THE FORMATION OF WOOD
IN FOREST TREES

THE FORMATION
OF WOOD
IN FOREST TREES

*The Second Symposium Held
under the Auspices of the
Maria Moors Cabot Foundation
for Botanical Research,
Harvard Forest, April, 1963*

Edited by

MARTIN H. ZIMMERMANN

*Lecturer on Forest Physiology,
Harvard University*

 1964

ACADEMIC PRESS • New York • London

ACADEMIC PRESS INC.
111 Fifth Avenue, New York 3, New York

United Kingdom Edition published by
ACADEMIC PRESS INC. (LONDON) LTD.
Berkeley Square House, London W.1

LIBRARY OF CONGRESS CATALOG CARD NUMBER: 63-23242

PRINTED IN THE UNITED STATES OF AMERICA

LIST OF CONTRIBUTORS

Asterisk indicates author of a paper in this volume

Numbers in parentheses indicate pages on which the authors' contributions begin

PETER ALBERSHEIM, Department of Biology, Harvard University, Cambridge, Massachusetts

*PAULO de T. ALVIM,[1] Inter-American Institute of Agricultural Sciences of the Organization of American States (Andean Zone), Lima, Peru (479)

IRVING W. BAILEY, Department of Biology, Harvard University, Cambridge, Massachusetts

*E. S. BARGHOORN, Department of Biology, Harvard University, Cambridge, Massachusetts (3)

*CLAUD L. BROWN, Department of Botany and School of Forestry, University of Georgia, Athens, Georgia[2] (389)

DUNCAN CLEMENT, Department of Biology, Harvard University, Cambridge, Massachusetts

*J. ROSS COLVIN, Division of Applied Biology, National Research Council, Ottawa, Canada (189)

WILFRED A. CÔTÉ, JR., State University College of Forestry, Syracuse University, Syracuse, New York

*J. DIGBY, Botany Department, University College of Wales, Aberystwyth, Wales (323)

*KATHERINE ESAU, University of California, Santa Barbara, California (37, 51)

*KARL FREUDENBERG, Forschungsinstitut für die Chemie des Holzes und der Polysaccharide, Organisch-Chemisches Institut der Universität, Heidelberg, Germany (203)

*A. FREY-WYSSLING, Swiss Federal Institute of Technology, Zürich, Switzerland (153, 457)

---

[1] Present address: Centro de Pesquisas do Cacau, Itabuna, Bahia, Brazil.

[2] This work was sponsored, in part, by the Georgia Forest Research Council, Macon, Georgia.

*C. E. A. HANNEY, Botany Department, University College of Wales, Aberystwyth, Wales (323)

*HENRY HELLMERS, Pacific Southwest Forest and Range Experiment Station, Forest Service, U. S. Department of Agriculture, and the California Institute of Technology, Pasadena, California (533)

*BRUNO HUBER, Forstbotanisches Institut, Universität München, Germany (497)[3]

*PAUL J. KRAMER, Duke University, Durham, North Carolina (519)

*PHILIP R. LARSON, Lake States Forest Experiment Station, Forest Service, U. S. Department of Agriculture, Rhinelander, Wisconsin (345)

*H. MEIER, Department of Botany, University of Fribourg, Switzerland (137)

*A. C. NEISH, Atlantic Regional Laboratory, National Research Council of Canada, Halifax, Nova Scotia (219)

*C. D. NELSON, Biology Department, Queen's University, Kingston, Ontario (243)

*R. D. PRESTON, The Astbury Department of Biophysics, The University of Leeds, England (169, 259)

HUGH M. RAUP, Harvard Forest, Harvard University, Petersham, Massachusetts

*S. D. RICHARDSON, Forest Research Institute, Rotorua, New Zealand (367)

*BRUCE R. ROBERTS,[4] School of Forestry, Duke University, Durham, North Carolina (273)[5]

LALIT M. SRIVASTAVA, Harvard University Herbarium, Cambridge, Massachusetts

*R. THAINE, Astbury Department of Biophysics, University of Leeds, England (259)

KENNETH V. THIMANN, Department of Biology, Harvard University, Cambridge, Massachusetts

*P. B. TOMLINSON, Fairchild Tropical Garden, Miami, Florida (65)

---

[3] This paper was read by Martin H. Zimmermann.

[4] Present address: U.S. Department of Agriculture, Delaware, Ohio.

[5] This paper was presented by P. J. Kramer.

JOHN G. TORREY, Department of Biology, Harvard University, Cambridge, Massachusetts

*WALTER TRANQUILLINI, Forstliche Bundesversuchsanstalt Mariabrunn, Forschungsstelle für Lawinenvorbeugung, Innsbruck, Austria (505)

*A. B. WARDROP, Division of Forest Products, Commonwealth Scientific and Industrial Research Organization, Melbourne, Australia (87, 405)

*P. F. WAREING, Botany Department, University College of Wales, Aberystwyth, Wales (323)

*HUGH WILCOX, State University College of Forestry, Syracuse, New York (459)

*BRAYTON F. WILSON, Maria Moors Cabot Foundation for Botanical Research, Harvard University, Petersham, Massachusetts (19)

*HUBERT ZIEGLER, Botanisches Institut, Technische Hochschule, Darmstadt, Germany (303)

*MARTIN H. ZIMMERMANN, Maria Moors Cabot Foundation for Botanical Research, Harvard University, Petersham, Massachusetts (289)

PREFACE

This volume is a record of the proceedings of the second Cabot Foundation Symposium, held at the Harvard Forest, in Petersham, Massachusetts, on April 15–19, 1963. The aims of the Cabot Foundation, originally more directly oriented toward improving the growth of trees, have gradually turned toward fundamental problems of tree growth, because it was realized that, before we can effectively improve the growth of trees, we have to learn a great deal more about how they grow.

Many symposia have been held during recent years on various aspects of tree growth, such as the chemistry and submicroscopic morphology of wood, the effects of the environment on growth, etc. Superficially seen, an additional conference might look superfluous. However, there was, and is, a serious need for bringing small groups of investigators of these different fields together in a quiet place, remote from distraction and the burden of administration. A few days of unhurried contact between representatives of these very different and yet so closely related fields proved to be a most stimulating experience.

Early in the planning stage it was agreed that the results of the symposium should be made available to everyone interested. The discussions were all recorded on magnetic tape. They were transcribed after the conference, edited, mimeographed, and sent to all participants for correction. Thus cleared and reduced to essentials, they were prepared for the printer.

I would like to thank all those who have made this volume possible: first of all the authors for their excellent contributions and for their cooperation and efforts to meet the various deadlines, Dr. Brayton F. Wilson for the transcription of the discussions from tape, Miss Margaret F. Stieg for her invaluable help in preparing the material for the publisher, and Professor Kenneth V. Thimann for his ever-available counsel and help in all editorial matters.

May 1963   MARTIN H. ZIMMERMANN

CHAIRMAN'S INTRODUCTION

It is my pleasant duty as chairman of the Maria Moors Cabot Foundation to welcome you all. We are very happy that everyone who was invited was able to come to the Symposium, with the single exception of Bruno Huber, whose health did not permit him to attend. Professor Huber was one of the most active and expert contributors to the previous Symposium, and we shall greatly miss him at this one.

I had hoped to have a message for you from Godfrey Lowell Cabot, who set up this Foundation just 25 years ago with the aim "to increase the capacity of the Earth to produce fuel by the growth of trees and other plants." Unhappily, however, Mr. Cabot died last year, some time after celebrating his 100th birthday amid a host of laughing children, grandchildren, and great grandchildren. Surely few men had a fuller and more satisfying life, for he lived to see the business which he founded and ran for many years become a great success, then turned his attention to his two hobbies, aviation and the utilization of solar energy. He became a Navy flier at the age of 57, and at the age of 75 endowed this Foundation. Mr. Cabot was disturbed at the rate at which man is exhausting the stocks of fossil fuel from the world, and foresaw the day when we should be forced to return to the use of the renewable fuels such as wood and water power. Fortunately, the coming of atomic power, which has appeared within about one generation of the time when many people foresee the beginning of the end of our oil supplies, is just in the nick of time and perhaps enables us to take a more detached view of the aims of our Foundation.

Because relatively little really scientific work is done on forest trees, we decided to devote our first Symposium, six years ago, to the Physiology of Forest Trees, and many of the topics discussed there were taken up further at the Tree Physiology session held during the International Botanical Congress at Montreal in 1959. For the present Symposium we thought it better to take somewhat less broad a field and decided that a good topic, with enough interrelations to interest workers in many areas, yet delimited enough to serve to crystallize our thoughts, was the formation of wood. This subject comprises, of course, the function and growth of cambium, the chemistry and physics of secondary wall formation and of specific polymers, the conditions, both internal and external, which govern these processes, and the role of wood formation in the world's economy.

We decided to hold the Symposium here at the Harvard Forest, partly because our previous one here was a success, partly because we are remote and undisturbed here, but partly because the size of the building automatically imposes a limitation on the size of the gathering, which we really need in order to keep our discussion within bounds. May I take this opportunity of thanking the Director of the Forest, Professor Hugh M. Raup, for his cooperation and hospitality.

Recently in England a competition was held for the composition of a chemist's prayer. I think one of the most appealing entries which I read was the following:

> O Lord, I beg upon my knees
> That all my various syntheses
> May not turn out to be inferior
> To those conducted by bacteria.

I can only hope that we, in our turn, may find that the syntheses of knowledge we shall hope to achieve during this week will not be too greatly inferior to those possessed by the living cells of the tree.

April, 1963   KENNETH V. THIMANN

CONTENTS

List of Contributors v

Preface ix

Introduction xi

Part I. The cambium and its derivatives

Evolution of cambium in geologic time.
    E. S. Barghoorn 3

A model for cell production by the cambium of conifers.
    Brayton F. Wilson 19

Structure and development of the bark in dicotyledons.
    Katherine Esau 37

Aspects of ultrastructure of phloem.
    Katherine Esau 51

Stem structure in arborescent monocotyledons.
    P. B. Tomlinson 65

The structure and formation of the cell wall in xylem.
    A. B. Wardrop 87

Part II. Biochemistry of cambial derivatives

General chemistry of cell walls and distribution of the chemical
    constituents across the walls.
    Hans Meier 137

Ultraviolet and fluorescence optics of lignified cell walls.
    A. Frey-Wyssling 153

Structural and mechanical aspects of plant cell walls with particular
    reference to synthesis and growth.
    R. D. Preston 169

The biosynthesis of cellulose.
    J. Ross Colvin 189

The formation of lignin in the tissue and in vitro.
    K. Freudenberg 203

Cinnamic acid derivatives as intermediates in the biosynthesis of
    lignin and related compounds.
    A. C. Neish 219

Part III. The translocation of photosynthetic products to the cambium

The production and translocation of photosynthate-C^{14} in conifers.
    C. D. Nelson 243

The role of transcellular streaming in phloem transport.
    R. Thaine and R. D. Preston 259

Effects of water stress on the translocation of photosynthetically
    assimilated carbon-14 in yellow poplar.
    Bruce R. Roberts 273

The relation of transport to growth in dicotyledonous trees.
    Martin H. Zimmermann 289

Storage, mobilization and distribution of reserve material in trees.
    Hubert Ziegler 303

Part IV. Internal and external control of wood formation

The role of endogenous hormones in cambial activity and xylem
    differentiation.
    P. F. Wareing, C. E. A. Hanney, and J. Digby 323

Some indirect effects of environment on wood formation.
    Philip R. Larson 345

The external environment and tracheid size in conifers.
    S. D. Richardson 367

The influence of external pressure on the differentiation of cells and
    tissues cultured in vitro.
    Claud L. Brown 389

The reaction anatomy of arborescent angiosperms.
    A. B. Wardrop 405

Cytology of aging ray cells.
    A. Frey-Wyssling 457

Xylem in roots of Pinus resinosa Ait. in relation to heterorhizy and
    growth activity.
    Hugh E. Wilcox 459

Tree growth periodicity in tropical climates.
Paulo de T. Alvim 479

Recording photosynthesis, respiration and transpiration.
Bruno Huber 497

Photosynthesis and dry matter production of trees at high altitudes.
Walter Tranquillini 505

The role of water in wood formation.
Paul J. Kramer 519

Distribution of growth in tree seedling stems as affected by temperature and light.
Henry Hellmers 533

Author Index 549

Subject Index 559

PART I

THE CAMBIUM AND
ITS DERIVATIVES

Evolution of Cambium in Geologic Time

E. S. Barghoorn

Department of Biology, Harvard University, Cambridge, Massachusetts

If major evolutionary events in the geologic history of plant life are considered in their broadest terms, irrespective of phylogenetic implications, certain fundamental advances in the course of evolution might be recognized as follows:

1. Origin of a stabilized genetic system for the replication of form from generation to generation.

2. Development of autotropic photosynthetic metabolism.

3. Emergence from an aquatic or free moisture dependent environment and adaption to withstand conditions of the terrestrial environment.

4. Development of an internal system of vascular tissues and the incorporation into it (and other tissues) of lignin as a chemical entity of the plant body.

5. Origin and development of cambium and the capacity for theoretically unlimited secondary growth and increase in size of the plant body.

Events 1 and 2 above are lost in the geologic record of life and at present may only be surmised through theories or concepts of chemical and biochemical evolution (Clarke and Synge, 1959). It should be noted, however, that quite highly organized and presumable photosynthetic (as evidenced by stable carbon isotope ratios of the organic matter present) primitive organisms are now known from sediments whose age approaches one-half that of the currently accepted value for the age of the earth (Tyler and Barghoorn, 1954; Rutten, 1962). The time of emergence of photosynthetic, presumably algal or protovascular plants into subaerial or terrestrial environments is likewise imperfectly known. It is conceivable that the moister or more humid continental surfaces were occupied in Late Precambrian or Early Paleozoic time by a shallow superficial covering of algal growth whose collective organic activities and residues would have facilitated the formation of a primitive sort of soil. The character of presumably terrigenous sediments of these units of geologic time are not incompatible with this view. However, the

3

subsequent events, viz., 4 and 5 above, are featured by a more perfectly known chronological and morphological documentation and it is to these that the present paper is directed.

The evolution of vascular plants possessing primitive adaptation, or structural modifications adequate to withstand the stress of terrestrial environments, was one of the broadest revolutionary advances in the plant kingdom (Bailey, 1953), enabling complete independence from the ambient aquatic or subaquatic environment. The play of natural selection operating on the primitive vascular plants in conjunction with the innumerable new ecological niches of the terrestrial environment allowed for rapid evolution of form and diversity, both of vegetative and reproductive structures. The rate of evolutionary change during the short segment of geologic time between the appearance of the earliest true land plants (i.e., vascular plants) of Silurian-Devonian time and the rich and varied flora of the Carboniferous is probably unique in the history of plant life. The only other segment of the geologic record which seems comparable is the rapid evolution and diversification of the flowering plants during Cenozoic time. In fact, it is even the more striking if we consider that all the major subphyla of the Trachophyta became highly diversified in the interval between the Middle Devonion and the later Carboniferous, an interval of approximately 75 million years (slightly longer than the duration of the entire Cenozoic era).

The question arises as to whether the seemingly explosive evolution of vascular plants after their establishment in terrestrial environments is an artifact of an incomplete fossil record, or of some other cause. It must always be recognized that a fossil assemblage is a mere fraction of its contemporary biota, yet the continuity of the fossil record, supported within the framework of absolute chronology lends confidence to our acceptance of the evolutionary sequences. Currently there is no tangible evidence that vascular plants existed prior to the Middle or Late Silurian and it is of interest to examine possible reasons for this fact, particularly in view of our recent knowledge of the existence of well-organized algal and related plants in sediments approximately 2000 million (2.0×10^9) years earlier.

It is my contention that one of the answers to this enigma is the "discovery," so to speak, of the chemical entity lignin. Lignin is one of the few chemical complexes which appears to be unique to the vascular plants as distinct from the nonvascular, i.e., algae, fungi, and their relatives. The physical properties imparted by lignin to the lignin-cellulose framework of tracheary tissues provides the essential physical characteristics of the plant body on which natural selection would operate in the adaptation of plants to the terrestrial environment. The increase in vertical dimensions of the plant body made possible by the rigidity of lignified cell walls places a survival value on the capacity to increase in height in competition for available light. It is entirely possible, particularly in view of the peculiar biochemical attributes of lignin (aromatic structure, physical dispersion, etc.), that all vascular plants are monophyletic. This would imply that the mutation providing the chemical pathways for lignin formation arose only once in the chemical evolution of plants and triggered the mechanism for evolution and selection of entirely new aspects of morphological expression and specialization. The fossil record, with its preponderance of small, simple, and poorly differentiated forms in the Early Devonian tends to support this concept. The recognition of the Psilophytales as a supposedly natural group of ancient and primitive land plants is an outgrowth of this monophyletic view.

Increase in height of a free-standing vascular plant which possesses no mechanism for increase in girth is obviously sharply limited by the rigidity of its primary vascular and associated tissues. Further increase in height, upon which natural selection operates in a positive direction as previously noted, necessitates increase in girth. Various mechanisms have evolved in relation to this biophysical necessity and it is of interest to examine these in some detail, particularly with respect to the expression of secondary vascular tissues. It should be kept in view, in this connection, that our survey of the evolution of cambium is based almost entirely on examining the products of secondary growth as expressed in the woody cylinder. Cytological and histological innovations in the cambium of plants which are known only as fossils may be inferred only by examination of the daughter cells or derivatives in the secondary xylem.

I. Psilophytales and Their Presumed Immediate Derivatives

Among Lower Devonian vascular plants there is little or no evidence of vascular cambium and this fact is correlated with their relatively small size. Unfortunately entire plants, unless of very small size, are seldom found as fossils. However, by piecing detached parts together in formulating a morphological entity it is sometimes possible to reconstruct a reasonable facsimile of an extinct plant as it grew in nature. It is quite possible that the ultimate height to which a plant possessing a simple protostele or actinostele and without excessive cortex of periderm could attain would be about 2 meters. This seems to have been attained in certain Lower Devonian forms in which some internal structure is recognizable (Höeg, 1942). The primary vascular tissues in the relatively few cases of three-dimensional preservation known among Early and Middle Devonian plants consist of simple or lobate strands of proto- and metaxylem with no indication of cambial activity, as expressed by secondary wood. By Middle Devonian time a number of plants had evolved which show directly or indirectly evidences of well-organized cambial activity and secondary growth. Again, structural preservation and critical evidence of the histology of secondary tissues is known in disappointingly few cases. However, the Middle Devonian genus *Schizopodium* is of particular interest inasmuch as it shows the probable nature of primitive secondary growth. Radially aligned xylem elements peripheral to the lobate primary xylem core of the stem appear to represent rudimentary cambial activity.

The earliest expressions of cambial activity throughout the not inconsiderable morphological range of Middle Devonian plants appears to be simple apposition of secondary elements to the well-defined single or multiple-stranded exarch protostele. This may be illustrated by the genus *Cladoxylon*, a probable progenitor of the ferns and which ranges from Middle Devonian into the Carboniferous.

By Upper Devonian time extensive secondary growth is to be found in all members of the various phyletic lines which attained full expression in the rich and varied floras of the Carboniferous. It is of interest to note two representatives of Upper Devonian plants which illustrate the complexity of form achieved in the geologically relatively brief interval of a few tens of millions of years. It should also be noted in this regard that a high degree of histological specialization of the secondary elements had been achieved.

It may be observed in the earliest and most rudimentary expression of secondary growth the prosenchymatous elements of the wood are accompanied by radially oriented files of cells representing rays. The association of ray tissue, with tracheary elements, regardless of their extent of development, appears to be an invariable relationship in the secondary xylem in all groups of those primitive vascular plants which possess cambial activity. The elimination or loss of ray tissue from the secondary xylem is a specialization to be found only among a few dicotyledonous groups in which cambial activity is suppressed or undergoing reduction in the phylogenetic transition to the herbaceous habit.

II. Lycopsida

Among the lycopods the rapid ascendency of arborescent forms is clearly documented in the Late Devonian and Early Carboniferous. Detailed knowledge of internal structure is best known from the widespread and highly distinctive genera *Lepidodendron* and *Sigillaria*. Both genera are of much interest in illustrating evolutionary "experimentation" in the achievement of arboreal stature and the formation of forest stands. It will be recalled that *Callixylon* achieved height and mass by what we may call the normal increment of the woody cylinder by extended cambial activity. In the arboreal lycopods size was achieved by a curious compromise between massive development of secondary cortical and periderm tissue and minimal development of secondary wood. *Lepidodendron* trees attained a known height of 120 feet (ca. 40 meters). Yet the maximal extent of the secondary wood appears never to have been more than a few centimeters of the radius of the vascular cylinder. Recent detailed studies of the probable ontogenetic sequences in development of these stems indicates that the massive development of the protostelic primary wood apparently increased acropetally as the size of the terminal meristem increased with increase in height up to the level of the primary dichotomy (Eggert, 1961). Concommitantly the relative proportion of secondary wood, hence of cambial activity decreased with increase in height of the main stem or trunk. However, in the ontogeny of an individual tree the vascular cambium seems never to have achieved a high degree of coordinated function nor quantitative expression. In relation to total size of the plant body, the giant lycopods seem to have achieved the extremes which have ever evolved in vascular plants with respect to the ratio of total mass of the plant to minimal development of secondary wood. Perhaps the nearest approach to it may be found among the present Cactaceae.

The arboreal lycopods, despite their size, worldwide distribution, and local dominance in coal swamps of the Later Carboniferous, declined abruptly in the Late Paleozoic. A few semiarborescent types persisted into the Early Mesozoic, but the entire lycopsid line of evolution has persisted to the present in the form only of dwarf plants devoid of secondary growth. The extant genus *Isoetes* possesses a vestigial form of secondary growth in the basal portions of its cormlike stem and there is evidence that this represents continued reduction from the *Isoetes*-like Cretaceous genus *Nathorstiana*. A recently discovered extant genus, *Stylites*, of the upland Andean region of Peru which possesses a somewhat woody cortex tends to corroborate this interpretation of gradual diminution of secondary growth extending to the present.

III. Sphenopsida

The paleontologic record of the articulate plants closely parallels that of the lycopods. It is probable, however, that they were even more diverse on what may be termed the generic level, than were the lycopods in the same level of time in the Paleozoic. Their attenuation during the Mesozoic was even greater than that of the lycopods, and as is well known, they are represented in the current flora by a small number of species contained in the single genus *Equisetum*.

Knowledge of the internal structure of the fossil sphenopsids is by no means limited to the genera *Calamites* (including its subgenera) and *Sphenophyllum*, but these two forms adequately illustrate the range of secondary development in the group. The calamites were arboreal plants of considerable size, possibly achieving a height approaching 100 feet, although there seems no doubt the bulk of them were of much lower stature. Support of the massive stems was achieved in large part through excessive periderm and secondary cortical expansion. The proportion of the vascular cylinder to the cross-sectional area of the stem, however, was considerably greater than that of the arboreal lycopods, indicating a more efficient and coordinated sequence in differentiation of cambial derivatives. Primary wood consisted of quite small collateral bundles, widely separated in many forms by broad interfascicular segments and the whole complex of primary vascular tissues surrounding a massive pith, which was hollow at maturity. Based on the size of the pith cavities and the coherent cylinder of secondary wood it may be presumed that in certain calamites the apical meristem exceeded 6 inches in diameter. It would be exceedingly interesting to know if this huge growing point were dominated by a single apical cell as in modern *Equisetum*. The secondary cylinder of the calamites developed immediately peripheral to the primary bundles and to the interfascicular wedges of the pith. Cambium developed completely concentrically and the broad inter-fascicular segments were extended in some forms by massive multiseriate rays of the secondary xylem.

Comparisons were long ago drawn to the similarity in structure of juvenile stems of *Calamites* and the mature structure of the stem in *Equisetum*. These similarities extend to the bundle canal system, cortical tissues and pith structure as well as the vascular bundles themselves. Whether or not there is a true lineal descent between the two genera is unproven and perhaps unlikely. However, in purely anatomical terms the structure of an *Equisetum* stem is essentially the analog of a *Calamites* stem devoid of cambial derivatives.

The stems of *Sphenophyllum* illustrate several interesting features of cambial development in Paleozoic plants. The plant body of the spheno-phylls was small and judging by the ratio of length to thickness of the stems the plants were semierect or possibly scandent in the understory of the coal swamp forests. The stems were protostelic with a highly angular triarch core of primary wood. The concentric layers of tracheary elements gradually assumed a cylindrical form by a curious combination of variable increase in radial and tangential diameter of the cambial derivatives and varying rates of pariclinal divisions in the cambium. The size of the early-formed secondary tracheids differentiated immediately peripheral to the protoxylem elements was commonly only a fraction of the cross-sectional area of those differentiated peripheral to the large metaxylem elements. With increase in girth the differences became correspondingly smaller and the secondary cylinder achieved essentially a cylindrical outline.

IV. Pteropsida

The number of diverse groups of plants which have been lumped into the subphylum Pteropsida is so great that this unit of classification is both unwieldy and unnatural. Not only the ferns, both living and fossil, but also all the gymnospermous assemblages as well as the angiosperms have been thus placed together. There is no need here to enter into a discussion of the morphological basis for the establishment of this grouping and for the purposes of our discussion representative forms may be selected from various orders with little or no reference to the degrees of phylogenetic affinity or relationship.

A. "FILICOPSIDA" (FILICINEAE)

The ferns and morphologically related extinct forms represent a complex phylogenetic problem which paradoxically has become increasingly difficult to unravel as knowledge of fossil forms accumulates (Andrews, 1961). If the group is defined along the broadest morphological parameters it appears to represent a fairly coherent phylogenetic line extending from the Middle Devonian to a currently rich representation in the extant flora. The suggestion has been made, and is probably well justified, to separate the group from the Pteropsid complex of seed-bearing plants and place them in a distinct subphylum, the Filicopsida (Newman, 1949). Anatomical evidence as well as that from reproductive structures tends to support this treatment.

A remarkable feature of the group is the extreme elaboration of the primary vascular tissues and failure of appreciable cambial activity to develop. Certain Middle and Late Devonian-presumed fern ancestors show a modicum of secondary growth associated with a multistranded primary vascular system, as previously noted in the case of *Cladoxylon* of the Devonian and Carboniferous time. However, the arboreal ferns of the Paleozoic as well as the tree ferns of the Mesozoic and Cenozoic, extending to the present, have achieved size and height through great elaboration of the primary vascular tissues, intensely lignified cortical tissues, and exaggerated enlargement of persistent leaf bases. Cambial activity is virtually unrepresented except as previously noted in a few Paleozoic members.

B. Cycadofilicales (Seed Ferns)

During the past decade major advances have been made in our understanding of the seed ferns of the Late Paleozoic and Early Mesozoic, particularly in the southern hemisphere. The century-old mystery of the affinities and the nature of the reproductive structures of *Glossopteris* have been in good part resolved (Plumstead, 1956). It is now evident that the seed ferns were a far more diverse group of plants than had previously been realized, and that their geologic record extends well into the Mesozoic.

The major part of our information concerning the anatomy and internal structure of the vegetative organs of the seed ferns, however, is still largely limited to that of Carboniferous and Permian forms. Insofar as the fossil record can be interpreted, it is evident that the seed ferns are featured throughout their geologic record by extensive secondary growth, although the size of the plant body in no cases known approaches that of the arboreal lower vascular plants. A wide range of structural patterns can be found among structurally preserved members of the seed ferns, including rather highly specialized eustelic types. It is of more interest here, however, to draw attention to certain of the bizarre expressions of cambial activity which the group developed in the late Paleozoic and which failed to survive into the Mesozoic. Indeed, some of the most peculiar forms of secondary growth known among vascular plants are to be found among the Medullosan group of the seed ferns of Carboniferous and Permian age. Certain of the Medullosan seed ferns developed complex systems of multiple protostelic vascular strands each possessing an independent vascular cambium. In the more highly modified Permian forms the so-called polystelic structure is commonly associated with accessory cambia, disjunct secondary cylinders, and intricate medullary bundle systems, each likewise possessing a cambium. The fundamental significance of these involved vascular systems are obscure, particularly those featured by excessive centripetally developed secondary xylem (Roberts and Barghoorn, 1952). With respect to the histology of the tracheary elements and rays of the secondary xylem, the Medullosan seed ferns, however, differ in no significant way from other contemporary groups of seed ferns.

C. Cordaitales–Coniferales

From their earliest recognizable occurrence in the fossil record the entire coniferous line of evolution is featured by highly organized and strongly developed secondary growth. From the ancestral Cordaitales extending through the evolutionary modifications leading to the modern conifers the arboreal habit has predominated. The stems of Cordaitean trees, as those of modern conifers, are comprised largely of thick cylinders of secondary wood featured by a minimal amount of wood and ray parenchyma tissue, and relatively little periderm. The emphasis, ontogenetically, on secondary growth and persistence of cambial activity in the Cordaitales probably accounts for the fact that these plants were certainly the tallest, if not the largest of Paleozoic trees. Similarly existing conifers are both the tallest and most massive of living plants. With respect to evolutionary innovations or abnormalities, neither the Cycadophytes, nor the Gnetales show any major features of cambial activity which had not already evolved in Paleozoic plants, although highly distinctive features may be observed in the cambial derivatives of these forms. These include the excessive parenchymatization of the secondary wood in the cycadeoids and certain cycads, and the curious mode of vessel formation in the Gnetales.

D. ANGIOSPERMAE

On the other hand, among the angiosperms virtually the entire range of cambial diversity is to be found. In this respect, as in so many other morphological features and anatomical specializations, the angiosperms represent the most variable of all known groups of plants. However, it is not within the scope of this discussion to consider the range of structure among the flowering plants except with respect to one fundamental feature in the Cenozoic evolution of the dicotyledonous groups, viz., the suppression of secondary growth. If we disregard for the moment the structural peculiarities of the monocotyledonae, in very few of which there is any semblance of normal secondary growth, it is apparent that suppression and loss of cambial activity is one of the most remarkable features of recent evolution in the angiosperms. The recency of the herbaceous habit among the many scores of families of the dicotyledonae has been abundantly documented by the massive evidence of palynology which has accumulated within the past decade. Herbaceous members of predominantly woody families, and strictly herbaceous families of the dicotyledonae are currently unknown in sediments older than the Lower Miocene. Within the context of what is now known of the history of Cenozoic paleoclimates is apparent that the survival value placed upon small size and brevity of the reproductive cycle has selected, in the operation of natural selection, for the herbaceous habit. It is quite reasonable to assign this selective pressure to the increasingly adverse climates in middle and higher latitudes during the Miocene and Pliocene, culminating in the Pleistocene (Barghoorn, 1951; Wolfe and Barghoorn, 1960). The evolution of the herbaceous habit relatively synchronously among so many families of angiosperms within such a short period of geologic time is certainly one of the more remarkable features of the geologic record of the vascular plants, and comparable in scope but in an inverse way to the worldwide dwindling and extinction of many groups during the Late Paleozoic.

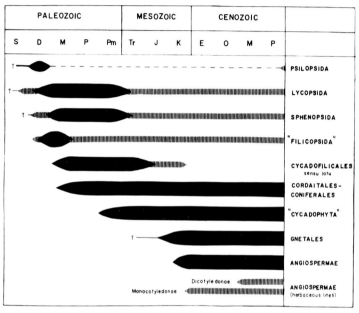

Fig. 1. Graph showing the occurrence of cambial activity and its persistence during geologic time in the major groups of the vascular plants. Secondary growth is indicated by broad black bars and occurrence of the herbaceous habit and hence of secondary growth by the narrow interrupted bars. The relative width of the bars is not intended to indicate relative abundance of representatives of the groups. The Ginkgoales are not shown but have a record very similar to that of the Cordaitales–Coniferales. The term "Filicopsida" is used here to designate those Pteropsid plants which belong to the phylogenetic line leading to the existing ferns. Note the loss of cambial activity in the various groups of the lower vascular plants during late Paleozoic and Mesozoic time and the origin of herbaceousness among dicotyledons during middle and later Cenozoic time.

The suppression of cambial activity is, as has been alluded to previously, to be found in other groups of vascular plants. Indeed it is the persistence of the herbaceous members which characterizes the evolutionary lines of most of the lower vascular plants. Inasmuch as the present flora is only a momentary expression, in terms of geologic history, of a continually evolving sequence of floras, it is of interest to speculate on the possible course of natural selection in the future with respect to the woody as opposed to the herbaceous lines of evolution.

A somewhat graphic and much-simplified scheme to show the trends of cambial expression and secondary growth in the major groups of vascular plants is shown in Fig. 1.

DISCUSSION

NEISH: Professor Barghoorn, how do you account for the disappearance of the cambium in the lycopods, for example?

BARGHOORN: These peculiar arborescent forms had little survival value if our understanding of late Paleozoic climates and the catastrophes of the early Mesozoic are right. This climatic change is borne out very well by various lines of evidence: chemistry and weathering, as well as by abundant paleobiological evidence, both floral and faunal.

NEISH: It seems to coincide with the emergence of the conifers. Do you think that they may have pushed them into extinction?

BARGHOORN: Conifers have a remarkably efficient mechanism for increasing size and yet carrying out transpiration. They could stand the very conditions that fostered adversity for the arborescent representatives of the lower vascular plants. The same is true of the angiosperms except that they have an even higher efficiency of the photosynthetic system.

ESAU: How did you determine lignification in fossil material?

BARGHOORN: Birefringence in the cell walls is present in some fossils as far back as the Eocene; that is, some cellulose persists. Older fossils do not have birefringent cell walls. Components of the wall other than cellulose are lignin plus the degradation and alteration products of cellulose. The fossil lignin can be extracted by the same chemical treatments that are used to extract lignin from present-day plants. We know that lignin has extraordinary resistance to reducing conditions of the sedimentary environment. Bacterial attack of lignin is at a minimum, or almost nonexistent under reducing conditions. So it all adds up that in fossil material the lignin is preserved at the expense of the cellulosic, hemicellulosic, pectic, and other constituents.

ESAU: But I don't presume you can identify the type of lignin—recognize the conifer *versus* the angiosperm lignin.

BARGHOORN: You get positive Mäule and phloroglucinol color reactions with lignin as old as 20 to more than 50 thousand years. This helps a little.

THIMANN: Is there any evidence for change in lignin type?

BARGHOORN: There is an increasing aromatic constituent in fossil residues and lignin is the most reasonable source of aromatic constituents. This is true for coal as well as for fossil wood.

FREUDENBERG: There is a change in lignin composition from lycopodia onwards, and it is very difficult to estimate and to characterize the lignin of lycopodia and of mosses because they contain hardly any methoxyl groups. But from the Gnetaceae and the conifers onwards, methoxyl groups appear and then it is possible to characterize the lignin. There is a development corresponding to the genealogy of the plants; the first lignins contain practically no methoxyl groups, then come the groups with one methoxyl on the C_9 unit, and then two methoxyl groups in the dicotyledonous wood. On the other hand, among the Gnetales, *Ephedra* contains also to some extent two methoxyl groups in its lignin. It resembles in some respects dicotyledonous wood (Manskaya and Kochneva, 1948).

BARGHOORN: Is it not true that with degradation of wood in nature there is an increase in methoxyl content?

FREUDENBERG: Methoxyl groups disappear during rotting. One would therefore not find much methoxyl in peat and in brown coal.

FREY-WYSSLING: I think Dr. Esau is right. You cannot declare all of these blackened cell walls as lignin, because if it were so, the coal belts would originate from lignin only; but it is known that cellulose and hemicelluloses can be carbonized as well.

BARGHOORN: Yes, there is no question about that; but these cell-wall residues have nothing to do with carbonization. They are not black but different degrees of translucent amber brown. From tissues of different stages in the geologic record one can trace the disappearance of cellulosic constituents. It is a difficult problem chemically to suggest how sugars and carbohydrates are transformed to compounds with aromatic properties. There is no doubt that the plant tissue as a whole contributes to coal formation. But I do feel that lignin as a biochemical substance very possibly came into existence as a biochemical transformation only once in the history of plant life. Once this happened, it made possible increase in girth, size, and all the other factors that go with secondary growth. Secondary growth without lignification would be, I think, a somewhat biophysically unselected mechanism in natural selection. Black lines on the chart, incidentally, have nothing to do with lignin but simply the existence of secondary growth.

THIMANN: Professor Freudenberg, is there any change in the physical or mechanical properties on the wall with the appearance of more methoxyl groups, so that the plant becomes more effective in supporting secondary growth?

FREUDENBERG: No, I think not. We have investigated dicotyledonous lignin, but we know more about coniferous wood lignin. The similarity is quite close. In my paper in this volume I show that the scheme for a constitutional formula of coniferous lignin can be transformed into a reasonable scheme of beech lignin by adding one methoxyl group to each second coniferyl unit.

BROWN: Dr. Barghoorn, you mentioned that ray cells in *Callixylon* were quite different from modern coniferous species. Can you comment on this?

BARGHOORN: They differ in a number of respects. In many *Callixylon* stems there are two types of ray cells; they appear almost like the tile cells of specialized angiosperms, small and large ray cells, a combination unknown in conifers. The multiseriate condition of the rays is occasionally found in some conifers, e.g., the Taxodiaceae, but they are very much more extensive in *Callixylon*.

SRIVASTAVA: Professor Barghoorn, would you comment on the relative time of origin of ray and fusiform initials?

BARGHOORN: They apparently originated simultaneously. Whenever you find in vascular plants expression of prosenchymatous tracheary elements of secondary origin, they are always associated with ray tissue. It is only in the angiosperms with the reduction of secondary growth or development toward the herbaceous habit that this is lost. The origin of the rayless condition in angiosperms is not so much a sequence of reduction as it is of the superenlargement of ray initials into fusiform initials.

ZIEGLER: You mentioned that lignin formation is a prerequisite for cambial activity, but it is interesting in this connection that cambial activity does not begin with the appearance of lignin formation. I think that a more important requirement is the presence of auxins to correlate the cambial activity with the activity of the leaves.

In this connection I have a question: Are there any leafless plants among the primary cormophytes that have extension growth with cambial activity?

BARGHOORN: The origin of the leaf as a fundamental morphological unit is rather interestingly shown by the Devonian forms. It seems clear that leaves originated by a flattening or "cladification" of the axis which initially was neither leaves nor stem, and this had already gone on before any appearance of cambium. Your suggestion is good because as soon as the plant body developed into a highly organized leaf-stem system, it had already achieved the essential features of a plant which has secondary growth. The earlier forms do not fit clear-cut morphological concepts of leaf, stem, and root.

ZIEGLER: Perhaps we can say that the "leaf" originates at the point where the flattened stem makes auxin.

BARGHOORN: That is a very reasonable idea.

THIMANN: Another point in connection with auxin struck me very forcibly. Apparently cambial activity came in while there was still a dichotomous type of growth. One of the most characteristic effects of auxin is its control of apical dominance. It is difficult to imagine how auxin-induced cambial activity could exist without apical dominance. It suggests that somewhere there has been a marked change in auxin physiology. In other words, auxin did not do in the old days what it does now.

BARGHOORN: Apical dominance seems to have appeared in these plants *before* secondary growth. Many Devonian plants which already show apical dominance do not have secondary growth.

THIMANN: That is very much more satisfactory.

LARSON: At what time, or in which groups, did cyclical development of the cambial derivatives, as evidenced by growth rings, first originate?

BARGHOORN: This is a difficult and involved question. All fossil plants which show pronounced growth rings grew in geographical areas which would indicate glaciation or seasonally cold environments. This gets involved in problems of paleomagnetism, continental drift, etc. All southern hemisphere trees of the late Paleozoic or early Mesozoic show very sharply differentiated growth rings. There are no cases known in contemporaneous deposits of the present northern hemisphere. This correlates very well with our knowledge of paleoclimates. The development of cyclical dormant and active periods is apparently largely imposed by external conditions, but once these are imposed, they may be carried over and built into physiological mechanisms. This may account for the fact that in certain tropical forests a tree may show growth rings while its neighbor does not. In the fossil forms there is a very definite association with external conditions.

BAILEY: It seems to me that a very critical point in the origin of vascular land plants, regardless of details of chemical composition, is the addition of material to the tracheid wall which produces rigidity and stiffness—lignin or any material which will stiffen the primary or secondary wall.

THIMANN: Is it thinkable that the entire evolution of land plants could have rested on cellulose instead of lignin?

PRESTON: I think the idea that lignin is essential to secondary wood formation perhaps needs looking at. In England apple root stocks seem to carry a virus which induces rubbery wood in some scions. This controls the development of the helices in the secondary walls of the fibers. The fibers appear quite normal but the steepening of the helix as the cell gets longer, from the inside to the outside of the stem, fails to occur so that the stem is potentially springy. The final step in lignin formation is also somehow inhibited so that in this wood there is no true lignin. Nevertheless, the affected trees are just as vigorous as others, almost as good bearers, have just as good a survival value; but the wood is rubbery (Preston and Nelmes, to be published).

BARGHOORN: Is this a sesquiterpene?

PRESTON: I don't know what step in lignin synthesis is stopped, but fresh, wet wood does not stain with lignin stains and the aromatic compounds with the U.V. absorption of lignin come out almost quantitatively in cold water.

WARDROP: A point on Preston's remark—trees containing rubbery wood usually do not possess the erect habit.

PRESTON: That is, in general, true although, oddly enough, the leader, insofar as there is a leader in apple, is normally straight. The branches tend to droop when they are bearing fruit though this tendency is offset by a reduction in extension growth, giving relatively sharply conical branches. They are just as successful trees as are the normal.

BROWN: If one completely defoliates pine seedlings while they are dormant, the first flush of growth from the terminal bud is very weak and poorly lignified. The terminal shoot still has apical dominance, but it is never rigid or stiff.

BARGHOORN: I think the record of the nonvascular plants shows that such substances as cellulose and hemicelluloses must have been in existence for something like 3 to 4 times as long geologically as the first vascular plants. That is why I try to lay this emphasis on lignin as an innovation in evolution, because algae do not have the structural attributes to make possible the free-standing erect habit and rigidity.

FREY-WYSSLING: I would like to ask two questions about your last slide (Fig. 1). (1) The development from plants without any cambial growth and secondary activity up to trees with good size was in Devonian times. There was no scale on the diagram; how many millions of years did this development take? (2) According to the slide secondary growth developed and then disappeared again in lycopods and others. Is it impossible that during the period involved both trees and herbaceous plants of these groups existed simultaneously and when the trees died out the herbs survived?

BARGHOORN: The Devonian period is about 45 million years. The period between the first appearance of cambium and the development of such a forest tree of the size of *Callixylon* was less than 20 million years. This is about the average period, for the geologic record as a whole, for the differentiation of any major group of vascular plants. So it is not inconsistent with the general picture. As to your second question, I think that the survival value associated with the herbaceous habit is the speed of reproduction. During the course of the development of trees over centuries, climatic or other adversities can inhibit reproduction except perhaps at very sporadic intervals. An annual or herbaceous plant, however, can pass through such periods of adversity as a species rather than an individual. In the case of the angiosperms this is clearly correlated with the deteriorating climate of high latitudes in the Cenozoic. All selective factors favored herbaceousness. As one goes toward the pole in either hemisphere, one finds fewer trees but a rich herbaceous flora, not only of lower vascular plants, but also of the highly specialized angiosperm herbaceous forms. So there is a natural selection operating in that direction. In general, the herbaceous habit has a survival value which the tree habit does not have. It is only in the favorable environments of the humid tropics at low latitudes that the tree habit is at a high premium in natural selection.

FREY-WYSSLING: But there is the question whether there has always been besides the trees a small number of herbaceous forms from which evolution of later herbs could take place, or whether trees and woody plants really lost their arborescent habit and became herbs again.

BARGHOORN: It is perhaps confusing but there is one evolutionary feature which always seems to be the same. In both plants and animals, morphological reduction is an irreversible process. Once a reduction has taken place it never goes back the other way. I think this is borne out by the record of the tree forms of all the major groups of the vascular plants. Throughout the geologic record from the Carboniferous into the Middle Mesozoic there is a progressive reduction in size and secondary growth in the lycopods and sphenopsids. In the case of the dicotyledonous angiosperms there is no evidence of herbaceous forms until Lower Miocene time (absence of pollen, seeds, fruits, or foliar organs). With regard to the monocotyledonous angiosperms, grasses seem to have been present in minimal numbers in Upper Cretaceous time although arborescent monocotyledons represented by palms were present much earlier.

WAREING: It is well known that size gives an advantage in competition for light. Under stable conditions there is a marked advantage in size, and this leads to the necessity for secondary growth. Under stable conditions, therefore, there is an advantage in this woody habit. Under conditions of rapid geological or climatic change, however, the herbaceous habit is advantageous.

BARGHOORN: That appears to be correct. As soon as conditions of optimal vegetative growth are eliminated, the selective pressure goes the other way.

REFERENCES

Andrews, H. N. (1961). "Studies in Paleobotany," Wiley, New York.

Bailey, I. W. (1953). *Am. J. Botany* **40**, 4-8.

Barghoorn, E. S. (1951). *J. Paleontol.* **25**, 736-744.

Clarke, F., and Synge, R. L. M. (eds.) (1959). "The Origin of Life on the Earth: Symposium." Pergamon Press, New York.

Eggert, D. A. (1961). *Palaeontographica Abt. B* **108**, 43-92.

Høeg, O. A. (1942). "The Downtonian and Devonian Flora of Spitsbergen," Skrifter om Svalbarg Og Ishavet, Oslo.

Manskaya, S. M., and Kochneva, M. N. (1948). *Doklady Akad. Nauk SSSR* **6**, 505. *Cited in* "The Chemistry of Lignins: Supplement Volume" (F. E. and D. A. Brauns), p. 13. Academic Press, New York, 1960.

Newman, I. V. (1949). *Trans. Roy. Soc. New Zealand* **77**, 154-160.

Plumstead, E. P. (1956). *Palaeontographica Abt. B.* **100**, 1-25.

Roberts, D. C., and Barghoorn, E. S. (1952). *Bot. Museum Leaflets Harvard Univ.* **15**, 191-200.

Rutten, M. G. T. (1962). "The Geological Aspects of the Origin of Life on Earth." Elsevier, Amsterdam.

Tyler, S., and Barghoorn, E. S. (1954). *Science* **119**, 606-608.

Wolfe, J. A., and Barghoorn, E. S. (1960). *Am. J. Sci.* **258-A**, 388-399.

A Model for Cell Production by the Cambium of Conifers[1]

Brayton F. Wilson

Harvard University, Cabot Foundation, Petersham, Massachusetts

The cambium is a cell-producing system, whose derivatives form the wood (xylem) and the inner bark (phloem). It is a population of meristematic cells which acts like a factory. Once the machinery of cambial activity is set in motion in the spring, the cambium takes assimilates from the phloem, water and minerals from the xylem, and, through the cell division cycle, produces a steady supply of new derivatives. Most of these derivatives differentiate to form new xylem; a few form new phloem.

In this paper, I will review the pertinent literature on the cambium of conifers; present some new data on cell division in the cambium of white pine; and set up a model for cell production by the cambium. Using the model it will be possible to estimate the rate at which cambial cells pass through the division cycle, to emphasize the major variables which affect the rates and amounts of cell production by the cambium, and to speculate on the basis of the uneven ratio of xylem to phloem cells produced by the cambium.

The model presented here is the result of interpreting the cambium as a homogeneous, dividing cell population. Its primary value is to provide a simplified representation of the dynamics of the cambium. This interpretation is compatible with the idea that the cambium is composed of initial cells plus xylem and phloem mother cells (Bannan, 1955). It stresses, however, the similarities rather than the differences between the cells in the cambium. Furthermore, it assumes that, with respect to capacity for cell division, there is no differentiation within the cambium caused by unequal cell divisions (Bünning, 1952).

[1] I gratefully acknowledge Dr. H. M. Raup for providing laboratory facilities and tree 3 at the Harvard Forest, Dr. E. M. Gould for providing trees 1 and 2 plus helpful advice, and Miss Sharon Hutchinson for her excellent technical assistance.

Derivative production by the cambium is the result of divisions within a population of cambial cells. The way in which the cambium is defined determines the limits of the population. Several definitions have been used, each depending on the approach of the particular investigator (Bannan, 1955). For the purpose of studying cell production, the cambium shall be defined in terms of cell division. Thus, the possible existence of true cambial initials (Bannan, 1955; Newman, 1956) is of little significance to this study. The term "cambium" will be used to include the entire population of dividing ray and fusiform cells between the xylem and phloem. Fusiform cells constitute more than 90% by

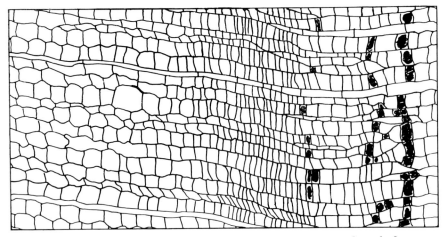

Fig. 1. Tracing from a photomicrograph of a transverse section through the cambium of *Abies concolor*. The narrow cells to the right of the center are fusiform cambial cells. To their left is the xylem, to their right the phloem. There are dark, tannin-filled cells in the phloem.

volume of the cambium and its derivatives (Wilson, 1963), so the model will be limited to fusiform cells. It is easy to define the cambium in words, but it is often difficult to define precisely the boundaries of the dividing cell population (Bannan, 1955; Wight, 1933). The actual limits of the cambial population in a particular part of a tree can be determined in two ways: by observing which cells actually do divide, or by seeing where radial cell enlargement, the first visible step in the differentiation of new xylem or phloem cells, has begun (Fig. 1). The accurate delimitation of a population is vital to any model concerned with cell division (Johnson, 1961).

The total cambial cell population of a tree includes the entire multicellular layer between the wood and bark, from behind the root tips to behind the shoot tips. In large trees this layer is composed of an astronomical number of individual cells. As the tree grows, the cambial layer increases in area (Forward and Nolan, 1962). The increase in area results primarily from an increase in the number of cells, rather than an increase in their average size (Bailey, 1923). The increase in cell number occurs in two ways: by the addition of new cells at the extremes of the cambium behind root and shoot tips (Sterling, 1947; Torrey, 1963) or by the interpolation of new cells within the cambium through pseudotransverse division of those cells already present (Bailey, 1923; Bannan, 1951, 1962a; Hejnowicz, 1961). The rate of increase in cell number is lessened by the transformation of individual fusiform cells, apparently through lack of nourishment (Bannan, 1953), and the loss of groups of cells through the death of roots and branches (Ovington, 1961). Ray cambial cells are derived either from reduction in the size of fusiform initials through successive anticlinal divisions, or through markedly unequal pseudotransverse divisions (Bannan, 1934; Barghoorn, 1940).

The total cambial cell population is composed of many radial files of cambial cells. Each radial file comprises a separate cambial population which produces radial files of xylem and phloem cells (Fig. 1). For the rest of this paper the radial cambial files will be called radial populations. New files are formed by pseudotransverse divisions of an initial cell (Bailey 1923; Bannan, 1951). I have calculated from Bannan's (1962a) data that 1–2% of all divisions in a radial file are pseudotransverse divisions, which are not directly related to derivative production. The rest of the divisions are parallel to the surface of the tree and divide the entire length of the cells (periclinal divisions). When a new initial has been formed, it soon begins to divide periclinally to form a new radial population. Periclinal divisions increase the number of cells in a radial population. Differentiation of cells adjacent to the xylem or phloem decrease the number. The balance between the rate of division within the population and the rate of differentiation at its edges determines the actual population size.

The cambium of conifers with growth rings passes through seasonal changes in the size of the radial populations (Brown, 1915; Wight, 1933). When the cambium is dormant the size is at a minimum, usually 2–4 cells. When cambial activity is initiated in the spring the number increases to 12–40 in fast-growing trees and 6–8 in slow-growing trees (Bannan, 1955). Once the size of the radial populations has been established, the number of cells stays the same during the grand period of xylem production. As latewood is formed the rate of cell production drops to zero and the radial number of cambial cells decreases to the dormant condition (Bannan, 1955; Brown, 1915; Wight, 1933).

The radial populations are the units in the cambium which produce cells, so it is important to determine whether all the cells in the population divide and whether they divide at comparable rates. Bannan (1955) has investigated the frequency of divisions across the cambium in *Thuja occidentalis*. His data (Fig. 2) show that divisions occur throughout the cambium, but that there is a peak in frequency approximately in the center of the cambium. There were about twice as many divisions in the middle as on the edges of both wide and narrow cambia. Brown (1915) and Wight (1933) have suggested that there is a relationship

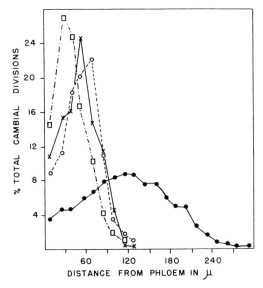

Fɪɢ. 2. The relative frequency of divisions across the cambia of four trees of *Thuja occidentalis*. (Adapted from M. W. Bannan, 1962b.)

between the width of the cambium and the width of the resulting growth rings. Bannan (1955) presented data on this relationship which suggest indirectly that in *Thuja* all cambial cells divide at approximately the same rate. Vigorous trees had cambia 100–150 μ wide and produced 60–120 xylem cells; slow growing trees had cambia 50–60 μ wide and produced 0.5–1.0 mm of xylem. When these data are all converted to cell number, by using Bannan's figure for average cambial cell, radial diameter of 7.9 μ and by assuming 30 xylem cells in a *T. occidentalis* growth ring 0.75 mm wide (Brown *et al.*, 1949, p. 494), the ratio of cambial cell number to final xylem cell number was 5.6 in vigorous trees and 4.3 in slow-growing trees. Thus, in these trees, cambial cells had divided about five times in both fast- and slow-growing trees. The rate of division seems to be *independent of the number of cells in the cambium.*

Cell division is the mechanism by which the cambium produces xylem and phloem derivatives. The division of fusiform cambial cells has been

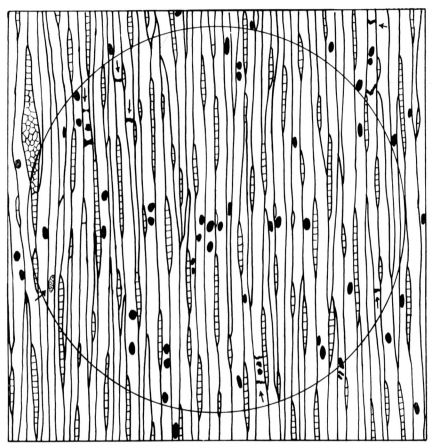

FIG. 3.   Tracing from a photomicrograph of a tangential section through pine cambium. The circle is 1.6 mm in diameter. To the left in the circle an arrow points to a nucleus in prophase of mitosis; other arrows point to phragmoplasts in dividing cells.

studied in detail by Bailey (1920). It is distinctive primarily because of the great length of the cells (2–4 mm) and because the cells divide parallel to their long axis (tangentially). The stages of mitosis are the same as in most plant cells. The nuclei average 20 by 35 μ in tangential view. It is, therefore, easy to spot mitoses, even at early stages of prophase, at only 100 × magnification. The dividing nucleus is located at the center of the cell. Towards the end of mitosis a cell plate, the first step in tangential wall development, forms between the two daughter nuclei. The cell plate is extended both up and down from the daughter nuclei by the activity of the phragmoplasts (Fig. 3). Over time the phragmoplasts move from the center of the cell to the tips, a distance of 1–2 mm. The two phragmoplasts in each cell are always at about the same distance from the daughter nuclei (Fig. 3), so they presumably move at the same rate. Bannan (1955) noted that he could not estimate the time for movement of the phragmoplasts, but that it was "obviously considerably greater than in terminal meristems." A good basis for assuming that the movement takes 1 or 2 days (Wilson, 1963), is that in sections there are usually many phragmoplasts at varying distances from recently divided nuclei even though mitoses themselves are relatively rare. Thus, the great length of the cambial cells results in the presence of phragmoplasts in recently divided cells for some time after mitosis. The phragmoplasts serve as a short-term record of mitotic activity.

Cell Division in the Cambium of White Pine

A quick summation of our knowledge of the cambium as a cell-producing system reveals some gaps. There are several studies of the cambium that essentially describe the limits of the radial populations; others that describe the seasonal changes in population size; a few that relate population size to the number of derivatives produced. There is one investigation of the relative frequency of divisions throughout the cambium. There are no data on the absolute frequency of divisions in the cambium, or in parts of the cambium, at different times, or in different parts of the tree. There are no estimates of the rate at which cells pass through any part of the division cycle, although information about the division cycle of apical meristem cells can serve as a useful guide. The sequence of events during cambial divisions has been studied intensively.

Thus, the major deficiency is information on the rate and frequency of cell division in the cambium. My study of cell division in the cambium of white pine (*Pinus strobus* L.) should clarify some aspects of the frequency of cell division: (1) within radial populations, (2) over time, (3) at different places in the tree, (4) in different trees.

Samples were taken from three trees growing at Petersham, Massachusetts; two were about 25 feet tall, growing in the open in a field; the third was about 65 feet tall, growing in a moderately dense stand. Blocks containing the cambium were removed from the trees, fixed in CRAF solution, and embedded in paraffin. Samples were taken from the first tree from the north, east, south, and west sides of the same internode (between branch whorls) at 12 noon for 4 days. Samples were taken from the second tree from the north side of one internode at 8 a.m., 11 a.m., 2 p.m., 5 p.m., and 8 p.m. for 3 days. Samples were taken from the third tree, the tall tree, from the north side of the tree at 2, 4, 6, and 8 meters above the ground at 8 a.m., 12 noon and 8 p.m. for 3 days.

Two unavoidable problems arise when trying to take successive samples from the same place on a tree. If the samples are too far apart then they are not really from comparable areas. If they are too close the wounding caused by removing one sample may stimulate division and callus formation in adjacent samples. To minimize these problems, samples were taken 1 inch apart. The resulting holes in the trees were filled with vaseline to reduce water loss and callus formation. There was no evidence, either externally or in sections, that removal of samples stimulated cell division or callus formation.

Serial, tangential 15 μ sections, and 15 μ transverse sections were cut through the cambium of each sample. The sections were stained with hematoxylin and orange G, and mounted as permanent microscope slides. Data were taken for each section through the cambium of every sample from the circular field using a 10 x objective and a 10 x eyepiece. The field was 1.6 mm in diameter (Fig. 3). For each sample the field was centered on a particular ray so that comparable fields were used in serial sections. The measurements taken were the total number of nuclei, the number of nuclei in mitosis, and the number of cells with phragmoplasts.

On the basis of the results of this study I shall assume that the frequency of cell division (including mitosis and phragmoplast movement) is the same throughout a radial cambial population. The relative frequency of cell divisions across pine cambia (Fig. 4) was similar to that in *Thuja* cambia (Fig. 2). Data for both species were based on 1200 mitoses; Bannan's data were from serial radial sections of the cambium from four trees, each at one place and time; my data for pine were from serial tangential sections from three trees, averaged for each tree from samples at different places taken over several days. In both species the frequency was highest in the middle of the cambium and dropped rapidly, to almost zero, in the quarter of the cambium nearest the xylem. In pine, the frequency in the half nearest the phloem was almost the same as in the middle, but in *Thuja* the frequency almost halved next to the phloem. The tail of low frequency near the xylem in all the curves probably reflects the variability in cambial width. Because there are fewer cambial cells at the extreme cambial widths, the frequency of mitosis apparently drops. In the two fast-growing pines, xylem production averaged 1.4 cells per day (Table I). The mixture of differentiating cells would have resulted in the sharp drop in frequency of divisions next to the xylem. Production of phloem derivatives was as little as one-tenth that of xylem derivatives, so there was slight mixing of differentiating cells and only a slight drop in frequency next to the phloem in pine.

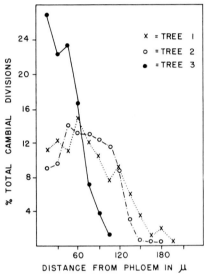

FIG. 4. Relative frequency of cell divisions at different distances from the phloem in three white pine trees (cf. Fig. 2).

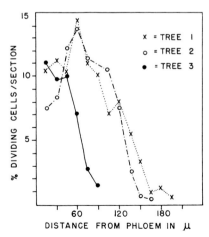

FIG. 5. The percentage of cells in division at different distances from the phloem in three white pine trees.

The data on the relative frequency of cell divisions throughout pine cambia may be presented as a percentage of the total number of cells in one microscope field, hereafter referred to as the absolute frequency of division (Fig. 5). In Fig. 4 the data were given as the percentage of the total number of cells in division across the whole cambium, or the relative frequency. When treated as absolute frequency the data show that about 10% of the cambial cells are in division in all three trees (Fig. 5). Thus, the assumption of a constant frequency of division applies to both

TABLE I

DATA RELATED TO CELL PRODUCTION BY THE CAMBIUM OF THREE WHITE PINE TREES

	Tree 1 (5/17/62; N,S,E,W; 4 days)	Tree 2 (6/13/62; 6 times/day; 3 days)	Tree 3 (4 heights; 6/20/62; 3 times/day; 3 days)
Number of samples	16	15	35
Average % cambial cells dividing	10.6	11.7	9.1
Range	0.4–28.7	4.8–25.0	4.0–22.7
Standard deviation	4.8	4.5	3.9
% Dividing cells in mitosis	22.0	18.2	24.5
Range	5–37	0–44	0–50
Standard deviation	10.7	12.2	17.8
Rate of derivative production/day	1.3–1.5	1.3–1.5	0.7–0.9
Radial population size	13–16	12–14	6–8
Average ½ cell length	1.17 mm	1.10 mm	1.71 mm

fast- and slow-growing trees (with wide and narrow cambia respectively). The curves for absolute frequency are the same shape as those for relative frequency. The same qualifications, discussed above, apply to the portions of the curves near the xylem. If each of these curves were simplified so that the same relative frequency held across the cambium, the absolute frequency would be about 10% in all three trees.

Not only is the averaged frequency of division across the cambium the same in all three trees, but it is nearly the same within these trees in different samples over time, around the tree, and at different heights (Table I). Thus, about 10% of the cells in a section through the cambium were dividing in any sample from these trees, regardless of where and when the samples were taken. This consistent level of division is the basis for assuming that the constant frequency of division applies to any part of the cambium at any time.

The Model

The two major assumptions on which the model for cell production in conifer cambium (Fig. 6) is based, are listed below. Some objections to these assumptions will be discussed later. These assumptions hold

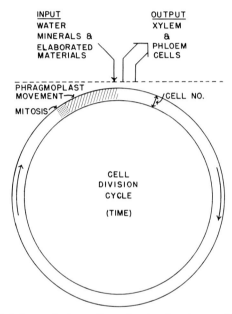

Fig. 6.   A model for analyzing cell production by the cambium of conifers.

only during the grand period of cell production, not at the beginning or end of cambial activity.

I. The size of a radial population is constant.
II. All cells in a radial population divide at the same frequency.

It is implicit in the first assumption that each cell division in the cambium is accompanied by the differentiation of a cambial cell. Each division produces two daughter cells. If a cell in the center of the population divides, then both daughter cells reenter the division cycle and a cell from the edge of the population differentiates. If a cell on the edge of a population divides, then one of the daughter cells differentiates and the other reenters the division cycle. In either case the net reentry to the cycle is one cell per division and there is no net gain in the size of the population. Thus, the rate of division = rate of derivative production (i.e., rate of loss through differentiation from the edge of the cambium) = rate of reentry to the division cycle.

It follows from the second assumption that the time for completion of the division cycle is the same for all cells in the population. With respect to times and rates in the division cycle the radial populations are completely homogeneous.

In the model the cambium is treated as a continuous factory (Fig. 6). Building materials and energy sources are fed in from the xylem and phloem. The materials are made into complex structures and returned to the xylem and phloem as cells. These cells differentiate according to their local environment. The machines which do the work are the self-duplicating individual cells of the cambial populations. At the beginning of each operation the cell, at minimum size, enters the division cycle, represented in the model as a circular, continuous pipeline. The length of the cycle is measured in days and is constant. The width of the pipeline is measured by cell number. The volume of the pipeline is equal to the size of the radial population. The rate of flow is the same throughout the system and the line is always full. During most of the cycle the cells are synthesizing cellular components and doubling in volume, all at the expense of materials from the xylem and phloem. Then the cells divide. The first step is mitosis and the second cytokinesis by phragmoplast movement. When phragmoplast movement is completed there are two new daughter cells and the population is overloaded by one cell. Therefore, a cell adjacent to the xylem or phloem differentiates. In large populations this cell is usually not one of the immediate daughter cells. It presumably starts differentiating fairly early in the division cycle, but just where is not known. A diagram of a series of divisions in a hypothetical cambium (Fig. 7) shows how extra cells in the cambial population may be removed by differentiation. The details of this diagram will be discussed later.

Now that the model has been set up, it is a good idea to consider some objections and limitations to the two assumptions above. The second assumption requires obvious simplification of the data on the frequency of cell division in the cambium (Figs. 2, 4, 5; Table I). There are no specific data which apply to the first assumption. General observation indicates that over periods of a week or so the average size of radial populations stays the same. It is quite likely, however, that for short periods the rate of division in the cambium does not equal the rate of loss through differentiation, so that the population varies in size.

There is no concrete evidence that *all* of the cells in the cambium divide. There might be certain cells or areas in the cambium comparable to the quiescent zone of apical meristems where divisions are infrequent

(Clowes, 1961). No such zone was picked up by Bannan (Fig. 2) or myself (Fig. 4). In addition, in radial sections, occasional radial populations are found in which up to six adjacent cells are all in some stage of division.

The length of the cell division cycle almost certainly varies from cell to cell (Johnson, 1961; Prescott, 1961). The morphological similarity of cambial cells is one of the few bases for assuming that the cells divide at

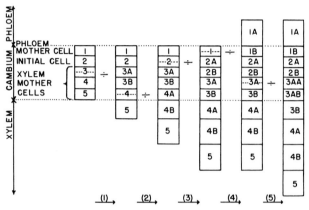

FIG. 7. A hypothetical radial cambial population of five cells, which shows how five successive divisions could affect the production of xylem and phloem cells.

anywhere near the same rate. Possibly variations in rate could be related to variations in cell size.

Rates and Times in the Cell Division Cycle in Pine Cambium

The total time for the cell division cycle in the cambia of the three pine trees can be determined by its relationship to the rate of derivative formation and the size of the radial populations. The rate of derivative production (Table I) was determined by counting the number of derivatives produced over a period of several weeks, dividing by the length of time and assuming that the rate was constant over the whole period. From assumption I, the rate of derivative production equals the rate of cell division. The rate of cell division equals the number of cells in a radial population divided by the length of the division cycle, if assumption II holds. The shorter the cycle, or the larger the population, the greater will be the rate of derivative production. These equations may be solved for the length of the division cycle by substituting the values for cambial cell number and rate of derivative production from the three trees (Table I). The length of time for the cycle in all three trees was about 10 days (Table II).

The cycle has two major parts: synthesis and enlargement, and division itself (Fig. 6). Cell division also has two major parts, mitosis and phragmoplast movement. The relative length of time of each of these three phases is the same as their relative occurrence in sections through the cambium. In the cambial population, 10% of the cells were in division at any one time (Table I), so it follows that 10% of the division cycle, about 1 day (Table II), is spent in division. Of the cells in division, about 20% are in mitosis and the rest in some stage of

TABLE II

ESTIMATED TIMES AND RATES IN THE CELL DIVISION CYCLE OF
THREE WHITE PINE TREES

Tree	Time for cycle (days)	Time for division (hr)	Time for mitosis (hr)	Time for phragmoplast movement (hr)	Rate of phragmoplast movement (μ/hr)
1	10.4	26.4	5.8	20.6	57
2	9.3	26.4	4.8	21.6	47
3	10.4	21.6	5.2	16.4	105

phragmoplast movement (Table I). Therefore, mitosis takes about 20% of the day used for division, or about 5 hours (Table II); the remaining 19 hours are spent in phragmoplast movement. The relative frequency of the stages of mitosis were: prophase 4.7, metaphase 1.5, anaphase 1.0, telophase 3.2. The approximate times based on these frequencies are: prophase 2.4 hours, metaphase 0.4 hours, anaphase 0.7 hours, telophase 1.6 hours.

The phragmoplast takes about 19 hours to move one-half the length of the dividing cells, from the daughter nuclei to the tips. In the three trees the average half-cell length was from 1.1 to 1.7 mm (Table I), so the over-all rate of phragmoplast movement was 50–100 μ per hour.

Other Aspects of Cell Production

The model for cell production by the cambium has made it possible to estimate the times involved in the cell division cycle. The length of the cycle seems to be a nonvariable component of cambial activity. It does not vary with the rate of derivative production. Two major variables are important in determining the rate and amount of cell production. These variables are: for the rate of production, the number of cells in a radial population; for total production, the length of time during which the cambium is active, a factor which varies in dominant and suppressed trees (Kozlowski and Peterson, 1962).

The estimates of times for the division cycle, based on the model, are in line with other estimates from plant meristems. The estimate of 10 days for the whole cycle compares to Bannan's (1955) estimate of 7 days between divisions during the initiation of cambial activity in the spring. In root and shoot apical meristems the entire division cycle takes about 1 to 1½ days (Clowes, 1961; Wimber, 1960). The volume of a root tip cell is of the order of $0.004 \times 10^5 \, \mu^3$ (Jensen and Kavaljian, 1958); the volume of a fusiform cambial cell is about $10 \times 10^5 \, \mu^3$ (computed from Wilson, 1963). Thus, cambial cells are about 2500 times larger than root tip cells. One might expect the division cycle of the larger cells to take considerably longer. The 5 hours for mitosis in pine cambial cells is well within the range of times reported for apical meristem cells (Clowes, 1961; Wimber, 1960). The 19 hours required for phragmoplast movement seems reasonable in view of the extreme length of the fusiform cambial cells. The phragmoplast moves up to $2000 \, \mu$ in cambial cells, as opposed to a few microns, if at all, in apical meristem cells (Bailey, 1920).

A constant time for the division cycle in fast- and slow-growing trees has interesting implications. It may be that once cambial activity is initiated, cell division occurs within the population at a maximum rate limited by the minimum time required for the division cycle. This minimum time would be determined by the large size of the cambial cells. Before a daughter cell redivides it doubles its nuclear and cytoplasmic components. During the grand period of growth this doubling may be limited, not by the availability of materials, energy sources or hormones, but by the time involved in the separate and sequential reactions in the growth process.

If control of cell production is desired, it must come through manipulation of the two variables in the process; the size of radial populations and the length of time available for cambial activity. Many of the factors which control the latter variable have been studied, e.g., the initiation and cessation of cambial activity. Most of them seem to be related to the flow of materials and hormones from the leaves (Larson, 1962; Wareing, 1958). The factors which determine the size of radial populations are unknown. Shortly after cambial activity is initiated, the size of a radial population is determined. After that it stays virtually constant until the end of the season. If the size of a population is due to the balance of the production of new cells by division and the loss of cells through differentiation, then either the rate of division or the rate of differentiation, or both, could determine the size of the population. Unfortunately there are no data on which to assess hypotheses on this subject.

The model is also helpful when considering the problem of the relative production of xylem and phloem derivatives. In fast-growing conifers the ratio of xylem to phloem cells is in excess of 10:1. In both fast- and slow-growing trees, however, the annual radial increment of phloem is about the same (Bannan, 1955; Grillos and Smith, 1959), so that in slow-growing trees the ratio approaches 1:1. There is evidence that all phloem cells are derivatives of the cambial cell immediately adjacent to the phloem, the phloem mother cell; the next cambial cell from the phloem is an initial, which never differentiates and produces both phloem and xylem mother cells; the rest of the cambial cells are xylem mother cells whose derivatives all eventually differentiate to form xylem cells (Bannan, 1955; Newman, 1956). From the point of view of the model, the cambial cells are differentiated from each other only by their position in the radial population.

A diagram of a hypothetical radial population during the grand period of derivative production is shown in Fig. 7. It consists of one phloem mother cell, one initial cell and three xylem mother cells. Phloem cells differentiate only after division of the phloem mother cell. The cell adjacent to the xylem differentiates after division of the initial cell or any of the xylem mother cells. All the cells in the population divide at the same frequency (assumption II). The first three divisions are of initial or xylem mother cells and produce xylem cells. The fourth division is of the phloem mother cell and produces a phloem cell. The fifth division produces another xylem cell.

In this hypothetical population the ratio of phloem to xylem derivatives is the same as the ratio of phloem mother cells to the other cambial cells, 4:1. The faster a tree grows the wider its cambium. The additional width comes from additional xylem mother cells; there is still only one phloem mother cell. The length of the division cycle is the same in fast- and slow-growing trees. Therefore, the annual increment of phloem cells is the same in fast- and slow-growing trees (given the same length of season), but the annual increment of xylem cells varies proportional to the size of the population.

The products of a hypothetical cambium, as in Fig. 7, are quite close to those from actual cambia. *Abies concolor* trees with cambia 14 cells wide produced xylem and phloem cells in a ratio of 14:1 (Wilson, 1963). If this 14-cell cambium were treated as the one in Fig. 7, the predicted ratio would be 13:1. This good fit is strong support for the assumptions made earlier and for the model. Also in *A. concolor*, one phloem cell was produced every 10 days, the length of the division cycle in pine. If the length of the cycle was the same in *A. concolor* as in pine, the phloem mother cell would divide every 10 days and the rate of phloem production would be one cell every 10 days. In fact, A. *concolor* produces derivatives at a rate of 1.4 cells per day, the width of the cambium was 14 cells, so according to the model, the length of the division cycle was 10 days. Here again, the model seems to hold.

DISCUSSION

BAILEY: It seems to me that there is considerable confusion and misuse of the word cambium, in the so-called tissue cultures of the cambium, in chemical analyses of the cambium, and in electron microscopy. What really is the cambium? In a slow-growing conifer or dicotyledon, the cambium is composed of a single layer of initials; in rapidly growing conifers or dicotyledons, there may be as many as three cells which appear to be potentially meristematic. If you study living material cytologically you can detect the beginnings of tracheid formation and of sieve-cell formation by changes in protoplasmic streaming and characteristic changes in the nucleus and nucleoli. It is quite clear that the derivatives of the initials do not lose their capacity for division, particularly in rapidly growing trees, but, because one finds cell divisions in a broad zone one cannot conclude that the whole zone is true cambium. Derivatives of the cambium, after going various distances in differentiation, retain the capacity for cell division, so that if one takes out a fairly thick section and grows it in tissue culture not only derivatives from the cambium but also derivatives from young tracheids and young phloem cells contribute to the callus. The thickness of the true cambial layer on a slow growing tree is from 6 to 8 microns. Rapidly growing trees may have three layers and this zone is three times as thick. We have no good techniques at present for getting out the true initials by themselves.

WILSON: Regardless of whether they are initials or not, if they divide, as far as production of derivatives is concerned, the division is just as good no matter where it occurs.

BAILEY: I cannot agree with that.

SRIVASTAVA: Possibly the actual cambial zone is where the cells in the center of the radial populations are dividing at a faster rate.

WILSON: I was surprised that using this approach I did not pick up any differences between initials and derivatives of initials which can still divide. There was no suggestion of anything like a quiescent zone.

BAILEY: A cytological study of the living material with vital stains, etc., would indicate the earliest stages of the transformation of a cell into a tracheid or phloem cell.

WARDROP: I would like to present the view that there is only one cell which is true cambium. Newman (1956) has looked at cambial divisions in transverse section. When a division occurs, the parent wall surrounds the initial and the xylem mother cell. The xylem mother cell may then divide again producing another parent wall and a new wall around each of the daughter cells. So in the differentiating zone one sees the cambium and groups of either two or more cells surrounded by a parent wall. In this way the cell which is the cambium can be distinguished. Newman's conclusion was that there is only one persisting cell; the others are already determined as xylem or phloem. In these terms one can hardly justify treating the cambial zone as a population.

WILSON: I would say that the populations are homogenous with respect to division. I do not intend to say that a phloem mother cell is the same as a xylem mother cell.

BARGHOORN: In studying the ontogeny of rays in both conifers and dicotyledons, it is quite evident that there is only a single initial. The origin and dropping out of the rays is very quickly expressed because of the geometry of the tissues. I would agree with the definition of the cambium as a single layer; it is not just a group of cells.

WILCOX: What were the dates on the three trees?

WILSON: The samples were taken in mid-May, mid-June, and late-June.

WILCOX: How can there be a constant rate of division of 10% throughout the season? I would expect the rate to be greater during the surge of activity in the early spring and again during the production of latewood. Did you not observe the midseason pause which is so common? Can the generalization you have made about the whole season be supported on the basis of three 3-day samples? I would think that seasonal periodicity must occur.

WILSON: I have a feeling, with little evidence to support it at present, that the cambium divides at more or less the same rate during a season and then stops. Those cells in the process of radial enlargement then turn into latewood.

ESAU: I think we can use the term "cambial initial" for the cell which presumably stays there indefinitely, barring the losses which have been discussed, and then speak of cambium as an indefinite zone of cambial initials plus their immediate derivatives, recognizing, of course, that these are already determined as phloem and xylem cells. In teaching, it is extremely difficult to say to the student, "This is cambium." You have to admit that you do not recognize the cambium unless you make a developmental study. One could simply call the zone of dividing cells cambium or cambial zone, and use cambial initials in speaking of the theoretical aspect that there is only one cell in proper position to give rise to cells in both directions.

BAILEY: I think it would be all right to use the term "cambial zone," provided one realizes what it is.

REFERENCES

Bailey, I. W. (1920). *Am. J. Botany* **7**, 417-434.
Bailey, I. W. (1923). *Am. J. Botany* **10**, 499-509.
Bannan, M. W. (1934). *Botan. Gaz.* **96**, 260-281.
Bannan, M. W. (1951). *Can. J. Botany* **29**, 421-437.
Bannan, M. W. (1953). *Can. J. Botany* **31**, 63-74.
Bannan, M. W. (1955). *Can. J. Botany* **33**, 113-138.
Bannan, M. W. (1962a). *Can. J. Botany* **40**, 1057-1062.
Bannan, M. W. (1962b). *In* "Tree Growth" (T. T. Kozlowski, ed.), pp. 3-21. Ronald Press, New York.
Barghoorn, E. S. (1940). *Bull. Torrey Botany Club.* **67**, 303-328.
Brown, H. P. (1915). *Botan. Gaz.* **59**, 197-241.
Brown, H. P., Panshin, A. J., and Forsaith, C. C. (1949). "Textbook of Wood Technology." McGraw-Hill, New York.
Bünning, E. (1952). *Surv. Biol. Progr.* **2**, 105-140.
Clowes, F. A. L. (1961). "Apical Meristems." Blackwell Scientific Publications, Oxford.
Forward, D. F., and Nolan, N. J. (1962). *Can. J. Botany* **40**, 95-111.
Hejnowicz, Z. (1961). *Acta Soc. Botan. Poloniae* **30**, 729-747.
Grillos, S. J., and Smith, F. H. (1959). *Forest Sci.* **5**, 377-388.
Jensen, W. A., and Kavaljian, L. G. (1958). *Am. J. Botany* **45**, 365-372.
Johnson, H. A. (1961). *Cytologia* **26**, 32-41.
Kozlowski, T. T., and Peterson, T. A. (1962). *Botan. Gaz.* **124**, 146-154.

Larson, P. R.   (1962).   *In* "Tree Growth" (T. T. Kozlowski, ed.), pp. 97-117. Ronald Press, New York.
Newman, I. V.   (1956). *Phytomorphology* **6**, 1-19.
Ovington, J. D.   (1961).   *Ann. Botany* **25**, 12-20.
Prescott, D. M.   (1961). *Intern. Rev. Cytol.* **11**, 255-282.
Sterling, C.   (1947).   *Am. J. Botany* **34**, 272-280.
Torrey, J. G.   (1963).   *In* "Symposia of the Society for Experimental Biology," Number XVII. Cambridge Univ. Press, Cambridge. (in press).
Wareing, P. F.   (1958). *J. Inst. Wood Sci.* **1**, 34-42.
Wight, W.   (1933).   *New Phytol.* **32**, 77-96.
Wilson, B. F.   (1963).   *Am. J. Botany* **50**, 95-102.
Wimber, D. E.   (1960).   *Am. J. Botany* **47**, 828-834.

Structure and Development of the Bark in Dicotyledons

Katherine Esau

University of California, Santa Barbara, California

The bark, or the tissue system outside the vascular cambium in a stem or root, shows variations in structure that are related to differences in structure and development of the component tissues. It includes at various times primary and secondary tissues, specifically, phloem, cortex, epidermis, and, later, also periderm. When periderms arise in deep layers of the bark and isolate blocks of tissue (cortex and, later, phloem) from the underlying tissues, the outer part of the bark thus isolated becomes the rhytidome. The bark is a more complex tissue system than the wood in both development and structure. It is also technically less accessible for study and, therefore, the information on the bark is much scantier, and often considerably less reliable, than that on the wood.

In the following, I shall discuss selected features of the bark and briefly mention others, chiefly by reference to illustrations.

The Phloem

Sclerenchyma

The dominant tissue in the bark is the secondary phloem. The most conspicuous variations in phloem structure result from differences in composition and in distribution of the component elements. Among the typical cell types in the phloem, the sclerenchyma cells give a particularly characteristic aspect to the secondary phloem (Holdheide, 1951; Santos, 1960; Zahur, 1959). In some species, sclerenchyma is lacking in the secondary phloem (Fig. 1), in others, fibers are present, and these may be distributed irregularly (Fig. 2) or in tangential bands (Fig. 3); still other species contain fibers and sclereids (Figs. 4 and 5) or sclereids only.

Older phloem usually shows more intense sclerification than the younger. Sclereids often differentiate in the older tissue whether or not fibers occur in the younger (Figs. 4, 5, and 7). Fibers themselves may develop only after the sieve elements have ceased to conduct (Fig. 9).

37

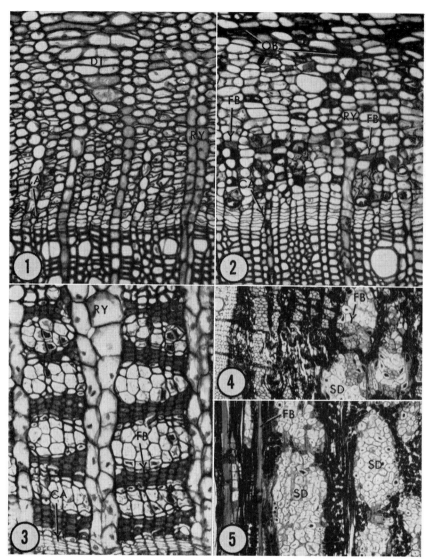

Figs. 1-5. Sclerenchyma in the secondary phloem.—Fig. 1. Transection of phloem of *Daphniphyllum* sp. (Daphniphyllaceae). Secondary phloem without sclerenchyma. Some dilatation of axial parenchyma at DI. Secondary xylem below cambium (CA). Fig. 2. Transection of phloem, above, and xylem, below, of *Litsea calicaris* Kirk (Lauraceae). Secondary phloem with scattered fibers (FB). Also scattered tannin cells (with dark contents). Crushed sieve elements at OB. Fig. 3. Transection of phloem of *Magnolia grandiflora* L. (Magnoliaceae). Fibers (FB) in tangential layers. Figs. 4 and 5. Phloem of *Quercus rubra* L. (Fagaceae) in transverse (Fig. 4) and radial (Fig. 5) sections. Some xylem to the left in Fig. 4. Fibers (FB) occur in the younger phloem, fibers and sclereids (SD) in the older. Details: CA, vascular cambium; DI, dilatation of parenchyma; FB, fibers; OB, obliteration of sieve elements; RY, ray; SD, sclereids. Figs. 1, 2, × 170; Fig. 3, × 150; Figs. 4, 5, × 60.

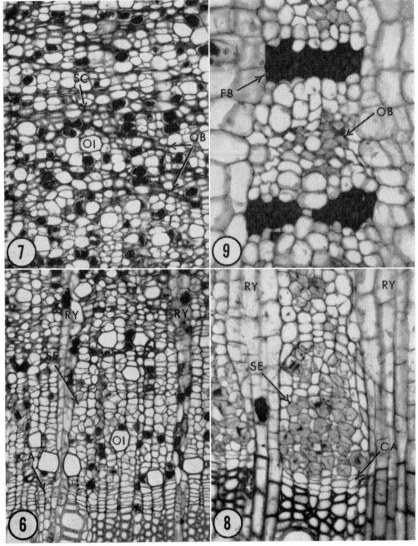

FIGS. 6–9. Obliteration in secondary phloem.—FIGS. 6 and 7. Transection of younger (Fig. 6) and older (Fig. 7) phloem of *Cryptocarya rubra* Skeels (Lauraceae). Sieve elements (SE) open in Fig. 6, crushed (OB) in Fig. 7. Tannin cells with dark contents. Sclerified parenchyma (SC) and sclereids occur in the old phloem. FIGS. 8 and 9. Transection of younger (Fig. 8) and older (Fig. 9) phloem of *Annona Cherimola* Mill. (Annonaceae). Sieve elements (SE in Fig. 8) have thick nacreous walls and are partly crushed (OB in Fig. 9) in the old phloem. Fibers (FB) differentiate in the old phloem. Details: CA, vascular cambium; FB, fibers; OB, obliteration of sieve elements; OI, oil cells; RY, ray; SC, sclerified parenchyma cells; SE, sieve element. Figs. 6, 7, × 160; Figs. 8, 9, × 190.

Parenchyma cells frequently become sclerified in the old phloem without necessarily assuming the characteristics of sclereids.

The classification of sclerenchyma cells and their delimitation from one another are problematical. One usually thinks of true phloem fibers as cells longer than the fusiform cambial initials from which they were derived and maturing in the conducting phloem. Yet, sclerenchyma cells that develop in the older, nonconducting phloem may also undergo elongation by intrusive growth (*Casuarina equisetifolia* L.) and, conversely, fibers differentiating near the cambium may fail to elongate (*Persea americana* Mill.; *P. lingue* Nees; Fig. 11). Thus, occurrence of intrusive growth is not correlated with the time of maturation of sclerenchyma cells.

The fibers that mature in the nonconducting phloem are sometimes classified as sclereids or sclerotic fibers (cf. Holdheide, 1951) despite their similarity to fibers in the conducting phloem. The use of the term sclereids for these cells stresses the lack of sharp distinction between sclereids and fibers. When the sclereids are relatively short and have heavily lignified walls with numerous pits, they are clearly distinguishable from fibers. Such sclereids may be also considerably wider than fibers (Figs. 4 and 5). But longer sclereids may intergrade with the fibers in both form and wall structure.

Sclereids also intergrade with sclerified parenchyma cells. The latter are considered to be cells that develop moderately thick lignified secondary walls but retain active protoplasts. Sclerified parenchyma cells, however, may become nonliving depositories of crystals. The "septate crystalliferous fibers," or Kristallkammerfasern of the German literature (Holdheide, 1951) are usually sclerified parenchyma strands (see also Chang, 1954; Milanez, 1942). A broad comparative study would, no doubt, increase our understanding of the differences between the representatives of sclerenchyma but could hardly be expected to eliminate the problem of intergrading.

One of the promising aspects for comparative studies of phloem sclerenchyma appears to be the degree of elongation of fibers during their ontogeny. The brief study of Santos (1960) comparing lengths of vessel members, xylem fibers, and phloem fibers of 25 species in 19 genera in 16 families of dicotyledons indicates that in a given species the degree of elongation of phloem fibers is similar, but not necessarily equal, to that of the xylem fibers. It also suggests an inverse relation between the initial length of the phloem fiber (as judged by the length of the vessel member) and the amount of increase of this length during fiber ontogeny.

THE CONDUCTING PHLOEM

When we relate the structure of the bark to that of the phloem we actually refer to the part of the phloem that has ceased to be concerned with longitudinal translocation. The conducting phloem constitutes only a small part of the bark. The characteristics of the conducting phloem have been dealt with in numerous publications and need not be reviewed here. But I would like to bring together the information on the amount of conducting phloem in the bark, a matter of importance for the characterization of the bark and of interest with regard to translocation. The recognition of the conducting part of the phloem depends, of course, on the knowledge of the developmental history of the sieve elements, particularly of that of their sieve areas.

The thickness of the active phloem may be expected to vary like the width of the annual increments of the wood in relation to the age of the tree and its growing conditions. The values given below should be regarded, therefore, merely as examples of the thickness of this phloem. The width of the conducting phloem in trees of the temperate zone usually measures in fractions of a millimeter (Fig. 10). Zimmermann's (1961) studies, for example, give 0.2 mm for *Fraxinus americana* L. and *Tectona grandis* L. Holdheide (1951, p. 205) recorded the following widths of annual increments in species whose sieve elements function only one season (in such species the width of conducting phloem may be considered equal to that of an annual increment): 0.2–0.3 mm for *Quercus, Fagus, Acer, Betula;* 0.4–0.7 mm for *Ulmus* and *Juglans;* and exceptionally large values of 0.8–1.0 mm for *Salix* and *Populus.* Whitmore (1962) assumes that a layer of 5–6 mm of the phloem is conducting in the Dipterocarpaceae but does not support this assumption by developmental studies of the sieve elements. Since he uses the estimated values for thickness of active phloem in his calculations of the longevity of sieve elements these calculations are also uncertain.

The determination of longevity of sieve elements depends on the recognition of the boundaries between conducting and nonconducting phloem and those between the successive annual increments. The early phloem frequently consists of more or less distinctly wider cells than the later formed tissue. The two parts of the phloem may also differ in the amount of parenchyma (Holdheide, 1951). If these differences are not obliterated in the senile phloem, annual increments may be recognized. In his major survey of the condition of the phloem in the bark, Holdheide (1951) found that in the majority of European dicotyledon trees the sieve elements function only one season. For the well-known exception, *Tilia,* Holdheide (1951) gives the value of 10 years for *T. cordata* Mill. and Evert (1962), 1–5 years for *T. americana* L.

Using the data on the width of conducting phloem and the transectional area of this phloem occupied by sieve elements, Holdheide (1951, p. 208) arrived at an average figure of 0.1–2.5 mm² of conducting area per 1 mm of stem circumference. Interestingly enough, *Tilia* had only 0.015 mm² of conducting area per 1 mm of stem circumference in a single annual increment, but for 10 annual increments—as mentioned, *Tilia* sieve elements may remain in functional condition for 10 years—

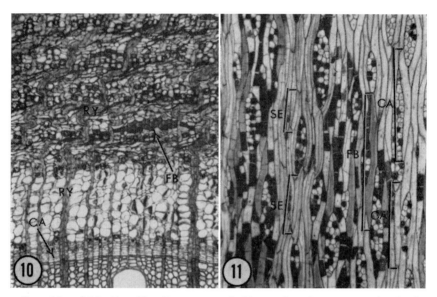

Figs. 10 and 11.—Fig. 10.   Transection of phloem of *Juglans regia* L. (Juglandaceae) illustrating contrast between conducting phloem with wide open sieve elements (above cambium CA) and the nonconducting phloem with crushed sieve elements and distorted rays (RY). The conducting phloem is approximately 0.25 mm wide. Fig. 11. Tangential section of phloem of *Persea lingue* Nees (Lauraceae) illustrating results of divisions in phloem mother cells: sieve elements (SE) are shorter and narrower than cambial cells (CA). Fibers (FB) are similar to cambial cells in length. Details: CA, cambium or cambial cells; FB, fiber; RY, ray; SE, sieve element. Both × 70.

the value for the conducting area was 0.15 mm². Holdheide's figures may be used to calculate the per cent of transectional area of active phloem occupied by sieve elements. For *Ulmus* and *Robinia* he gives, respectively, the values of 0.15–0.20 mm² and 0.18 mm² of conducting area per 1 mm of stem circumference. In both genera the annual increments of phloem measured 0.4–0.7 mm in width. These figures would give approximately 25–50% for the conducting area in the active phloem.

Although the conducting phloem constitutes only a small proportion of the bark, this part of the tissue alone is suitable for determination of such characters as shape and length of sieve elements; presence of nacreous walls in these cells; inclination and structure of the sieve plates; size, shape, and numbers of companion cells; full range of variation of parenchyma cells (some may be obliterated in the nonconducting phloem); and, finally, the recently discovered occurrence of divisions in phloem mother cells that reduce the potential size of sieve elements (Fig. 11). The rays also should be examined in the active phloem because they may become much modified in the older tissue especially through dilatation. All the characters listed above are of first importance in comparative studies of the bark.

THE NONCONDUCTING PHLOEM

The changes that occur in the phloem after the sieve elements cease to conduct varies considerably in different species. As already reviewed, intensive sclerification affects this tissue in many species. Then, there are differences in pattern and degree of obliteration of sieve elements (compare Figs. 7, 9, and 10). The collapse of the sieve elements may cause a large reduction in the width of an increment (Holdheide, 1951, p. 206). Crystals are common inclusions in the phloem. They occur in the conducting as well as the nonconducting phloem but are more abundant in the latter partly because their deposition is often a concomitant of sclerification. The types and distribution of crystals are valuable characteristics for comparative studies (cf. Holdheide, 1951; Moeller, 1882). Deposition of other ergastic substances, especially of starch and phenolic compounds, and the presence and kind of secretory structures are also of diagnostic value (Moeller, 1882).

Profound changes in the appearance of the aging phloem are brought about by dilatation, or expansion, resulting from enlargement and division of axial and ray parenchyma cells. Some enlargement of axial parenchyma commonly occurs concomitantly with the collapse of sieve elements (Figs. 6–9) but there may be a more intensive growth of the parenchymatous elements so that wide wedges of tissue are interpolated among existing cell complexes. The great increase in width of rays in many species is a familiar phenomenon. This increase may occur through repeated orderly divisions in the median part of the ray so that one might speak of a dilatation meristem (Schneider, 1955). Axial parenchyma may form similar wedges with a meristematic layer in median position (e.g., *Eucalyptus;* Chattaway, 1955). Whitmore (1962) found that the Malaysian Dipterocarpaceae differ in the pattern and amount of dilatation, some showing this phenomenon mainly in the rays, others

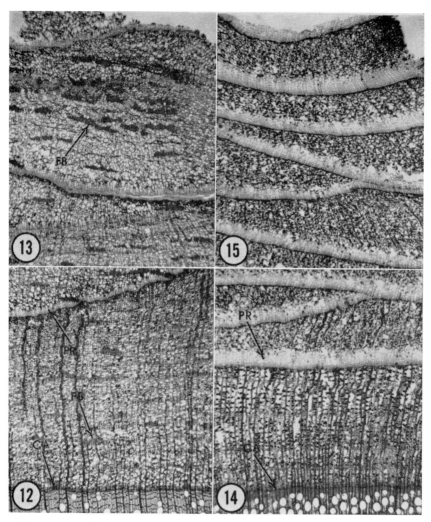

Figs. 12–15. Rhytidome—Figs. 12 and 13. Transections of innermost (Fig. 12) phloem and outermost (Fig. 13) parts of bark of *Juglans nigra* L. (Juglandaceae). Secondary phloem between cambium (CA) and innermost periderm (PR in Fig. 12) is 2–3 mm wide; a layer only 0.2 mm wide, near the cambium, was in conducting state. The rhytidome begins with the innermost periderm (PR). It consists of narrow layers of periderm and wide layers of secondary phloem. In this phloem the parenchyma cells are markedly enlarged (above PR in Fig. 12 and in Fig. 13) and the rays obscured. The total width of rhytidome was 5–6 mm. Figs. 14 and 15. Transections of innermost (Fig. 14) and outermost (Fig. 15) parts of bark of *Cephalanthus occidentalis* L. (Rubiaceae). Secondary phloem between cambium (CA) and innermost periderm (PR) is 1.5 mm wide. The rhytidome begins with the innermost periderm (PR). Its total width was 4.5 mm. In the *Cephalanthus* rhytidome the layers of periderm are wider and those of phloem are narrower than in *Juglans*. Details: CA, vascular cambium; FB, fibers; PR, periderm. All × 20.

44

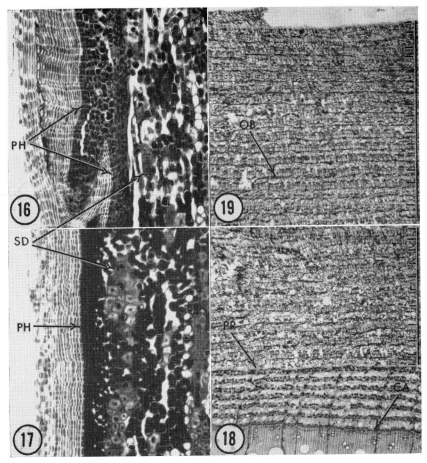

Figs. 16–19.—Figs. 16 and 17. Transverse (Fig. 16) and radial (Fig. 17) sections of bark of *Myrica pennsylvanica* Loisel (Myricaceae). To the right in each figure is the lacunose cortex with sclereids (SD). Fig. 16 illustrates the beginning of rhytidome formation: below in the figure phellogen (PH) has arisen at a new, deeper position. The phellem cells have thick walls. A considerable amount of phelloderm is present, well defined at the right of phellogen (PH) in Fig. 16. Figs. 18 and 19. Transections of innermost (Fig. 18) and outermost (Fig. 19) parts of the bark of *Sassafras albidum* Nees (Lauraceae). Secondary phloem from the vascular cambium (CA) to the innermost periderm (PR) 0.75 mm wide. Conducting phloem 0.1 mm wide. Rhytidome beginning with the innermost periderm in Fig. 18 and throughout Fig. 19. Total width of rhytidome was 4.5 mm. The secondary phloem consists of tangentially alternating layers of (1) sieve elements and associated nucleate cells (light layers in figures) and (2) fibers and parenchyma cells (dark layers in figures). In the rhytidome the parenchyma cells in the light-colored bands are enlarged and the sieve elements crushed (OB). The horizontal dashes at the right edge in Figs. 18 and 19 indicate positions of successive periderms. They arose in the darkly stained tangential layers. Details: CA, vascular cambium; OB, obliteration of sieve elements; PH, phellogen; PR, periderm; SD, sclereids. Fig. 16, × 80; Fig. 17, × 100; Figs. 18 and 19, × 20.

in the axial parenchyma. Of particular interest is Chattaway's (1953) observation that in *Eucalyptus* the enlargement of parenchyma cells may occur outside the most recently initiated periderm. Figure 12 indicates the same timing for dilatation in *Juglans*: the parenchyma cells on the outside of the innermost periderm (PR) are larger than those on the inside of it.

The dilatation of rays increases their conspicuousness in the tissue. In some species the rays do not enlarge and may become displaced (Fig. 10), or even obscured (Figs. 1, 7, and 12, above PR), by changes in the axial part of the phloem.

Periderm and Rhytidome

As is well known, the periderm itself varies in structural details such as amount, kind, size, and shape of cells. Moreover, it shows developmental variations as expressed in timing, depth, and frequency of origin. These characteristics of the periderm affect in great measure the nature of the rhytidome and the manner in which it separates from the tree. The thick-walled phellem in Figs. 16 and 17 may be contrasted with the thin-walled cork in Fig. 14. Figures 16 and 17 show the first periderm in cross and radial sections and Fig. 16 illustrates the appearance of the first deeper seated periderm initiating the rhytidome. Figures 12–18 give examples of variability in thickness of periderm layers. According to Bamber (1962), differences in the phellem appear to be most significant in regard to classification of the tribe Leptospermoideae on the basis of bark structure.

In the rhytidome of *Juglans nigra* L. (Figs. 12 and 13) narrow periderms cut off relatively wide layers of secondary phloem and these are compact because of dilatation of parenchyma. Phloem fibers are present in this rhytidome. The layers of periderm in *Cephalanthus occidentalis* L. (Figs. 14 and 15) are rather wide and the phloem of the rhytidome is lacunose and devoid of sclerenchyma. *Sassafras albidum* Nees (Figs. 18 and 19) illustrates rhytidome with exceptionally narrow layers of both periderm and phloem. The small amount of overlapping of periderm layers in *Sassafras* suggests a ring-bark type of rhytidome as contrasted with the scaly type in which the periderms overlap (Figs. 12–15) and cut off more or less restricted portions of phloem.

The differences in spatial frequencies of periderms in the three species just discussed are probably expressions of differences in frequencies with reference to time of initiation of the successive periderms. Holdheide (1951, p. 232) states that variable numbers of annual increments are included between successive periderms in different species, but that yearly initiation of periderms is exceptional (*Salix, Populus*).

Rhytidomes vary in total thickness depending on the manner of abscission of their layers and probably also in relation to environmental conditions. Growth habit too plays a role, with shrubs frequently having thinner bark. Some figures for the thickness of rhytidome are given in the legends to Figs. 12–15 and 18–19, but it is not certain whether all of the original thickness of the bark was present in the finished slides. Holdheide (1951, p. 201) cites the following values for the thickness of the entire bark: *Clematis*, 0.8–1.0 mm; *Robinia*, 2–3 mm; *Cornus sanguinea* L., 0.3–0.6 mm; *Cornus mas* L., up to 2.2 mm; *Sorbus*, up to 10 mm; and *Juglans* and *Fagus* up to 14 mm. According to Holdheide, the bark becomes thinner as the stem ages.

Whitmore (1962) has calculated that faster rate of growth of phloem is correlated with greater width of layers cut off by the periderms. He also reports that in the Dipterocarpaceae a greater ratio of xylem to phloem formation results in more pronounced dilatation and thinner rhytidome. Finally, the greater amount of rhytidome is associated with deeper fissuring of the surface.

The causal relations in the initiation of periderms are little known. Species apparently have inherent differences in this regard but environmental conditions also play an important role. Zeeuw (1941), for example, has supplied the following data on the influence of exposure to sun on the time of production of the first periderm. The mean age of the stem with deep periderm formation under conditions of insolation and shading, respectively, was 7.1 and 12.9 for *Fraxinus*, 16.0 and 21.4 for *Liriodendron*, and 19.6 and 34.9 for *Pinus*. Thus, insolation hastened the formation of deep cork in these species without obliterating the basic differences between species.

Conclusion

The principal part of the bark of trees consists of secondary phloem. Thus, the proper characterization of the bark presupposes first of all the knowledge of the structure and development of the phloem, particularly of the part of the phloem that is no longer conducting but constitutes the bulk of the bark. The periderm affects the character of the bark by its own structural details and by the timing, depth, and frequency of its initiation in the bark. In older bark, the periderm and phloem together determine the characteristics of the rhytidome; in younger bark, cortex also is included. The cortex, of course, constitutes a prominent part of the bark before the rhytidome develops.

Discussion

Tomlinson: What criteria do you use to decide that sieve tubes are still conducting? All your preparations seemed to show the presence of callose in the region of conducting phloem. Do conducting sieve tubes include callose?

Esau: As far as we know, at least with reference to the methods that we use in the preparation of phloem, one does not find sieve elements without callose, except in the very early stages of their ontogeny. If the callose is massive, we say that the sieve element is approaching cessation of conduction, or that it has been injured. Sieve tubes that we consider functioning show an intermediate stage: Callose is present, but the pores are not closed. In addition we ordinarily can recognize stainable material within these pores, which we loosely describe as connecting strands. I consider this appearance an abnormal phenomenon, but at the same time, we do not find the same situation in the nonconducting elements. I should add that in conducting cells we sometimes do not recognize the stainable material because of effects of processing. So we look for not too massive callose and open pores or pores filled with stainable material. Naturally we also expect the cell to be enucleate.

Tomlinson: Are you aware to what extent callose deposition is an artifact?

Esau: This is the big argument of today. There is some evidence that callose deposition is triggered very rapidly. The question is whether *all* of the callose that we *ever* see in the plant is the result of this mechanism of response to wounding. There is a recent paper by Eschrich (1963) describing "blitz" reaction in callose deposition.

Zimmermann: Callose may provide a very good means of determining whether or not a sieve tube is functioning. Only a functioning sieve tube has the ability to form callose rapidly. But this does not mean that callose has a function in translocation. It is probably only a sealing compound.

Esau: I would add the following. With our methods we see callose and use its presence as a criterion, but do not guarantee that it is not an artifact.

Tomlinson: Do you know of any studies on trees with anomalous secondary structure that have included phloem? I am interested in the problem of longevity of sieve tubes.

Esau: I know of no such studies specifically with reference to longevity.

Wilcox: You mentioned dimensions of under a millimeter of functioning phloem, and figures for *Tilia* for long life. I want to put the two together and ask if this means that phloem mother cells are cutting off derivatives much more slowly in a species like *Tilia*, or that an annual increment of phloem is very much less.

Esau: The paper by Holdheide (1951) includes a statement about that. To his amazement, he had to include all of the 10 years in order to obtain the same figure for conducting area per millimeter of circumference as he obtained from the others with just one increment. Apparently that would mean that the increments are narrower.

Wilcox: There is then, no study of the course of seasonal ontogeny of a species such as this?

Esau: One is under way, by R. F. Evert at Wisconsin.

Brown: In maturation of sieve elements in *Populus*, the nucleoli remain for quite some time after the nuclei disintegrate. Is this a fairly general phenomenon for nucleoli?

Esau: It is not a general phenomenon.

Brown: I wonder if this could be related to cellular metabolism in some way?

Esau: I do not know; it deserves more consideration, especially in view of our present knowledge of the relationship between nucleoli and RNA.

NELSON: When growth starts in the spring in this part of the country, is last year's phloem conducting? Does callose disappear?

ESAU: As a rule not. In a majority of species new phloem is formed. I think that as we study more species we will find that generally a small amount of phloem is left in an undifferentiated state in the cambial zone which differentiates before new phloem is formed. It is rather exceptional for the old phloem to begin functioning again. Of course, *Vitis* shows this kind of behavior. When callose is removed, the sieve tubes acquire the same characteristics as they had when they were newly differentiated. Later, new phloem is formed and the previous year's phloem develops definitive callose and ceases to function. In our deciduous trees, either some phloem differentiates from last year's phloem mother cells and begins to function before new elements are formed, or new elements are formed immediately.

BAILEY: In white pine the first sign of approaching cambial activity can be seen during a warm day as early as February. It is a change from a dry to a watery appearance. The second sign is the appearance of starch which had disappeared during the winter, and the third, if I remember correctly, is the maturation of new sieve cells. This maturation is one of the symptoms of the beginning of new growth.

ESAU: The question is whether the new sieve cells are produced by the cambium during the current season, or whether they are remnants of last year's cambial activity.

BAILEY: They seem to be elements which had started development in late summer, wintered over in an undifferentiated condition, and completed maturation in early spring.

ESAU: I think this is general. We just finished studying *Liriodendron* at Davis and found the same behavior. There are incompletely differentiated sieve elements with companion cells already cut off, both still with nuclei, in our winter collections. I think that a quick maturation of these elements occurs in the spring.

PRESTON: Is there any evidence as to the length of the sieve tubes, in the sense of files of cells, each end terminated by a complete wall? Does the sieve tube run the whole length of the plant, or is it quite short? I am thinking of sieve tubes in analogy with vessels.

ESAU: There is no exact analogy to vessels, because the same kind of sieve plates occur throughout. The concept of a sieve tube is entirely theoretical. I have not seen a sieve element with a sieve plate on one end only.

WAREING: The formation of the first sieve elements in the spring presumably normally precedes bud break. Is there any evidence that disbudding shoots prevents the appearance of new sieve elements?

ESAU: I know of no experiments in that direction.

ZIEGLER: To come back to the question of the longevity of sieve tubes, I think we should differentiate between deciduous and evergreen trees. In gymnosperms the phloem functions for more than 1 year; in *Picea,* according to Huber (1939), at least 2 years and sometimes 3. Are there specific differences between evergreen angiosperms and deciduous angiosperms concerning the longevity of the sieve tubes?

ESAU: Not that I know of. I would not rely on any data of longevity unless the study had been carried through several years with careful determination of development of the sieve elements and studies of cambial activity.

ZIEGLER: Since sieve-tube exudate can be obtained from evergreen oaks during the whole year, there must be functioning phloem. In this case the phloem does not cease to function in autumn. The phloem of evergreen dicotyledons probably functions longer than that of deciduous species. I would like to emphasize the necessity for a careful study of evergreen dicotyledons.

REFERENCES

Bamber, R. K. (1962). *Australian J. Botany* **10**, 25-54.

Chang, Y.-P. (1954). *Tappi Monograph Ser.* **14.**

Chattaway, M. M. (1953). *Australian J. Botany* **1**, 402-433.

Chattaway, M. M. (1955). *Australian J. Botany* **3**, 170-176.

Eschrich, W. (1963). *Planta* **59**, 243-261.

Evert, R. F. (1962). *Am. J. Botany* **49**, 659.

Holdheide, W. (1951). *In* "Handbuch der Mikroskopie in der Technik" (H. Freund, ed.), Vol. 5(1), pp. 195-367.

Huber, B. (1939). *Jahrb. wiss. Botanik* **88**, 176-242.

Milanez, F. R. (1942). *Chronica Botanica* **7**, 68-69.

Moeller, J. (1882). "Anatomie der Baumrinden." Springer, Berlin.

Santos, C. R. de Oliveira (1960). *Rev. Agr. Brazil* **35**, 199-206.

Schneider, H. (1955). *Am. J. Botany* **42**, 893-905.

Whitmore, T. G. (1962). *New Phytol.* **61**, 191-220.

Zahur, M. S. (1959). *Cornell Univ. Agr. Expt. Sta. Mem.* **358.**

Zeeuw, C. De. (1941). *N. Y. State Coll. Forestry, Syracuse Univ. Bull.* **56.**

Zimmermann, M. H. (1961). *Science* **133**, 73-79.

Aspects of Ultrastructure of Phloem[1]

KATHERINE ESAU

University of California, Santa Barbara, California

Electron microscopy is revealing ontogenetic and structural details in phloem unforeseen in studies with the light microscope, but it also raises new questions the answers to which require further refinements in techniques. Although we may be justified in feeling encouraged, and even enthusiastic, about the discoveries at the ultrastructural level, the circumstance that the material must be killed and dehydrated for examination with the electron microscope cannot be ignored. We are forced to rely heavily on speculation in our efforts to relate living phenomena to the information derived from electron microscopy.

In studies of phloem with the electron microscope the sieve element attracts the principal attention for obvious reasons. The explanation of the mechanism of translocation of organic substances depends on the full understanding of the structure of this cell. Of particular interest are the nature of the protoplast of the sieve element and the structure of the sieve areas by means of which the individual sieve elements are connected with one another.

Since the sieve elements are rather sensitive to manipulations necessary in microscopic work, it is not surprising that the results obtained by various investigators are not uniform and views on the characteristics of the sieve element continue to be contradictory (Duloy *et al.*, 1961; Esau and Cheadle, 1961, 1962a; Kollmann, 1960). I am presenting one of these views by describing the results obtained in our laboratory, mainly those on the sieve elements of *Cucurbita maxima* Duchesne and *Vitis vinifera* L.

The *Cucurbita* phloem was killed by injection of the KMnO₄ solution into the hollow petiole (Esau and Cheadle, 1961). The phloem of *Vitis* was pretreated with sucrose solution according to Currier *et al.* (1955)

[1] The research that served as a basis for this presentation was supported in part by the National Science Foundation Grant G-14424 and the Public Health Service Grant R.G. 5868.

51

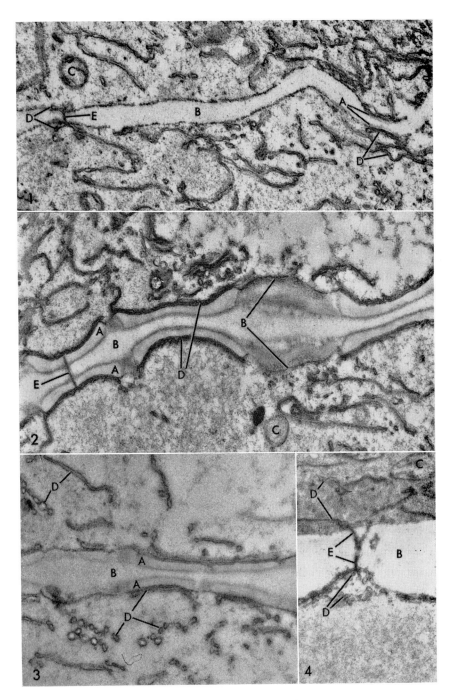

before it was killed with KMnO₄. The illustrations used in this presentation are all from material imbedded in methacrylate. We think that, with regard to the protoplasts, the *Cucurbita* tissues were less denatured by the preparation for microscopy than those of *Vitis*.

Sieve Areas and Protoplasts of *Cucurbita* Sieve Elements

The structure of the sieve plate is best understood when followed through its development (Esau *et al.*, 1962). In young sieve elements the future sieve plate appears like any other primary wall except that it shows fewer plasmodesmata than walls separating parenchyma cells from one another. Sieve-plate differentiation is first indicated by the application of units of the endoplasmic reticulum to localized parts of the wall and the appearance of callose beneath the endoplasmic reticulum (Fig. 1). These parts of the wall are the pore sites. Each has one plasmodesma in the center, but because of the thin sectioning required in electron microscopy many sections of the same pore site have to be made to reveal the plasmodesma. As soon as the pore site is delimited the cellulosic part of the wall appears thinner here than where no pore sites are visible (Fig. 1). The significance of this phenomenon is still obscure. It appears as though some of the original wall material is removed and replaced by callose.

In the initial stages, the pore sites are narrow. Subsequently they widen and the callose depositions thicken (Fig. 2). The callose forms conspicuous platelets each approximately as wide as the future pore. The endoplasmic reticulum continues to be associated with the callose platelets. The cellulosic parts of the wall between the pore sites thicken conspicuously, and differential staining suggests a structural complexity in this part of the wall (Fig. 2). The cellulosic part of the wall between the callose platelets of a pore site also appears to increase in thickness (compare Figs. 1 and 2).

The perforation of the pore site is initiated by removal of the cellu-

---

Figs. 1–4. Longitudinal sections through sieve elements of *Cucurbita*.

Figs. 1 and 2. Sieve plates in two stages of development. Callose platelets (A) and endoplasmic reticulum (D) at each pore site. In each figure one pore site is cut through the single plasmodesma (E). Fig. 3. Part of immature sieve plate. The endoplasmic reticulum (D) is partly broken up into vesicles. There are possibly two pore sites close together at the right. Fig. 4. Part of wall between sieve element and companion cell with a plasmodesma, branched on the companion-cell side. Details: A, callose platelet; B, cellulosic part of sieve plate; C, mitochondrion; D, endoplasmic reticulum; E, plasmodesma. Figs. 1, 2, × 19,000; Fig. 3, × 22,500; Fig. 4, × 30,000.

losic part of the wall between the callose platelets in the center of the pore site, probably in relation to the single plasmodesma. The opposing platelets fuse (Fig. 5, arrow) and then are broken through (Fig. 5, open pores). Thus a pore lined with callose is formed. At this stage the pore is still narrow and is surrounded by a ledge tapering toward the pore

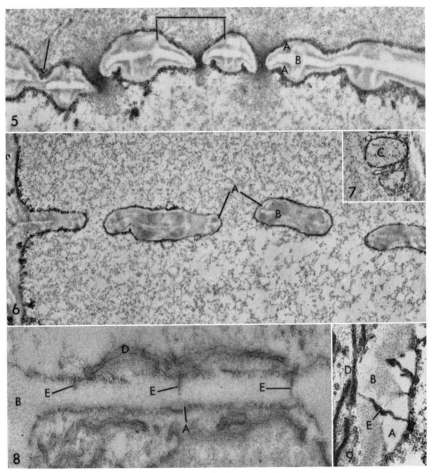

Figs. 5–9. Longitudinal sections through sieve elements of *Cucurbita* showing wall structures.—Fig. 5. Sieve plate with recently opened pores. Arrow indicates a still closed pore site with fused callose and the bracket delimits two halves of one callose platelet. Fig. 6. Mature sieve plate. Fig. 7. Mitochrondria from one of the cells in Fig. 6. Fig. 8. Lateral sieve area between immature sieve elements. Fig. 9. Part of wall between mature sieve elements. Fig. 9. Part of wall between mature sieve element (right) and parenchyma cell (left). Details: A, callose; B, cellulosic part of sieve plate; C, mitochondrion; D, endoplasmic reticulum; E, plasmodesma. Fig. 5, × 14,000; Fig. 6, × 10,000; Fig. 8, × 41,000; Fig. 9, × 28,500.

and consisting of cellulosic wall part coated with callose. In many views this ledge appears bent, all ledges of one plate pointing in the same direction (Fig. 5) just as though they were displaced by a unidirectional flow of material. Subsequently the ledges diminish in extent and the pores widen (Fig. 6). Enzyme action is probably involved in bringing about the original perforation and the later removal of the ledges.

Before the pore sites become perforated the protoplasts of the sieve elements undergo the characteristic changes that eventually distinguish these cells from ordinary nucleate ones. The disappearance of the nucleus, familiar from studies with the light microscope, has been substantiated by electron microscopy, although the sequence of events in this disappearance has not been worked out at the ultrastructural level. The nucleus becomes very much lobed before it disappears as a discernible entity.

Young sieve elements have abundant endoplasmic reticulum, mitochondria, and dictyosomes (Figs. 1 and 2). In mature sieve elements, only the mitochondria continue to be discernible, but they assume an appearance suggesting reduction in metabolic activity: their internal membranes disappear and the stroma becomes thin (Fig. 7). Incidentally, Figs. 6 and 7 show that sieve-plate pores are large enough to permit the passage of mitochondria. The endoplasmic reticulum undergoes a characteristic change. It breaks up into vesicles (Fig. 3) which subsequently occur in parietal position (Figs. 5 and 6), separated from the cell wall by the ectoplast (Esau and Cheadle, 1961). Possibly the nuclear envelope undergoes a similar change, for its basic similarity to the endoplasmic reticulum is well established. Mature sieve elements contain no dictyosomes, but the manner of their breakdown is not known. Perhaps they too disintegrate into vesicles. The slime bodies, characteristic of young sieve elements, disperse throughout the cell lumen. At this time the tonoplast ceases to be discernible (Esau and Cheadle, 1962a). A particularly significant feature of these changes is that they occur before the pore sites become open (Esau and Cheadle, 1962b; Esau *et al.*, 1962). It thus appears that the highly modified protoplast is characteristic of the functioning element.

In *Cucurbita* phloem, killed by injecting the $KMnO_4$ solution into the hollow petiole, many of the sieve plates were found to be free of the slime accumulations—the slime plug—characteristic of phloem sectioned live without special precautions. The sieve plates without slime plugs suggest that the pores are lined with the ectoplast and the vesicular endoplasmic reticulum and that the vacuolar material is continuous through the pores (Fig. 6). Since no tonoplast is present at this time, it is perhaps inappropriate to speak of the vacuole, especially in view

of the incorporation of protoplasmic material—the slime—into this vacuole. The terminological problem needs further thought.

The common opinion is that the accumulation of the slime on the
sieve plate indicates rapid flow of material through the plate and filter-
ing out of the slime. Sectioning of live phloem brings about such a flow
but whether all slime plugs result from such injury is impossible to state
at present. Indications of plugging may be present in most carefully
prepared material and even in sieve elements with newly opened pores
(Fig. 5).

Thus far, vacuolar continuity has been recognized only in sieve plates
(Fig. 6). Lateral sieve areas, whether in young sieve elements (Fig. 8)
or mature ones (Esau et al., 1962), usually show relatively thin, apparently homogeneous strands. Such sieve areas give no evidence of becoming perforated, at least in the manner the sieve plates are perforated.

Sieve elements have protoplasmic connections resembling plasmodesmata with companion cells—typically branched on the companion-
cell side (Fig. 4)—and with parenchyma cells (Fig. 9). These connections require special attention. As is well known, in ordinary nucleate
cells plasmodesmata are connected to the endoplasmic reticulum (upper
cell in Fig. 4). In the sieve element the endoplasmic reticulum is disin-
tegrated into vesicles. The endoplasmic reticulum-plasmodesmata relationship could hardly be expected to be identical on the two sides of
the wall between the sieve element and the nucleate cell.

Sieve Areas in *Vitis*

The information on development of *Vitis* sieve areas is less complete
than that for *Cucurbita,* but considerable evidence indicates that the
formation of sieve-plate pores is a similar phenomenon in both plants.
Young sieve plates in *Vitis* have paired callose platelets in the pore sites,
each of which is penetrated by a single plasmodesma. Figure 10 shows
the paired platelets of one sieve area of a compound sieve plate (cf. Esau,
1948) in sectional view, that is, from a tangential section of the tissue.
In Figs. 11 and 12 parts of a sieve area are seen in surface view as they
appear in a radial section of the tissue. The section in Fig. 10 includes
no plasmodesmata; several of these appear in Figs. 11 and 12 (arrows).
Where most of a platelet is present in a section (Fig. 11) the plasmodesma
is seen to be located in central position. Stages intermediate between
the sieve plates with closed pores (Figs. 10–12) and those with completely
open pores (Figs. 15 and 16) have not been observed as yet.

A comparison of the sieve areas of the sieve plate—sieve areas of type
A, according to my earlier designation (Esau, 1948)—with the lateral,

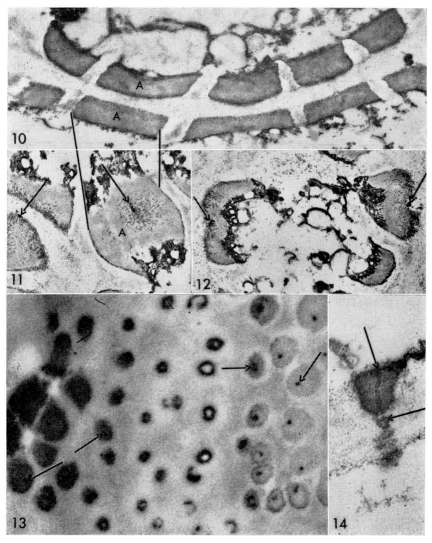

Figs. 10-14. Longitudinal sections through *Vitis* sieve elements showing wall structures.—Fig. 10. Sectional view of immature sieve area of a sieve plate with callose platelets (A). Figs. 11 and 12. Surface views of parts of callose platelets (A), each with a plasmodesma (arrow). Fig. 13. Lateral sieve area sectioned obliquely so that the plasmodesmata (arrows) are seen at different levels in the wall. Callose surrounds one or two plasmodesmata right and left. The ring-like structures occur in median position in the wall (median nodules). Fig. 14. One plasmodesma (upper arrow) from a sieve area as in Fig. 13 imbedded in callose. Median nodule (lower arrow) is open in center. No callose at lower side of wall. Fig. 10, × 17,500; Figs. 11 and 12, × 17,000; Fig. 13, × 24,500; Fig. 14, × 51,750.

type B, sieve areas reveals a difference that is more than merely difference in width of the pores. When the sieve-plate pores are filled with slime (in this study none were obtained without) they appear to be penetrated by thick strands of uniform thickness (Fig. 16). In the lateral sieve areas the strands resemble plasmodesmata in thickness but they have distinct "nodules" in the median position in the wall. The peculiar structure of these median nodules is illustrated in Figs. 13 and 14. Figure 13 shows a lateral sieve area cut obliquely in such a way that all levels of the wall appear in one view. Near the two surfaces of the wall (right and left) the callose plugs, each with a plasmodesma (arrows), are in view. Deeper in the wall (middle) no callose is present and the plasmodesmata widen out and become hollow in the center. Entirely satisfactory longitudinal sections of lateral sieve areas were not obtained, but the oblique section of one plasmodesma in Fig. 14 shows one callose plug with the plasmodesma imbedded in it (upper arrow) and the open median nodule (lower arrow) below the callose plug. From Figs. 13 and 14 one may deduce that the median nodule is a hollow sphere of protoplasmic material. The structure revealed in Figs. 13 and 14 obviously does not fit the description of sieve areas type B given by Hepton and Preston (1960), although those authors were correct in stating that one callose plug may include more than one plasmodesma.

The $KMnO_4$ fixation gives rather satisfactory differentiation between the cellulosic wall parts and the callose. It is not yet clear, however, why sometimes the callose stains darker (Figs. 10–12), sometimes lighter (Figs. 15–18) than the cellulosic wall. The difference does not seem to be related to age, for I have seen dormancy callose stained both light (Fig. 17) and dark. Contrary to Hepton and Preston's (1960) statement, the callose may appear layered in electron micrographs as well as in light-microscope views (Esau, 1948; Kessler, 1958). The callose lining the pores in Fig. 15 shows a detail not revealed by light microscopy, plasmodesmata-like structures oriented radially with reference to the center of the pore.

Reactivation after dormancy involving the removal of dormancy callose is one of the particularly interesting phenomena in the life of the Vitis sieve element. Light-microscope studies suggest the participation of slime in the removal of callose. The remarkable feature of the process is the accuracy with which the new strands of slime, that appear to penetrate the plugs of callose from their surfaces, come to pass exactly through the pores of the plate. On the basis of light-microscope studies I suggested that possibly thin cytoplasmic strands remained imbedded in the callose during dormancy (Esau, 1948, pp. 243, 244) and that the

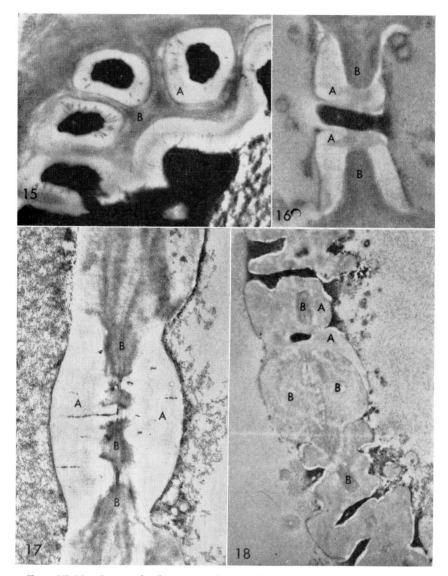

Figs. 15–18. Longitudinal sections through *Vitis* sieve elements showing wall structures.—Fig. 15. Part of mature sieve plate in face view (radial section) showing pores filled with slime (black) and lined with callose (A). Fig. 16. Sectional view (tangential section) of one pore. Fig. 17. One sieve area of a sieve plate in sectional view closed with dormancy callose (A) but with fine strands traversing the callose. Fig. 18. Part of sieve plate in sectional view during reactivation. Irregular openings indicate removal of dormancy callose. Details: A, callose; B, cellulosic part of the wall. Fig. 15, × 13,000; Fig. 16, × 11,500; Fig. 17, × 13,800; Fig. 18, × 6,600.

dissolution of this callose occurred along these strands. Electron-micro-
scope views indeed reveal thin strands in the dormancy callose (Fig. 17).
Hepton and Preston (1960) claim to have discovered these strands but
their material was collected after cambial reactivation, too late for being
certain that dormancy callose was still unaffected (Esau, 1948). Electron-
microscope pictures also suggest that the removal of dormancy callose
involves an enzymic dissolution of callose. As Hepton and Preston (1960)
have shown, the callose in contact with the material penetrating it—
slime, in my opinion—appears modified (white layer along the dense
strands in Fig. 18). Moreover, the irregularity in the outlines of the
callose at this stage suggests a rather intense degradation of callose.

Conclusion

With regard to phloem, electron microscopy has confirmed and
deepened some of our findings with the light microscope, has failed to
confirm some others, and has revealed features not visible at the microscopic level. But the work is still new and only few techniques have
been explored. On the basis of our present information we are not justified in drawing definitive conclusions regarding the relation between
the structure and the function of the phloem. We can only speculate.
My speculation is that among the phloem cells—and perhaps among
plant cells in general—the sieve element is one of the most peculiar
cells and that this peculiarity is an indication of specialization making
the cell dependent on the associated nucleate cells in its functional
activity.

Discussion

PRESTON: Dr. Esau has found almost exactly what we have seen ourselves, so the
basic facts are the same, I think. It is the interpretation that is in question. I have no
doubt that in Vitis, for instance, a good deal of the plugging which is seen is an
artifact in the sense that the plugs are probably not solid and structureless. I tend to
think of this in terms of the work of Kollmann (1961, 1963; Kollmann and Schumacher, 1961), particularly his work on Metasequoia, in which he sees tubules passing through the sieve pores, apparently continuous with the endoplasmic reticulum.
I wonder if in Vitis our sections are not thin enough—whether, if we had better
sections, we would have seen tubules. With Cucurbita, I wondered how sure you
were that the contents of the sieve pores and the granular material on each side are
in fact vacuolar, not cytoplasmic. I don't think myself that it matters much whether
this material is vacuolar or not. The fact that this material accumulates in the pores
symmetrically suggests that there is no damage. Doesn't that mean that there can be
no mass flow? Mass flow should displace this accumulation.

ESAU: Concerning the question whether this is vacuolar material or not, I have
a series of photographs showing the disappearance of the tonoplast. There is no
question in my mind that to begin with the vacuole is nicely delimited, and completely separated from all the walls, including the sieve plate. Subsequently the

tonoplast disappears. This development suggests continuity of the material which was present in the vacuole. As far as symmetrical accumulation is concerned, in the wounding of sieve elements there is a gradation of accumulation. Close to the wound surface accumulation is very asymmetrical, a so-called slime plug. Farther away, the asymmetry is less pronounced, and in the intermediate zone accumulations are completely symmetrical. We can also obtain material without accumulations, which suggests that the pore of the living element is not filled with such accumulation. As far as the tubules are concerned, are you specifically thinking of *Metasequoia* (Kollmann and Schumacher, 1962) or are you thinking of *Passiflora* which Kollmann studied originally? For *Passiflora* he showed large pores with many tubules. I do not think he has really supplied proof that those are tubules. The pertinent electron micrograph was not entirely satisfactory, so he made a drawing to help interpret it. Subsequently he said that he saw tubules in sieve areas of *Metasequoia* in oblique and cross sections; indeed one can see circles in the cross sections there. Many people claim that plasmodesmata contain tubules of endoplasmic reticulum. That would parallel the situation in sieve areas of *Metasequoia*. Of course, *Metasequoia* has much smaller connecting strands than *Cucurbita,* an indication that the conifers are less highly evolved in that respect than the dicotyledons. We need more information regarding this complex problem, but I am inclined to think that the dense accumulations in the pores do not truly reflect the condition in the living cell.

FREY-WYSSLING: I would like to return to the question of when the tonoplast breaks down. I cannot understand how the plasmalemma could exist without any protoplasmic covering. You have suggested that the material inside the pore is proteinaceous and comes from the vacuole. Callose plugs are attacked; enzymic reactions take place, so that this material is not as passive as ordinary vacuolar sap; it is metabolically active. It is just a matter of definition whether this fluid is called "cytoplasm" or "vacuolar content." "Vacuole" and "cytoplasm" are often used as purely morphological terms. As soon as there is no tonoplast the situation is very similar to the laticifers in which many people claim the contents of the vacuole to be diluted cytoplasm.

ESAU: I have been thinking along similar lines. One could visualize an element in which there is no longer any definition of protoplasm and vacuole, a cell containing thin cytoplasm enveloped by an ectoplast. The question is whether rapid conduction could take place through such a system. What is the state of the proteinaceous material in the vacuole? Is it oriented in some way so that materials could go through easily? Or are there surfaces along which materials are moving?

ZIMMERMANN: We have to consider that there is a pressure of about 20 atm in these sieve elements. Somehow the cell wall, which is continuous with the xylem, has to be separated from the inside of the sieve element. There must be a cytoplasmic barrier.

ESAU: Do you not think that the ectoplast could do that? Sieve elements can be plasmolyzed and deplasmolyzed just like normal cells. The lateral cell walls are lined with the ectoplast and lying next to it are the mitochondria and the remnants of the endoplasmic reticulum in the form of little vesicles. The slime, which originally appeared as discrete slime bodies, now is dispersed throughout. There does not seem to be any delimitation between vacuolar and nonvacuolar contents.

BAILEY: There is a similarity here with the rubber cells of the guayule, where the tonoplast breaks down and then the particles migrate across the cell. There seems to be a fusion of the protoplasm and the vacuolar contents so that rubber particles can go back and forth.

ESAU: That was what Dr. Frey-Wyssling mentioned with regard to laticifers in the rubber plant.

THIMANN: All the same, I cannot see how mass flow could occur in this system. Let us accept everything you say, Dr. Esau, about slime and callose; it is all artificial and is not normally there. Let us try to visualize a functioning sieve tube without them. Still the fact remains that there is some living cytoplasmic material. You say yourself that it is possible to plasmolyze and therefore you must have some plasmalemma or tonoplast. One cannot plasmolyze down the sides without plasmolyzing across the cell. Yet these sieve plates must be open, and must transmit 20% sucrose or whatever it is. I do not see any getting around that. And no enzymic or cytoplasmic material could possibly be in there if there is mass flow. Either there is mass flow, or there is non-sugar cytoplasmic material in those pores. I can see no intermediate position.

PRESTON: This is really my point. The whole contents of the sieve tube would be displaced with mass flow.

THIMANN: Will you explain, please, how sugar solution can flow through the pores while they still contain cytoplasm.

ZIEGLER: There is no cytoplasm in the pores of the Angiosperms. There is slime material, according to Dr. Esau.

ESAU: The important question is, in what form is this slime present in an undisturbed sieve element. When it is disturbed, slime accumulates in the pores. When it isn't disturbed, then the slime must be somewhere in the cell, perhaps in the form of fibrils, and perhaps even continuous across the pores. The fibrils may be oriented in such a way that materials can move past them and leave them in position.

THIMANN: Is it possible that it is only on the side and not on the plates under normal conditions, and that it is displaced to the pores only upon injury?

ESAU: We have illustrations showing, step by step, the disintegration of slime. At the stage when it leaves the parietal cytoplasm, and the tonoplast breaks down, practically the whole lumen is filled with that material, which can be seen both with the light microscope and with the electron microscope.

THIMANN: Well, we are confronted with the problem of unifying the physiological and the anatomical data. The physiological data tell us that the inside of the sieve tube is a concentrated sugar solution, in free flow, but the anatomical data seem to show that there is something else.

ESAU: Kollmann thinks that the slime is cytoplasm and he sees tubular structure in it, not only in the pores, but also within the lumen. He visualizes that movement occurs either on the surface of these tubules or within them. He would like to see the tubular structure because it agrees with the idea of endoplasmic reticulum. I don't see the tubular structure. Perhaps my technique is not good enough. I have a graduate student who paid particular attention to this matter. He explored fixations, using osmic acid and potassium permanganate, and concluded that the material is fibrous rather than tubular. He recognized the slime in the form of very fine fibrils. Such fibrils would be no obstruction to the movement of the lighter material across. It is only on wounding that the pore would be sealed.

WAREING: When you plasmolyze this sieve tube, what happens in the region of the sieve plate?

ESAU: That is a good question. We saw a very peculiar phenomenon of surge within the cell. But we didn't recognize any movement across the sieve plate. So I am beginning to think that, even though we had elements in a condition that was close to the natural, we may have caused the pores to be sealed to a moderate degree by the slime. The plastids, however, were lying against the wall; they didn't release the starch grains. We were actually dealing with individual cells rather than with a sieve tube.

ZIMMERMANN: The question of whether or not there is callose in the uninjured plant can be broken up into two parts. On the one hand, there is the question of whether there are traces of callose present at all times. Such traces may have something to do with the sieve-plate formation, and they may play a role in the rapid formation of wound callose, but from the point of view of translocation we are not concerned with these traces. On the other hand, there is the question of whether or not there are relatively substantial callose cylinders in *conducting* sieve tubes. Substantial callose cylinders would offer serious restriction of the pores. If the connecting strand is only one-third of the diameter of the whole pore, then the transverse sectional area of the pore available for translocation is only 10% of the whole pore. It is these large callose cylinders that I consider artifacts due to wounding.

ESAU: It may be the same kind of wound response that Currier found in pits of parenchyma cells.

ZIEGLER: Dr. Eschrich (1963) now has pictures from *Cucurbita ficifolia* of developed sieve pores without any callose.

ESAU: I have seen some like that too. Do you suppose that these are older sieve tubes?

ZIEGLER: No, he sees pores without any callose in quite young sieve tubes. He believes your callose platelets to be fixation artifacts, but with a distinct meaning, an artifact that can be used as an indication of special differentiation within this region.

FREY-WYSSLING: I think platelets really exist around the pores during the growth of the secondary wall. There has to be a plug which prevents the deposition of microfibrils. In macerated material one can see that there is no deposition of microfibrils in the pore area. Earlier we had thought of a cytoplasmic plug, but Prof. Esau's slides show that it consists of callose. It seems important to me that there be some mechanism preventing secondary thickening in the pore areas.

REFERENCES

Currier, H. B., Esau, K., and Cheadle, V. I. (1955). *Am. J. Botany* **42**, 68-81.
Duloy, M., Mercer, F. V., and Rathgeber, N. (1961). *Australian J. Biol. Sci.* **14**, 506-518.
Esau, K. (1948). *Hilgardia* **18**, 217-296.
Esau, K., and Cheadle, V. I. (1961). *Proc. Natl. Acad. Sci.* **47**, 1716-1726.
Esau, K., and Cheadle, V. I. (1962a). *Proc. Natl. Acad. Sci.* **48**, 1-8.
Esau, K., and Cheadle, V. I. (1962b). *Bot. Gaz.* **124**, 79-85.
Esau, K., Cheadle, V. I., and Risley, E. B. (1962). *Bot. Gaz.* **123**, 233-243.
Eschrich, W. (1963). *Planta* **59**, 243-261.
Hepton, C. E. L., and Preston, R. D. (1960). *J. Exptl. Botany* **11**, 381-393.
Kessler, G. (1958). *Ber. Schweiz. Botan. Ges.* **68**, 5-43.
Kollmann, R. (1960). *Planta* **55**, 67-107.
Kollmann, R. (1961). *Ber. Deut. Botan. Ges.* **74**, 54-55.
Kollmann, R. (1963). *In* "Recent Advances in Biophysics" (R. D. Preston, ed.). To be published.
Kollmann, R., and Schumacher, W. (1961). *Planta* **57**, 583-607.
Kollmann, R., and Schumacher, W. (1962). *Planta* **58**, 366-386.

Stem Structure in Arborescent Monocotyledons[1]

P. B. TOMLINSON

Fairchild Tropical Garden, Miami, Florida

The majority of larger living Tracheophyta are constructed like a dicotyledonous hardwood tree, most of the axis and branches being secondary tissue derived from an initial cambial layer capable of producing secondary xylem on its inner and secondary phloem on its outer face. This construction is also typical of many extinct plants. Tree physiologists have been concerned wholly with living plants of this general type. However, large plants with other methods of construction do occur, but little attention has been given to their development and physiology. The present article draws attention to one such anomalous group, the arborescent monocotyledons. Apart from describing their method of growth in comparison with that of dicotyledonous trees, certain peculiar physiological attributes are emphasized.

Because of fundamental differences of construction between large dicotyledons on the one hand and monocotyledons on the other, the term treelike or arborescent is preferred for the latter group. Arborescent forms occur in a variety of unrelated monocotyledonous families. They dominate certain groups, as in the Palmae, Pandanaceae, Strelitziaceae,[2] and to a lesser extent in the Agavaceae. Otherwise arborescent forms occur as small assemblages in taxa which are predominantly herbaceous, like Strelitziaceae in Scitamineae; Bambuseae in Gramineae; species of *Kingia, Lomandra, Xanthorrhoea* in Xanthorrhoeaceae; of *Aloe* in Aloineae (Liliaceae); of *Puya* in Bromeliaceae; of *Aristea, Klattia, Witsenia* in Iridaceae; of *Alocasia, Montrichardia, Philodendron* in Araceae. These forms are connected via transitional types to herbaceous species. The phylogenetic relation between arborescent and herbaceous forms in the monocotyledons is not clear. Evidence has been presented, however,

---

[1] The author's research on the anatomy of monocotyledons is supported by grants from the National Science Foundation and the American Philosophical Society.

[2] Strelitziaceae in the limited sense indicated in Tomlinson (1962b). Otherwise family names are according to Hutchinson (1959).

that in the Scitamineae at least, the arborescent forms are primitive (Tomlinson, 1962b).

One common feature of these monocotyledons is that they are virtually restricted to the tropics, and this may be very significant. It certainly is one reason for our relative ignorance of them. Few arborescent mono-cotyledons rival dicotyledonous trees in over-all stature and they infrequently dominate a particular vegetation type. However, palms which are capable of growing to 100 feet are not uncommon and some may achieve 200 feet. There are no reliable records of maximum palm stature. Nevertheless, although these plants scarcely compare with tall dicotyledons they undoubtedly reach a size which subjects them to the same physical stresses. Both kinds of plant therefore have similar requirements of mechanical strength and long-distance internal conducting mechanisms.

This article presents only a brief summary of the development of the arborescent monocotyledons, which is all that is possible in our present limited state of knowledge. Even quite elementary information is lacking and no quantitative studies have been made. No attempt is made here to rectify these shortcomings, but it is hoped that such a survey may provide a stimulus for the careful and detailed studies which are needed.

Much of the information included herein has been presented in greater detail by Schoute (1902, 1903, 1906, 1907, 1909, 1912, 1918) in a series of papers which deserve wider recognition, and more recently Holttum (1954, 1955) has presented fundamental observations. Some new ideas and facts relevant to this article have also been presented in Tomlinson (1964a).

Among the groups of arborescent monocotyledons mentioned above I have first-hand familiarity with only a few. Subsequent discussion is therefore restricted largely to the Palmae, Pandanaceae, and Agavaceae. If only essential features are regarded each of these groups is represented by a distinctive growth-form:

(i) *Palmae*—unbranched axis consisting wholly of primary tissue.

(ii) *Pandanaceae*—branched axis consisting wholly of primary tissue.

(iii) *Agavaceae*—branched or unbranched axis consisting of both primary and secondary tissues in varying proportions.

This simplified outlook does not exclude other growth forms. A fourth group might include the palm *Hyphaene* of which there are species with branched axes consisting wholly of primary tissues, the branching being a true dichotomy, unlike branching in Pandanaceae and Agavaceae. However, little detailed information is available about *Hyphaene*. The bamboos also constitute a peculiar and distinctive fifth group with regard to their growth form. On the other hand, the majority of arborescent monocotyledons in the families mentioned above probably belong to one of the three main groups (i)–(iii). In this article only the first group is dealt with in any detail, the ways in which the other groups differ are described very briefly.

Single-Stemmed Palms *(Cocos)*

The growth habit of palms varies considerably (e.g., Tomlinson, 1961b, e) but they are all variants of a common type (Holttum, 1955). The simplest, but not necessarily the most primitive, habit is represented by single-stemmed palms. The coconut (*Cocos nucifera* L.) may be used as a familiar example of this type, other palms being mentioned only to illustrate features not shown by *Cocos*. Growth of its axis involves three successive phases. There is a gradual transition from one phase to another so that the limits of the phases cannot be defined too precisely. Throughout these three phases the axis is built of successive inter-nodes, each internode associated with a single leaf. The nodes may be delimited externally by distinct leaf scars, but there is no nodal plate or other internal boundary between adjacent internodes as in bamboos. This is a purely descriptive concept and each stem segment of internode plus leaf is in no way equivalent to the unit of shoot growth established for certain monocotyledons on a developmental basis (e.g., by Priestley *et al.*, 1935).

In the development of the axis of the coconut there is an initial juvenile phase, succeeded by an adult phase divided into an early vegetative phase and a later reproductive phase. In coconut and most other palms the reproductive phase is largely superimposed on the vegetative phase, but in the Caryotoideae and palms like *Corypha*, *Raphia*, and *Nannorrhops* flowering is determinate and there is a com-plete change from a vegetative to a reproductive phase (Tomlinson, 1964a).

Juvenile Phase

This begins with the establishment of a narrow seedling axis (cf. Fig. 1). The first internodes of this axis are short, narrow, and associated with incompletely developed leaves, the earliest represented by bladeless scales. Subsequent leaves show a gradual increase in size and com-plexity, most evident in the blade, so that the adult is approached gradually (Tomlinson, 1961a). Internodes associated with juvenile leaves always remain short but successively are gradually wider. (Figs. 2, 3). This eventually produces a massive obconical axis, the distal, widest internodes situated at or a little above soil level usually being wider than those produced in the later stages of growth (Fig. 4) (Tom-linson, 1960). Tissues of these short, basal internodes are not direct products of the apical meristem proper but of a primary thickening meristem. They are, however, wholly primary and there is no secondary increase in diameter with age. The development of the obconical axis in the juvenile phase is largely due to the gradual establishment of the primary thickening meristem. Once a massive apical vegetative cone has

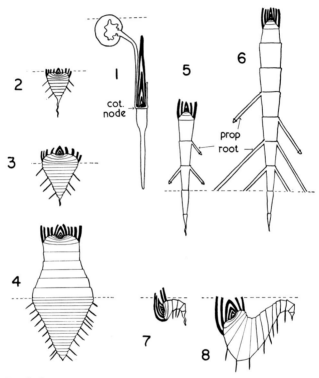

FIGS. 1–8. (After Tomlinson, 1960.) Juvenile phase in palms; vertical section shown, with only base of leaves represented. Cotyledonary attachment is ignored.
FIG. 1. Young seedling, e.g., of *Phoenix*. FIGS. 2–4. Three successive stages in development of basal region of the axis in a single-stemmed palm like *Cocos*. FIGS. 5–6. Two successive stages in development of basal region of a monocotyledon with elongated seedling internodes, as in Iriartoid palms and *Pandanus* spp. FIGS. 7–8. Two successive stages in development of basal region in *Sabal* spp. Apart from its outline this is essentially the same as in other palms.

been established, the subsequent configuration of the axis results entirely from its activity.

The part of the axis produced in this juvenile phase of growth may be referred to simply as the basal region of the stem. It is actually the oldest part of the axis and to continue to refer to it as "juvenile" would be misleading. In *Cocos* three features distinguish it from later-formed, distal parts of the axis. First, the internodes are congested; second, during its development juvenile foliage is produced; third, adventitious roots are restricted to it.

Almost all palms show these distinctive features in the basal axial regions. A few of the more conspicuous exceptions may be noted. In some Iriartoid palms the basal internodes are elongated, producing an unstable axis which is supported by massive prop roots (Figs. 5, 6). Another exceptional basal region is shown by *Sabal* (Figs. 7, 8) (Bailey, 1944). In some small palms a persistent juvenile condition is retained, the leaves being permanently of the juvenile type as in species of *Chamaedorea, Geonoma, Reinhardtia* (Tomlinson, 1961a). In contrast to the single-stemmed *Cocos* the most conspicuously different growth habit is in the multiple-stemmed or caespitose palms. Buds occur in the axils of the basal leaves and grow out as suckers capable of becoming new erect axes. As these develop they repeat the growth characteristics of the parent axis. Their physiological dependence on the parent axis is short lived because they soon establish an independent adventitious root system (Holttum, 1955). In caespitose palms suckers are almost invariably restricted to the basal region of the axis and thereby constitute another important morphological criterion for this region.

In conclusion, the juvenile phase of palm growth is significant because in it is established the primary thickening meristem and massive vegetative cone. The basal region established during this phase differs from the later-formed part of the axis in significant physiological ways which are outwardly expressed in distinctive morphological features. Mechanically the region is efficient because it provides a broad foundation on which the aerial axis rests.

Adult Phase (Vegetative)

Subsequent growth of the axis involves the production of internodes all more or less equal in width and length. In *Cocos* they are a little longer than the basal internodes. In some palms the aerial internodes remain congested, like those of the basal region. In others they are much longer, the extreme limit being represented by the rattans and other scandent palms. The vegetative phase is distinguished by the production of the adult kind of foliage, the absence of either vegetative or reproductive lateral branches, and the absence of adventitious roots. A few exceptions to these generalizations may be noted. In *Phoenix dactylifera* and sometimes in *Chrysalidocarpus lutescens* aerial axillary suckers appear, but their growth is restricted. Aerial adventitious root primordia of limited growth occur on the stems of a few palms such as *Chamae-*

dorea tepilijote. Aerial roots may otherwise be present but modified as short spines, as in *Cryosophila nana* and *Mauritia armata.*

Attention must now be paid to the development and internal structure of the axis. Because a system of many thousands of vascular bundles is involved, these aspects are only understood in very general, qualitative terms. Only a few general concepts can be presented. There is, however, little disagreement about these concepts. The apical meristem proper of a palm is not significantly larger than the average size of that of other angiosperms (Ball, 1941). It is largely a leaf-producing meristem. The crown of the axis, within the apical vegetative cone is occupied by a shallow bowl-shaped depression at the center of which the apical

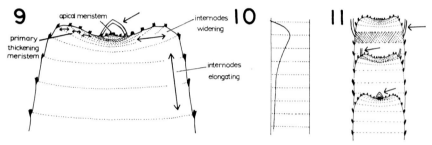

Figs. 9–11. (After Tomlinson, 1961c.) Developmental processes in the apical vegetative cone of the palm during adult vegetative phase. Vertical section; leaf bases (black) only shown; limits of internodes shown by dotted lines. Fig. 9. Diagrammatic longitudinal section of vegetative cone. Fig. 10. Diagrammatic representation of the course of a single leaf trace in the mature stem. Fig. 11. Three successive stages (from below upwards) in development of a single internode (cross hatched); the base of the leaf associated with this internode is indicated by the arrow.

meristem is situated (Fig. 9). The bulk of the tissue of each internode is produced by a thickening meristem which is continuous below the successive leaf primordia. The general shape of this meristem corresponds to the surface of the bowl. This thickening meristem is primary, and its main activity takes place before elongation growth of the internode commences. However, the distinction between primary and secondary meristems in the vegetative cones of palms can scarcely be made with any certainty and to adopt rigid concepts for these expressions serves no useful purpose (Queva, 1907). The precise structure of this meristem and its homologies are outside the scope of this article (cf. Helm, 1936; Eckardt, 1941). The configuration of the apical cone is a result of the activity of the primary thickening meristem. Each internode becomes wider by the continued activity of the meristem. It achieves approximately its maximum diameter before it begins to elongate (Fig. 11).

In different palms the onset of elongation growth occurs earlier or later in relation to thickening growth and through this variation the shape of the apical vegetative cone varies. Later growth of the internode is largely elongation. Some thickening growth continues as primary tissues continue to expand.

Association of developing leaves with internodes which originate in this distinctive way accounts for the terminal rosette of congested leaves typical of the coconut, as of most palms. The structure and behavior of the closed tubular leaf base in palms is also correlated with the distinctive development of the massive vegetative bud since mechanical stresses are set up to which the leaf base is structurally and functionally adapted in a variety of striking ways (Tomlinson, 1962a, 1964b).

The gross anatomy of the mature *Cocos* stem (Fig. 12) also results from the way in which innumerable individual vascular bundles (leaf traces) originate in a meristematic region which behaves in the above distinctive way. This correlation has been generally appreciated from the time of von Mohl (1858); (see also Schoute, 1903; Arber, 1925, p. 34) but still defies mathematical analysis. The best account of this correlation is that of Branner (1884) which still, however, is not wholly satisfactory.

Each leaf is vasculated by many hundreds of leaf traces continuous into the stem and since there are many closely succeeding leaves a detailed analysis of such a complex structure is yet scarcely possible. The general course of the vascular bundles in the mature palm stem is well known (e.g., Tomlinson, 1961c, e) but there is great variation between individual bundles (Monoyer, 1925). Many essential facts are obscure. Adopting the style commonly used in describing the distribution of leaf traces in stems, each bundle enters the stem from the leaf at an acute angle, passing rapidly to the center of the stem, its subsequent course back to the periphery of the stem extending through many internodes (Fig. 10). The structure of each trace changes throughout its length. Distally, that is, close to its entrance from a leaf, it has well-developed proto- and metaxylem, well-developed phloem tissues, but a relatively poorly developed fibrous sheath. Proximally, that is, remote from its leaf insertion, the bundle has no protoxylem, reduced metaxylem, and a massive fibrous sheath encircling the phloem. An axis containing many such bundles with, at any one level, different parts of many different bundles, has a narrow peripheral region of congested vascular bundles with well-developed mechanical tissues and a wide central region of diffuse vascular bundles with less well-developed mechanical tissues (Fig. 12). Mechanically this is a very strong system. Physiological continuity through this axis is maintained by frequent bundle fusions. However, it is not known whether these fusions are restricted to any one part of each leaf trace, which is suggested in several analyses of vascular bundle distribution (e.g., von Mohl, 1849; Branner, 1884), or whether their occurrence is variable (Monoyer, 1925). Possibly bundle fusions occur at random. Continuity of the conducting system is, however, maintained and there is intimate contact between stem vascular bundles and root traces in the basal region of the stem, these unions often being quite deep seated (Drabble, 1904).

The study of the development of the palm stem has scarcely yet begun. Our present ignorance has several causes. Little material has been examined since palms are mostly tropical and few botanists have had unlimited access to them. The technical difficulties involved in making sections of palm stems are enormous. Nor can the traditional approach of the wood anatomist be used since the whole axis of the palm must be considered. A small sample is not representative of the whole palm as it largely is in a dicotyledonous tree. Some further aspects of growth in the palm stem must be considered before this can be appreciated.

The essential features of the development of the *Cocos* stem outlined above show that the stem tissues are derived from a primary thickening meristem which forms the massive vegetative cone. The distribution of the leaf traces in the stem, which itself determines the general skeletal construction of the axis, is solely the outcome of the differentiation of vascular bundles within this meristem. Growth as represented by cell division is more or less restricted to the apical vegetative cone, but growth as represented by cell expansion continues for some time below the primary meristematic region. Thus there is appreciable widening of the axis some distance below its apex. This late widening is one of the major sources of mechanical stress imposed on old leaf bases (Tomlinson, 1962a). Widening is not the result of meristematic activity, but is merely diffuse secondary growth (Tomlinson, 1961e, p. 20), largely of ground parenchyma cells, but also of bundle sheath fibers. The axis has no cambial layer and no new tissues are produced once the internode has completed elongation growth. However, the ground parenchyma cells retain a vitality which is expressed in a variety of ways. The most obvious, found in many palms, but not in *Cocos*, is for the ground parenchyma cells to continue their expansion whilst still thin walled. A very spongy ground tissue with wide intercellular spaces may develop. This activity, which rarely includes cell division, accounts for detectable increase in stem thickness in the older part of palm stems (Schoute, 1912). It is most noticeable in *Roystonea*. Ground parenchyma cells also accumulate starch, often in great quantities. They usually continue to deposit wall material so that in the older parts of stems the ground parenchyma is very sclerotic, as in *Cocos*. In contrast to changes in the ground paren-chyma there seems to be no change in the vascular tissue.

These changes are of significance to the systematic anatomist attempt-ing to relate stem structure to classification or to identify palms from stems alone. In addition to the differences between central and peripheral regions of the stem at a single level there are the differences in different levels throughout a single palm stem. The analysis by Monoyer (1925) of a stem of *Arecastrum romanzoffianum (Cocos botryophora)* shows this well. Considering that few diagnostic features have so far been recog-nized in the microscopic structure of palm stems, the lack of progress in this field of systematic anatomy can well be appreciated (Tomlinson, 1961d). It has been suggested, however, that the way in which the ground parenchyma changes with age does differ in different palms but is constant for a single species and therefore may itself be of diagnostic value (Kaul, 1960).

ADULT PHASE (REPRODUCTIVE)

After a limited period of vegetative growth the onset of the reproduc-tive phase is marked by the appearance of axillary inflorescences. In *Cocos* these arise singly and their development is intimately associated with that of the subtending leaf and its node. Inflorescences develop, expand, and mature in the order of their age. Their growth is limited. Although quite a significant physiological change is involved in the onset of the reproductive phase, in *Cocos* it is morphologically less striking than in palms with determinate flowering, like *Corypha, Raphia, Nan-norrhops,* and Caryotoideae. In these the axis becomes wholly reproduc-tive after a very long vegetative period. However, a discussion of repro-ductive phenomena in palms is outside the scope of this article. Certain aspects have been dealt with elsewhere (Tomlinson, 1964a).

Pandanaceae *(Pandanus utilis)*

Pandanus is a large genus and includes species of varying life form. The essential feature in which it differs from *Cocos* is its ability to pro-duce aerial vegetative branches. The juvenile phase in *Pandanus* may be one of two fairly distinct kinds (Schoute, 1907). In one, seedling inter-nodes are elongated and the axis becomes supported by prop roots. This corresponds to the seedling state in the Iriartoid palms (e.g., Figs. 5, 6). In the second, the seedling internodes are congested and a broad obconi-cal base is developed, like that of *Cocos*. This is shown by *Pandanus utilis* (e.g., Figs. 2–4) and this species is used as a continued example. *Pandanus utilis* shows the basic morphological, developmental, and anatomical features of *Cocos*. It passes through a similar juvenile phase, in which a broad apical vegetative cone is formed, and by continued activity of this cone a similar axis develops in the adult vegetative phase. Root primordia occur on all parts of the aerial stem, unlike *Cocos*. The most conspicuous anatomical difference between *Pandanus* and *Cocos* is that the axis of the former includes, in addition to simple vascular bundles, compound vascular bundles which contain two or more separate vascular strands. This type of bundle is said to result from peculiar fusions between simple bundles (Meyer, 1933) which themselves have certain peculiarities in their vertical course (Carano, 1906a, b; Solereder and Meyer, 1933). The ground parenchyma also becomes lacunose in a manner unlike that of palms. Despite early records which suggested that secondary tissues could be produced (Strasburger, 1906; Warburg, 1900) subsequent observations have revealed no secondary meristem (Schoute, 1907). Schoute suggested that the secondary vascular bundles recorded by Strasburger and Warburg are actually root traces. This conclusion is supported by my own observations in which no cambial activity has been seen.

The significant way in which *Pandanus utilis* differs from a palm like *Cocos* is its ability to produce axillary buds and branch systems of un-limited growth. Each leaf axil includes a minute bud. These are mostly suppressed. The reason that they also fail to grow out belatedly is dis-cussed below. Root primordia are produced throughout the aerial axis, but their growth is also strongly inhibited. The stimulus causing a few buds to grow out is precise since branches are arranged according to a definite pattern. Except for the few first-formed branches on the lower part of the main axis, branching is associated wholly with flowering and a regular pattern of sympodial growth is established. Flowering on each segment of the sympodium is determinate, the vegetative growth of the segment ending in a terminal inflorescence. Growth of the axis is, how-ever, continued by a branch developing from a bud in the axil of a foliage leaf immediately below the inflorescence. The inflorescence is short lived and becomes evicted by growth of the lateral axis in such a way that growth of the lateral continues that of the parent axis (Schu-mann, 1897). This process of eviction has been described in detail by Schoute (1906). Multiplication of branch systems is possible because two or even three buds may grow out below a single inflorescence. The distribution of these branches is such that well-grown specimens of *P. utilis* have a regular candelabra habit. The over-all appearance of the plant suggests a dicotyledonous tree because there is a massive main trunk, with branches becoming progressively narrower in the distal direc-tion. However, this effect is achieved by reduction in the size of the apical vegetative cone of branch systems of successively higher order

and the origin of this form is quite different from that in a dicotyledonous tree with secondary growth. *Pandanus utilis* has wide aerial
roots, but these are restricted to the base of the stem. Stability is maintained largely by the development of a massive main axis and branches
of diminishing diameter. In some ways each new segment of each sympodium in *Pandanus* can be regarded as equivalent to the entire axis of
a coconut, since each segment essentially repeats the three phases of
growth described for the palm. This concept is elaborated elsewhere
(Tomlinson, 1964a). The best analogy is between *Pandanus* and a multiple-stemmed palm. In the palm, suckers which repeat the construction
of the parent axis are inserted basally on the stem; in *Pandanus* the new
branch units of successively higher order are each inserted distally on
the axis of the previous order.

Agavaceae (*Agave* and *Dracaena*)

A distinctive feature of stems in the Agavaceae is their cambium,
which produces secondary tissues in varying amounts (Cheadle, 1937).
This tends to obscure the essential similarity between the Agavaceae on
the one hand and the Palmae and Pandanaceae on the other, a similarity
which becomes clear when the primary construction of the axis in the
three groups is examined (Schoute, 1903). In their primary construction
members of the Agavaceae with unbranched axes, like some species of
Agave and *Furraea*, resemble *Cocos*. They have an obconical basal region to which roots are restricted, they develop a massive vegetative cone,
and the anatomical arrangement of primary tissues is like that in a palm,
except for differences in the detailed construction of vascular bundles.
Resemblance between *Cocos* and *Agave* is rather obscured by the very
sharp demarcation between a vegetative and a determinate flowering
phase in the latter. *Agave* is most like palms with determinate flowering
(Tomlinson, 1964a). Suckering of many *Agave* species recalls that of
multiple-stemmed palms.

Agavaceous genera with well-developed, branched aerial stems, like
Dracaena and *Yucca*, are not obviously like *Cocos*. They compare with
Pandanus in their primary construction. Branching is sparse and in most
species takes place only in the primary stages of growth so that no secondary tissues are involved. Branching, like that of *Pandanus*, is sympodial
below a terminal inflorescence (Schoute, 1918) and there are only minor
differences of detail between Agavaceae and Pandanaceae in the method
of eviction of the terminal inflorescence by the lateral branch. The essential similarity between the two types is shown by the obconical form
of the primary axis, revealed in the measurements quoted by Schoute

(1903). A similar obconical primary axis is recorded by Adamson (1926) for shrubby Iridaceae with secondary growth.

The cambium which adds secondary tissue to the primary axis is not an initial cambium, as in a dicotyledon, but a tiered (*etagen*) cambium (Schoute, 1902; Cheadle, 1937). Its behavior differs from that of the dicotyledonous cambium. It produces only a limited amount of undifferentiated parenchyma externally (secondary cortex). Internally it produces secondary vascular strands within secondary parenchymatous ground tissue. Within each secondary bundle both phloem and xylem differentiate, the xylem tracheids undergoing considerable elongation growth as they mature (Röseler, 1889; Scott and Brebner, 1893; Cheadle, 1937). The function of this secondary tissue may differ in different plants. In *Dracaena*, for example, it has an obvious mechanical function, since without it the primary structure would be unstable. In others, for example *Agave*, the secondary tissue is of such restricted development that its mechanical significance may not be large. It may possibly be associated with the development of a root system. In other plants a storage function has been suggested for the secondary tissue (Cordemoy, 1894; Holm, 1894). Experiments by Cheadle (1937) suggest that conduction is most rapid in the outer part of the secondary tissues.

The presence of this secondary tissue largely obscures the essential similarity between the Agavaceae on the one hand and arborescent monocotyledons without secondary tissue, on the other. Because of this secondary vascular tissue in certain monocotyledons much of the discussion of their phylogeny has been an attempt to relate them to dicotyledons in which secondary vascular tissues are fundamental (e.g., Lindinger, 1908). In view of the considerable differences between these two types of secondary tissue, a close relationship can scarcely be expected. The close similarity in primary construction of all arborescent monocotyledons does, however, warrant consideration.

Conclusions

GROWTH-LIMITING CHARACTERISTICS

The growth-limiting characteristics of plants without vascular cambia and therefore without the ability to produce unlimited amounts of secondary conducting tissues have been discussed in detail by Schoute (1906, 1918) and Holttum (1954, 1955). Physiological limitations imposed on such plants have also been pointed out. The growth habits of monocotyledons are largely a result of the absence of a vascular cambium (Holttum, 1955). Establishment of the plant in the juvenile phase clearly shows this. The primary root or radicle of the seedling has no cambium and cannot become wider and so increase its capacity to supply the increasing demand for water and dissolved mineral salts imposed by an enlarging leafy shoot. Adventitious roots replace the first root. Development of the massive obconical base by superposition of short but successively wider internodes is a method of producing a wide axis from a narrow seedling axis, the internodes of which have no means of secondary increase in diameter. The bluntly obconical base provides a wide area of insertion for adventitious roots close to the soil. This form of axis is also mechanically stable. Basal regions in which internodal elongation is marked require an independent supporting system, of either thick, aerial prop roots, as in *Pandanus* and the Iriartoid palms, or, possibly, of secondary tissue, as in the Agavaceae. All these plants are therefore well adapted mechanically and physiologically to growth restrictions imposed upon them.

Absence of a vascular cambium from the aerial axis also severely restricts branching. Dicotyledonous trees with vascular cambia are typically much branched; arborescent monocotyledons without vascular cambia are typically little branched. The former branching, dicotyloid (Schoute, 1918), is not limited. New branches are slender twigs which arise readily on both young and old parts of trees since the cambium, and consequently the secondary vascular tissues, of twig and main axis become continuous and mechanical and physiological continuity is maintained. The latter branching, monocotyloid (Schoute, 1918), is limited. New branches develop relatively massive apical vegetative cones and in the absence of a vascular cambium vascular tissues of branch and main axis cannot become continuous, especially if one is much older than the other. Physiological and mechanical continuity is difficult to maintain. Buds may be present, as in *Pandanus*, but if they grow out belatedly only branches of limited growth can be produced and these may serve simply as propagules (e.g., *Pandanus gemmiferous;* St. John, 1962). Root primordia in *Pandanus*, on the other hand, develop in such a way that physiological continuity between root and axis is possible, even if the primordia develop into roots very belatedly, because a well-developed root-trace system, continuous with the vascular system of the stem, is differentiated as the root primordium originates. This trace system anticipates future development of the root.

Apart from this inherent restriction of branching in monocotyledons, the elaboration of a much-branched leafy crown in plants without secondary vascular tissue is limited by the size of the main axis. The weight it can ultimately support and the maximum rate at which it can supply water are fixed at the time of its initiation. These restrictions are overcome in two ways. Either direct contact to soil water is made by new wide aerial roots which arise on the main axis and even on the branches themselves, thus providing new independent channels of water and also mechanical support, or the subsequent demands for physical strength and an adequate water supply are anticipated in the production of a very wide axis which is formed before branching begins, as in *Pandanus utilis.*

One would therefore expect agavaceous and other monocotyledonous plants with well-developed secondary tissues not to be restricted in their branching. It is notable, however, that monocotyledons with the ability to adopt a dicotyloid method of branching rarely do so. Schoute (1918) lists a number of species of *Dracaena, Aloe,* and related genera which are much branched and resemble dicotyledonous trees, but the majority branch sparingly. This again might suggest that the vascular cambium is not a fundamental feature of these plants.

In view of these restrictions, circumstances under which the arborescent monocotyledons branch are reviewed in the following paragraphs. It will be noted that there is less restriction on the production of lateral axes of limited or determinate growth (e.g., inflorescences) than on laterals with unlimited or indeterminate growth (e.g., vegetative branches).

A. Branches of Unlimited Growth

1. Branching wholly absent; e.g., single-stemmed palms, a few species of *Agave, Furcraea.*

2. Branching from basal suckers. Since these are situated basally they rapidly develop an independent root system and become physiologically independent of the parent axis (Holttum, 1955). Competition between lateral and parent axis may be alleviated when early growth of the sucker is stoloniferous or rhizomatous; e.g., several palms, *Phenakospermum* of Strelitziaceae, species of *Agava* and *Aloe.* Suckering is otherwise common in all the major groups of arborescent monocotyledons.

3. Branching by equal dichotomy of the parent axis as in species of *Hyphaene.* This is a true dichotomy according to Schoute (1909) and is remarkable as the only known instance of such branching in angiosperms. Its presence is suspected in a few other palms.[3] The system is mechanically and physiologically efficient since the branches are few and progressively narrower.

4. Branching by sympodial development of lateral axes below a terminal inflorescence. This is the method characteristic of Agavaceae, Aloineae, and Pandanaceae. Buds occur in the axils of all leaves but only

---

[3] From preliminary observations made in the company of Dr. H. E. Moore, Jr., it appears that vegetative branching in *Nypa* is equally dichotomous.

those close to, and probably stimulated by, a terminal inflorescence grow out. Their expansion involves an immediate enlargement of the basal region of the branch in such a way that intimate fusion of the primary tissue of main axis and branch occur whilst the terminal inflorescence is displaced into a lateral position (Schoute, 1906, 1918). Maturation of tissues on parent and lateral axes takes place simultaneously and by this distinctive procedure a mechanically and physiologically efficient union is effected without the intervention of secondary tissues. An interesting comparison has been made by Schoute (1918) between the development of the basal region of a main axis at the seedling stage and the development of the basal region of each lateral branch in a sympodium. In some ways the two kinds of axis are homologous (Tomlinson, 1964a). However, in the former example establishment of the primary thickening meristem is slow and involves a gradual enlargement in a long series of internodes. In the latter, establishment of the wide vegetative cone takes place almost immediately and, at least in *Pandanus* (Schoute, 1906), may be largely the result of activity of the prophyllar internode (the first internode on the branch). This can happen only because growth of the lateral axis is precocious.

5. Branching which may or may not be sympodial, essentially of the last-described type but independent of flowering, occurs at the base of the main axis in *Pandanus* and possibly distally in *Aloe* and *Dracaena* species (Schoute, 1906, 1918). This type of branching is problematical and to what extent it is a modification of sympodial branching is not known.

The above methods of branching are normal phenomena.

6. Branching as a pathological condition in otherwise unbranched axes has been recorded in many palms (Morris, 1893; Ridley, 1907). This usually results from damage to or even destruction of the apical meristem. Since such branches are unpredictable nothing is known of their development.

B. Branches of Limited Growth

7. Branching to produce lateral inflorescences occurs in most palms and in Strelitziaceae. Such axes, although relatively short lived, are subjected to the same growth-limiting characteristics as vegetative branches. Vascular continuity between axis and lateral branch is ensured by the close association in development of the main axis and branch. Tissues of main axis and branch insertion develop together. Consequently, the branch insertion is always wide and encircles a considerable sector of the stem, almost the whole circumference in some Arecoid palms. This affords an efficient union without involving secondary tissues.

8. Branching in the elongated terminal inflorescence of other monocotyledons is more comparable with that in the primary shoots of dicotyledons since it takes place on a primary axis in which elongation growth
is dominant. Lateral branches in such panicles have a relatively narrow
insertion.

PHYSIOLOGICAL CONSIDERATIONS

The previous discussion has established in very general terms the
method of development of larger monocotyledons and the way this
determines their growth habit. Consideration of mechanical requirements
has shown how these plants are well adapted to withstand physical
stresses imposed upon them even though their adaptive methods are
limited compared with those in dicotyledonous and gymnospermous
trees. Similar comparison of the requirements for long-distance conduction is also instructive. Is the trunk of an arborescent monocotyledon
less efficient in conducting water than a dicotyledonous tree trunk? There
is no evidence for this. In their gross anatomy the leaves of many arborescent monocotyledons have xeromorphic features usually regarded as
mechanisms which reduce transpiration. These structures include a thick
cuticle (e.g., Agavaceae), a well-developed colorless hypodermis (e.g.,
Palmae, Pandanaceae, Strelitziaceae), sinking of the stomata within the
epidermis (e.g., Agavaceae, Strelitziaceae), partial occlusion of the outer
stomatal chamber (e.g., Pandanaceae), development of abundant sclerenchyma (e.g., Palmae, Pandanaceae, Xanthorrhoeaceae), and a wide suc-
culent mesophyll (e.g., Agavaceae). This might indicate that movement
of water through the trunks of these plants is difficult and that water
supply to leaves is therefore inadequate. But these xeromorphic features
may have different causes. Simplest and most obvious is that arborescent
monocotyledons inhabit dry regions, as in the Agavaceae and Xanthorrhoeaceae. Otherwise, each leaf has a large area of lamina (Palmae,
Strelitziaceae). Also individual leaves, being long lived, often persist
on the plant for several seasons. There is no good evidence that the
trunks of large monocotyledons are inefficient water conductors. Rather,
they must be overefficient, since they anticipate a demand for water
which increases as the size of the leafy crown increases with age, whereas
the primary axis cannot increase its capacity to conduct, as already
mentioned for *Pandanus*.

A further comparison between dicotyledons and monocotyledons on
the basis of longevity of conducting tissues is also instructive (cf. also
Figs. 12, 13). In the dicotyledonous tree, conduction of water in the
xylem and elaborated foodstuffs in the phloem continually involves
new tissues. These are produced, usually seasonally, on each side of
the cambium. Inner (xylem) conducting tissue persists throughout the

life of the plant, but largely in a nonconducting capacity. Xylem vessels apparently function for one or few seasons, subsequently becoming air filled and often occluded by tyloses. A new generation of vessels assumes the conducting function. Parenchyma cells of the wood retain their vitality much longer (Barker, 1953) but are not associated directly with vertical conduction. Thus the bulk of the wood in a dicotyledonous tree is inert and the conducting ability of any one growth layer is ephemeral.

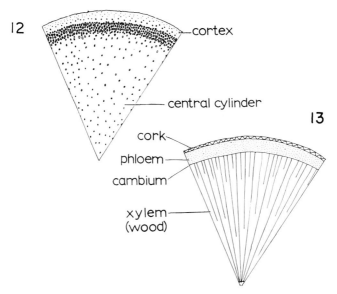

Figs. 12–13. (After Tomlinson, 1961c.) Sectors of the palm stem and the trunk of the dicotyledonous hardwood tree compared diagrammatically in transverse section.

The ephemeral nature of the secondary phloem is evident from its anatomy. Sieve tubes largely function during the season in which they are produced (except for those which overwinter in an undifferentiated state) because their sieve plates are occluded with callose at the end of that season. Reactivated sieve tubes in which callose is dissolved in spring may function for a limited period in the early part of the next season. Subsequently all sieve tubes produced by one growth increment collapse or are crushed by expansion of adjacent tissues. Exceptionally it is known that phloem may function for more than one season as in *Vitis* (Esau, 1948). Likewise little is known of the functional life span of the sieve tubes in tropical trees of nonseasonal climates, but it is not very long because secondary phloem tissues are all eventually incorporated as dead cells in the bark. It is a reasonable conclusion, therefore, that the normal situation in dicotyledons is for the sieve tubes to function for one, and rarely a few seasons.

Most arborescent monocotyledons are in sharp contrast to dicotyledons in this respect. In the Palmae and Pandanaceae, for example, all conducting tissues of the stem are primary and there is no mechanism by which they can be renewed. They are not functionally ephemeral but conduct so long as the plant is alive. There are no accurate records of the life span of palms whereby the maximum age of their conducting tissues might be determined, but in slower-growing species it must be more than a century. No detailed studies of these conducting tissues have been made and there are no obvious special features which would account for their longevity. Xylem vessels resemble those in other monocotyledons and in the primary tissues of dicotyledons. Tyloses are rarely developed and when they do occur this may be always a pathological phenomenon.

Longitudinal transport of elaborated foodstuffs continues in the phloem in even the oldest part of the stem. No violent demands on this conducting system are made, but vertical transport continues throughout the stem since nutrients are supplied by the leafy crown to its basal region and to the root system. Rapid mobilization and transport of food reserves may occur in palms with determinate flowering. The continued functioning of sieve tubes in palms for periods of over a century is doubly remarkable when their cytoplasmic structure is considered. Detailed studies of sieve tubes in arborescent monocotyledons have not been made, but my own casual observations show no obvious differences between them and those of other angiosperms. Callose, for example, occurs in sieve tubes of both primary and secondary vascular bundles, but its detailed distribution and fluctuation are not known. The angiosperm sieve tube is remarkable because as it matures the nucleus breaks down and the boundary between cytoplasm and vacuole becomes indistinct. This has been likened to a "premortal" condition by Esau (1950) and this accords well with the brief conducting life of most sieve tubes. The application of this concept to the sieve tubes of a palm are obvious, because if these cells are also in a "premortal" state, truly they are "an unconscionable time a-dying!"

The significance of a detailed study of the phloem in large monocotyledons, particularly the palms, need now scarcely be emphasized. What distinctive mechanism do these cells have which permits them to stay functionally alive for tens or hundreds of years, even though their cytoplasm is in a semidisorganized state? This itself is just one of the many perplexing problems in these organisms which only more intensive study can answer.

Summary

An analysis of the growth habit of certain arborescent monocotyledons is attempted, although it is pointed out that detailed developmental studies are largely lacking. Three main growth forms are considered, represented respectively by examples from the Palmae, Pandanaceae, and Agavaceae. Certain fundamental features in which these plants resemble each other are emphasized. Each has an obconical basal region, developed in the juvenile phase of growth. In this growth phase foliage is juvenile, internodes are usually short, and always successively wider as a massive apical vegetative cone is formed; roots and axillary suckers are often restricted to this basal region. Primary meristematic activity in the apical cone is fundamentally identical in the three classes and is responsible for the primary vascular skeleton in a simple causal way, although the size of the cone makes detailed mathematical analysis difficult. Agavaceae differ from Palmae and Pandanaceae in augmenting primary stem tissues with secondary vascular tissue from a continuous cambium. Pandanaceae differ from Palmae chiefly in undergoing sympodial branching in the aerial parts, the peculiar mode of branch development being largely associated with flowering. Agavaceae, like *Dracaena* and *Yucca*, have essentially the same method of primary branching as in Pandanaceae. Because of the basic resemblance of the Agavaceae in their primary construction to the Palmae and Pandanaceae it is suggested that the presence of the secondary cambium in the former group is not a fundamental feature.

The growth-limiting characteristics of large plants like arborescent monocotyledons without a vascular cambium are discussed, and a causal relation between primary growth and branching is described, the available methods of branching being reviewed. A brief discussion of some physiological properties of the conducting tissues in long-lived monocotyledons constructed wholly of primary tissue draws attention to the ability of these conducting cells and notably the sieve tubes to function in an unaltered state for periods of time much longer than is considered normal for dicotyledonous trees.

Discussion

ZIMMERMANN: Is it actually known, anatomically, where the conducting bundles of newly formed leaves attach to the old bundles of the stem?

TOMLINSON: According to Branner (1884) fusions (or branching) of bundles occur in the meristematic tissues of the apical vegetative cone, all bundles being of the same age and wholly procambial; in each, one branch continues directly into a leaf primordium, the other eventually passes into a leaf much higher up the stem which has still to be developed. A regular system of bundle branching is implied in this scheme, but actual observation suggests that branching is rather haphazard. Physiological continuity is assumed rather than proved. Branner also talked about "blend-ing" of bundles, as distinct from "fusions."

FREY-WYSSLING: As new leaves are formed, old ones are shed, so that the con-ducting capacity of functioning leaf traces remains constant. As to the longevity of the sieve tubes, old leaf traces surely go out of function. But since the number of axial bundles is the same at the top and the bottom of the palm, there must be a connection of the new bundles to the old ones. I thought this had been studied by the old anatomists.

TOMLINSON: Admittedly the distal part of vascular bundles which immediately lead into leaves must cease to function when those leaves fall. However, the proxi-mal parts, occupying the center of the stem, ramifying perhaps haphazardly in the man-ner I have just stated, must serve partly or wholly as longitudinal conducting channels. According to the classical interpretations, e.g., of von Mohl (1849), fusions are most common in the peripheral region, but my own feeling is that significant fusions are further toward the center of the stem, possibly Branner's "blendings." The peripheral fusions cannot be very significant physiologically; the peripheral bundles have re-duced vascular tissues and there is only the possibility of them fusing with the distal parts of traces which will pass soon into a leaf. The peripheral zone of con-gested bundles is of mechanical importance, however. One often finds palms with the peripheral portion of the stem injured, by fire for example, so that there is a damage to or constriction of the stem. Stems with conducting tissues reduced in this way show no obvious impairment of their conductability. No experimental work has been performed with palms although simple surgical experiments would indicate which regions of the stem at any one level actively conduct.

ALVIM: Palms do not usually branch, but one occasionally observes repeated branching in coconut.

TOMLINSON: I mentioned this as a pathological phenomenon. This is usually ascribed to damage to the apical bud, for example by disease. Unless there was regularity in the repeated branching, I would still be inclined to ascribe it to a re-peated pathological or abnormal effect.

ZIMMERMANN: You said that the crown of *Hyphaene* gets smaller each time after the stem branches. Is this because the vascular system of the stem is here a limiting factor?

TOMLINSON: It is likely to be a mechanical as well as a physiological limitation. The trunk has no mechanism for increasing strength and conducting capacity by adding new tissue, so that even if the stem base was physiologically overefficient and could accommodate an increasing demand, e.g., for water, imposed by multiplication of the crown, the size of distal branches must be limited by mechanical require-ments.

ESAU: You have related the inefficiency of the plant to the observation that the secondary growth doesn't assist the growth of the plant in the way that it does in the dicotyledons. Is it not true that the secondary growth is just intensified primary growth, in the sense that the secondary vascular bundles are continuations of the leaf traces as suggested by Strasburger (1891)? This concept makes secondary growth, in a way, similar to primary growth except that it extends farther down.

TOMLINSON: There is no good evidence that secondary growth bundles are merely downward continuations of primary bundles. The amount of secondary tissues formed bears no relation to the vigor of the apical vegetative cone and rate of development of leaves. There is commonly a marked anatomical difference between primary and secondary bundles.

WAREING: Surely if you trace these vessels upward they terminate in leaves?

TOMLINSON: Presumably these vessels ending in a leaf scar must become plugged by tyloses. This needs careful vertification, however. This point further emphasizes the central tissues as being most actively concerned with long-distance and long-term conduction.

WAREING: The fact that these vessels originate in the leaves supports Dr. Esau's point.

ESAU: They do not originate *in* the leaves, but they are continuous with those of the newest leaf traces. I presume that the xylem is differentiating downwards. If it did, it would connect with the secondary tissue in the same manner as we find in the dicotyledons, in which there is a continuity between the latest annual increment and the newly formed leaf traces.

TOMLINSON: All this is interpreting arborescent monocotyledonous stems in the light of what we know about dicotyledons. For example, there is no information as far as I know about the course of xylem differentiation in leaf traces.

BARGHOORN: Palms are very sharply delimited geographically to within latitudes of 30° on both sides of the equator, in spite of the ability of many of them to stand freezing. Do you think that failure of the translocation system is the limiting factor?

TOMLINSON: Surprisingly, few palms are frost resistant and these are invariably those whose natural range extends into climatic zones normally subjected to seasonal frost. I think that the limitation of palm distribution is that they have no mechanism for dormancy. The characteristic feature of growth of palms is its uninterrupted continuity. Under normal circumstances they don't become dormant, even when subjected naturally or artificially to adverse conditions. Perhaps the continued stimulation of distal growth processes is necessary to maintain the activity of conductivity channels.

BARGHOORN: In your discussion, does *Cordyline* fit in anatomically with *Agave?*

TOMLINSON: *Cordyline* is essentially a small *Dracaena*, anatomically as well as morphologically. *Agave* shows many close histological similarities with *Dracaena*, but a detailed, systematic anatomical survey of these forms and other liliflorous families still needs to be done.

ALVIM: In *Caryota urens* flowering begins at the upper nodes and then gradually descends to older nodes until it reaches a certain height; then the plant dies. Is there any physiological explanation for this?

TOMLINSON: I know of none. This type of basipetal sequence in flowering is quite anomalous in the arborescent monocotyledons as a whole, which makes the *Caryota* group of palms particularly interesting.

REFERENCES

Adamson, R. S. (1926). *Trans. Roy. Soc. S. Africa* 13, 175-194.

Arber, A. (1925). "Monocotyledons—A Morphological Study." Cambridge Univ. Press, London and New York.

Bailey, L. H. (1944). *Gentes Herbarum* 6(7), 367-459.

Ball, E. (1941). *Am. J. Botany* 28, 820-832.

Barker, E. (1953). *Am. J. Botany* 40, 773-778.

Branner, J. C. (1884). *Proc. Am. Phil. Soc.* 21, 459-483.

Carano, E. (1906a). *Rend. Accad. Lincei Roma* 15(2), 243-246.

Carano, E. (1906b). *Ann. Botan. (Rome)* 5, 1-45.

Cheadle, V. I. (1937). *Botan. Gaz.* 98, 535-555.

Cordemoy, A. J. de (1894). Ph.D. Thesis. Paris. p. 108, see *Compt. Rend. Acad. Sci.* 117, 132-134 (1893) and *Beih. Botan. Zentr.* 5, 89-91 (1894).

Drabble, E. (1904). *Trans. Linn. Soc. London, Botany* [2] **6**, 427-490.

Eckardt, T. (1941). *Botan. Arch.* **42**, 289-334.

Esau, K. (1948). *Hilgardia* **18**, 217-296.

Esau, K. (1950). *Botan. Rev.* **16**, 67-114.

Helm, J. (1936). *Planta* **26**, 319-364.

Holm, T. (1894). *Botan. Gaz.* **19**, 66-67.

Holttum, R. E. (1954). "Plant Life in Malaya." Longmans Green, London and New York.

Holttum, R. E. (1955). *Phytomorphology* **5**, 399-413.

Hutchinson, J. (1959). "Families of Flowering Plants. II. Monocotyledons," 2nd ed. Clarendon Press, Oxford.

Kaul, K. N. (1960). *Bull. Natl. Botan. Gardens Lucknow, India* **51**, 52.

Lindinger, L. (1908). *Beih. Botan. Zentr.* **24** (1), 211-253.

Meyer, F. J. (1933). *Planta* **19**, 607-613.

Monoyer, A. (1925). *Mem. Acad. Roy. Belg.* **8**, 1-44.

Morris, D. (1893). *J. Linn. Soc. (Botany)* **29**, 281-298.

Priestley, J. H., Scott, L. I., and Gillett, E. C. (1935). *Ann. Botany (London)* **44**, 1-19.

Queva, C. (1907). *Beih. Botan. Zentr.* **22**, (2), 30-77.

Ridley, H. N. (1907). *Ann. Botany (London)* **21**, 415-422; **23**, 338-339.

Röseler, P. (1889). *Jahrb. Wiss. Botan.* **20**, 292-348.

St. John, H. (1962). *Pacific Sci.* **16**, 88-125.

Schoute, J. C. (1902). *Verhandel. Koninkl. Akad. Wetenschap.* **9**, 59.

Schoute, J. C. (1903). *Flora (Jena)* **92**, 32-48.

Schoute, J. C. (1906). *Ann. Jardin Botan. Buitenzorg* **20**, 53-87.

Schoute, J. C. (1907). *Ann. Jardin Botan. Buitenzorg* **21**, 115-137.

Schoute, J. C. (1909). *Rec. Trav. Botan. Neerl.* **6**, 211-232.

Schoute, J. C. (1912). *Ann. Jardin Botan. Buitenzorg* [2]**11**, 1-209.

Schoute, J. C. (1918). *Rec. Trav. Botan. Neerl.* **15**, 263-335.

Schumann, K. (1897). *Botan. Jahrb.* **23**, 559-572.

Scott, D. H., and Brebner, G. (1893). *Ann. Botany (London)* **7**, 21-62.

Solereder, H., and Meyer, F. J. (1933). *In* "Systematische Anatomie der Monokotyledonen," Vol. 1, pp. 28-50. Borntraeger, Berlin.

Strasburger, E. (1891). "Ueber den Bau und die Verrichtungen der Leitungsbahnen in den Pflanzen." Histologische Beiträge. Band 3. Fischer, Jena.

Strasburger, E. (1906). *Jahrb. Wiss. Botan.* **43**, 580-628.

Tomlinson, P. B. (1960). *Principes (J. Palm Soc.)* **4**, 140-143.

Tomlinson, P. B. (1961a). *J. Arnold Arboretum* (Harvard Univ.) **41**, 414-428.

Tomlinson, P. B. (1961b). *Principes (J. Palm Soc.)* **5**, 83-89.

Tomlinson, P. B. (1961c). *Principes (J. Palm Soc.)* **5**, 117-124.

Tomlinson, P. B. (1961d). *Abstr. Symposium Papers, 10th Pacific Sci. Congr., Honolulu.* p. 282.

Tomlinson, P. B. (1961e). "Anatomy of the Monocotyledons. II. Palmae." Clarendon Press, Oxford.

Tomlinson, P. B. (1962a). *J. Arnold Arboretum (Harvard Univ.)* **43**, 23-46.

Tomlinson, P. B. (1962b). *Evolution* **16**, 192-213.

Tomlinson, P. B. (1964a). *J. Arnold Arboretum (Harvard Univ.)* **45**, (in press).

Tomlinson, P. B. (1964b). *Phytomorphology* (in press).

von Mohl, H. (1849). "On the Structure of the Palm Stem" (English translation). Rept. Ray. Soc., London.

von Mohl, H. (1858). *Botan. Zeit.* **16**, 185-190; 193-198.

Warburg, O. (1900). *In* Engler's "Das Pflanzenreich," Vol. 4 (9), p. 97.

The Structure and Formation of the Cell Wall in Xylem

A. B. WARDROP

Division of Forest Products, Commonwealth Scientific and Industrial Research Organization, Melbourne, Australia

I. Introduction

The general anatomy of the secondary xylem has been described in great detail in a publication on plant anatomy (Esau, 1953). It may be recalled that two systems of cells, viz., the axial and the radial system, may be recognized. The proportion of the various cells varies greatly between species so that, for example, in the angiosperms the volume of the xylem occupied by the fibers may range between 25% *(Erythrina)* and 70% *(Eucalyptus)*. In gymnosperms the tracheids usually occupy 90–95% of the xylem volume (Frey-Wyssling and Aeberli, 1942).

The walls of most mature cells of the xylem can be shown to consist of two structures, the primary wall and the secondary wall. In general application, this terminology presents some difficulties (Wardrop, 1962), but, for the present discussion, the primary wall may be defined as the structure formed at cell division in the cambium and which encloses or which enclosed the protoplast during the phase of surface growth of the cell during differentiation. The secondary wall is the structure which is formed after the surface growth has ceased (Fig. 10).

The composition and physical texture of the cell walls in the elements of the xylem are qualitatively similar, so that in this discussion these aspects may be considered before discussion of the differing organization of the wall in the cells constituting the xylem.

II. Composition of the Cell Wall

1. CLASSIFICATION OF WALL CONSTITUENTS

In terms of structure the constituents of cell walls fall into three groups: the matrix substances, framework substances, and the encrusting substances. Matrix and framework constituents are formed simultaneously

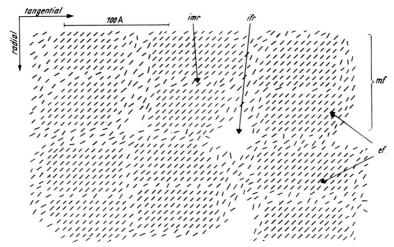

FIG. 1. The texture of the cell wall according to Frey-Wyssling (1955). Imr, intramicrofibrillar spaces; ifr, intermicrofibrillar spaces; mf, microfibril; ef, elementary fibril.

during the wall formation, whereas the encrusting constituents begin to form after some degree of cell-wall formation has taken place. In wood fibers the framework substance is cellulose. The matrix constituents consist of non-cellulosic polysaccharides, and the main encrusting substance is lignin. During the formation of heartwood some secondary encrustation by polyphenolic constituents may take place. (See the paper by Meier in this volume.)

2. DISTRIBUTION OF WALL CONSTITUENTS

Methods used to study the distribution of constituents in the cell wall include the use of optical and electron stains (Albersheim et al., 1960), the application of cytochemical methods based on differential solubility (Bailey and Kerr, 1935; Dadswell, 1931), ultraviolet microspectrophotometry, interference microscopy associated with immersion refractometry (Lange and Kjaer, 1957), and studies of differentiating xylem (Meier, 1961; Stewart et al., 1953).

From the application of these methods it has been concluded that, for the tracheids of spruce, 70% of the lignin is located in the region external to the layer S_2, that the cellulose is present in greatest concentration in the inner part of the layer S_2 or the layer S_3 (Asunmaa and Lange, 1953, 1954), and that the uronic acid-containing constituents are present in greatest concentration in the middle lamella and primary wall (Meier, 1961). The distribution of constituents in the cell walls of ray parenchyma and vessels has not been studied in the same detail as for wood fibers.

However, in ray parenchyma the lignin content is undoubtedly higher than that of the fibers, as has been shown by analysis of dissected parenchyma by A. J. Bailey (1936) and by more recent interference microscope investigations (Harada and Wardrop, 1960).

III. Texture of the Cell Wall

Both the matrix and encrusting substances which occur in the xylem cells are amorphous, whereas the framework of cellulose is aggregated in the form of microfibrils.

The existence of the microfibrils as structural units of cellulose was predicted by Frey-Wyssling (1937) and they were demonstrated in cellulose from a variety of sources following the development of the shadow-casting techniques by Williams and Wyckoff (1946). The microfibrils are of indefinite length and vary from 100 to 300 Å in width (Mühlethaler, 1960). In wood fibers the microfibrils are approximately 100 Å in width (Hodge and Wardrop, 1950). Different concepts have been proposed for the molecular organization of the microfibril. The reason for this is that in earlier X-ray diffraction and polarized light studies it was established that cellulose is in part crystalline. In ramie the crystalline regions (micelles) were calculated to be 50–70 Å wide and at least 600 Å in length (Hengstenberg and Mark, 1928). Later work showed that breadth of the crystalline regions varies in cellulose from different sources and in wood is considerably less than in ramie (Mühlethaler, 1960; Wardrop, 1954a). From physical measurements of the degree of polymerization of cellulose and the length of the crystalline regions calculated from X-ray diffraction measurements, it was concluded that the cellulose molecules are arranged in a manner such that, over limited regions of their length, perfect three-dimensional order exists and that these crystalline regions are separated by regions of less perfect molecular order. Because of the discrepancy between the breadth of the microfibrils measured in the electron microscope and the breadth of the crystalline regions it may be assumed that the microfibrils must consist of lateral aggregations of longitudinal micellar strings. This general concept is in agreement with the electron microscopic observations that microfibrils may be broken down into finer fibrillar elements termed "elementary fibrils" (Mühlethaler, 1960) and by acid hydrolysis into particles apparently corresponding to the crystalline regions (micelles) (Rånby, 1949).

These observations are generally consistent with the model of the structure of the microfibril by Frey-Wyssling (1954) (Fig. 1). The existence of the paracrystalline phase separating the elementary fibrils and surrounding the microfibrils results in the increase in apparent micelle size which accompanies acid hydrolysis of cellulose (Howsmon,

1949; Wardrop, 1949), and the fact that a similar change accompanies the removal of lignin and of matrix substances from the wall suggests that at least the paracrystalline phase surrounding the microfibril is intimately associated with these constituents.

It should be pointed out that within the microfibrils the 101 (6.1 Å spacing) planes lie parallel to its surface. This has been shown for films formed from cellulose sols by Mukherjee and Woods (1953), and it is known for the large cells of certain algae such as *Valonia* and *Chaetomorpha* that the 101 plane also tends to lie parallel to the surface of the cell (Fig. 1). Because of the circular form of fibers this point has not been demonstrated in these cells, but it is generally assumed to be so. The 101 plane is the richest in hydroxyl groups, and Frey-Wyssling (1954, 1955) considers it to be the plane of lamellation of the cell wall and that the microfibrils tend to be aggregated laterally within cell wall lamellae. Evidence of this in wood fibers can be seen from the longitudinal sections of cell walls cut in the radial and tangential planes (see Figs. 16 and 17 in the paper by Wardrop later in this volume). The secondary walls of xylem cells all exhibit lamellation. These lamellae are not generally visible in mature cells because of the presence of matrix substances, and because of encrustation by lignin, but they can be seen in developing cells before lignification begins or in mature cells after delignification.

The form and magnitude of regions of the cell wall not occupied by cellulose was first established by Frey-Wyssling (1937). He concluded from X-ray diffraction measurements of the size of metal crystals deposited within the delignified fibers that two systems of capillaries were present, one between the microfibrils measuring 100 Å in width, and another within the microfibrils measuring some 10 Å in width (Fig. 1). These general conclusions were subsequently confirmed by electron microscopic studies of metal-impregnated fibers (Frey-Wyssling and Mitrakos, 1959; Wardrop, 1956). The regions in which the metal crystals were deposited in the delignified fibers are normally partly or wholly occupied by matrix substances. It is also in these regions that the water present in the cell wall is located, so in living cells the matrix substances and lignin are present in a greatly swollen condition. Although some water may penetrate minute fissures in the microfibrils, the crystalline regions are not penetrated by water. This is demonstrated by the fact that the X-ray diffraction diagram of cellulose in both wet and dry cell walls is similar. From the composition of the walls and the shrinkage on drying, the volume of the fresh wall occupied by the cellulose framework can be calculated. For the primary wall before lignification this is less than 8%. The corresponding value for secondary walls is less than 50%.

In the fresh condition, therefore, the microfibrils in both the primary and the secondary walls are relatively widely separated from each other. In the secondary wall, however, because of its lamellated structure the separation would be greater in the radial than in the tangential plane. In recent years attempts have been made to relate the above physical texture of the cell wall to the known distribution of constituents within it and to the distribution of mass across the wall. From the mass distribution, and the density of the cell-wall constituents, some information of the relative porosity of different regions of the wall has been obtained. Thus it was concluded from X-ray microradiographic studies by Lange (1954) and Asunmaa (1960) that the relative packing density of cell-wall substances in the middle lamella would be 81% and 89% of that in the secondary wall for spruce and birch, respectively. These results would imply that the compound middle lamella is relatively more porous than the secondary wall.

A similar conclusion was reached by Lange and Kjaer (1957) from interference microscope measurements of the effective thickness (i.e., the thickness the structure would have if all capillaries were eliminated) of different regions of the wall. These results showed that the effective thickness of the compound middle lamella was approximately 80% of that of the secondary wall.

Results which in general agree with these conclusions were obtained by Asunmaa and Steenberg (1957), who found that the electron-scattering power of the middle lamella was less than that of the secondary wall in sapwood, but greater in heartwood. It was not known, however, to what extent these observations reflected the distribution of mineral constituents. It may also be noted that the uptake of dyes such as Congo red is greater in the layer S_1 than in the true middle lamella or the layer S_2 (Wardrop and Davies, 1961), which suggests that the spaces in which the dye micelles are deposited are greatest in the layer S_1. These observations in general suggest that the region external to the layer S_2 is one of relatively high porosity, although most of the methods used do not precisely distinguish between the true middle lamella, primary wall, and layer S_1.

IV. Cell Wall Organization

Studies of cell-wall organization are concerned particularly with the pattern of microfibril orientation in relation to the morphological axes of the cell, i.e., to the form of the cell, and with the nature of layering within the secondary wall. Such investigations have been made in greatest detail on the cell wall of angiosperm fibers and gymnosperm tracheids. Since these cells show a very similar pattern of organization they may be considered together.

1. FIBERS AND TRACHEIDS

(a) *The Primary Wall.* Early optical investigation by Kerr and Bailey (1934) established that the primary wall is birefringent in both transverse and longitudinal section. Van Iterson (1935) showed that in tracheids the major extinction position lies approximately transverse to the cell axis. These observations together with the low magnitude of birefringence in transverse section [e.g., 0.001 in *Pinus sylvestris* (Preston and Wardrop, 1949a)] were consistent with the view that the micelles (microfibrils) are considerably dispersed about a mean transverse direction of orientation. X-ray diffraction studies confirmed these optical observations and it was concluded by Preston and Wardrop (1949a) that most of the micelles (microfibrils) lie between the angles of 0° and 16° to the transverse axis of the cells.

The application of the electron microscope to the study of the primary wall in differentiating xylem and in fragments detached from mature cells yielded a specific interpretation of the indirect optical and X-ray observations. (Hodge and Wardrop, 1950; Wardrop, 1954c; Wardrop and Harada, 1963). From these studies it has been established that on the inner surface of the primary wall the microfibril orientation is approximately transverse to the cell axis but differs considerably from this orientation on the outer surface (Figs. 2 and 3). The significance of this difference in orientation is discussed further, below, in relation to the surface growth of the cells. Furthermore, at the cell corners there can be seen longitudinal ribs of microfibrils which in mature cells are heavily lignified. The primary walls do not show lamellation and the microfibrils appear to be intertangled. These observations are consistent with the earlier optical studies in that the dispersion of the microfibrils in the outer regions of the wall is sufficiently great to account for the birefringence observed in both transverse and longitudinal section and for the low magnitude of birefringence in transverse section. The relatively regular transverse orientation in the inner part of the wall would be expected to confer an approximately transverse major extinction position on the wall. In the middle region of the wall thickness it may be assumed that the microfibril orientation would be random (see below).

(b) *The Secondary Wall.* The secondary walls of fibers and tracheids exhibit two features of organization apparent in many cells with thickened walls. The cell walls show both microscopic layering and submicroscopic lamellation. The layering of the cell wall is associated with differences both in composition (see above) and organization. When examined in transverse section between crossed nicols the cell wall shows conspicuous optical heterogeneity (Fig. 4). This was interpreted by Bailey and Kerr (1935) as due to a differing helical orientation of the micelles (micro-

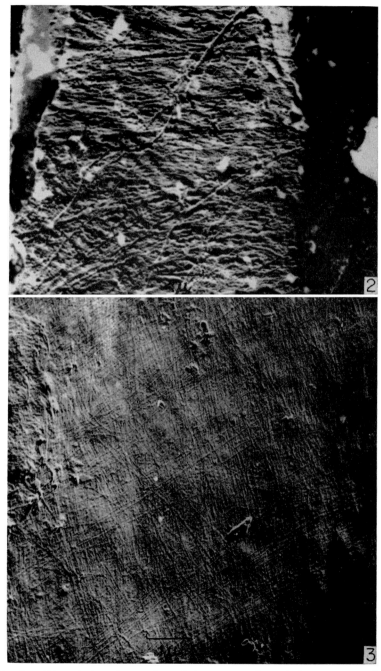

FIG. 2. (Upper) A carbon replica of the inner surface of the primary wall of a fiber of *Eucalyptus elaeophora*. (Wardrop and Harada, 1963.)

FIG. 3. (Lower) The outer surface of a fiber of *Eucalyptus elaeophora*. (Wardrop and Harada, 1963.)

fibrils) in the different layers. This view was confirmed in the optical study of Wardrop and Preston (1951). The contribution of the different layers to the wide-angle X-ray diffraction diagram, as well as in low-angle scattering diagrams, can be recognized.

The outer (S_1), middle (S_2), and inner (S_3) (Figs. 4 and 10) layers of the cell walls of fibers or tracheids are typically present. The birefringence of the S_1 layer is somewhat greater than that of the layer S_3. The layer S_3, however, is frequently considerably thinner than the layer S_1 and in some instances may be absent (e.g., *Picea*). The variation in thickness of the cell walls in earlywood as compared with that of latewood is due

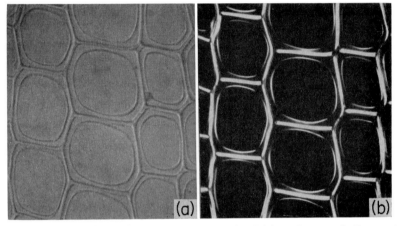

Fig. 4. *Pinus radiata.* A transverse section (a, left) with normal illumination and (b, right) photographed between crossed nicols showing the optical heterogeneity of the secondary cell wall.

mainly to a variation in the degree of development of the layer S_2 (Kerr and Bailey, 1934).

Apart from the observed optical heterogeneity of the cell walls in the transverse section, evidence that each of the secondary wall layers possessed a helical organization was established by such observations as the direction of striations in the walls (Bailey and Kerr, 1935; Bailey and Berkeley, 1942), the swelling behavior of the walls in strong acids and alkalies (Bucher, 1953; Bucher and Wiederkehr-Scherb, 1948), the direction of growth of iodine crystals in swollen walls (Bailey and Vestal, 1937a), the pattern of enzymic degradation of the walls by fungi (Bailey and Vestal, 1937b), and the direction of the major extinction position of isolated walls and fragments of them.

Direct confirmation of these observations was obtained by the application of the techniques of electron microscopy to the study of these cells.

The application of such methods also adds details not indicated by the indirect methods of observation. That the layer S_1 was itself a complex structure had been indicated by the optical studies of Nagatomo (1952). Early electron microscopic studies showed that the layer consists of at least two lamellae of apparent helical microfibrillar orientation (Emerton and Goldsmith, 1956; Frei *et al.*, 1957; Hodge and Wardrop, 1950; Meier, 1955) and subsequently it was proposed by Wardrop (1957a) that this layer contains some four lamellae of alternating S and Z helical orientation (Fig. 5). These lamellae were shown to be symmetrically disposed about the longitudinal axis of the cell. The further studies of Harada *et al.* (1958), however, showed that in conifer tracheids additional lamellae in which the microfibril orientation was intermediate between that of those present in layer S_1 and those of the layer S_2 may be present. Further studies, however (Wardrop and Harada, 1963), showed that these lamellae of intermediate orientation are not always present, so that there is some variation in the organization of the walls of these cells.

The middle layer of the secondary wall (S_2) consists of numerous concentric lamellae of which the microfibrils are orientated at only a small angle to the longitudinal cell axis. The orientation in successive lamellae appears to be similar. It may be noted that the microfibrils are less obvious than in primary walls and in some instances appear to be aggregated in sheafs (Fig. 6), so that there is some dispersion of the microfibrils about the general direction of orientation.

The presence of concentric rings of lignin referred to in the investigations of Kerr and Bailey (1934) and Dadswell and Ellis (1940) in the layer S_2 are consistent with the location of lignin between the lamellae of the layer. The radio-concentric patterns which were also observed would imply the existence of radial fissures in the cellulose lamellae, which are occupied by lignin. These have not been observed in longitudinal sections of intact walls but can be seen in the electron microscope studies of lignin residues by Sachs (1962).

The birefringent inner layer of the secondary wall (S_3) varies considerably in the degree of its development so that in some instances (as in *Fraxinus, Alnus,* and *Picea*) it is absent or so poorly developed that it is not apparent when transverse sections are examined between crossed nicols. The magnitude of birefringence in transverse section is less than that of the layer S_1, although in view of its composition (Meier and Yllner, 1956) this does not necessarily reflect a steeper microfibrillar orientation than the layer S_1. Electron microscopic studies have shown the layer S_3 to be lamellated with successive lamellae having alternating S or Z helical orientation of the microfibrils (Fig. 7). The perfection of orientation of the microfibrils is, however, less than that of the layer S_1. As between the layers S_1 and S_2. Harada *et al.* (1958) have observed lamellae in which the microfibrillar orientation was intermediate between that of the layers S_2 and S_3.

The layering of the cell wall described above can be seen in electron micrographs of transverse sections of the wood. This is shown for *Pinus radiata* and *Eucalyptus regnans* in Figs. 8 and 9 respectively. It may be

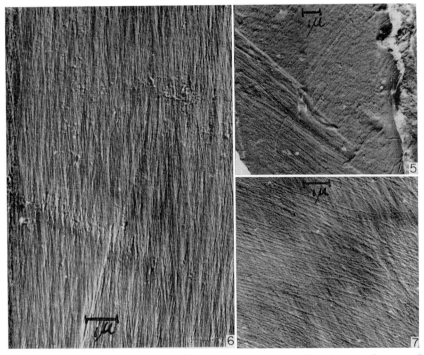

FIG. 5.   (Upper right) *Acacia podalyriaefolia*. A carbon replica showing the crossed fibrillar texture of the outer layer of the secondary cell wall (S_1).

FIG. 6.   (Left) *Pinus radiata*. A carbon replica of the middle layer of the secondary cell wall (S_2) showing the sheaf-like aggregates of microfibrils.

FIG. 7.   (Lower right) *Pinus radiata*. An early stage in the deposition of the layer S_3 (carbon replica). The layer S_2 can be seen underlying it.

noted that in Fig. 9 the S_3 layer is difficult to distinguish. The apparently greater shrinkage of the S_1 layer apparent in these electron micrographs is consistent with the physical texture of the layer discussed above as well as the microfibril orientation. From the preceding discussion the general organization of the different wall layers may be represented diagrammatically as in Fig. 10.

From the standpoint of morphogenesis it is of interest that the orientation of the microfibrils in the secondary wall of tracheids is related to

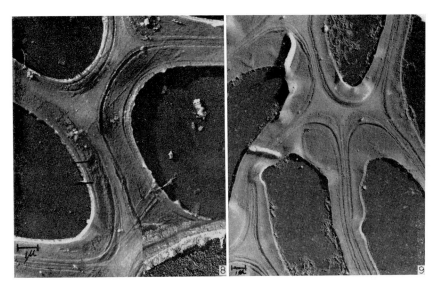

FIG. 8. (Left) *Pinus radiata.* A transverse section showing the three layers of the secondary cell wall, together with the terminal lamella, shown at greater magnification (Inset, at bottom).

FIG. 9. (Right) *Eucalyptus regnans.* A transverse section showing the three layers of the secondary cell wall.

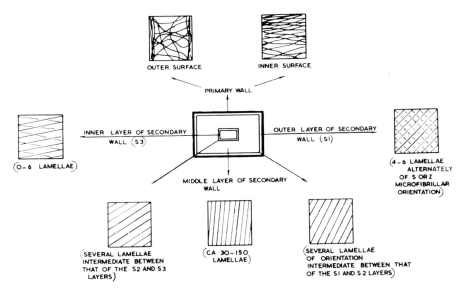

FIG. 10. A diagrammatic representation of the cell-wall organization of a typical fiber or tracheid showing the texture of the different cell-wall layers. (Wardrop and Harada, 1963.)

the dimensions, and presumably to the form, of the cell. This relation was first recognized by Preston (1934) and later elaborated as a result of additional work (1948). It was observed for many conifers that, for tracheids of average length L in which the average inclination of the micellar (microfibrillar) helix to the cell axis was θ, a relation existed of the form $L = A + B \cot \theta$ (A and B are constants). It was shown by Preston that the breadth of the cells also influenced the value of θ and the data more exactly fitted a relation of the above form, if a hypothetical value $\theta_{1.00}$ was calculated corresponding to unit (arbitrary) breadth. This relationship was shown to apply to the tracheids from successive annual rings in which the tracheids are of increasing length and to random samples of tracheids from a number of annual rings so that the relation did not reflect a process of aging of the meristem from which the tracheids were derived.

Some evidence that the orientation of the S_1 layer may also change in cells of increasing length was obtained by Preston and Wardrop (1949a). It was shown that the magnitude of birefringence of the S_1 layer in transverse sections decreased in the tracheids from successive growth rings. Assuming that the observed differences in birefringence reflected changes in microfibril orientation, then these observations would imply a decrease in the value of θ for the S_1 layer as well as that for the layer S_2.

Since Preston's original work, this phenomenon has been observed in the abnormal tracheids of reaction wood of gymnosperms (compression wood) (Wardrop and Dadswell, 1952b), the fiber tracheids of *Eucalyptus*, and cotton fibers (Meredith, 1946).

The orientation of the microfibrillar helix in compression wood tracheids is of interest since the secondary walls of these cells are characterized by well-developed helical fissures which are parallel to the microfibrillar orientation of the layer S_2, so that the orientation of the microfibrils can be observed at any point along the length of the cell. The observations of Wardrop and Dadswell (1952b) have shown that within one cell the angle of orientation (θ) varies along the length of the cell, being greatest near the broad central part of the cell and less near the narrower tips. Since all gradations of structure between compression and normal wood exist, it is reasonable to suppose that the general relationship established on a statistical basis by Preston may also apply to variations within the tracheids. A further feature which can be observed in the compression wood tracheids is that the number of turns of the microfibrillar helix increases with the cell length; again, in view of the continuity of structural transition which exists between normal and compression wood it would seem reasonable that this is also a feature of the microfibrillar organization in the normal cells. These features of secondary wall organization in tracheids are discussed further in relation to the problem of cell-wall formation (below).

2. Xylem Parenchyma

Although xylem parenchyma may comprise a significant fraction of the wood volume its cell-wall organization has not been investigated in such detail as that of fibers and tracheids.

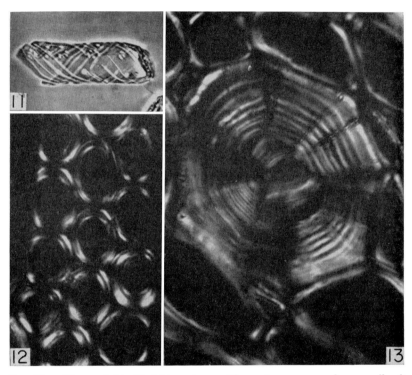

Fig. 11. (Upper left) *Hodgkinsonia ovatiflora*. A ray parenchyma cell after fungal attack—illustrating the helical organization of the secondary cell wall. Phase contrast. (Wardrop and Dadswell, 1952a.)

Fig. 12. (Lower left) *Dialium laurium*. Ray parenchyma photographed between crossed nicols showing the optical heterogeneity of the cell wall. (Wardrop and Dadswell, 1952a.)

Fig. 13. (Right) *Persoonia lanceolata*. Sclerozed ray parenchyma photographed between crossed nicols. (Wardrop and Dadswell, 1952a.)

In the primary wall of ray parenchyma the major extinction position lies transverse to the cell axis and, when viewed in the electron microscope, shows an intertangled arrangement of the microfibrils (Cronshaw, 1960; Harada and Wardrop, 1960). The existence of an helical organization in the secondary wall was suggested by the initial observation of Tuszon (1903) that isolated cells frequently possessed helical fractures in the walls. That the helix was relatively flat in relation to the major cell axis was shown by the fact that the cells had a negative sign of birefringence (Ritter and Mitchell, 1939) and from a study of the X-ray diffraction diagram of the isolated cells (Gross, Clarke, and Ritter, 1939). Confirmation of this helical organization of the secondary wall was obtained from the more detailed optical studies of Wardrop and Dadswell (1952a), and from the study of cells attacked by fungi (Fig. 11). In transverse sections the secondary wall of ray parenchyma is optically heterogeneous, consisting of relatively broad birefringent outer and inner layers separated by a central, narrow, nonbirefringent layer (Fig. 12).

The electron microscope studies of Harada and Wardrop (1960) confirmed that the microfibril orientation in the outer and inner layers of the secondary wall are oriented as a flat helix while those of the central layer are oriented axially. The inner layer, however, showed some complexity of organization and may consist of a number of lamellae of opposed helical orientation. In *Eucalyptus* this complexity of organization of the inner layer does not exist and the layer consists of a single, flat helix of microfibrils.

In some angiosperms such as *Persoonia* some ray parenchyma cells may become sclerozed and the secondary wall formed in such cells has an extreme complexity of organization, consisting of alternate layers in which the microfibrils are oriented in steep and flat helices with respect to the major cell axis (Fig. 13) (Wardrop and Dadswell, 1952a).

The cell-wall organization of vertical parenchyma cells has been investigated (Wardrop and Dadswell, 1952a) and has been shown to be similar to that of ray parenchyma.

3. VESSELS

Initial optical studies on the cell-wall organization in vessels were made by Frey (see Frey-Wyssling, 1959) and these were followed by the investigations of Bailey and Vestal (1937a,b) and of Preston (1939). When examined in transverse section between crossed nicols the cell walls show varying degrees of optical heterogeneity as shown in Fig. 14. It was pointed out by Bailey and Vestal (1937a) that the vessel walls in the less specialized dicotyledons (such as that illustrated for *Sassafras* in Fig. 14a) show a typical three-layered structure resembling that of tracheids, whereas when the vessels are more specialized the layering is less obvious and they may appear quite uniformly birefringent as shown for *Fraxinus* in Fig. 14b. In vessels in which the secondary wall possesses the typical three-layered structure the differences in birefringence reflect differences in helical microfibril arrangement, similar to that observed in tracheids.

In those vessels in which the birefringence in transverse section is uniform it is difficult to determine if this results from an absence of layering, from the presence of layers differing only slightly in helical micro-

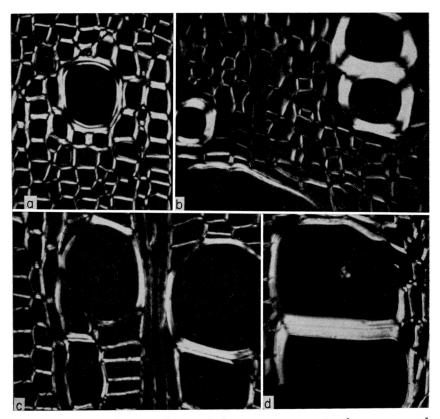

Fig. 14. Vessel elements photographed in transverse section between crossed nicols. (a) *Sassafras verifolium;* (b) *Fraxinus nigra;* (c) *Eugenia kuranda* (cf. Fig. 15); (d) *Papuodendron lepidotum.*

fibril orientation, or from the disturbance of microfibril orientation within the layers due to the presence of pits. The second possibility was apparently the case in *Eugenia*, the vessel walls of which show uniform birefringence (Fig. 14c), but which an electron microscope examination shows to possess three quite definite layers in the secondary wall (Fig. 15). That these layers differ only slightly in microfibrillar orientation can be seen in Fig. 16a. The extent to which the microfibril orientation

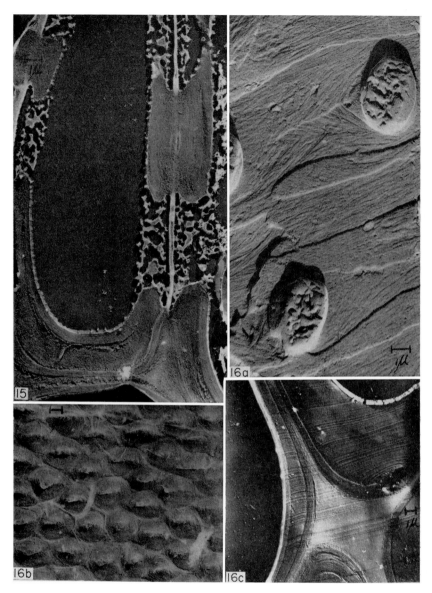

Fig. 15. (Upper left) *Eugenia* sp. An electron micrograph of a transverse section through a vessel showing three layers of the secondary cell (cf. Fig. 14) and well-developed vestures on the pits (cf. Fig. 14c).

Fig. 16. (a, Upper right) Carbon replica of the surface of a vessel of *Aeschynomene* sp. Some lamellae are partly removed from the wall showing the complexity of the microfibrillar orientation around the vestured pits. (b, Lower left) Carbon replica of a densely pitted area of a vessel of *Papuodendron lepidotum* (cf. Fig. 14d). (c, Lower right) Electron micrograph of a transverse section through a thin vessel of *Sassafras verifolium* showing the layering of the cell wall (cf. Fig. 14a).

can be disturbed by the presence of pits is apparent in the carbon replica
of the vessel pits of *Papuodendron* (Fig. 16b; cf. Fig. 14d).

V. Sculpturing of the Cell Wall

1. THE STRUCTURE OF PITS

As already indicated, in the case of vessels, the secondary cell-wall
organization described above for the different tissue elements of xylem
is modified locally to form the pits connecting adjacent cells. The nature
of this modification varies depending upon the nature of the cells in
which the pits are present.

(*a*) *The Xylem Pits of Gymnosperms.* The bordered pits in gymnosperm
tracheids were demonstrated by Sachs (1882) to be initiated by the
deposition of a ring of cellulose on the primary wall of the differentiating
cell. This ring (here designated as the "initial pit border") delineates the
outer boundary of the pit in the mature cell. The optical studies of Frey-
Wyssling (1955) and the studies of Bailey and Vestal (1937a) on the
orientation of iodine crystals in the cell wall served to demonstrate that
the cellulose micelles constituting the ring were arranged concentrically.
This was subsequently confirmed by electron microscope studies of
differentiating tracheids (Wardrop, 1954c). It should be emphasized that
the formation of initial border thickening begins before deposition of the
layer S_1 and in mature cells may be detached from cells after delignification by mechanical disintegration. It must therefore be structurally
distinct from the layer S_1. This was recognized by Bailey and Vestal
(1937a) and has been demonstrated directly in the electron microscope
studies of Harada *et al.* (1958) and of Liese and Hartmann-Fahnenbrock
(1953) and in the optical observations of Wardrop and Davies (1961).
In view of these studies the deposition of the wall layers in the region of
a bordered pit may be represented as in Fig. 17a.

Simultaneously with the initiation of the secondary wall and the
elaboration of the pit border, the pit membrane, i.e., the primary wall
delineated by the inner edge of the initial pit border, undergoes changes
in organization. At first the pit membrane possesses a typical primary
wall organization (Frey-Wyssling *et al.* 1956; Wardrop, 1958), and
is in intimate contact with the cytoplasm. The membrane then increases
in thickness near its center through the deposition of circularly arranged
microfibrils which constitute the torus, and the microfibrils of the pit
membrane become rearranged to form bundles of radially oriented
microfibrils suspending the torus across the pit chamber and thus providing direct communication between adjacent cells. This change is not
common to all tracheids, and the mechanism by which it is achieved

has not been elucidated although Jayme and Hunger (1960) have suggested that it may result from stress generated by the aspiration of the pits at the conclusion of differentiation of the cells. The magnitude of the spaces between the radial microfibril bundles has been estimated by the size of particle suspensions which can be made to pass through them (Bailey, 1913; Frenzel, 1929; Liese, 1956). For a number of genera Liese (1956) has observed that particles up to 2000 Å in diameter can pass through the pores of the membrane in this way. It may be noted

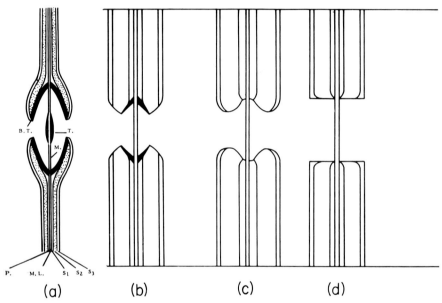

(a)   (b)   (c)   (d)

Fig. 17. Diagrammatic representation of the disposition of the cell-wall layers in the region of the pits of (a) a gymnosperm tracheid; (b) an angiosperm fiber tracheid; (c) an angiosperm vessel; (d) a parenchyma cell. M = Pit membrane; T = torus; S_1, S_2, S_3 = outer, middle, and inner layers of the secondary wall, respectively; P = primary wall; M. L. = middle lamella; B. T. = initial pit border.

that in mature cells the pit membrane becomes heavily encrusted with cytoplasmic debris (Stemsrud, 1956).

In the half-bordered pits between tracheids and parenchyma cells the primary wall texture is retained and no torus is formed. The pit membrane between parenchyma cells is similar (Harada et al., 1958).

(b) The Xylem Pits of Angiosperms. The disposition of the cell-wall layers around the pits in tracheids, and fiber tracheids, of angiosperms is essentially similar to that existing in gymnosperms tracheids (Cronshaw, 1960; Harada, 1962; Liese, 1951, 1957a). An initial pit border is deposited on the primary wall, which as in conifer tracheids is not overlain by the layer S₁, but is covered by the layers S₂ and S₃ (Bosshard, 1952; Wardrop, 1958; Fig. 17b). The pit membrane retains the primary wall texture.

In vessels the initial secondary thickening is not formed separately around each pit area but the microfibrils may follow a sinuous course between adjacent pits, as was demonstrated in the studies of vessel pits in *Fraxinus* by Bosshard (1952) and in *Ulmus* by Wardrop (1958). Since this secondary thickening of the vessel walls constitutes a general thickening of the cell wall and is not a localized initial thickening as seen in conifer tracheids, no "initial pit border" in the sense used above can be recognized in vessels. This is apparent in electron micrographs of replicas of vessel walls such as those of Harada *et al.* (1958), Liese (1957a), and Cronshaw (1960). It can also be seen in sections such as that of the vessel of *Eugenia* shown in Fig. 15, and in the observations of Harada (1962). The disposition of the wall layers in vessels of this type may be represented as in Fig. 17c. The pit membrane as in the fiber tracheids and fibers retains the primary wall texture.

The pits between ray parenchyma cells are not bordered so that the pit is simply an area of the cell over which secondary thickening does not occur and the pit membrane retains its primary wall texture. In instances so far examined it appears that the layers of the secondary wall, as in vessels, are not confluent at the pit border, so that the structure of the parenchyma pits may be represented as in Fig. 17d.

In addition to the well-defined sculpturing of the cell wall apparent in the structure of pits the walls of many cells of both angiosperms and gymnosperms show localized thickening to form such characteristic structures as annular, helical, and reticulate thickenings, vestures of some pits of dicotyledons, the crassulae, callitroid thickenings, and the wart structure of conifer tracheids, and the dentate thickenings of ray tracheids in conifers. The function of these structures is not known but they are frequently of taxonomic significance and although their general nature was recognized from optical studies, the application of the electron microscope has clarified their nature and the manner of their formation and contributed especially to elucidating their relation to the different layers of the secondary wall.

2. HELICAL THICKENINGS IN CONIFER TRACHEIDS

From optical studies it was shown by Frey (see Frey-Wyssling, 1959) that helical thickenings consist of micellar (microfibrillar) aggregates of parallel orientation. They are relatively easily detached from the cell wall and are usually more obvious near the middle of cells and tend to

cease before reaching the cell tips. The relation of the orientation of the
thickenings to cell dimensions was investigated by Wardrop and Dadswell in *Pseudotsuga* (1951). It was observed that the angle of inclination of the thickening to the longitudinal cell axis was less in longer

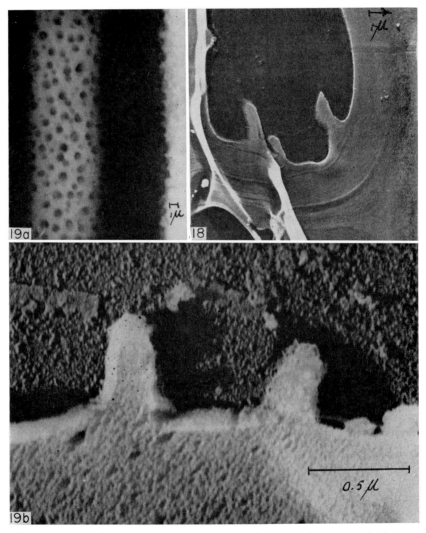

Fig. 18. *Taxus baccata.* A transverse section of a tracheid showing the layering
of the cell wall and a number of helical thickenings.

Fig. 19. (a) *Actinostrobus pyramidalis.* An ultraviolet photomicrograph of a
longitudinal section of a tracheid seen in surface view and in profile. (b) An electron
micrograph of a transverse section showing the continuity of the wart structure with
the cell wall.

than in shorter cells and furthermore that the number of turns of the helix per cell increased with increasing cell length. Thus the relation of the orientation of the helical thickenings to cell dimensions is similar to that observed for the layer S_2 described above.

In an electron microscope study of *Pseudotsuga* it was observed by Hodge and Wardrop (1950) that the thickenings consist of microfibril aggregates, formed in addition to the layer S_3, and differing in their direction of orientation from that of the microfibrils present in this layer. This was also observed by Liese and Hartmann-Fahnenbrock (1953). In a more recent investigation of *Taxus* (Wardrop and Davies, unpublished), the helical thickenings can be seen to be separate from the layer S_3 (Fig. 18) although this is not always obvious. In view of the composition of these structures and the similar pattern of variation of their orientation with cell dimensions it would seem reasonable to regard them as homologous with the layers of the secondary cell wall, although they differ in the lateral extent of their development.

3. Dentate Thickenings in Ray Tracheids

These structures are characteristic of the ray tracheids in some species of *Pinus*. In surface view they do not possess the regularity of form of helical thickenings of tracheids. From the studies of Meier (1960) they appear to be localized thickenings of the innermost layer of the secondary wall of the parenchyma cells (see above) rather than a structure formed in addition to the normal layering of the cell wall.

4. Callitroid Thickenings

These thickenings, which are characteristic of some species of *Callitris*, have been investigated by Cronshaw (1961). They have been shown to lie within the limits of the pit border and appear in tangential section as arches adjacent to the pit aperture. They are covered by the wart structure and so are presumably elaborations of the layer S_3 where it crosses the pit border although this point has not been demonstrated. It is consistent with this interpretation, however, that the wart structure can be seen to be present on the thickenings as well as in the remainder of the cells.

5. The Wart Structure of Conifer Tracheids

The wart structure of conifer tracheids was first described by Kobayashi and Utsumi (1951) and by Liese (1951). Although these structures were first recognized in the electron microscope as small protruberances on the inner surface of this cell wall measuring from 0.05 to 0.5 microns in diameter, frequently they can be seen in the optical microscope (Liese, 1957b). They were considered by Frey-Wyssling (1959) to be features of the terminal lamella (see below). In a further investigation it was shown by Wardrop *et al.* (1959) that in *Actinostrobus* the wart structure consists of a membrane system lining the cell lumen which was extended into a series of protruberances which showed ultraviolet absorption (Fig. 19a). This structure could be isolated by dissolution of the cell wall, and chemical analysis showed it to contain nitrogen. Further investigation of the wart structure by Wardrop and Davies (1962) demonstrated that, as seen in mature cells, it is a form of cell-wall sculpturing encrusted by denatured cytoplasm. This can be seen in Fig. 19b, which is a cross section of a tracheid showing the wart structure which appears to be continuous with the inner layer of the secondary wall. Most recent investigations show that during maceration of the xylem the wart structure tends to undergo hydrolytic attack more readily than the remainder of the wall and suggest that the polysaccharides of which it is constituted may differ from those of the other wall layers. It may be noted that Meier and Yllner (1956) have obtained evidence that the layer S_3 is rich in glucuronoarabinoxylan and it is possible, in view of its structural continuity with the layer S_3, that similar differences in composition may extend to the wart structure.

In sections cut through the wart structure but which were not shadow-cast, the localized wall thickening could be seen to be overlain by a membrane which was extremely dense to electrons. The origin of this membrane was established by a study of the cytology of differentiating tracheids (Wardrop and Davies, 1962). Stages in the development of the wart structure showed that the development of the wart structure was accompanied by the movement of the plasmalemma away from the wall. In some instances various organelles could be seen to be associated with the protruberances. As the cells matured the zone of cytoplasm between the plasmalemma and tonoplast narrowed, confining the particulate and membranous organelles of the cytoplasm between them, until at the death of the cells the denatured remains of the plasmalemma, the tonoplast, and any organelles confined between them were flattened onto the wall. This process may be represented as show in Fig. 20. Thus in the mature (dead) cell the wart structure may be regarded as possessing both cell-wall and cytoplasmic components. However, the cytoplasmic components may be expected to be deposited at the death of the cell irrespective of the formation of the cell-wall protuberances so that in instances where a wart-like structure can be recognized but in which no localized wall thickening occurs, such as that described by Liese and Ledbetter (1963) in *Plantago*, it would seem

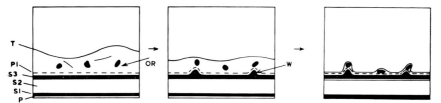

Fig. 20. Diagrammatic representation of three stages in the formation of the wart structure. P = primary wall; T = tonoplast; Pl = plasmalemma; OR = organelle; W = wart structure; S_1, S_2, S_3 = the outer, middle, and inner layers of the secondary wall respectively.

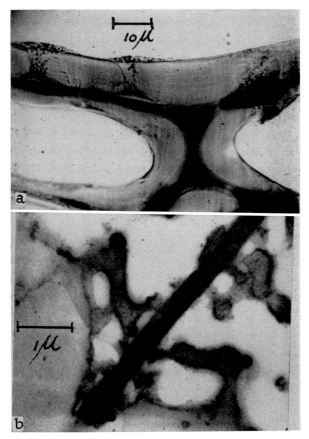

Fig. 21. (a) *Eucalyptus regnans*. An ultraviolet photomicrograph showing absorption in the vestures of a vessel pit. Note the extension of the vestures laterally from the pit aperture. (b) *Eugenia* sp. A section through the pit membrane showing the continuity of the vestures with the secondary wall and the electron-dense nature of the membrane compared with the cell wall.

unjustified to regard such structures as analogous to the wart structure of conifer tracheids.

6. VESTURED PITS IN ANGIOSPERMS

In the vessel pits of more specialized dicotyledons, extensions of the pit border into more or less ramifying outgrowths were described by Bailey (1933). These were shown to be highly refractive and were recognized as outgrowths of the cell wall. This interpretation has been confirmed in recent electron microscope studies by Côté and Day (1962) and by Wardrop *et al.* (1963). In the latter investigation it was observed that vestures show absorption in ultraviolet light (Fig. 21a). In *Eugenia* it was demonstrated that the vestures were outgrowths of one or more of the layers S_1, S_2, and S_3 (Fig. 21b) depending on the disposition of the layers at the pit border. Instances exist in which the vestures also appear to arise from the pit membrane, although this has not been established with certainty. It could be seen, however, that the vestures and the pit membrane were heavily encrusted with a denatured cytoplasmic membrane (cf. the wart structure) which (Fig. 21b) appeared dense to electrons. It is considered that the encrusting cytoplasmic membrane is responsible for the observed ultraviolet absorption. It was observed further that vestures frequently extended away from the pits as less elaborate outgrowths into the cell lumen and that they closely resembled in form the warts of conifer tracheids. These studies clearly confirm the conclusions of Bailey that vestures are elaborations of the cell wall and in this sense may be regarded as similar to the wart structure in conifers. The encrusting membrane seen in the mature structures is assumed to be similar in origin to that covering the wart structure.

VI. Cell-Wall Organization and the Differentiation of Fibers and Tracheids

The change of composition and organization of the walls of xylem elements, associated with the differentiation of the mature cells from the cambium, may be regarded as being composed of four arbitrary phases. The phases into which the process of differentiation may be divided are cell division in the cambium; the phase of surface growth of the daughter cells of such divisions; the phase of secondary thickening; and the phase of lignification. The phases following cell division are not strictly consecutive so that secondary wall formation may begin locally in a differentiating fiber or tracheid before growth at the tip has ceased, and lignification may commence before the formation of the secondary wall has been completed.

1. Cell Division in the Cambium

The cytological organization of the cambium was studied in investigations by Bailey (1920a, b, 1930) in which its essentially vacuolate condition and its seasonal variability in organization were recognized. The cytological changes associated with the development of the cell plate in the cambium were also studied (1920b). The formation of a complete primary wall around each daughter protoplast following cytokinesis was recognized by early investigators and later was studied in some detail (Newman, 1956; Wardrop, 1952a). It may be noted that, as a result of the repeated divisions within the xylem mother cells, parent walls in the intercellular region accumulate to a greater extent between radial walls than between tangential walls so that this phenomenon may account for the apparently greater width of the middle lamella between radial than between tangential walls.

Electron microscopic studies of the cytological organization of the cambium have to this stage been largely exploratory in nature. The cambium and differentiating xylem of *Datura* were studied by Hohl (1960) and those of *Pinus* and *Eucalyptus* have been investigated by Cronshaw and Wardrop (1963). In the cambium or cells immediately adjacent to it the cambium shows great cytological complexity—containing numerous small vacuoles, mitochondria, plastids, and Golgi apparatus—and endoplasmic reticulum which in some instances shows a tendency to be aligned parallel to the wall surface.

The primary wall of the differentiating xylem shows numerous pit fields and possesses conspicuous corner thickenings of longitudinally arranged microfibrils.

The intercellular readjustments following periclinal and anticlinal divisions in the cambium have been studied extensively by Bannan and Whalley (1950) and Bannan (1956). Bannan (1956) has also summarized the literature on the nature of these changes.

2. Surface Growth in Differentiating Fibers and Tracheids

The phase of surface growth of the daughter cells of cambial divisions in general precedes the formation of the secondary wall although this latter process may commence locally before the cessation of surface growth in other parts of the cell. Although this sequence of wall development is accepted for most cells, reference to the possible influence of dimensional changes in cells resulting in changes in the orientation of microfibrils in the secondary wall is sometimes made. Because of the irregular arrangement of the cells in the differentiating xylem it is a difficult matter to establish the sequence of surface growth and secondary

wall formation. One recent approach to this problem has been to measure
the perimeter of successive cells from the cambium in which the degree of development of the secondary wall could be established. This

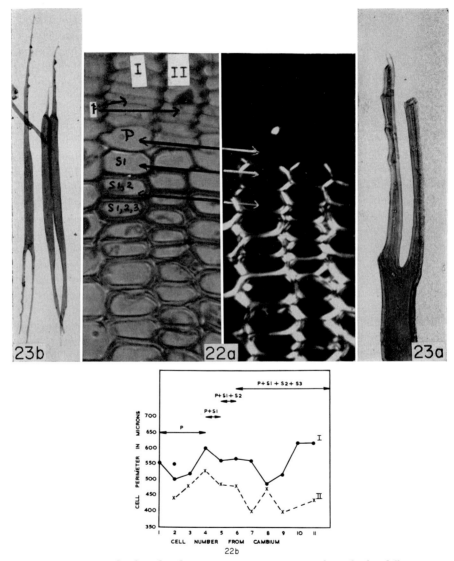

FIG. 22. *Papuodendron lepidotum.* A transverse section through the differentiating xylem under normal (left) illumination and between crossed nicols (right)
showing the progressive deposition of the secondary wall. (b, Lower) Measurements
of the cell perimeter in the two files of cells shown in (a).

FIG. 23. (a and b) *Papuodendron lepidotum.* Showing the form of isolated fibers.

is best done using species with regular storied structure, so that the effect of the tapered form of the fibers is largely eliminated in that most cells at any level of cross section are cut at the same point along their length. One result of such a study using *Papuodendron* is shown in Fig. 22b. It can be seen that the perimeter of the cell I-4 in which only the primary wall was present was as great as that in any of the cells of the same radial file irrespective of the degree of secondary wall formation which had taken place.

It may also be noted that although the increase in the radial dimensions of the differentiating fibers may be up to 400% of that of the cambium, the growth in perimeter is very much less than this (120%), so that the increase in radial diameter results from a change in cross-sectional form of the cell as well as its actual growth.

In the examination of this species it was also observed that the number of tips of cells observed in cross sections tended to be greater in the more mature xylem so that it might be assumed that lateral surface growth of the cells precedes the process of elongation.

The degree of extension growth of the differentiating fiber and tracheids compared with the cambial initials was studied extensively by Bailey (1920a, b), who showed that in gymnosperms the tracheids were up to 20% longer than the cambial initials, although the study of individual cells by Bannan (1956) showed that the average change in length may be greatly exceeded in individual cells. In angiosperms Bailey found that the length increase was greater than that observed for gymnosperms and in some instances may amount to nearly 500% of the initial length.

Several lines of evidence indicate that the growth in length of differentiating fibers and tracheids is confined to the tips or the region near the tips of the cells. The occurrence of bifurcated and otherwise distorted tips in mature cells (Fig. 23) when these are not observed in the cambial initials, and the further observations of Schoch-Bodmer that the areas of pits in fibers, fiber tracheids, and phloem fibers correspond with the length of the vessel segment (i.e. the length of the cambial initials) also support this view. A similar conclusion was reached by Bannan (1956) on the basis of his studies of the intercellular readjustments which take place during differentiation.

The fine structure of differentiating fibers and tracheids has been studied by Bosshard (1952), Wardrop (1958), and Wardrop and Harada (1963). As indicated above, the microfibril orientation is approximately transverse to the cell axis on the inner surface of the primary wall (Fig. 2) but greatly differs from this orientation on the outer surface of the cells (Fig. 3).

These observations constitute evidence similar in kind to that which

led Roelofsen and Houwink (1953) to the formulation of the multinet
hypothesis of the growth of primary walls in parenchyma and hair
cells. According to this hypothesis, the microfibrils are deposited in an
initial, approximately transverse, orientation to the major cell axis and
during surface growth become progressively disoriented from this direction, so that the microfibrils on the outer surface of the cells (i.e. the
oldest microfibrils) are most changed in orientation from their initial
transverse arrangement. As a corollary to this it was pointed out by
Wardrop (1958) that the final orientation on the outer surface of the
cells should reflect the amount and polarity of growth which has taken
place. Furthermore the microfibrils on the outer surface should be more
widely separated from each other. The near-longitudinal orientation of
the microfibrils observed at the tips of differentiating fibers (Wardrop,
1958) is consistent with this conclusion, but this is not observed in all
fibers since, during the intercellular readjustments taking place during
differentiation, elongation does not always occur (Wardrop and Harada,
1963; Bannan, 1956).

Evidence relating to the operation of the multinet mechanism in fibers
has been obtained in recent work in this laboratory. In this approach the
orientation of microfibrils on the outer surface of mature cells has been
studied. This has been done using wet carbon replicas to avoid distor-
tion of the surface during drying. As experimental material the mature
fibers of *Papuodendron* were used. As already pointed out, this species
has a storied structure and the fibers possess a well-defined broad central region which narrows steeply toward the tip (Fig. 23). The broad
central region may be assumed to correspond approximately with the
cambial initial length. This is supported by the fact that the average
length of this region in the material used was 0.30 mm compared with
0.26 mm for the vessel element length, the overall length of the fibers
being 0.79 mm, so that the increase in length of the fibers was approximately 2.5 times that of the initials from which they were derived.
It may also be noted in the photomicrographs of the bifurcated fiber
shown in Fig. 23 that the bifurcation began immediately beyond the
broad central part, which also suggests this region does not participate
in the elongation of the fiber.

The variation of microfibril orientation along the length of such cells
is shown in Fig. 24. It could be seen qualitatively that at the tip the
orientation was random. At position (c) the orientation was nearly
axial, at position (d) there was evidence of a definite, crossed, microfibrillar texture, and near the middle of the cell, at position (e), the
orientation was random with a tendency to be transverse. A preliminary
attempt has been made to express these observations quantitatively using

the method used by Probine and Preston (1961) of measuring the percentage of microfibrils oriented in a series of directions with reference to the fiber axis. The results obtained to date are shown in Fig. 25. These measurements agree with the qualitative estimates except in posi-

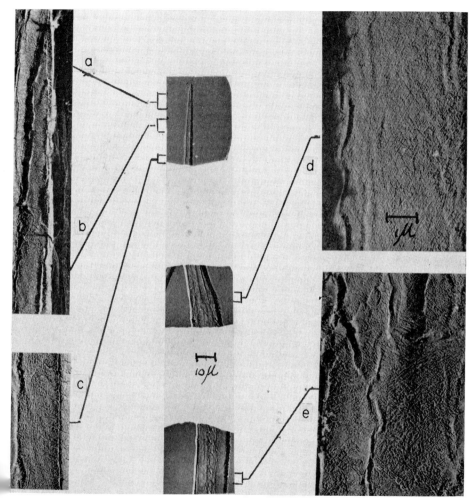

Fig. 24. A carbon replica of a single fiber of *Papuodendron lepidotum* showing the variation of microfibril orientation along the cell.

tion (b), where there appeared to be a tendency to orientation in two directions although much less regular than that in position (d).

If as suggested by Roelofsen (1958) the wall pressure of growing cells is exerted by the innermost microfibrils then all microfibrils external

to these would be expected to undergo passive reorientation reflecting
the extent and polarity of the growth which occurred. On such an assumption the axial orientation observed would imply that the major
extension growth occurs somewhat behind the cell tip and that the

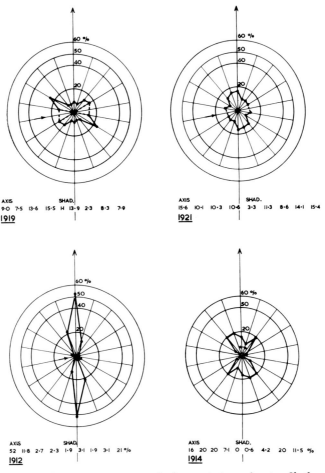

Fig. 25. A graphic representation of the variation of microfibril orientation
shown in Fig. 24. Upper left, cf. Fig. 24a; upper right, cf. Fig. 24b; lower left, cf.
Fig. 24c; lower right, cf. Fig. 24d.

relatively regular, crossed microfibrillar, helical texture results from a
simultaneous lateral expansion accompanied by elongation. Frey-Wyssling (1962) has drawn attention to these different textures in various
cell types. In general his findings are consistent with these conclusions.
Further evidence which is consistent with the multinet hypothesis has

been obtained by Wardrop and Harada (1963) from autoradiographic studies. In plants administered $C^{14}O_2$ the radioactivity was observed in the zone of xylem differentiation. In cells obtained by maceration and in which, as indicated by their optical properties, only the primary wall was present, the distribution of radioactivity was quite uniform (Fig. 26).

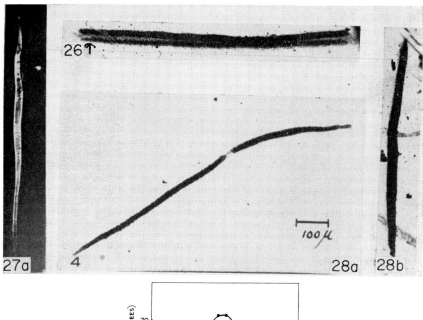

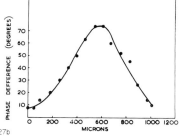

FIG. 26. An autoradiograph of two tracheids isolated by maceration from a plant grown in $C^{14}O_2$. The cell marked by an arrow was uniformly labeled and it was shown by its optical properties that only the primary wall was present.

Fig. 27. (a) A partially differentiated fiber of *Eucalyptus elaeophora* of positive optic sign and in which presumably both the S_1 and S_2 layer were present; photographed between crossed nicols. (b) The variation in phase difference along a fiber such as that in (a).

FIG. 28. (a) *Eucalyptus elaeophora*. An autoradiograph of a cell similar to that in Fig. 27a. Note the decreasing radioactivity toward the cell tips (layer S_1 and S_2 present). (b) *Pinus radiata*. An autoradiograph of a cell in which only the layer S_1 was present (negative sign of birefringence) showing decreased radioactivity toward the cell tips.

This would indicate that, although in the differentiating fibers the growth was localized, the synthesis of cellulose was quite uniform over the cell surface. Since these results would imply the uniform deposition of microfibrils over both the extending and stationary regions of the cell surface it might be expected that the walls of the central (nonextending) regions of the cell would become thicker relative to the extending tips. It is extremely interesting, therefore, to speculate whether the continued deposition of cellulose microfibrils in this region while the tips of the cells are growing may be a factor governing the initiation of secondary cell-wall formation, especially as the secondary wall is initiated near the center of the cells (see below). If further observations show that such a view can be sustained, then the classical concepts of intussusception and apposition would appear to involve essentially similar processes except that in one instance (intussusception) the microfibrils are deposited on an expanding surface and in the other (apposition) they are deposited on a stationary surface.

3. Secondary Wall Formation in Fibers and Tracheids

(a) *The Pattern of Deposition of the Secondary Wall*. The first indication of cell-wall thickening in tracheids and fibers is the formation of the initial border thickening, limiting the pit membrane area of the future pits. As pointed out above, this structure is independent of the secondary wall layers and its development is followed by the successive formation of the layers S_1, S_2 and S_3 which overlie it to varying degrees.

The structures of the secondary wall layers in differentiating cells have been studied by Wardrop and Harada (1963). These do not differ in appearance from that in mature cells (Figs. 5-7). However, there is some evidence from the examination of mature cells that successive lamellae of the layer S_1 increase in the degree of perfection of microfibril alignment as successive lamellae are formed (Wardrop, 1957a).

In an optical investigation by Wardrop and Dadswell (1953) of partially differentiated tracheids of *Pinus* it was observed that the cell wall appeared to be thinner nearer the tips of the cells and that there was a decrease of birefringence from the middle of the cell toward its tips. In some instances only the primary wall was present at the cell tips, so it appeared reasonable to conclude that formation of the secondary wall began near the center of the cell and proceeded toward its ends. Since this initial study, similar observations have been made of the sclerenchyma fibers of *Phormium tenax* and the phloem fibers of *Nerium oleander*. A more detailed study of the variation of birefringence along the length of tracheids of *Pinus* and the fibers of *Eucalyptus* was made by

Wardrop and Harada (1963). One result of this investigation is shown in Fig. 27 in which the quantitative variation in phase difference is shown for the fiber illustrated. From the sign of birefringence (positive) it was concluded that in this cell the layer S_2 was in process of formation. Similar observations were made for fibers in which the layer S_1 was being formed (sign of birefringence negative).

Further evidence of the progressive development of the secondary wall layers toward the cell tips was obtained by the study of autoradiographs of partially differentiated cells obtained from plants grown in an atmosphere of labeled carbon dioxide. As pointed out above, cells in which only the primary wall was present showed a uniform distribution of radioactivity. In cells undergoing secondary wall formation (as determined by their optical properties) the radioactivity decreased from the center of the cells toward the tips in a manner similar to the birefringence. This is illustrated for a tracheid undergoing formation of the layer S_1 (Fig. 28b) and a fiber in which the layer S_2 was being formed (Fig. 28a).

Two additional observations support these optical and autoradiographic observations. Thus as already described, in the tracheids of the reaction xylem of gymnosperms (compression wood), the layer S_3 is absent and the layer S_2 of the secondary wall is characterized by a system of helical fissures parallel to the direction of microfibril orientation. In partially differentiated tracheids of compression the fissures are very obvious near the middle of the cells but are difficult to distinguish or absent toward the tips of the cells (Wardrop and Dadswell, 1952b). This may be interpreted as a progressive formation of the S_2 layer toward the cell tips. Since all stages of variation between typically normal tracheids and the compression wood tracheids exist it may be argued that such observations support this general pattern of secondary wall deposition.

A second type of observation which supports the idea of a progressive longitudinal deposition of the secondary wall consists in examining cross sections of fibers at their centers and near the tips and determining the degree of secondary wall formation. Thus Fig. 29 shows a cross section of *Papuodendron lepidotium* photographed under ordinary illumination and between crossed nicols. In cells A the S_1 layer had formed, in cells B both the layers S_1 and S_2 were present, and in cells C the layers S_1, S_2, and S_3 were present. However, from the birefringence it appeared that, in the intruding tip of the cell marked by the arrows, no secondary wall formation had taken place. Since all the cells surrounding this cell were undergoing secondary thickening it is reasonable to assume that,

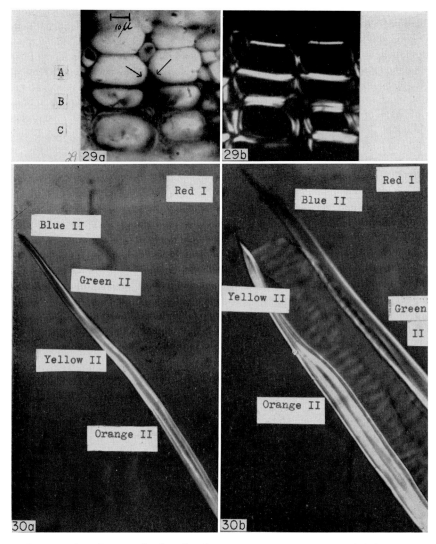

FIG. 29. (Top) *Papuodendron lepidotum*. A transverse section of differentiating xylem. In the tip of the fiber marked by the arrows, apparently only the primary wall was present although the secondary wall was present in the cells surrounding it. (a, Upper left) Normal illumination. (b, Upper right) Crossed nicols.

FIG. 30. (Bottom) *Acacia podalyriaefolia*. Partially differentiated reaction wood fibers photographed between crossed nicols with a retardation plate of 550 mμ. The interference colors observed are indicated. In (b) the cell at the left was judged to be nearly mature.

near its center this was also undergoing secondary wall formation, but had not reached the point along the length of the cell through which the section passed.

Further evidence of this kind was obtained from a study of the differentiating fibers of the reaction wood of angiosperms (tension wood, q.v.). In these cells the layer S_2 or the layer S_3 may be replaced by the formation of an extremely thick unlignified layer $S(G)$ in which the microfibrils are axially oriented. In a specimen of *Acacia* the tension wood fibers were shown to have the organization in which the layer $S(G)$ replaced the normal layer S_3. Because of the considerable thickness of the layer $S(G)$ and the fact that both the secondary wall layers S_1 and S_2 were present, such fibers are extremely birefringent, so that in fibers in which formation of the $S(G)$ layer was taking place the variation in birefringence was sufficiently great to be apparent as differences in interference colors when they were examined between crossed nicols using a suitable retardation plate (550 mµ). Thus in one fiber (Fig. 30a) the color at the tip was blue (second order) ranging through green to yellow and orange near the middle of the fiber, whereas mature fibers showed a nearly uniform orange color (Fig. 30b). Quantitative determinations of the magnitude of birefringence showed that its variation was similar to that in Fig. 27 so that development of the layer $S(G)$ also took place progressively toward the tips of the cells. Direct confirmation of this conclusion was obtained by the electron microscopic examination of the differentiating xylem from which the cells shown in Fig. 30 were obtained by maceration. Thus Fig. 31 shows a cross section of a group of fibers of tension wood in which the layer $S(G)$ was undergoing formation. The variation in breadth of the cells shown can be attributed to the point along their length at which the section was cut and results from the nonstoried nature of the xylem in this species. Thus fibers A and B were cut near the tips, whereas the cell C was cut near its center. Examination of the electron micrograph shows that in the cell C, and indeed all the other cells in the section with the exception of A and B, the layers S_1, S_2, and $S_3(G)$ are present. In cells A and B which were sectioned near their tips, however, only the layers S_1 and S_2 can be recognized, so that in the optical observations (Fig. 30) the variations in birefringence can be attributed to the progressive development of the layer $S_3(G)$.

It will be apparent that all the above observations are consistent with the concept of the progressive longitudinal deposition of the secondary wall layers. It is of interest that at the tips of the cells there is a minute terminal canal so that the primary wall remains in contact with the cell lumen. This was observed in conifer tracheids by Wardrop and Dadswell

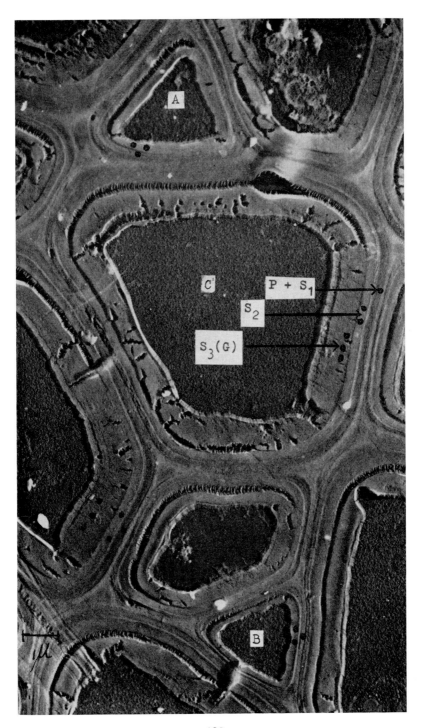

122

(1952b) and a similar feature was observed by Krabbe in the phloem fibers of *Nerium oleander*. This arrangement of the lamellae in the region of the canal has not yet been established, but in *Nerium* it could be seen that the lamellae are interrupted by a pore through which the cytoplasm penetrates.

In view of the above pattern of cell-wall formation it is relevant to consider its implication in terms of cell-wall organization. As described above the layers of the secondary wall are lamellated. It may therefore be assumed that the lamellae are deposited successively on the existing wall. In view of the observed variation in birefringence along the cell length and other observations described it is implied that in a developing cell more lamellae are present near the center of the cell than at its tips so that each lamella must extend from the middle toward the

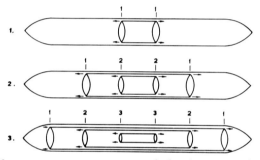

FIG. 32. A diagrammatic representation of the formation of three successive lamellae of the outer layer of the secondary wall of a differentiating fiber. The primary wall is not shown to be undergoing growth simultaneously.

end of the cell. This process is represented diagrammatically in Fig. 32.

The above concept has some interesting speculative implications. Let it be supposed that Fig. 32 represents the formation of three successive lamellae of the layer S_1. If at stage 3, the cytoplasm in the region 1-2 was depositing a Z helix of microfibrils in the first lamella, then in the region 2-3 there would be an S helix in the second lamella and in the region 3-3 of the third lamella, a Z helix. Obviously this would not be consistent with the operation of an overall mechanism of apposition and, if the cytoplasm acts as a template directing the orientation of microfibrils (see below), then the organization of the template must vary along the cell length. On the other hand, the work of Colvin and

FIG. 31. *Acacia podalyriaefolia*. A transverse section of differentiating reaction wood from which the cells shown in Fig. 30 were obtained by maceration. In cell C the layers S_1, S_2, and $S_3(G)$ can be seen, whereas in cells A and B sectioned near their tips only the layers S_1 and S_2 were present. P = primary wall.

Beer (1960) demonstrating the longitudinal growth of the microfibrils in *Acetobacter xylinum* would appear consistent with the longitudinal extension of the lamellae of microfibrils in the direction of their orientation.

Some indication of the longitudinal distance separating successive lamellae can be obtained from the data shown in Fig. 27b by calculating the change in phase difference corresponding to a lamella 300 Å thick with the optical properties of cellulose. In this way values of the order of 10 µ were obtained. This does not appear to correspond to any known structural feature of the cell wall, such as the length of the crystalline regions within the microfibrils, or to the sheaf-like aggregate seen in the layer S_2 (Fig. 6). These observations might be interpreted as indicating that the process of cell-wall formation does not proceed by a stepwise crystallization of the cellulose.

(b) *The Cell Wall—Protoplast Relation during Differentiation.* In the relatively few studies of the changes in cytoplasmic organization during differentiation of xylem which have been made (Cronshaw and Wardrop, 1963; Hohl, 1960) there is no positive evidence of penetration of the cell wall by the cytoplasm, except for the presence of plasmadesmata. Indeed these structures are rarely apparent even in differentiating pits, although they can be seen in immature cells.

As already described in relation to the formation of the wart structure the cells become conspicuously vacuolate at an early stage and are certainly so by the time secondary wall formation begins. The increasing proximity of the plasmalemma and the tonoplast has been shown to influence the form of the organelles and may lead to the apparent parallelism of elements of the endoplasmic reticulum to the wall surface (Cronshaw and Wardrop, 1963).

In cells such as tracheids and fibers undergoing secondary wall formation no evidence of the incorporation of cytoplasmic components in the wall has been found, and even in the stone cells of phloem in which the walls are conspicuously lamellated they appear to be free of cytoplasmic structures, although Whaley et al. (1959) have reported elements of the endoplasmic reticulum in maize root cells and Lamport and Northcote (1960) have reported the presence of hydroxyproline in the cell wall of *Acer pseudoplatanus*. In the interesting case of the secondary walls of the reaction wood of gymnosperms the conspicuous helical fissures of the layer S_2 are penetrated by the cytoplasm, but on plasmolysis of the wall the ribs of cytoplasm are withdrawn and show no close association with it. Likewise during the development of the warts and the vestures of pits there is a localized withdrawal of the plasmalemma as the structures develop.

Furthermore the examination by Wardrop and Harada (1963) of cells which were fixed under conditions involving intense plasmolysis (as with formalin–acetic acid) in general showed a clear separation of the cell wall and the protoplast (Fig. 33) and there was no evidence of partially formed cellulose microfibrils in the retracted protoplast.

In the retracted protoplast both the outer (plasmalemma) and inner (tonoplast) surfaces could be recognized. The structure exhibited by

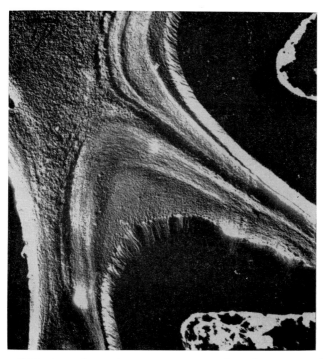

Fig. 33. *Tristania conferta.* A transverse section through a group of fibers in which the layer S_2 was being formed. Note the absence of adhering cytoplasm on the wall.

the protoplast was strongly influenced by the fixative, and conspicuously fibrillar (from formalin–acetic acid fixation) (Fig. 34a) and granular (from permanganate fixation) (Fig. 34b) textures were apparent. In the formalin-fixed material the tonoplast surface appeared more fibrillar than that of the plasmalemma, but both structures did have a fibrillar texture which, however, was much less apparent with permanganate fixation. The coarser granular structures seen in Fig. 34 were assumed to be denatured organelles. Irrespective of the method of fixation, however, the whole complex tended to fracture parallel to the cell axis. In none of

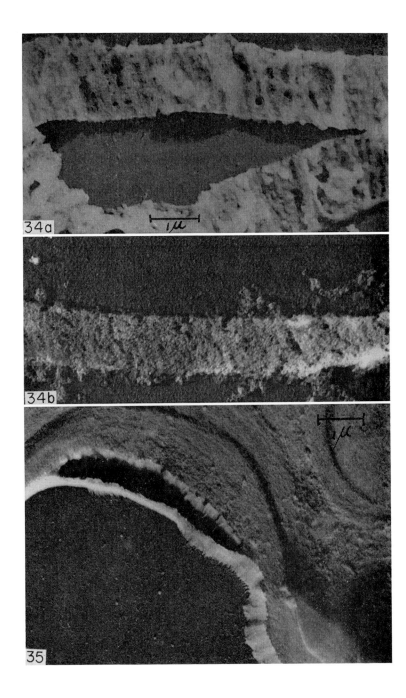

these structures, however, was any evidence obtained of fibrils of the magnitude of cellulose microfibrils.

In cells in which the cytoplasmic membranes had not separated from the wall the fibrillar texture was in both the tonoplast and plasmalemma (Fig. 35), so it is reasonable to suppose that the texture did not result from the presence of cellulosic microfibrils. The fibrillar texture of the denatured cytoplasm could also be seen in mature cells. The absence of cellulose from the plasmalemma was also suggested by the nature of the properties of the protoplasts in the formalin-fixed material. They were shown by Wardrop and Harada (1963) to lack birefringence and to show strong ultraviolet absorption. They stained strongly with lipoid dyes, such as Sudan black, and with osmium tetroxide and gave a negative reaction with iodine and sulfuric acid. They stained faintly for carbohydrate using the Hotchkiss reagent and were stained strongly with Victoria Blue B.

The above evidence does not in general suggest the likelihood of an intracytoplasmic origin of the microfibrils such as has been suggested in studies relating to wall formation in some algae (Frei and Preston, 1960). Indeed, the directed synthesis of the lamellae of the different wall layers is more consistent with the extracytoplasmic origin of the lamellae.

In considering factors governing the orientation of the microfibrils in the cell wall the directed growth of the lamellae is not consistent with the view that the cytoplasm acts as a template on the surface of which lamellae are replicated. To a degree the orientation of the microfibrils is related to the amount of cellulose present, those layers richest in cellulose being oriented more nearly parallel to the cell axis. The relation of microfibril orientation to the dimensions of the cells described by Preston (1934, 1948) suggests that, although the overall orienting mechanism in the cell may be related to its form, the mechanism governing changes in orientation is obviously independent of the form of the cell, since changes from S to Z helices and the change in orientation from the S_1 to S_2 layer, or the S_2 to S_3 layer, take place in cells of constant form.

In tracheids and fibers the plasmalemma does not show any obvious organization at the supermolecular level—although in young cells some evidence of a surface organization could be seen this has not been

---

FIG. 34. (a, Top) *Tristania conferta.* The structure of the protoplast after fixation in formalin–acetic alcohol. (b, Middle) Similar to (a) after permanganate fixation. Note the absence of microfibrils.

FIG. 35. (Bottom) *Tristania conferta.* Similar to Fig. 33, showing the denatured protoplast adhering to the partly formed S_2 layer. Note that microfibrils appear to protrude from the edge of the detached part of the cytoplasmic membrane (formalin–acetic fixation).

established with certainty. Whatever the means by which the cytoplasm may govern the microfibrillar orientation in the wall the above considerations suggest that this mechanism is one which, at least initially, governs the direction of microfibril growth.

In relation to the wall formation of fibers and tracheids, however, reference may be made to the so-called tertiary wall or terminal lamella (Frey-Wyssling, 1959) which can be demonstrated in mature cells. The terminal lamella was demonstrated in the extensive studies of Bucher (1953) and Bucher and Wiederskehr-Scherb (1948) in isolated fibers after staining with basic dyes such as Victoria Blue B, and subsequent swelling. What was considered to be a similar structure remaining in the xylem of birch and spruce after fungal attack was investigated in the electron microscope by Meier (1955). It was shown to possess a fibrillar texture in which the orientation was parallel to that of adjacent lamellae of the secondary wall. This showed little ultraviolet absorption and was birefringent. From a subsequent investigation, Meier and Yllner (1956) concluded that the tertiary wall contained some uronic acid–containing substances and xylan, but little cellulose. Frey-Wyssling (1959) also considered that the wart structure was a feature of the terminal lamella and that its fibrillar texture arose from microfibrils in process of formation. As pointed out above it has since been demonstrated that the wart structure consists of a localized thickening of the cell wall and is not to be regarded as characteristic of the terminal lamella, which, it is clear from the above discussion, consists only of the denatured membranous components of the cytoplasm, and arises in the manner shown in Fig. 20.

4. LIGNIFICATION

The final phase in the differentiation of fibers and tracheids is that of lignification of the cell wall. As described above (Section II) the lignin is deposited in association with the matrix substances in the intercellular layer and the intermicrofibrillar spaces of the wall. The biochemical aspects of this process and the nature of the association of lignin with other wall constituents are described by Frey-Wyssling and by Freudenberg elsewhere in this symposium.

In the context of the differentiation of the xylem, however, it may be noted that lignin is first deposited at the cell corners of the primary wall and subsequently extends to the intercellular layer and the various layers of the secondary wall. The deposition of lignin continues until the death of the cell and continues in the intercellular layer while deposition takes place in the secondary wall (Wardrop, 1957b). The sequence of secondary thickening and lignification is illustrated in Fig. 36.

Lignification of the cell wall is associated with changes in its properties such as its staining reactions, and in some instances the wall increases in thickness. The functional significance of lignification is not known, but the possibility of its association with matrix constituents through uronic acid ester linkages and the fact that the initiation of the process is coincident with the cessation of surface growth suggests that it may be part of a mechanism limiting further surface enlargement of the cells by immobilizing those components of the matrix which permit surface

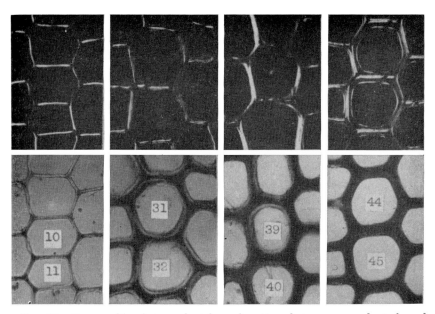

Fig. 36. Comparable photographs taken of sections between crossed nicols and in ultraviolet light showing the relation between cell wall formation and lignification. The numbers refer to the cell number counted from the cambium.

growth to take place, apart from any changes in the physical properties of the cell wall resulting from its deposition.

Acknowledgments

The author acknowledges the cooperation of his colleagues Mr. G. W. Davies and Dr. R. C. Foster for helpful discussion during the preparation of this paper.

Discussion

Esau: If the wall of a growing tracheid or fiber is extending, will the wall of an associated cell grow the same way or will there be gliding growth?

Wardrop: The evidence suggests that there is a zone of extension below the tip, pushing the tip forward, at the same time as the tapering portion of the cell expands laterally. I see nothing wrong with the idea of intrusive growth under these conditions. It does agree with Dr. Schoch-Bodmer's work on *Sparmannia* (Schoch-Bodmer, 1960). In similar cells there is pitting in the central region but not at the tip.

BAILEY: It depends on the tissue it is in contact with whether another developing fiber or ray parenchyma. Whether or not it is gliding growth depends on the contacts.

To raise another point, in latewood tracheids of conifers, vessels, fiber tracheids, or libriform fibers of dicotyledons, in which the secondary layers are very thick, there is a clue to the orientation of the microfibrils that is very simple. The slitlike orifices of the pits follow exactly the orientation of micellar texture. If one follows the pit orifice through the wall with the fine adjustment of the microscope, the change in orientation of cell-wall texture is indicated by the change in orientation of the pit orifice.

Now to my question. In the case of the wart that you describe, do you think that there is a cellulosic inner part to the wart? Have you any clues to what the surrounding substance, the dark layer, is chemically?

WARDROP: On the inner surface of all these cells one can see a very thin ultraviolet-absorbing membrane. It is, no doubt, the remains of the protoplast adhering to the wall.

BAILEY: In the thick radial walls of gymnosperm cambium there are very prominent sieve areas. They are difficult to find in the tangential walls. In a periclinal division the phragmoplast travels down the center of the cell and splits the primary pit fields in two. When a daughter cell enlarges for the next division, the primary pit fields are now in the center. I can see the successive formation of new walls inside of a mother cell, and that new sieve fields might be formed in the center, but what becomes of the old halves of the mother cell wall? What happens to the microfibrils?

WARDROP: They probably just lie around in the intercellular region and that is why the intercellular layer between radial walls is thicker than that between tangential walls.

BAILEY: Of course in the dicotyledons there are sieve areas in the tangential wall as well.

COLVIN: I take it that the various lamellae of the layers of the secondary walls grow simultaneously. Some of these layers are remote from the cytoplasmic membrane.

WARDROP: The implication would be that, looking at a cell undergoing secondary thickening, there would be steps between successive lamellae. In conifer tracheids and in the phloem fibers of *Nerium* there is a canal at the tip of the cells through which the cytoplasm remains in contact with the primary wall.

MEIER: I believe that Dr. Colvin thinks that the cytoplasm is still in contact with the deeper layers. So he seems to question apposition growth. Do you suggest, Dr. Colvin, that the cytoplasm penetrates the cell wall?

COLVIN: No, I do not think that, but I do believe that it has some influence on the orientation of the microfibrils deep within the wall. I will explain what I mean tomorrow. (See the paper by Colvin in this volume.)

CÔTÉ: Could you explain more fully the wet carbon replica that you used in your primary wall studies?

WARDROP: We place a drop of a suspension of cells on a slide, clamp a plate of methacrylate on it, and then warm it in water to about 80°C. The initial replica is then shadowed with carbon.

BAILEY: What do you think about the terminology now? In simple cases it is nice to say S_1, S_2, S_3, but how about some of the fibers in certain tropical dicotyledons or the gelatinous layer in reaction wood? These show a multilayered structure in which the successive lamellae seem to be separated by layers which either are non-cellulosic nor have very low cellulosic content. What shall we call that type of cell wall?

FREY-WYSSLING: The terminology must be general. The cotton fiber has 25 such layers. How can you then say S_1, S_2, S_3, S_4, and so on? And in a lacticifer wall complications will be even worse. While it is correct to describe most tracheids in terms of S_1, S_2, and S_3, this cannot be general terminology for describing secondary cell walls.

WARDROP: I could not agree more; it is purely a matter of convenience.

BAILEY: The answer in dealing with the angiosperms as a whole is the concept of two types of walls, the wall of the cambium that is carried over, i.e. the primary wall, and then the wall layers that are formed subsequent to that, secondary walls. Then you can define as many layers internally in the secondary wall as you wish. That would apply to all vascular plants.

WAREING: Is the orientation of the spiral thickening of the wall in the reaction wood of *Taxus* changed in relation to the normal wall?

BAILEY: Yes, there is a change in the orientation of the helix between the whole compression wood and the normal helices of the secondary wall.

FREY-WYSSLING: I appreciate that Dr. Wardrop has not explained the cell-wall texture as a result of mechanical forces. There has been a tendency among persons who work on cell walls to explain these elaborate structures as induced by external forces. But this is an excellent example that the cytoplasm "knows ahead" how it must place the microfibrils so that the cell serves its purpose when it is fully differentiated. Of course, there are changes in orientation in the primary wall which is stretched passively, but in the apposition layers the cytoplasm acts in accordance with the future function of the cell wall.

SRIVASTAVA: Have you any idea what kind of inclusions are in these wartlike thickenings?

WARDROP: The core of the wart is a wall elaboration as shown in Figure 20, in which its formation is represented diagrammatically. It is a matter of whether some of these organelles may settle on the wall elaboration or in between them. In a mature cell one can see in addition to the normal three layers a very strong ultra-violet-absorbing layer adjacent to the lumen. This layer is the same, I think, as the one that stains with Victoria Blue B. The central part is cellulosic.

ESAU: I am disturbed that these organelles appear like little pebbles which have settled down. Actually, when they die and dry up they will not be recognizable as little bodies, will they?

WARDROP: It always surprises me how solid the cytoplasmic membranes look in shadowed material from which the embedding medium has been removed.

MEIER: Have you any idea about the orientation of microfibrils in the warts?

WARDROP: No.

BAILEY: Having been involved in cell-wall work for 60 years, I find the encouraging thing is the progress that has been made. One cannot hope to solve all the problems at the present moment, but they will be solved.

REFERENCES

Albersheim, P., Mühlethaler, K., and Frey-Wyssling, A. (1960). *J. Biophys. Biochem. Cytol.* **8**, 501.

Asunmaa, S. (1960). *Intern. Conf. Electron Microscopy, Berlin, 1958,* **4**, 722.

Asunmaa, S., and Lange, P. (1953). *Svensk Papperstidn.* **56**, 85.

Asunmaa, S., and Lange, P. (1954). *Svensk Papperstidn.* **57,** 501.

Asunmaa, S., and Steenberg, B. (1957). *Svensk Papperstidn.* **60,** 751.

Bailey, A. J. (1936). *Ind. Eng. Chem. Anal. Ed.* **8,** 389.

Bailey, I. W. (1913). *Forestry Quart.* **11,** 12.

Bailey, I. W. (1919). *Proc. Natl. Acad. Sci. U.S.* **5,** 283.

Bailey, I. W. (1920a). *Am. J. Botany* **7,** 355.

Bailey, I. W. (1920b). *Proc. Natl. Acad. Sci. U.S.* **6,** 197.

Bailey, I. W. (1930). *Z. Zellforsch. Mikroskop. Anat.* **10,** 651.

Bailey, I. W. (1933). *J. Arnold Aboretum (Harvard Univ.)* **14,** 259.

Bailey, I. W., and Berkeley, E. E. (1942). *Am. J. Botany* **29,** 231.

Bailey, I. W., and Kerr, T. (1935). *J. Arnold Arboretum (Harvard Univ.)* **18,** 273.

Bailey, I. W., and Vestal, M. R. (1937a). *J. Arnold Arboretum (Harvard Univ.)* **18,** 185.

Bailey, I. W., and Vestal, M. R. (1937b). *J. Arnold Arboretum (Harvard Univ.)* **18,** 196.

Bannan, M. W. (1956). *Can. J. Botany* **34,** 175.

Bannan, M. W., and Whalley, B. E. (1950). *Can. J. Res., Sect. C* **28,** 341.

Bosshard, H. H. (1952). *Ber. Schweiz. Botan. Ges.* **62,** 482.

Bucher, H. (1953). "Die Tertiärlamelle von Holzfasern und ihre Erscheinungs-formen bei Coniferen." Untersuchungen des Labors der Cellulosefabrik Attisholz, Solothurn, Switzerland.

Bucher, H., and Wiederskehr-Scherb, L. P. (1948). "Morphology and Structure of Wood Fibers." Cellulosefabrik Attisholz A. G., Solothurn, Switzerland.

Colvin, J. R., and Beer, M. (1960). *Can. J. Microbiol.* **6,** 631.

Côté, W. A., and Day, A. C. (1962). *Tappi* **45,** 906.

Cronshaw, J. (1960). *Australian J. Botany* **8,** 51.

Cronshaw, J. (1961). *J. Inst. Wood Sci.* **8,** 12.

Cronshaw, J., and Wardrop, A. B. (1963). Unpublished data.

Dadswell, H. E. (1931). *J. Council Sci. Ind. Res.* **4,** 185.

Dadswell, H. E., and Ellis, D. J. (1940). *J. Council Sci. Ind. Res.* **13,** 45.

Emerton, A. W., and Goldsmith, V. (1956). *Holzforschung* **10,** 108.

Esau, K. (1953). "Plant Anatomy." Wiley, New York.

Frei, E., and Preston, R. D. (1960). *Proc. Roy. Soc. Ser. B* **154,** 70.

Frei, E., Preston, R. D., and Ripley, G. W. (1957). *J. Exptl. Botany* **8,** 139.

Frenzel, P. (1929). *Planta* **8,** 642.

Frey-Wyssling, A. (1937). *Protoplasma* **27,** 372.

Frey-Wyssling, A. (1954). *Science* **119,** 80.

Frey-Wyssling, A. (1955). *Biochim. Biophys. Acta* **18,** 166.

Frey-Wyssling, A. (1959). "Die pflanzliche Zellwand." Springer, Berlin.

Frey-Wyssling, A. (1962). *In* "The Interpretation of Ultrastructure," Symposium of the International Society for Cell Biology, Vol. 1, p. 307. Academic Press, New York.

Frey-Wyssling, A., and Aeberli, H. (1942). *Holz Roh- u. Werkstoff* **5,** 265.

Frey-Wyssling, A., and Mitrakos, K. (1959). *J. Ultrastructure Res.* **3,** 228.

Frey-Wyssling, A., Mühlethaler, K., and Bosshard, H. H. (1956). *Planta* **47,** 115.

Frey-Wyssling, A., Mühlethaler, K., and Bosshard, H. H. (1959). *Holzforsch.* **5,** 107.

Gross, S. T., Clarke, G. L., and Ritter, G. J. (1939). *Paper Trade J.* **109,** 303.

Harada, H. (1962). *J. Japan Wood Res. Soc.* **8**, 252.

Harada, H., and Wardrop, A. B. (1960). *J. Japan Wood Res. Soc.* **6**, 34.

Harada, H., Meyazaki, Y., and Wakashima, T. (1958). *Bull. Govt. Forest Expt. Sta. No.* **104**.

Hengstenberg, J., and Mark, H. (1928). *Z. Krist.* **69**, 271.

Hodge, A. J., and Wardrop, A. B. (1950). *Australian J. Sci. Res.* **B3**, 265.

Hohl, H. R. (1960). *Ber. Schweiz. Botan. Ges.* **70**, 395.

Howsmon, J. A. (1949). *Textile Res. J.* **19**, 152.

Iterson, G. van (1935). *Proc. 6th Intern. Botan. Congr. Amsterdam, 1935* **2**, 291.

Jayme, G., and Hunger, G. (1960). *Papier* **14**, 549.

Kobayashi, K., and Utsumi, N. (1951). See Harada (1953).

Kerr, T., and Bailey, I. W. (1934). *J. Arnold Arboretum (Harvard Univ.)* **15**, 327.

Lamport, D. T. A., and Northcote, D. H. (1960). *Nature* **188**, 665.

Lange, P. (1954). *Svensk Papperstidn.* **57**, 501.

Lange, P., and Kjaer, A. (1957). *Norsk Skogind.* **11**, 425.

Liese, W. (1951). *Ber. Deut. Botan. Ges.* **64**, 31.

Liese, W. (1956). *Proc. Intern. Conf. Electron Microscopy, London, 1954*, p. 550.

Liese, W. (1957a). *Holz Roh- u. Werkstoff* **15**, 449.

Liese, W. (1957b). *Naturwissenschaften* **7**, 240.

Liese, W., and Hartmann-Fahnenbrock, M. (1953). *Biochim. Biophys. Acta* **11**, 190.

Liese, W., and Ledbetter, M. C. (1963). *Nature* **197**, 201.

Meier, H. (1955). *Holz Roh- u. Werkstoff* **13**, 323.

Meier, H. (1960). *Beih. Z. Schweiz. Forstv.* **30**, 49.

Meier, H. (1961). *J. Polymer Sci.* **51**, 11.

Meier, H., and Yllner, S. (1956). *Svensk Papperstidn.* **59**, 395.

Meredith, R. (1946). *J. Textile Inst.* **37**, T205.

Mühlethaler, K. (1960). *Beih. Z. Schweiz. Forstv.* **30**, 55.

Mukherjee, S. M., and Woods, H. S. (1953). *Biochim. Biophys. Acta* **10**, 499.

Nagatomo, S. (1952). *Botan. Mag. (Tokyo)* **65**, 765.

Newman, I. V. (1956). *Phytomorphology* **6**, 1.

Preston, R. D. (1934). *Phil. Trans. Roy. Soc. London Ser. B* **224**, 131.

Preston, R. D. (1939). *Ann. Botany (London)* **3**, 507.

Preston, R. D. (1948). *Biochim. Biophys. Acta* **2**, 370.

Preston, R. D. (1952). "Molecular Architecture in Plant Cell Walls." Chapman and Hall, London.

Preston, R. D., and Wardrop, A. B. (1949a). *Biochim. Biophys. Acta* **3**, 549.

Preston, R. D., and Wardrop, A. B. (1949b). *Biochim. Biophys. Acta* **3**, 585.

Probine, M. C., and Preston, R. D. (1961). *J. Exptl. Botany* **12**, 261.

Rånby, B. (1949). *Acta Chem. Skand.* **3**, 649.

Ritter, G. J., and Mitchell, G. L. (1939). *Paper Trade J.* **108**, 33.

Roelofsen, P. A. (1958). *Acta Botan. Neerl.* **7**, 77.

Roelofsen, P. A., and Houwink, A. L. (1953). *Acta Botan. Neerl.* **2**, 218.

Sachs, I. B. (1962). Rept. No. 2256. U.S. Dept. Agr., Forest Prod. Lab., Madison, Wisconsin.

Sachs, J. (1882). "Textbook of Botany." Oxford Univ. Press, London and New York.

Schoch-Bodmer, H. (1960). *Beih. Z. Schweiz. Forstv.* **30**, 107.

Stemsrud, F. (1956). *Holzforschung* **10**, 69.
Stewart, C. M., Amos, G. L., and Harvey, L. J. (1953). *Australian J. Biol. Sci.* **B6**, 21.
Tuszon, J. (1903). *Ber. Deut. Botan. Ges.* **21**, 276.
Wardrop, A. B. (1949). *Nature* **164**, 366.
Wardrop, A. B. (1952a). *Nature* **170**, 329.
Wardrop, A. B. (1952b). *Textile Res. J.* **22**, 288.
Wardrop, A. B. (1954a). *Holzforschung* **8**, 12.
Wardrop, A. B. (1954b). *Australian J. Botany* **2**, 154.
Wardrop, A. B. (1954c). *Australian J. Botany* **2**, 165.
Wardrop, A. B. (1956). *Biochim. Biophys. Acta* **21**, 200.
Wardrop, A. B. (1957a). *Holzforschung* **11**, 102.
Wardrop, A. B. (1957b). *Tappi* **40**, 225.
Wardrop, A. B. (1958). *Australian J. Botany* **6**, 299.
Wardrop, A. B. (1962). *Botan. Rev.* **28**, 241.
Wardrop, A. B., and Dadswell, H. E. (1951). *Nature* **168**, 610.
Wardrop, A. B., and Dadswell, H. E. (1952a). *Australian J. Sci. Res.* **B5**, 223.
Wardrop, A. B., and Dadswell, H. E. (1952b). *Australian J. Sci. Res.* **B5**, 385.
Wardrop, A. B., and Dadswell, H. E. (1953). *Holzforschung* **7**, 33.
Wardrop, A. B., and Davies, G. W. (1961). *Holzforschung* **15**, 129.
Wardrop, A. B., and Davies, G. W. (1962). *Nature* **194**, 497.
Wardrop, A. B., and Harada, H. (1963). In press.
Wardrop, A. B., and Preston, R. D. (1951). *J. Exptl. Botany* **2**, 20.
Wardrop, A. B., Liese, W., and Davies, G. W. (1959). *Holzforschung* **13**, 115.
Wardrop, A. B., Ingle, H. D., and Davies, G. W. (1963). *Nature* **197**, 202.
Whaley, W. G., Mollenhauer, H. H., and Kephart, J. E. (1959). *J. Biophys. Biochem. Cytol.* **5**, 501.
Williams, R. C., and Wyckoff, R. W. G. (1946). *J. Appl. Phys.* **17**, 23.

PART II

BIOCHEMISTRY OF
CAMBIAL DERIVATIVES

General Chemistry of Cell Walls and Distribution of the Chemical Constituents across the Walls

H. Meier

Department of Botany, University of Fribourg, Switzerland

Cellulose, hemicellulose, and lignin are the three main constituents of the cell walls of xylematic elements in forest trees. Cellulose, having by far the simplest molecular structure, is made up of β-1,4-linked glucose residues. It has often been discussed whether there are present in the cellulose chain, intermixed with the glucose residues, a few other sugar residues, as e.g., xylose. This, however, could never be verified and, indeed, more recent investigations have shown that this most likely is not the case.

The degree of polymerization (DP) of wood celluloses has continuously increased during the last 10 or 20 years. The reason for this is, of course, not that forest trees have improved the quality of their cellulose but that chemists have improved their methods for the isolation and DP determination of wood celluloses. For birch cellulose, for example, it was recently reported a DP of about 9000 (Goring and Timell, 1960), that is of the same order of magnitude as it has earlier been reported for cotton and ramie celluloses.

The complex molecular structure of lignin from coniferous woods is illustrated schematically by Formula I (from Adler and Gierer, 1957). The formula shows how the various elements may be combined by linkages that have been claimed to occur in the lignin molecule. The guiacylglycerin-β-guiacyl ether structures are most abundant. To a smaller extent the phenyl cumaran structures, the pinoresinol structures and the diphenyl structures are present. About one-third of all the phenylpropan units are phenolic in nature. In the lignin from angiospermous woods there are syringyl units present besides the guiacyl units.

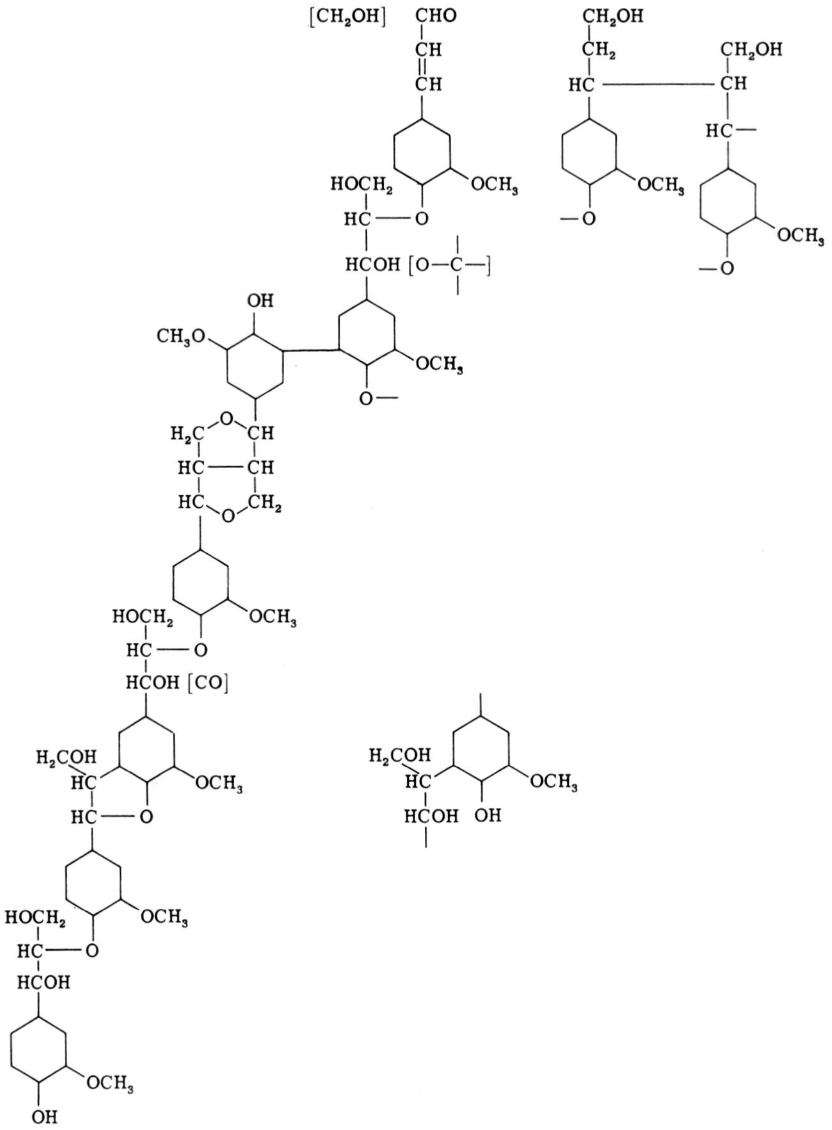

[CH₂OH] CHO
         |
         CH
         ‖
         CH

CH₂OH
|
CH₂
|
HC

CH₂OH
|
CH
|
HC—

HOCH₂   OCH₃
|
HC — O

HCOH [O—C—]

$[CH_2OH]$ CHO
CH_2OH CH_2 CH_2OH
$HOCH_2$ OCH_3

OH
CH₃O

OCH₃

O—

H₂C   O   CH
| |
HC — CH
| |
HC   O   CH₂

HOCH₂   OCH₃
|
HC — O
HCOH [CO]

H₂COH
HC   OCH₃
|
HC — O

H₂COH
HC   OCH₃
|
HCOH OH

HOCH₂   OCH₃
|
HC — O
HCOH

OCH₃
|
OH

FORMULA I

The former are responsible for the higher methoxyl content of this lignin in contrast to lignin from gymnospermous woods (21% and 15 to 16%, respectively).

The study of the chemistry of the hemicelluloses has been neglected for a long time, in spite of the fact that especially in angiospermous woods the hemicelluloses are present in a much larger quantity than lignin. The development of the different chromatographic separation and identification methods, however, has changed the situation very quickly and during the past 10 years the chemical structure of wood hemicelluloses has been elucidated to a large extent.

The term hemicellulose (half-cellulose) is not a very good one. It is a collective name used by most authors for noncellulosic polysaccharides of plant cell walls. However, pectins are usually exempted from the term hemicellulose, and certain very water-soluble cell wall polysaccharides are often designated as mucilages. Polysaccharides which are present in the cell walls of grains and which are consumed during germination are sometimes called "storage celluloses" (in German: Reservezellulosen).

Older classifications of hemicelluloses which use such names as cellulosanes, polyuronides, polyosanes, etc. have been more or less abandoned in modern literature. As in many other fields of the chemistry of natural products, when the molecular structures of the compounds became obvious, they were designated by proper chemical names and there was no longer any need for complicated half-scientific classifications. Thus it may be that the term hemicellulose will also disappear in time, and that we may then just speak of noncellulosic cell wall polysaccharides.

It might be worthwhile to indicate briefly the general procedure which is followed for the isolation, the purification, and the determination of the chemical structure of wood polysaccharides. For the isolation of the polysaccharides, the wood is usually ground to a particle size of about 1 mm. The wood meal is then deresinized, for example, with acetone in a Soxhlet apparatus. After that, the polysaccharides are either extracted directly from the wood meal or the wood meal is first delignified by a mild procedure to give holocellulose. Direct extraction of polysaccharides from undelignified wood meal is possible only in a few cases. The arabinogalactans which are present in large amounts in larch wood can, for example, be obtained in this way by direct extraction with water. However, it is doubtful whether these arabinogalactans which are also present in small amounts in other coniferous woods, are cell wall constituents or not. From angiospermous woods about half of the hemicelluloses can be obtained directly from the undelignified wood meal by extraction with 16% sodium hydroxide solutions. If a more complete extraction of hemicelluloses is desired, the wood meal must be delignified first. For coniferous woods a delignification prior to polysaccharide extraction is always necessary. The delignification has to be carried out by a mild method which alters the hemicelluloses as little as possible. The most widely applied standard procedure is delignification with sodium chlorite. During delignification a small amount of hemicelluloses is usually extracted from the wood meal. Further amounts of hemicelluloses can be obtained after delignification by extraction with boiling water, with dimethylsulfoxide and with dilute alkaline solutions.

To prevent oxidative degradation during extraction with alkaline solutions, the extraction has to be performed in a nitrogen atmosphere. The extracted hemicelluloses are usually recovered by precipitation with ethanol after a slight acidification of the extracts.

Some alteration of the chemical structure of the hemicelluloses during the extraction procedure cannot be avoided, except when a direct extraction of hemicelluloses with water is possible. During delignification with sodium chlorite the aldehydic end groups of the polysaccharides are oxidized to carboxyl groups and during extraction with alkaline solutions all ester linkages, which may be present, are split.

A short review will now be given of the chemical structure of hemicelluloses of coniferous and of angiospermous woods. The most important hemicellulose in coniferous woods is a glucomannan with a DP which may vary from about 60 up to about 140 (Lindberg and Meier, 1958). This glucomannan contains glucose and mannose residues in the ratio 1:3 to 1:4, as well as a small amount of galactose residues.

The galactose content of different glucomannans varies from almost zero to about 15%. Recent studies of glucomannans extracted with inert solvents from pine wood have revealed that they are partially acetylated *in situ* (Meier, 1961a). This has hitherto been overlooked since the glucomannans which had been studied earlier had always been extracted with alkaline solvents from the wood.

Formula II shows the chemical structure of a part of a galactoglucomannan molecule. This structure has been ascertained by the usual

FORMULA II

techniques used in polysaccharide chemistry such as methylation, partial hydrolysis, and periodate oxidation. Complete methylation of the glucomannans, hydrolysis, chromatographic separation of the monomers obtained, and their quantitative determination revealed that the molecule was essentially a straight chain in which the glucose and mannose residues were linked by 1,4-linkages (Croon *et al.*, 1959), and the galactose residues probably by 1,6-linkages (Hamilton and Thompson, 1959). By partial hydrolysis of a galactoglucomannan the oligosaccharides shown in Table I have been obtained (Meier 1960). The presence of a trisac-

TABLE I

DI- AND TRISACCHARIDES FROM A PARTIAL HYDROLYZATE OF
A GALACTOGLUCOMANNAN[a]

Disaccharides	Trisaccharides
M $\xrightarrow[\beta]{1\quad4}$ M	M $\xrightarrow[\beta]{1\quad4}$ M $\xrightarrow[\beta]{1\quad4}$ M
M $\xrightarrow[\beta]{1\quad4}$ G	M $\xrightarrow[\beta]{1\quad4}$ M $\xrightarrow[\beta]{1\quad4}$ G
G $\xrightarrow[\beta]{1\quad4}$ M	G $\xrightarrow[\beta]{1\quad4}$ M $\xrightarrow[\beta]{1\quad4}$ M
G $\xrightarrow[\beta]{1\quad4}$ G	M $\xrightarrow[\beta]{1\quad4}$ G $\xrightarrow[\beta]{1\quad4}$ M
Ga $\xrightarrow[\alpha]{1\quad6}$ M	G $\xrightarrow[\beta]{1\quad4}$ G $\xrightarrow[\beta]{1\quad4}$ M
	Ga $\xrightarrow[\alpha]{1\quad6}$ M $\xrightarrow[\beta]{1\quad4}$ M

[a] Symbols: M = Mannose; G = Glucose; Ga = Galactose.

charide containing two adjacent glucose residues and of another one containing one glucose residue between two mannose residues makes it probable that the distribution of glucose and mannose units in the molecule is at random. This hypothesis is also supported by the fact that in the same wood glucomannan fractions with varying glucose to mannose ratios are found.

The position of the acetyl groups in the molecule has been studied by periodate oxidation of a galactoglucomannan which had been extracted with hot water from a pine holocellulose (Meier, 1961a). On periodate oxidation those nonterminal mannose and glucose residues survive which carry an acetyl group on carbon atom 2 or 3, whereas those which have no substituent on one of these two carbon atoms are oxidized to dialdehydes. It could be shown that all the acetyl groups were linked to carbon atoms 2 or 3 of mannose residues.

Another very important hemicellulose type in coniferous woods is the arabino-4-O-methylglucuronoxylan (Formula III). This contains arabinose, 4-O-methylglucuronic acid and xylose residues in the approximate molar proportions 1:1.5:7.5. It has a DP of about 120 and consists of a backbone of β-1,4-linked xylose residues. L-Arabinofuranose residues are linked to carbon atom 3 of every 7.5 xylose residue and 4-O-methyl-

FORMULA III

glucuronic acid residues are linked to carbon atom 2 of every fifth xylose residue (Garegg and Lindberg, 1960).

Beside the glucomannans, galactoglucomannans, and arabino-4-O-methylglucuronoxylans, some other hemicelluloses occur in coniferous woods, but usually only in very small quantities. Among these there may be mentioned the arabinogalactans (Bishop, 1957; Bouveng, 1961), which contain, in addition to galactose residues, 5 to 20% arabinose residues. The arabinogalactans are highly branched molecules and hence very water soluble. The galactose residues are mainly linked to each other by β-1,3- and β-1,6-linkages. The arabinose residues are partly present in the furanoside and partly in the pyranoside form and are linked either to each other by 1,3-linkages or to galactose residues by 1,6-linkages. From certain larches arabinogalactans have been obtained in yields up to about 16% of the dry weight of the wood. Other conifers usually contain less than 1% of this type of hemicellulose.

Also there are present in very small quantities in coniferous woods the three polysaccharides which form the so-called pectic triad, namely, a partially esterified polygalacturonic acid, an arabinan, and a galactan. Of these three which may be partially linked to each other, only the galactan has been structurally investigated. Galactan occurs in very large amounts in compression wood and has been shown (Bouveng and Meier, 1959) to consist essentially of a straight chain of β-1,4-linked galactose residues.

In angiospermous woods 4-O-methylglucuronoxylan is quantitatively by far the most important hemicellulose (Bouveng *et al.*, 1960; Glaude-mans and Timell, 1958). It has been shown that it consists of about 200 β-1,4-linked xylose units. Every tenth unit is substituted at carbon atom 2 by a 4-O-methylglucuronic acid residue. About seven out of ten xylose units carry an O-acetyl group preferentially at carbon atom 3 and to a minor extent at carbon atom 2 (Formula IV). Also a glucomannan is pres-

FORMULA IV

ent in small quantities in angiospermous woods (Timell, 1960a). It differs, however, from the glucomannans in coniferous woods by having no galactose residues and by a much higher content of glucose residues, the ratio of glucose to mannose being 1:1 to 1:2. Also in this glucomannan the hexose residues are linked by β-1,4-linkages.

The polysaccharides of the pectic triad seem also in angiosperms to be present in very small amounts. A galactan which has recently been isolated from tension wood of beech (Meier, 1962), where it is relatively abundant, contained both β-1,4- and β-1,6-linked galactose residues as well as 4-O-methylglucuronic acid groups which were linked to carbon atom 6 of some of the galactose residues. Also rhamnose residues were found in this tension wood galactan, which differs markedly in its structure from the galactan found in coniferous woods.

This short review on the chemical structure of the cell wall constituents shall be concluded with a few remarks about the lignin carbohydrate linkage. Freudenberg (1962) has shown that such linkages can easily be produced *in vitro* when artificial dehydrogenation lignin is produced in the presence of sugars. A quinon methide can then combine with a sugar hydroxyl—or a polysaccharide hydroxyl if a polysaccharide is present—and produce a polysaccharide ether of a guaiacyl carbinol which can be incorporated in lignin. There are many indications that lignin-carbohydrate linkages really exist in wood, especially between hemicelluloses and lignin whereas a linkage between cellulose and lignin is less probable. Absolute proof for a linkage between lignin and hemicellulose in the wood, however, has not yet been offered, and it is not yet known with which sugar residues and with which carbon atoms of the sugar residues the linkages are formed.

TABLE II
OVER-ALL COMPOSITION OF NORMAL WOOD AND REACTION WOOD

Wood	% Lignin	% Cellulose	% Hemicellulose
Pinus silvestris	29	40	31
Picea abies	28	44	28
Betula verrucosa	20	40	40
Fagus silvatica	20	38	42
Picea abies (compression wood)	39	30	31
Fagus silvatica (tension wood)	13	57	30

The differences in chemical composition of the xylematic elements of different woods shall now be discussed. Table II shows the over-all composition of two coniferous woods and two angiospermous woods as well as that of reaction woods. In coniferous woods the noncellulosic polysaccharides are present in similar amounts as is lignin; in angiospermous woods, the amount of noncellulosic polysaccharides is approximately twice that of lignin. Compression wood is extremely rich in lignin and poor in cellulose, whereas the reverse is true for tension wood.

Table III shows the polysaccharide composition of normal wood and reaction wood of different species. Normal wood of conifers and angiosperms differ mainly in the proportions of mannans and xylans. In coniferous woods the main hemicellulose is of the mannan type, but there are also considerable amounts of xylan present. In angiospermous woods the xylan type hemicellulose is very dominant. Reaction wood differs markedly from normal wood in the proportions in which the individual polysaccharides are present. Reaction wood always has a much higher galactan content than normal wood. In tension wood of angiosperms the

TABLE III

POLYSACCHARIDE COMPOSITION OF NORMAL WOOD AND REACTION WOOD

Polysaccharide	*Picea abies* (%)	*Betula verrucosa* (%)	*Picea abies* (compression wood) (%)	*Betula verrucosa* (tension wood) (%)
Cellulose	62	50	50	62
Galacto-glucomannan[a]	22	4	14	1
Arabino-4-O-methylglucuronoxylan[b]	13	44	17	24
Pectic group and others (in reaction wood mainly galactan)	3	2	19	13

[a] Glucomannan in *Betula verrucosa.*

[b] 4-O-methylglucuronoxylan in *Betula verrucosa.*

4-O-methylglucuronoxylan content is usually about half that of normal wood, whereas the cellulose content is much higher than in normal wood.

The differences in the polysaccharide composition of the woods of conifers belonging to different genera and families are not very large. At least the principal structural features of the hemicelluloses seem always to be the same. However, the proportions in which the different types of hemicelluloses are present can vary somewhat from one genus or one family to the other. From the four recent classes of the gymnosperms, the *Cycadinae*, the *Gynkgoinae*, the *Coniferae*, and the *Gnetinae*, besides the *Coniferae*, only the single recent representative of the *Ginkgoinae*, *Ginkgo biloba*, has been investigated more thoroughly. The types of hemicelluloses and also their quantitative proportions in *Ginkgo biloba* were practically the same as in most conifers (Timell, 1960b; Mian and Timell, 1960).

The wood of dicotyledons of different genera and families seems to vary mainly in the proportions in which the individual polysaccharides are present, and to have almost no variations of the structural features of the hemicelluloses. The hemicelluloses of the stems of monocotyledons, however, show structural differences from those present in dicotyledonous woods. The xylans may, as for instance in esparto grass, be devoid of uronic acid residues, or they may, as the xylans from wheat straw, contain large amounts of arabinose residues in addition to glucuronic acid residues (Aspinall, 1959).

Within a single wood species the polysaccharide composition varies widely in the cell walls of different types of xylematic cells. Table IV [values calculated from Perilä (1961)] illustrates the differences between vertical tracheids and parenchyma cells (including ray tracheids) from pine and between libriform fibers, vessels and parenchyma cells from birch. In parenchyma cells of birch the xylan content is extremly high and the material is therefore very suitable for studying the overmolecular structure of this hemicellulose. X-ray diffraction studies on birch parenchyma cells showed clearly that the xylan is X-ray amorphous. This, of course, does not imply that there is no order at all.

The chemical composition varies widely not only between cell walls of different cell types but also in the individual cell wall layers within a single wall of a certain cell type.

The distribution of lignin through the fiber wall has been studied most thoroughly. The following techniques have been used: staining reagents, dissolution of the nonlignin compounds, microdissection followed by chemical analysis, ultraviolet and fluorescence microscopy. All the techniques gave similar results, and it has now been known for some time that between 60 and 90% of the lignin of the wall is localized in the region of the middle lamella and the primary wall. For softwoods, the lignin content of the middle lamella lies somewhere near the lower figure and for hardwoods, near the higher one.

The location of the cellulose and hemicellulose in the fiber wall is more difficult to determine than that of lignin. Asunmaa and Lange (1954) sought to obtain such information by a microspectrographic method. This, however, involved various drastic pretreatments of the fibers and the results must, therefore, be interpreted with care. Furthermore, the method suffered from the drawback that it did not enable differentiation between the various types of hemicelluloses. The most reliable technique for studying their location would be the microdissection of single fibers into the single wall layers and the analysis of them,

TABLE IV

POLYSACCHARIDE COMPOSITION OF DIFFERENT XYLEMATIC CELL ELEMENTS

	Pinus silvestris		*Betula verrucosa*		
Polysaccharide	Vertical tracheids (%)	Parenchyma cells and ray tracheids (%)	Libriform fibers (%)	Vessels (%)	Parenchyma cells (%)
Cellulose	56	50	51	53	14
Galacto-glucomannan[a]	25	20	2	–	1
Arabino-4-O-methyl-glucuronoxylan[a]	17	28	46	45	84
Others	2	2	1	2	1

[a] See Table III footnotes.

after hydrolysis, for their sugar composition. However, no one has yet succeeded in isolating each of the fiber cell wall layers completely. An alternative approach is, therefore, required and has been devised at the Swedish Forest Products Research Laboratory (Meier and Wilkie, 1959; Meier, 1961b). During the ageing of the young fiber, successive polysaccharide layers are deposited next to one another. Fibers are then isolated and analyzed at various stages of maturation. From a knowledge of the polysaccharides found in these fiber fractions an attempt has been made to deduce the nature of the cell wall layers in the mature fiber. This approach to the problem entails the assumption that, once a cell wall layer has been deposited, its polysaccharide composition does not subsequently alter.

The young fibers in radial sections through the outermost part of the wood xylem were separated into four fractions: (M + P)-fibers, (M + P + S_1)-fibers, (M + P + S_1 + S_2 outer part)-fibers and (M + P + S_1 + S_2 + S_3)-fibers. This separation was carried out under the polarizing microscope where the different layers exhibit different optical

properties. Each fiber fraction was hydrolyzed and the sugars were estimated quantitatively. The results were then used to calculate the
polysaccharide composition in each of the four fractions.

It is thus possible to deduce very roughly the proportions of the
individual polysaccharides in each cell wall layer. Micrographs of
transverse sections taken with the polarizing microscope and with the
electron microscope gave a certain volume fraction for each layer in the
fiber wall. The density is certainly not the same in all the different layers,

TABLE V

PERCENTAGES OF POLYSACCHARIDES IN THE DIFFERENT LAYERS OF THE FIBER WALL

Polysaccharide	$M + P^a$	S_1	$S_{2 \text{ outer part}}$	$S_{2 \text{ inner part}} + S_3$
Birch				
Galactan	16.9	1.2	0.7	0.0
Cellulose	41.4	49.8	48.0	60.0
Glucomannan	3.1	2.8	2.1	5.1
Arabinan	13.4	1.9	1.5	0.0
Glucuronoxylan	25.2	44.1	47.7	35.1
Pine				
Galactan	16.4	8.0	0.0	0.0
Cellulose	33.4	55.2	64.3	63.6
Glucomannan	7.9	18.1	24.4	23.7
Arabinan	29.3	1.1	0.8	0.0
Glucuronoarabinoxylan	13.0	17.6	10.7	12.7
Spruce				
Galactan	20.1	5.2	1.6	3.2
Cellulose	35.5	61.5	66.5	47.5
Glucomannan	7.7	16.9	24.6	27.2
Arabinan	29.4	0.6	0.0	2.4
Glucuronoarabinoxylan	7.3	15.7	7.4	19.4

^{a} Contains also a high percentage of pectic acid.

but, as a first approximation, the volume percentages can probably be
taken as weight percentages. It must, however, be emphasized that this
estimate is very tentative and the carbohydrate composition of the different layers as presented in Table V can, therefore, show only the main
trends.

For all three woods investigated, the cellulose content is lowest in the
$(M + P)$-layer which contains a high percentage of pectic material
(galactan, arabinan, and pectic acid). There is, however, a marked
difference between birch and the two coniferous woods in the arabinan
content of the $(M + P)$-layer; in birch it is only half as high as in pine.
For the xylan content it is the reverse. In birch, the cellulose content
is highest in the inner part of the S_2-layer and in the S_3-layer. The S_1-

layer and the outer part of the S_2-layer have a very high content of glucuronoxylan.

In spruce and pine the composition of the different cell wall layers is similar. The glucomannan content increases steadily from the outer parts of the cell walls to the inner parts. The glucuronoarabinoxylan content is very high in the S_3-layer. The same was found by Bucher (1960) who made a controlled hydrolysis of the tertiary wall in spruce wood. There seems to be practically no arabinan in the secondary wall layers of spruce and pine. The galactan value in these layers may be due to the presence of a galacto-glucomannan.

The uneven distribution of the chemical compounds through the single fiber wall also reflects the chemical differences of spring wood and summer wood from conifers. Spring wood tracheids and summer wood tracheids differ from each other mainly by the much thicker S_2-layer

TABLE VI

RELATIVE PERCENTAGES OF POLYSACCHARIDE IN SPRING WOOD AND SUMMER WOOD FROM PINE (*P. silvestris* L.)

Polysaccharide	Spring wood	Summer wood
Galactan	3.4	3.1
Cellulose	56.7	56.2
Glucomannan	20.3	24.8
Arabinan	1.0	1.8
Glucuronoarabinoxylan	18.6	14.1

in the summer wood. As a consequence, as is shown in Table VI, the summer wood has a higher glucomannan and a lower glucuronoarabi-noxylan content than spring wood, where the glucomannan-rich S_2-layer makes up a lower percentage and the glucuronoarabinoxylan-rich S_3-layer a higher percentage than in summer wood.

Our knowledge of the chemical structure of the constituents of wood and of the chemical and physical fine structure of wood has greatly increased in recent times. The biological processes which produce these structures are, however, still rather obscure, and it appears that it will need considerable efforts to throw some light on this side of the subject.

DISCUSSION

BAILEY: You are right in the case of the water-soluble galactans; they do not seem to be constituents of the cell wall. Years ago I studied these in western larch; in the dry wood it appears quite clear that most of the galactan is in the lumen of the cell. In both transverse and longitudinal sections of the cambial zone the walls exhibit some birefringence.

ZIMMERMANN: Structural polysaccharides, like cellulose, always seem to have a configuration in which the next molecule is turned over; glucose is in the β form, galactose in the α form. Is there any explanation?

MEIER: In the galactans, for instance it is β.

ZIMMERMANN: The β-galactose in compression wood seems to be an exception. Still, structural polysaccharides often have this configuration. Depending on the hydroxyl on the 4 position it is either α or β.

COLVIN: One can see from a model that this is about the only way it can be, a twofold screw axis. It settles down this way; this is just the shape of the molecule.

PRESTON: It is true that the only way one can make a model is through the anti-parallel arrangement, but nevertheless, the physical evidence is not all that good. I think the structure rests entirely on the difficulty of making a model without this particular arrangement.

FREY-WYSSLING: How do we know that hemicelluloses and pectin chains are straight in wood. Many seem to be amorphous, would this be an indication that they are not straight?

COLVIN: We do not know. As a matter of fact there is a strong school of thought (to which I do not subscribe) that the chains are not straight in cellulose.

PRESTON: There is some evidence that the chains are straight in hemicellulose, which I have presented in my paper on p. 169 of this volume.

FREUDENBERG: It is convenient to write cellulose as Haworth did, turned over from one residue to the next, but this is not necessarily the true conformation; cellulose could be written in another way as well. Crystalline cellulose has a diagonal structure.

Dr. Meier, you said that *Ginkgo biloba* behaves in your case just like a conifer. It does the same in respect to lignin. *Ginkgo* is chemically a conifer. But in other plants, for instance in *Podocarpus,* there are two out of about twenty species which have lignin constituted like angiosperms. Are they richer in arabinose, these Japanese *Podocarpus?* Most of them behave in respect to lignin like conifers. Another case of taxonomic interest is *Ephedra* of the Gnetales, which has lignin like the angiosperms. I wonder if there is a parallelism with the hemicelluloses.

MEIER: As far as I know the hemicelluloses of the *Podocarpaceae* and of the *Gnetinae* have not yet been investigaaed. Many ferns, however, are intermediate between conifers and angiosperms in their hemicellulose composition.

WARDROP: I was interested in the high xylan content you observed in the rays. Have you any idea where it is located.

MEIER: No.

PRESTON: A few weeks ago H. I. Bolker (1963) claimed to have shown by difference infrared spectra that there is an acetal or hemiacetal link between lignin and some fraction of the holocellulose, probably a hemicellulose. He used a double beam spectrometer, with whole wood, pressed into a bromide disk in one beam and holocellulose in the other beam. The difference spectrum thus included the infrared spectrum of the linkage group. His method seems to be a powerful way of looking into this problem. Is there not, incidentally, some evidence from jute for a lignin-cellulose link in that, if on delignification only 5% lignin is left, the cellulose still cannot be mercerized in caustic soda.

FREUDENBERG: Attempts have been made to produce lignin by dehydrogenating coniferyl alcohol or isoeugenol in the presence of cellulose. This experiment is not conclusive, because amorphous and insoluble lignin-like preparations are obtained. One cannot distinguish in the presence of cellulose whether insoluble lignin is linked or not. Attempts to form open chain hemiacetals have not been successful. They only exist as formulated in these cellulose chains or in all these polysaccharides, as closed acetals. The link between lignin and the polysaccharides is partially with the hemicelluloses, but the last residue of glucose in Björkman lignin belongs to the cellulose. I believe that lignin is linked as an ether between the polysaccharides and the benzyl alcohols. Either cellulose or hemicellulose may participate, or both. (See the paper by Freudenberg in this volume.)

MEIER: How do you know that you are dealing with cellulose? There are reports that small amounts of glucans are present. Thus the glucose need not always be from cellulose.

FREUDENBERG: There is always a small amount of sugar in Björkman's lignin. When the whole is methylated and hydrolyzed, 2,3,6-trimethylglucose is obtained. This means, probably, a cellulose residue.

THIMANN: When you say that every tenth unit is a 4-O-methylglucuronic acid group, is this a statistical value, or is it based on studies of isolated units?

MEIER: It is statistical. There is probably random distribution.

REFERENCES

Adler, E., and Gierer, J. (1957). *In* "Die Chemie der Pflanzenzellwand" (E. Treiber, ed.), pp. 446–486. Springer, Berlin-Göttingen-Heidelberg.

Aspinall, G. O. (1959). *Adv. Carbohydrate Chem.* **14**, 429-468.

Asunmaa, S., and Lange, P. W. (1954). *Svensk Papperstid.* **57**, 501.

Bishop, C. T. (1957). *Can. J. Chem.* **35**, 1010-1119.

Bolker, H. I. (1963). *Nature* **197**, 489.

Bouveng, H. O. (1961). *Svensk Kem. Tidskr.* **73**, 113-129.

Bouveng, H. O., and Meier, H. (1959). *Acta Chem. Scand.* **13**, 1884-1889.

Bouveng, H. O., Garegg, P. J., and Lindberg, B. (1960). *Acta Chem. Scand.* **14**, 742-748.

Bucher, H. (1960). *Papier* **14**, 542.

Croon, I., Lindberg, B., and Meier, H. (1959). *Acta Chem. Scand.* **13**, 1299-1304.

Freudenberg, K. (1962). *Pure Appl. Chem.* **5**, 9-20.

Garegg, P. J., and Lindberg, B. (1960). *Acta Chem. Scand.* **14**, 871-876.

Glaudemans, C. P. J., and Timell, T. E. (1958). *J. Am. Chem. Soc.* **80**, 1209-1213.

Goring, D. A. I., and Timell, T. E. (1960). *Svensk Papperstid.* **63**, 785-790.

Hamilton, J. K., and Thompson, N. S. (1959). *Tappi* **42**, 752.

Lindberg, B., and Meier, H. (1958). *Svensk Papperstid.* **60**, 785-790.

Meier, H. (1960). *Acta Chem. Scand.* **14**, 749-756.

Meier, H. (1961a). *Acta Chem. Scand.* **15**, 1381-1385.

Meier, H. (1961b). *J. Polymer Sci.* **51**, 11-18.

Meier, H. (1962). *Acta Chem. Scand.* **16**, 2275-2283.

Meier, H., and Wilkie, K. C. B. (1959). *Holzforschung* **13**, 177-182.

Mian, A. J., and Timell, T. E. (1960). *Svensk Papperstid.* **63**, 769-774, 884-888.

Perilä, O. (1961). *J. Polymer Sci.* **51**, 19-26.

Timell, T. E. (1960a). *Svensk Papperstid.* **63**, 472-476.

Timell, T. E. (1960b). *Svensk Papperstid.* **63**, 652-657.

Ultraviolet and Fluorescence Optics of Lignified Cell Walls

A. FREY-WYSSLING

Swiss Federal Institute of Technology, Zürich, Switzerland

The lignified cell wall is a composite body of essentially cellulose and lignin (minor constituents being neglected). Whilst the ultrastructure of the constituent cellulose is extensively explained by X-ray analysis and electron microscopy, this is not the case for lignin, because it yields very poor X-ray patterns and does not show any contrast to cellulose in the electron microscope. Indirect methods have therefore been applied to clarify the ultrastructure of the incrusting lignin, using its capacities of UV absorption and intrinsic fluorescence.

Structural State of Lignin in the Cell Wall

As far back as 1928 (A. Frey, 1928) it was shown that the incrustation of lignin does not sensibly change the birefringence of cell walls. Sections

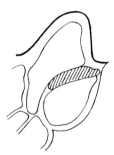

FIG. 1. Lignified island in the lignin-free stomatal cell wall of *Ginkgo biloba* (A. Frey, 1928).

across the stomata of *Ginkgo* leaves proved to be a suitable object for this demonstration (Fig. 1), because one side of the cell is incrusted with lignin forming a lignified island in the otherwise cellulosic wall. Both parts are conspicuously birefringent. But there is no measurable path difference between the two regions. It is true that they show up indifferent shades in the phase microscope; but this is due to different densities in the lignified and cellulosic parts of the wall, and not to a perceptible difference of birefringence. On the basis of such observations it was concluded that lignin is incrusted in an amorphous state and its incorporation into the cell wall was interpreted as a swelling phenomenon.

This view was confirmed, when Freudenberg *et al.* (1929) showed that, after quantitative extraction of cellulose, lignified cell walls yield a framework of amorphous lignin. The double refraction it displays is pure *form birefringence* of a rodlet composite body which disappears after imbibition with liquids of the same refractive index as lignin ($n_D = 1.61$). Also, in the electron microscope such lignin residues have quite an amorphous aspect (Mühlethaler, 1949).

However, in 1944 Lange (1944-1945) discovered a striking UV dichroism of lignified cell walls. Since cellulose and other carbohydrates in the cell wall do not absorb ultraviolet light, he attributed this dichroic effect to lignin and assumed an orientated adsorption of its molecules by the cellulosic microfibrils, similar to the dichroism induced to cellulose fibers (ramie, linen, cotton) by iodine or direct cotton dyes. This dichroic staining is due to the intrinsic absorption anisotropy of the dye molecules lined up along the surface of cellulose. In analogy an intrinsic UV dichroism was ascribed to the lignin molecule.

This view seems plausible since isolated lignin shows a graphite-like layer lattice (Jodl, 1942). According to Freudenberg (1956) the monomeric molecules of the highpolymeric lignin are coniferylic (I) and sinapinic (II) alcohols:

These building units dispose of a system of conjugated double bonds which causes the absorption of ultraviolet light. It is easily conceivable that the amount of absorbed light differs when the electric vector of the polarized light oscillates parallel or perpendicular to the aromatic ring of the molecule. Thus, a sufficient number of equally orientated molecules should yield a dichroic effect visible in the polarizing microscope.

The dichroism of plant cell walls is evaluated by measuring the light extinction parallel $E_{\parallel}$ and perpendicular $E_{\perp}$ to the axis of cells with fiber texture. For lignified fibers observed in UV light, Lange found for the dichroic quotient $E_{\parallel}/E_{\perp}$ values up to 1.2.

Owing to these findings, we are faced with a discrepancy of the results gained by different optical methods. While studies on the birefringence of lignified cell walls infer an incrustation of amorphous isotropic lignin, the discovered UV dichroism implies the presence of orientated anisotropic lignin. It is the scope of this paper to clarify this contradictive inconsistency.

We started by repeating the experiments of Freudenberg *et al.* (1929) with lignin ghosts of cell walls. These are produced by dissolving the carbohydrates with cuoxam (copper tetrammonia hydroxide) so that a porous skeleton of lignin is left as a rodlet composite body (Fig. 2A) which is birefringent. However, this double refraction is not constant but depends on the refractive index of the imbibing liquid. According to Wiener (1912) the birefringence of such a system is

$$n_\parallel{}^2 - n_\perp{}^2 = \frac{\delta_1 \delta_2 (n_1{}^2 - n_2{}^2)^2}{(\delta_1 + 1)\, n_2{}^2 + n_1{}^2}$$

In this formula $n_\parallel$ represents the extraordinary refractive index (parallel to the axis of the composite body) and $n_\perp$ the ordinary index (perpendicular to the axis); n_1 the refractive index of the isotropic rods, and n_2 that of the imbibition liquid; δ_1 and δ_2 are the volume fractions (relative volume) of the two components ($\delta_1 + \delta_2 = 1$). Clearly, $n_\parallel{}^2 - n_\perp{}^2$ is a measure of the double refraction $n_\parallel - n_\perp$. The formula shows how this double refraction depends on the refractive index n_2 of the imbibition medium (Frey-Wyssling, 1940). It is zero when $n_1 = n_2$ (Fig. 2B), and positive for all other values of n_2, because the numerator contains the square of $n_1{}^2 - n_2{}^2$. Since in birefringent objects the larger index is denoted by n_γ and the smaller one by n_a, it follows that $n_\parallel = n_\gamma$ and $n_\perp = n_a$ (Fig. 2A).

It is significant that besides the volume fractions δ_1 and δ_2 no quantities depending on the dimensions of the rods occur in the equation. The double refraction is independent of the thickness of the rods. This is of particular importance to the study of sublight-microscopic textures, as long as the size of the structural units is not known. The double refraction of the composite bodies has been termed form birefringence (A. Frey, 1924), because its nature depends on the form of the textural elements of the solid phase.

When we are dealing with lignified cell walls, the composite body consists of not only two, but three components: parallelized cellulose rodlets (microfibrils), incrusting lignin, and free space where the imbibition liquid penetrates. For the application of the Wiener theory they must be reduced to two, either by destroying one of them (e.g., cellulose when preparing lignin ghosts) or by grouping two of them in but one component. Doing so, we distinguish (1) the UV-absorbing component lignin (n_1 and δ_1) and (2) the nonabsorbing component (n_2 and δ_2), consisting of cellulose + imbibition liquid. The relative volume δ_2 consists then of the relative volumes of cellulose + available capillary space, and n_2 must be calculated as a mean value of the refractive power of cellulose and the variable refractive indices n_0 of the imbibition liquid.

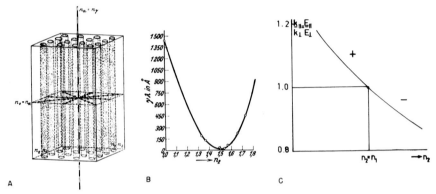

A   B   C

Fig. 2. (A) Rodlet composite body with sublight-microscopic rods. Refractive indices: of rods n_1, of imbibition liquid n_2, of composite body $n_\parallel$ and $n_\perp$. (B) Wiener curve for form birefringence $n_\parallel - n_\perp = f(n_2)$ of rodlet composite body. $\gamma\lambda$ path difference proportional to $n_\parallel - n_\perp$. (C) Wiener curve for form dichroism $E_\parallel/E_\perp = k_\parallel/k_\perp = f(n_2)$ of rodlet composite body. E, extinction, k, absorption exponent.

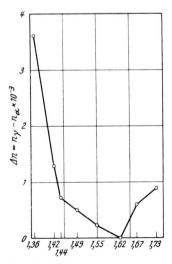

Fig. 3. Experimental form birefringence curve on radial sections of lignified ghost from spruce tracheids. Ordinate: birefringence Δn. Abscissa: refractive index n_2 of imbibition liquid.

Figure 3 displays the form birefringence measured on radial sections of lignin ghosts from spruce tracheids. As imbibition liquid, mixtures of ethanol ($n_2 = 1.36$) and carbon disulfide ($n_2 = 1.62$) were used; for stronger refractive power monobromonaphthalene ($n_2 = 1.66$) and methylene iodide ($n_2 = 1.73$) had to be applied. With the mixture $n_2 = 1.61$ which has the same refractive index as lignin, the birefringence disappears completely. This means that the lignin under observation is isotropic; if it had intrinsic anisotropy a certain amount of birefringence had to show up at the minimum of the form birefringence curve (residual birefringence). Since the monomeric building unit of lignin has a pronounced morphologic anisotropy, lignin itself can be isotropic only if it is amorphous.

To find out why there is UV dichroism although the lignin of the cell wall seems to be amorphous, Wiener's theory, extended to absorbing composite bodies, was applied. It permits one to decide whether the dichroism is due to the rodlet system (form dichroism) or to the anisotropy of the rodlets (intrinsic dichroism). If absorption is moderate the formula for form dichroism reads (Wiener, 1926)

$$\frac{k_{\parallel}}{k_{\perp}} = \frac{n_{\perp}}{n_{\parallel}} \frac{[(n_1^2 + n_2^2) - \delta_1(n_1^2 - n_2^2)]^2}{4n_2^2}$$

$k_{\parallel}$ represents the absorption coefficient parallel and $k_{\perp}$ perpendicular to the rodlet composite body. The other quantities are the same as in the formula for the form birefringence. $k_{\parallel} > k_{\perp}$ means positive; $k_{\parallel} < k_{\perp}$, negative; and $k_{\parallel} = k_{\perp}$, lacking dichroism. Here again the optical behavior must be considered to depend on the refractive index of different imbibition liquids, $k_{\parallel}/k_{\perp} = f(n_2)$. If such a liquid with $n_2 = n_1$ is brought between the rods, $n_{\parallel}$ equals $n_{\perp}$ so that the numerator of the formula becomes $4n_2^2$ and $k_{\parallel}/k_{\perp} = 1$. This means that not only the effect of form birefringence but also that of form dichroism disappears when $n_2 = n_1$. $n_2 < n_1$ causes positive and $n_2 > n_1$ negative form dichroism (Fig. 2C).

More easily than the absorption coefficient k, the extinction E can be measured by photometry. Therefore, in measuring dichroism the quotient $E_{\parallel}/E_{\perp}$ is determined. Since E is proportional to k the form dichroic curves of both $k_{\parallel}/k_{\perp}$ and $E_{\parallel}/E_{\perp}$ are identical.

The difficulty is to find a liquid with a refractive index of lignin ($n_D = 1.61$) which does not absorb ultraviolet light. H. P. Frey (1959) used the above-mentioned mixtures of ethanol and carbon disulfide. With the aid of the dispersion of those mixtures their refractive indices were extrapolated for the UV wavelength $\lambda = 280$ mμ where lignin has its absorbing maxima. The relevant index n_1 of lignin is $n_{280} = 1.88$. The dichroism $E_{\parallel}/E_{\perp}$ was measured by a device designed by Ruch (1951).

In Fig. 4 the results of such imbibition measurements with spruce tracheids are shown. The slope of the curves proves that there is a form effect. They clearly tend toward 1 (lacking dichroism) with rising n_{280}. But isotropy is not completely reached at n_1 of lignin which is $n_{280} = 1.88$.

This can be due to a slight intrinsic dichroism of lignin or to the fact that the above formula is simplified by the assumption that there is only a weak absorption. Evidently this is not the case for lignin at $\lambda = 280$ mµ. Therefore, the form dichroism of the system under consideration has

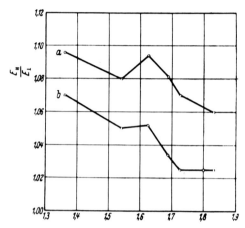

FIG. 4.   UV dichroism of spruce tracheids in 280 mµ light: (a) on radial wall; (b) on tangential wall (H. P. Frey, 1959). Ordinate: dichroism $E_{\parallel}/E_{\perp}$. Abscissa: refractive index n_{280} of imbibition liquid.

been calculated according to the more complicated formulas of Wiener (1926) considering high absorption as well.

For this calculation the constants of Table I have been used. Since in imbibition experiments the nonabsorbing component consists of cellulose fibrils + imbibition liquid, n_2 must be calculated by alligation of the

TABLE I
WALL COMPONENTS OF SPRUCE TRACHEIDS

Absorbing component (lignin)	
k	UV absorption index for 280 mµ = 0.118
n_1	Refractive index for 280 mµ = 1.8769
δ_1	Relative volume = 0.1, 0.25, or 0.35

Nonabsorbing component (cellulose + imbibition solution)	
n_γ	Index $n_{\parallel}$ of cellulose for 280 mµ = 1.865
n_a	Index $n_{\perp}$ of cellulose for 280 mµ = 1.795
n_0	Variable index of imbibition liquid
δ_2	Relative volume cellulose + imbibition liquid = 0.9, 0.75, or 0.65

amount and the refractive power of both cellulose n_λ or n_α and penetrated liquid n_0 (see Table II). In doing so, the curves of Fig. 5 are obtained. To stress the theoretical nature of these curves as compared with the experimental curves in Fig. 4, the dichroism is not indicated by the extinction quotient $E_\parallel/E_\perp$ which can be measured, but by the calculated index quotient $k_\parallel/k_\perp$. Numerically these quotients have the same value.

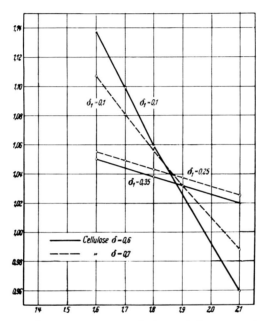

FIG. 5. Theoretical Wiener curves of form dichroism, calculated for n_{280} (H. P. Frey, 1959). Ordinate: form dichroism $k_\parallel/k_\perp$. Abscissa: refractive index n_{280} of imbibition liquid.

Figure 5 shows that with low lignin content ($\delta_1 = 0.1$) the curve of form dichroism runs from positive ($k_\parallel/k_\perp > 1$), to negative ($k_\parallel/k_\perp < 1$) effects as requested by the above formula. However, if the content of lignin is larger ($\delta_1 = 0.25$ up to 0.35), this is no longer the case; then the curves display a slope similar to the experimental ones. Since spruce tracheids contain 28% lignin by weight (Jayme and Finck, 1944), δ_1 must be of the order of 0.3, so that there is an astonishing conformity of the experimental and theoretical findings. As a conclusion the observed UV dichroism of lignified cell walls must be declared as form anisotropy due to the rodlet composite body imposed by the parallel texture of the cellulosic microfibrils. There is no appreciable intrinsic UV dichroism and, therefore, no proof for any lignin orientation.

A third optical effect inherent to lignin is its intrinsic fluorescence.

Lignified cell walls illuminated by UV emit a striking blue light in the fluorescence microscope. The fluorescence light is slightly polarized, being stronger parallel than perpendicular to the cell axis. The effect is known as *difluorescence*. Here again the question arises whether it is caused by orientated lignin molecules or by a form effect depending on imbibition.

This problem has been solved by Helen Hengartner (1961). To secure an equal excitation of all lignin molecules throughout the whole preparation, the slightly absorbed 366 mμ band of mercury light instead of the highly absorbed 280 mμ band was used. Since tracheids have a pronounced helical texture, jute fibers, which are known for their almost

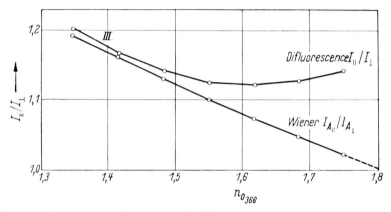

Fig. 6. Comparison of experimental difluorescence $I_{\parallel}/I_{\perp}$ of jute fiber with theoretical Wiener absorption $I_{A\parallel}/I_{A\perp}$ curve (Hengartner, 1961). Ordinate: light intensity $I_{\parallel}/I_{\perp}$. Abscissa: refractive index n_{366} of imbibition liquid.

ideal fiber texture, served as object. The intensity quotient $I_{\parallel}/I_{\perp}$ of the emitted fluorescence light was measured with a dichroscopic eyepiece or by depolarization with a compensator.

The liquid for imbibition must not show any fluorescent effect nor any absorption of the incident UV light at 366 mμ. The best results were obtained with the mixture water–Clerici solution (containing thalium formiate and malonate). This mixture covers a range of refractive power from $n_{366} = 1.35$ up to 1.75. The result of the imbibition experiments is presented in Fig. 6.

It shows that even the effect of difluorescence is not constant, but depends on the refractive index n_0 of the penetrating liquid. Although lignin is characterized by intrinsic fluorescence the difluorescence of lignified fibers is a form effect.

There is no Wiener formula for form difluorescence. But since in sufficiently dilute systems the amount of emitted fluorescence light I_F is proportional to the amount of absorbed light I_A the quotients $I_{F\parallel}/I_{F\perp}$ and $I_{A\parallel}/I_{A\perp}$ must be alike. Therefore, the simplified Wiener formula for dichroism given in this paper can be used to calculate form difluorescence depending on $f(n_2)$.

For this calculation all refractive indices must be measured for or interpolated to n_{366}. The figures of Table II were used.

TABLE II

WALL COMPONENTS OF JUTE FIBERS

Absorbing component (lignin)	
n_1	Refractive index for 366 mμ = 1.71
δ_1	Relative volume = 0.035
	(in jute there is 3.5% lignin by volume)

Nonabsorbing component (cellulose + imbibition liquids)	
n_γ	Index $n_\parallel$ of cellulose for 366 mμ = 1.690
n_a	Index $n_\perp$ of cellulose for 366 mμ = 1.630
n_0	Index of water up to Clerici solution = 1.348 up to 1.752
$\delta_2 = \delta_{\text{Cellulose}} + \delta_{\text{Capillaries}} = 0.665 + 0.30 = 0.965$	
$n_{2\parallel} = (30/96.5)n_0 + (66.5/96.5)n_\gamma$	
$n_{2\perp} = (30/96.5)n_0 + (66.5/96.5)n_a$	

The absorption calculated in terms of absorption coefficients k or measured as extinction E has been transformed into light intensities I by the relation $I = e^{-E} = e^{-4\pi kd/\lambda}$ (d is the thickness of the absorbing layer and λ the wavelength of the light used). However, the form curve for $I_\parallel/I_\perp$ is qualitatively the same as for $E_\parallel/E_\perp$ in that for both cases the quotient is 1 for $n_1 = n_2$; only the slope of the dichroism curve differs depending on whether E or I is used for its construction.

Figure 6 shows the result together with the experimentally determined difluorescence. There is an astonishing quantitative agreement of the two curves. Whilst the theoretical one $I_{A\parallel}/I_{A\perp}$ is almost a straight line, the experimental curve of emitted fluorescence light $I_{F\parallel}/I_{F\perp}$ is slightly bent. The reason for this deviation is not known. But the quantitative similarity of the measured and the calculated values of $I_{F\parallel}/I_{F\perp}$ proves that also the observed difluorescence in lignified cell walls is a form effect, indicating again an amorphous incrustation of lignin.

Marchessault (1962) comes to the same conclusion because, in contrast to cellulose and xylan, lignin does not show any dichroism in the infrared.

Distribution of Lignin in the Cell Wall

UV optics and fluorescence can also be used for quantitative evaluations of the content and the distribution of lignin in the cell wall. This allows us to answer the controversial question concerning the lignification of the primary and the secondary wall.

Densitometer curves in 280 mµ UV light across two adjacent lignified cells yield an absorption maximum in the middle lamella. From there the curve symmetrically slopes down across the neighboring two primary walls and the outer parts of the secondary walls, where finally it indicates a plateau with a fairly constant absorption level. The same

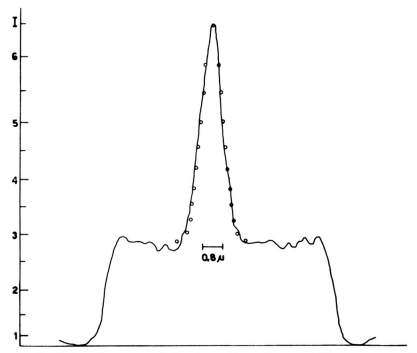

FIG. 7. Emitted fluorescence light of jute fibers (Ruch and Hengartner, 1960). Solid line, densitometer curve; Open circles, calculated values. Width of middle layer, 0.8 µ. Ordinate: light intensity I. Abscissa: radial section across cell walls of two adjacent tracheids.

is true for the intensity I of the emitted fluorescence light (Figs. 7 and 9b).

Lange (1954) concluded from these findings that there was an increasing lignification in the outer layers of the secondary wall and in the primary wall toward the maxima in the middle lamella. However, the pronounced inhomogeneity of the boundary between primary and secondary wall causes considerable light diffraction. This effect can be calculated and Ruch and Hengartner (1960) found the intensity of fluorescent light emitted as indicated by open circles in Fig. 7. For their calculation they made the assumption of evenly distributed lignin amounts in both parts of the cell wall as indicated in Fig. 8. The coincidence of the densitometric curve with the calculated values for *I*, if the effect of light scattering is duly considered, proves that the lignification is uniform throughout the whole secondary wall. The same is true for the primary wall, but the lignin content is considerably higher.

Besides diffraction, another reason that the abrupt discontinuity of the lignin content at the boundary of primary and secondary walls is obscured to a gradual one is the numerical aperture of the microscopic objectives used. The higher the aperture, the more obliquely the rays cross the preparation, exciting fluorescence in both parts of the cell wall; therefore, photometry requires rays which cross the object as

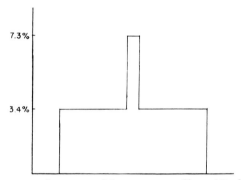

Fɪɢ. 8. Distribution and content of lignin in jute fibers (Ruch and Hengartner, 1960). Ordinate: lignin content. Abscissa: radial section across cell walls of two adjacent tracheids.

nearly parallel to the axis of the microscope as possible. In contrast to diffraction this effect of concealing the true distribution of lignin cannot be calculated. So the coincidence of experimental and theoretical intensity curves (Fig. 7) is only evident when low apertures, for instance 0.65, are used.

To find out the lignin content of the primary and the secondary wall the law of Beer-Lambert must be applied (Ruch and Hengartner, 1960). It reads

$$E = \varepsilon \cdot c \cdot d$$

where ε is the extinction coefficient (21.5 liters/gm cm for lignin with UV = 280 mμ), c the lignin concentration (gm/liter) and d the thickness (cm) of the lignin layer. From this it follows for the mass of lignin per unit area (gm/cm²) of the microscopic preparation that

$$M_L = c \cdot d = E/\varepsilon$$

E can be measured, ε is known.

The lignin mass M_L must be brought into relation with M_W, the mass per unit area of the total cell wall. This can be measured with the aid of the interference microscope.

$$M_W = \frac{\phi \lambda \rho}{n_W - n_{H_2O}}$$

ϕ is the measured phase difference, λ the wavelength of the light used, ρ the density, and n_W the refractive index of the relevant parts of the cell wall. The immersion liquid is water whose refractivity must be deduced from that of the wall.

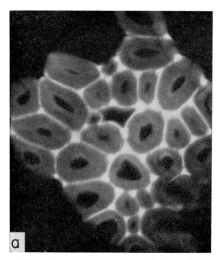 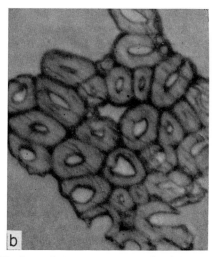

Fig. 9. Cross section of jute fibers (Ruch and Hengartner, 1960). (a) In fluorescence microscope; (b) in UV microscope, $\lambda = 280$ mμ.

For the secondary wall n_W can be measured by the classical immersion method and is found to be $n_W = 1.546$. Since that part of the wall is only slightly lignified, its density is near to that of cellulose, $\rho = 1.55$.

For the primary wall, both strata and the middle lamella in between must be considered jointly as middle layer. It contains 57% cellulose ($n = 1.555$, $\rho = 1.55$) and 43% hemicelluloses ($n = 1.532$, $\rho = 1.49$); from these data a mean refractive index and a mean density are calculated.

Measuring E and ϕ at the same spot of the secondary wall or the middle layer the amount of lignin in percent by weight $[(M_L/M_W) \cdot 100\%]$ is found. With this procedure Ruch and Hengartner (1960) find for jute fibers: 3.4% lignin in the secondary wall, and 7.3% lignin in the primary wall.

Thus the primary wall contains more than twice as much lignin. This is confirmed by Figs. 9a, b, micrographs showing fluorescence emission and UV absorption ($\lambda = 280 \, \text{m}\mu$). It is conceivable that in the primary wall with its random texture of the cellulosic microfibrils there is more space for lignin incrustation than in the secondary wall with its parallel texture.

Summary

The apparent anisotropy of lignin in lignified cell walls is mere form anisotropy. This is shown by the analysis of three different optical effects in lignified fibers: birefringence of lignin ghosts, UV dichroism of tracheids and bifluorescence of jute fibers. It must be concluded that the structural state of incrusted lignin is amorphous.

The concentration of lignin in the primary wall is more than twice as high as in the secondary wall. Within either of the two layers the lignin distribution is uniform.

Discussion

MEIER: If it is a question of space which layers are most heavily lignified, how can you explain the difference in lignification between secondary walls of angiosperms and those of conifers? The secondary wall of angiospermous wood is very little lignified; on the other hand, secondary walls of coniferous woods have a rather high lignin content.

FREY-WYSSLING: We have to consider all the incrusting material, not only lignin. If there are more hemicelluloses there is less space for lignin.

BAILEY: Some of the tropical dicotyledons are probably almost as highly lignified as some of the conifers. The S_2 structure in these plants is quite coarse. It is obvious that there are larger microspaces than in the less heavily lignified secondary walls of other dicotyledons.

FREUDENBERG: There may be a way to reconcile your opinion with that of Lange. The glucose units of cellulose are of about the same shape and size as lignin units. Lignin may partially penetrate the outer layer of the fibrils. When this occurs in the living cell, and finally in the mature wood cell, the lignin may give a very fine image of the surface of the cellulose chains. But when lignin is isolated in the presence of some acids, it is coagulated and probably loses the fine structure. It is therefore possible that in wood itself one can find a certain orientation of the lignin.

FREY-WYSSLING: That is the reason that we did not make any extractions; we used whole cell walls without any chemical treatment. The only requirement was that they were not completely dry; they were just air dried. The water can then be replaced with a liquid and the effect of form anisotropy results.

FREUDENBERG: It would be form anisotropy because it is an image of the cellulose.

FREY-WYSSLING: But if there were some orientation of the lignin itself, one should find some intrinsic anisotropy. This is not the case. Infrared measurements show the same.

FREUDENBERG: I agree with you, but the orientation found by Lange may be so fine and so superficial that it does not show with your methods.

FREY-WYSSLING: Of course, if there is some chemical bonding anisotropic relations must result. However, there may be random arrangement which results in statistical isotropy.

FREUDENBERG: When we did this refraction work you mentioned, 30 years ago, Dr. Zocher actually did the work (Freudenberg *et al.*, 1929). And Bailey (1936) was the first to find the high amounts of lignin in the middle lamella by micromanipulation.

BAILEY: In the thick S_2 layers microfibrils are very commonly aggregated into macrofibrils, which are easily visible under the regular light microscope. The intercellular spaces are correspondingly larger. Frequently lignin is present in these large capillaries. The situation there would quite agree, I think, with the residues I obtained.

WARDROP: About the concentration of lignin in the middle lamella rather than in the outer parts of the secondary wall, I think there are some points of agreement in some admittedly imperfect work using electron stains, which show enormously higher concentration in the primary wall and middle lamella. Certainly lignification will be greatest where there is most space. But we also have to consider that, as the cell develops, lignification begins at the primary wall and middle lamella and goes on there much longer than in the rest of the wall. UV absorption increases in the middle lamella just before the cell dies, so there is a longer time for lignin deposition. There is even a third explanation. It may be that lignin can link more effectively in the middle lamella to the uronic acid–containing polysaccharides than in the more cellulose-rich regions.

You referred to the use of sections 3 microns thick for measurements of ultraviolet dichroism. Were these sections cut through the middle layer of the secondary wall where all the microfibrils are oriented uniformly? I imagine that any material with a crossed texture, or containing the middle lamella with its isotropic structure, would present an enormously complicated system. Your theory can only apply in a parallel system.

FREY-WYSSLING: Yes, that is why we have taken tangential sections 3 microns in thickness.

WARDROP: One of your curves did not seem to reach 1. Why is that?

FREY-WYSSLING: That could be explained by Dr. Freudenberg's suggestion that there is a very small amount of intrinsic dichroism. Furthermore, the simplified Wiener formula which yields $E_\parallel/E_\perp = 1$ for $n_1 = n_2$ applies only for weak absorptions, which is not quite true for lignin in ultraviolet. If the absorption is high enough so that the square of the absorption coefficient can no longer be neglected, then the dichroism does not disappear completely at $n_1 = n_2$.

WARDROP: As we remove the lignin from the wall, however carefully, subsequent X-ray diffractions of line breadth always show some apparent crystallization of the paracrystalline phase. This is a bit indirect, but it would agree with the point that crystallization could occur as the result of the removal of lignin.

FREY-WYSSLING: In any case, the bulk of the optical effects are from amorphous lignin, and if there is any oriented lignin, it is very little indeed.

REFERENCES

Bailey, A. J. (1936). *Ind. Eng. Chem. Anal. Ed.* **8**, 52.
Freudenberg, K. (1956). *Angew. Chem.* **68**, 84.
Freudenberg, K., Zocher, H., and Dürr, W. (1929). *Ber. Deut. Chem. Ges.* **62**, 1814.
Frey, A. (1924). *Kolloidchem. Beih.* **20**, 209.
Frey, A. (1928). *Ber. Deut. Botan. Ges.* **46**, 444.

Frey, H. P. (1959). *Holz Roh- Werkstoff* **17**, 313.

Frey-Wyssling, A. (1940). *Kolloid-Z.* **90**, 33.

Hengartner, H. (1961). *Holz Roh- Werkstoff* **19**, 303.

Jayme, G., and Finck, F. (1944). *Cellulosechemie* **22**, 102.

Jodl, R. (1942). *Brennstoff-Chem.* **23**, 163, 175.

Lange, P. W. (1944-1945). *Svensk Papperstid.* **47**, 263; **48**, 241.

Lange, P. W. (1954). *Svensk Papperstid.* **57**, 525.

Marchessault, R. H. (1962). *Pure Applied Chem.* **5**, 107.

Mühlethaler, K. (1949). *Biochim. Biophys. Acta* **3**, 15.

Ruch, F. (1951). *Exptl. Cell Res.* **2**, 680.

Ruch, F. and Hengartner, H. (1960). *Beih. Z. Schweiz. Forstver.* **30**, 75.

Wiener, O. (1912). *Abhandl. Sächs. Ges. Wiss.* **32**, 507.

Wiener, O. (1926). *Kolloidchem. Beih.* **23**, 189.

Structural and Mechanical Aspects of Plant Cell Walls with Particular Reference to Synthesis and Growth

R. D. Preston

The Astbury Department of Biophysics, The University of Leeds, England

Introduction

With some exceptions which seem at the moment to be rare, plant cell walls are built upon a common plan. It therefore seems reasonable to suppose that, insofar as those features of structure generally regarded as ubiquitous are decisive in controlling the physical nature of these walls, then observations made on one type of cell will be applicable to another type of cell even though technical difficulties prevent verification. This might carry with it important consequences, for it could be possible both to predict the lines along which explanation might be sought of behavior specific to the second type of cell and even to anticipate behavior of this cell which could then be looked for. It is the purpose of the present paper to outline the features of structure which seem basic to cell walls, using in the main seaweed cell walls as illustrative material, and to examine their possible relevance to the fine structure of xylem elements and to plant cells generally.

By far the majority of plant cell walls may be taken, broadly speaking, to be constituted of a two-phase system, a mesh-work of long, thin threads—the microfibrils—in various order, embedded in a matrix of so-called incrusting substances. Each of these phases is composed of long linear arrays of sugar residues and their derivatives, together with other types of polymeric substances such as lignin in xylem, suberin in cork, and so on. The two phases are never completely separable and the molecular interactions between them are without doubt of material significance. The microfibrils can, however, be extracted without signs of contamination with incrusting substances visible in the electron microscope (Cronshaw et al., 1958) and on hydrolysis they yield glucose together with other sugars in varying degree. In xylem the nonglucose fraction amounts to only a few per cent of the microfibril weight—though it can reach 15% in beech wood—and this might be thought of as a contaminant and therefore of no particular significance. With some seaweeds, however, the microfibrils, which are not significantly different in size from those of higher plants, contain 50% or more of xylose (Cronshaw et al., 1958). This carries with it of necessity the concept that in these seaweeds—and by implication in higher plants, too—xylose and other sugars play a material role in the constitution of these biological units of structure. The content of xylose is rarely sufficient fully to clothe the microfibrils even with a monolayer of xylan and the microfibril may therefore be conceived as a central crystalline rod which on hydrolysis yields glucose only (Dennis and Preston, 1961), consisting therefore of cellulose *sensu strictu,* surrounded by a "cortex" of mixed chains of glucan and xylan in less perfect crystalline order (Frey-Wyssling, 1959; Preston and Cronshaw, 1958).

The microfibrils are commonly arranged in cell walls in some specific way. They are usually flattish ribbons within which certain crystal planes, spaced 6.1 Å apart, lie parallel to the flatter faces and it has been found with some plants that these planes, and therefore the flatter faces of the microfibrils, tend to lie parallel to the wall surface. This is true of all plant cells which are large enough to allow the relevant observation to be attempted—the marine algae *Valonia* (Preston and Astbury, 1937), *Chaetomorpha* (Nicolai and Frey-Wyssling, 1938; Frei and Preston, 1961a), *Cladophora* (Astbury and Preston, 1940; Frei and Preston, 1961a) and many other cellulosic seaweeds (Frei and Preston, unpublished)— whether or not the microfibrils have any other higher orientation (Frei and Preston, 1961a). It seems reasonable to suppose that the same tendency exists in higher plant cells including the elements which constitute the xylem.

Again, the microfibrils are commonly distributed through a wall in lamellae within which they lie more or less parallel to each other. It is moreover striking to note how often it is now found that, as first demonstrated with, and still found most beautifully exemplified by, the seaweeds to which attention has been called above, the microfibrils of adjacent layers are crossed, often at about 90°. Such a crossed microfibrillar structure has been now verified not only for the tracheids and fibers of higher plants (see Wardrop, this volume, p. 87) but for the hyphal walls in some fungi (Aronson and Preston, 1960a, b), many parenchymatous cells and some root hairs and root epidermal cells (Foster, 1962); indeed for almost every cell in which this structure has been sought. The circumstances under which this kind of structure can develop are much more easily looked for in the larger cells of the seaweeds than they are in the smaller cells of the xylem. Moreover, interrelations between changes in cell dimension and wall structure can also be more readily studied, and placed on a firmer quantitative basis, in the larger seaweeds. It then remains to be decided whether or not the resultant findings can be generalized to cover the cells of higher plants.

Finally, it is always pertinent to inquire how far the incrusting substances are involved in determining the physical properties of the walls. Here again the algae lend themselves to the appropriate investigations especially on account of the wide limits between which the incrusting substance content ranges.

The Constitution of Cellulose and the Yielding of Cellulosic Walls to Stress

The central crystalline core of cellulose microfibrils probably consists always of linear chains of β-1,4-linked glucose residues (Fig. 1) arranged with respect to each other in a regular way which no doubt varies slightly from one species to another (Preston, 1962). The particular kind of order involved depends among other things upon a particular feature of the β-1,4-link. A chain of sugar residues linked in this particular way is potentially straight; in cellulose the chain is held straight by internal intrachain hydrogen bonding, but the fact that it can be straight depends upon the inter-glucose link and familiarity should not be allowed to blind us to the beautiful simplicity which this involves. When the link is an α-1,4-link, as in starch, the chain can no longer be straight; when the link is a β-1,3-link, as is the case in laminarin, in yeast glucan (Houwink and Kreger, 1953), and also in the structural xylan of some Siphonales (Frei and Preston, 1961c), again the chain is not straight. In neither of these cases could the chains be laid side by side to produce straight microfibrils. It is in fact known that the molecular chains in starch are coiled into helices; and it has recently been shown that, although β-1,3-linked xylan does form microfibrils, the molecular chains within the microfibrils are wound around each other in pairs in a slow helix (Frei and Preston, 1963). It is not yet known how far this peculiar arrangement affects the properties of these microfibrils, except that the optical properties are quite different from those of cellulose, but differences from cellulose must be extensive. Since, for instance, the tensile properties of thickened cell walls are attributed to the microfibrils, the particular tensile properties of cellulosic walls may therefore depend in no small degree on the β-1,4-link involved. It should be re-

membered, however, as a *caveat*, that the β-1,4-linked mannan found to
constitute the skeletal material in the walls of some Siphonales (Frei
and Preston, 1963) and of the cuticle in *Porphyra*, the structure of which
has now been worked out (Frei and Preston, unpublished), does not
form true microfibrils even when the chains are well oriented. The cell
walls are nevertheless coherent and firm.

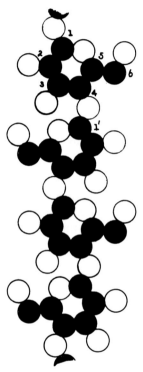

Fig. 1. Diagrammatic representation of two cellobiose residues in a cellulose
chain. Solid circles, carbon atoms; open circles, oxygen atoms; hydrogen omitted.
The chain is straight and is held in this particular configuration by intrachain hydrogen bonding. The linearity of the chain depends upon the β-1, 4-link.

Most cell walls are mechanically anisotropic; they may more easily be
stretched in some directions than others, for example. This is usually
associated with anisotropy of structure. If a wall lamella consists of
parallel cellulose microfibrils embedded in a matrix then it is under-
standable that the lamella will yield least easily to stress along the microfibrils and most easily to stress applied across them. The value of Young's
modulus, a property of materials which measures the resistance to stress,

is greater along the microfibrils than across them. When the lamella is wrapped round a cell in such a way that the microfibrils lie in a helix, then it becomes a matter of some mathematical difficulty to decide how the cell will react when blown up from within. If, however, understanding of the growth of cells is fully to be reached this problem must be solved even when the wall consists of several lamellae each with a different helical construction. In considering elastic effects, the first need

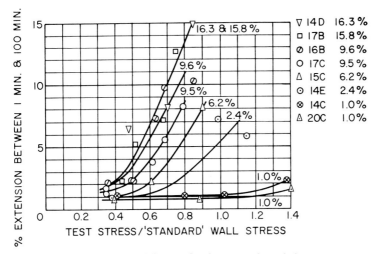

FIG. 2. The rate of creep of longitudinal strips of wall from growing *Nitella* internodal cells, under different loads (abcissa). The creep rate (ordinate) is expressed as the % extension between 1 and 100 minutes application of load. The figures on the graph give the growth rate over the 24-hour period before the cell was killed.

is to know the value of Young's modulus for each lamella parallel and perpendicular to the microfibrils and these two cannot be measured with the small cells found in higher plants. Here again, however, figures have been obtained for the larger cells of algae which should be applicable to preliminary calculation; careful choice of cells with respect to structure could refine the values. In the walls of internodal cells of *Nitella opaca*, for example, Young's modulus for stress parellel to the (moderately well-aligned) microfibrils is ca. 32×10^9 dynes/cm² and across the microfibrils ca. 7×10^9 dynes/cm², a ratio of about 4:1 (Probine, 1959). These figures refer to a growing cell wall; when the wall has stopped growing the ratio has dropped to a value of 2:1. In these cylindrical internodal cells the microfibrils lie almost transversely, somewhat dispersed about their common direction, and the whole cell resembles in this regard the fusi-

form initials of conifer cambium. The walls come under the tensions
due to the cell's internal turgor pressure and these tensions are borne
by the walls alone since the cells grow quite free in the aqueous environment. In such a cylindrical cell the tension is twice as great transversely
as longitudinally, an anisotropic ratio of 2:1 and, since the corresponding
ratio of Young's moduli is about 4:1, then the cell must extend elastically
parallel to the cell axis more readily than it does transversely.

There is however serious reason to doubt whether elastic yield has
anything to do with cell growth. Probine has shown (Probine, 1959,
Probine and Preston, 1961) that the walls of *Nitella* internodal cells
creep rapidly longitudinally under small loads but barely show any
creep at all transversely. The rate of creep increases the rate of growth
increases (Fig. 2) and there seems no reason to doubt that this is the
mechanical phenomenon associated with growth. Probine (1959) has
found, further, that the rate of creep in isolated walls is markedly affected by the content of cations; an excess of K^+ over Ca^{++} causes an
increased rate of creep and of Ca^{++} over K^+ a decreased rate. This presumably is actuated through the strength of bonding between the cellulose microfibrils and the (parallel, see following section) molecular chains
of the hemicelluloses, and the interchain bonding between the latter. It is
well recognized that K^+ is accumulated in the main at the growing points
of plants and this effect of ions may well be a very general phenomenon.
There is no reason to doubt that it is involved in the differentiation of
xylem elements.

The Orientation of the Hemicelluloses

The relevance of the β-1,4-link with regard to the mechanical properties of a wall may not, therefore, be confined to, and indeed under
some circumstances need not involve, the microfibrils. Let us compare,
for example the Young's modulus in, on the one hand, a *Valonia* wall
lamella 80% of which is cellulose in the form of well-aligned microfibrils,
and a *Nitella* cell wall, only 10% of which is microfibrils and those not
so perfectly aligned. In both walls Young's modulus varies with direction
of stretching, being a maximum when the wall is stretched parallel to
the general run of the microfibrils and least at right angles to this. The
degree of anisotropy is not largely different in spite of the wide difference in microfibril content (Probine, 1959). It could be that the deficiency in cellulose is counterbalanced by an abundance of incrusting
substances and that the mechanical anisotropy of walls is due in appreciable part to molecular chains other than those in microfibrils, which
are also in the main β-1,4-linked and are potentially straight.

This could happen if the chains of the incrusting substances tend to

lie parallel to the cellulose microfibrils. There is now complete documentation that this is true in some seaweeds and evidence that it applies
equally to the xylem of higher plants. The most striking case has been
found in the brown seaweeds. The walls of these plants have a relatively
low microfibril content, and if the microfibrils were uniformly distributed
they would be disposed in transverse section as shown to scale in Fig. 3a.

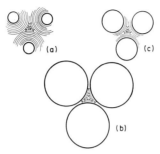

FIG. 3. Diagrammatic cross sections of microfibrils (drawn circular and to scale)
and their mutual dispositions in three plant types. The thinner concentric part-circles
are drawn about the thickness of a hemicellulose chain apart. (a) brown seaweeds;
(b) *Valonia;* (c) xylem elements.

The intermicrofibrillar spaces are so extensive that one of the incrusting
substances can form crystallites sufficiently large to be detectable on
X-ray diagrams. This particular substance is the poly-*l*-guluronic acid
component of alginic acid (Frei and Preston, 1962). The point to be
noted for present purposes is that the cellulose microfibrils and these
crystallites are similarly oriented. The most significant observation perhaps is that in the cells of *Chorda filum* (Fig. 4) the crystallites of alginic
acid and the microfibrils of cellulose lie around the cell in helices of the
same pitch. Incrusting substances which are far removed from the direct
influence of surface forces associated with the microfibrils therefore take
up microfibril orientation. At the other end of the scale, the microfibrils
of the *Valonia* wall, similarly represented to scale in Fig. 3b, are closely
crowded and, except in the larger interstices which must occur, none of
the molecular chains of the incrusting substances is far removed from
a microfibril surface. It can safely be expected that these chains are here,
too, oriented with the microfibrils, since nonglucose chains at or near the
microfibril surfaces are known to be specifically oriented in this way (see
below). It follows as a reasonable extension that, in the intermediate
condition found in xylem cell walls (Fig. 3c), the molecular chains of
almost all the incrusting substances with linear chains might be oriented
like the cellulose microfibrils.

There is evidence that this extension is valid. This comes from three sources. Firstly, when longitudinal sections of wood are treated with copper sulphate, the copper is strongly adsorbed by the cell walls. As shown by Belford *et al.* (1957, 1958, 1959a, b) the copper may then be fixed as a complex with dithiooxamide and the walls become dichroic, with the line of double bonds of the long molecule of the complex paral-

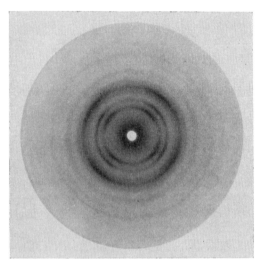

Fig. 4. X-ray diagram of a bundle of air-dried cortical tissue of *Chorda filum;* cell length vertical. Holocellulose after washing in cold dilute HCl. The acid treatment converts calcium alginate to alginic acid but does not affect orientation. The inner two sets of arcs are due to poly-*l*-guluronic acid and the outer set to cellulose I. Note that the arcs lie along the same straight line. All these arcs represent planes parallel to the respective chain lengths; the two kinds of chains therefore lie parallel.

lel to microfibril length. The complex is clearly associated with xylans and/or mannans in the wall (Dennis, 1962) so that the long chains of these compounds must lie parallel to microfibril length. Secondly, Liang *et al.* (1960) have observed that certain bands in the infrared absorption spectrum of whole wood sections referring specifically to xylan are polarized, and that the sense of the polarization demonstrates again this parallel arrangement of xylan and cellulose. Thirdly, it is clear that at least the xylan chains sitting immediately upon the cellulose chains of a microfibril must be oriented parallel to the microfibril. As shown by Dennis (1962), when xylans are extracted from whole wood by treatment with progressively increasing strengths of KOH solution there is no break in the curve relating weight loss to alkali concentration. This implies no abrupt change in the associations of xylan as the microfibril surface is approached.

The Crossed Microfibrillar Structure

Since the walls both of some seaweeds and of xylem tracheids and fibers show crossed microfibrillar structure though in varying degrees, and since dimensional changes in both the kinds of cells concerned are

FIG. 5. Electron micrograph of inner lamellae of a side wall of a cell of *Chaetomorpha melagonium,* viewed from the outside. Cell axis vertical. × 30,000; shadowed Pd-Au.

associated with a yielding of the wall to the hydrostatic pressure of the vacuole, then the reaction of the wall of the one group of cells to dimension change should in broad outline be the same as that of the other. Again these reactions have been observed in seaweeds and could be looked for in xylem elements though with very much greater difficulty.

The relevant observations have been made with a number of members of the Cladophorales (Frei and Preston, 1961b) but attention here will be confined to *Chaetomorpha melagonium.* This plant consists of a single filament of cylindrical cells placed end to end, with walls containing two sets of cellulose microfibrils crossing each other almost at right angles (Fig. 5), segregated as in *Valonia* to separate lamellae. One set forms a slow left hand spiral and the other a steep right hand spiral round the cell, geometrically equivalent to the S_1 and S_2 layers of tracheids. As each cell elongates during the growing season, the flatter spirals already laid down become steeper and the steeper spirals flatter, while on the inside new lamellae continue to be laid down with the original orientations. As a consequence, on passing through the wall from inside to outside the flatter spiral becomes steeper and the steeper spiral flatter. This is true multinet growth in the sense of Roelofsen (1951; Roelofsen and Houwink, 1951, 1953). Insofar as tracheids and fibers elongate during differentiation while clothed with a secondary wall, similar accommodations in structure must occur and since these cells grow by tip growth the adjustments made might be considerable. Signs of such adjustments have in fact been found by A. B. Wardrop (private communication). These adjustments are not perhaps so important as is a concomitant phenomenon observed with *Chaetomorpha*. The observed changes in the spirals with growth could come about only if, as it elongates, a cell twists about its own axis in the same sense as the steeper structural spiral. This *spiral growth* of the whole filament, forecast from the wall structure, has actually been observed (Frei and Preston, 1961b). A filament 60 mm long, for instance, will twist at a rate of one complete revolution of one end relative to the other for each 1 mm of growth, i.e., about 200° per day. The rate of twisting and the changes in wall structure are quantitatively related (Frei and Preston, 1961b). On the same point, it has been shown by Green (1954) and by Probine and Preston (1961, 1962) that the long internodal cells of *Nitella*—with walls resembling in architecture the walls of cambial initials—also twist as they grow and Probine (1963) has attributed this to an interplay between cell turgor and the mechanical properties of the wall in terms of its structure, just as in *Chaetomorpha*. This recalls earlier explanations given of the spiral growth of sporangiophores of *Phycomyces* (Preston, 1948; Preston and Middlebrook, 1949; Middlebrook and Preston, 1952). If the observation on *Nitella* can be transferred to conifer cambium and that on *Chaetomorpha* to differentiating tracheids, then if these elements are free to move they must twist about their axes. One consequence could be a tilting of the grain away from the vertical, i.e., the production of spiral grain. It has already been shown that the quantitative aspects of spiral grain in some trees are not inconsistent with such a view (Preston, 1949). One apparent demerit of such an explanation would be that all conifer trees should show spiral grain to some degree; the odd thing is, however, that it is in fact difficult to find a tree the grain of which is not demonstrably spiral. If the corresponding cells are not free to twist then consequences should follow such as observed when *Chaetomorpha* filaments are restrained, namely distortions of wall structure.

Microfibril Synthesis and Orientation

It was shown by Colvin *et al.* (1957; see also Colvin's article in this book, p. 189) that the microfibrils of the extracellular cellulose of *Acetobacter xylinum* are produced by end synthesis, the constituent molecular chains resembling in this respect those of synthetic amylose. It could be expected that such cellulose synthesis, like starch synthesis, would need a primer which would presumably be a microfibril end. Observations have also been made on the mature walls of *Chaetomorpha melagonium* which point to the same conclusion for this cellulose too. These are of two kinds.

The wall lamellae within which the microfibrils lie parallel to each other can usually be stripped from the wall as coherent, individual sheets. The microfibrils are largely confined to the lamella but even then they are frequently twisted round each other (Preston and Kuyper, 1951). Such twisting has frequently been observed or suspected with other celluloses including those of higher plants. Of still more significance, one lamella is, over some part of its area, inextricably attached to the next by an interweaving of microfibrils between the lamellae (Frei and Preston, 1961a). One such case is illustrated in Fig. 6. There is no question of this appearance being an artifact due either to accidental removal of microfibrils or to the drying down on the specimen grid. This is real interweaving. It suggests most strongly that the microfibrils are not produced by aggregation of preformed chains and, moreover, that they are not produced at an interface. The implication is clearly that the microfibrils are produced by end synthesis by a synthesizing machinery which has considerable spatial extent.

The second type of evidence comes from observation of cells both of *Chaetomorpha* and *Cladophora* (Frei and Preston, 1961a) both after plasmolysis and immediately before preparation for sporulation. In either case, the cytoplasm continues to produce cellulose microfibrils but the power to orient them has been lost and the microfibrils of the new lamella lie at random. This particular circumstance will be recalled below. The point at the moment is that both at the edge of the perforation in the wall already prepared for the exit of swarmers, and at the edge of the random wall lamella being laid down after plasmolysis, the microfibrils terminate in a tapering blunt end. These do not at the least suggest synthesis by lateral aggregation.

If, as is imagined above, the synthesizing machinery is of considerable spatial extent, then it must also be so ordered in space as to allow microfibrils in these particular plants to be oriented accurately in two directions (or in some species three) and in no others. Moreover, if the organ-

ization is destroyed, then power of orientation would be lost but not
necessarily that of synthesis. This would explain the randomization of
the microfibrils mentioned above, associated with plasmolysis and with
sporulation, and this gives some encouragement in the further examination of this general idea. The orienting machinery seems to be the same

FIG. 6.   Electron micrograph of side wall lamellae of *Chaetomorpha melagonium*.
× 20,400; shadowed Pd-Au. Cell axis vertical. Note transverse microfibrils interwoven with longitudinal fibrils of the next lamella.

in all members of the Cladophorales examined and there seems no
reason why it should be different in any cell with crossed microfibrillar
structure, whether of higher or lower plants. For instance, as shown by
Frei and Preston (1961a), if the cells of the species of marine algae
concerned are represented as rectangles with the longer side parallel
to cell length, then the microfibril directions in each can be represented
by placing the rectangles on a common grid of these intersecting sets of
straight lines (Fig. 7). The grid as a whole symbolizes the common

orienting mechanism and the part of it within each rectangle the particular expression in the species concerned.

The standard criticism of the concept of end synthesis as applied to microfibrils incorporated in cell walls concerns the mobility of the system and this must be met if the concept is to be retained. There is no

FIG. 7.   Diagram representing the relationships between the structure of the wall in *Chaetomorpha, Cladophora,* and *Valonia.* The two major orientations of microfibrils correspond to the two sets of double lines. The third orientation is represented by single lines. The longer edge of each rectangle is taken parallel to the axis of the corresponding cell. *a, Chaetomorpha melagonium; b, Cladophora rupestris; c, Chaetomorpha princeps; d, Cladophora prolifera; e, Valonia ventricosa.*

problem of this kind with the extracellular cellulose of bacteria, the only cellulose for which end synthesis has been proved. If we imagine an enzyme complex associated with either or both ends of a microfibril, there is no difficulty in envisaging movement of either or both through the medium as the microfibril grows; for the medium offers little resistance and the microfibril need not remain straight so that the movement does not need to be linear. With cell walls the case is different. While the enzyme complex is engaged in synthesis it must either push out microfibrils forward or itself retreat backward. This is perhaps no serious matter for the first few microfibrils in a new lamella, but as the microfibrils become crowded the resistance to movement could become considerable. More seriously, movement of either kind would seem irreconcilable with deposition of straight microfibrils. There can clearly have been no movement involved in the synthesis of well-ordered walls.

A clue to the way out of this dilemma is given by observations made on the inner face of the wall of *Chaetomorpha* and *Cladophora* when the cytoplasm has been removed as, for instance, by plasmolysis. There then still remains, on this inner wall face, files of granules oriented either along the existing microfibrils or at right angles to them (Fig. 8). These

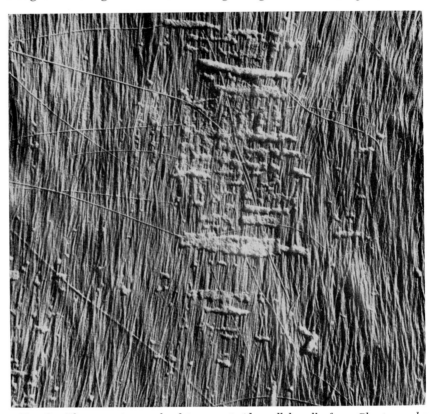

Fig. 8.   Electron micrograph of innermost side wall lamella from *Chaetomorpha melagonium*, cell plasmolyzed immediately before fixation. Granular bodies are arranged in files at about 90° to the microfibrils of the last complete lamella. Note the few fibrils of a new lamella, interwoven with those of the old and ending in the files of granules. × 20,400.

are never seen except on the inner face of the wall and the presumption is that these aggregates of granules are cytoplasmic, representing remnants of the cytoplasmic surface. They are always associated with microfibrils which appear to end within them, and those visible in Fig. 8 clearly form the first microfibrils of a new lamella. It is not to be supposed that these aggregates present more than a hint as to the nature of the active cytoplasmic surface. One can however hazard a guess, on the basis of these observations, as to the basic principles underlying the synthesis and orienting machinery and to present a model structure embodying them.

The model, which should be considered as a formal scheme not necessarily related to real structure, rests upon the following considerations.

(1) Microfibrils are produced by end synthesis.

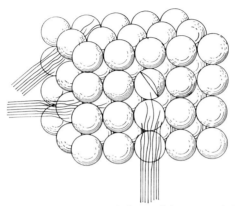

FIG. 9.   Diagrammatic representation of the model suggested for the synthesizing and orienting machinery in cell walls.

(2) Neither the microfibril nor the synthesizing enzyme complex moves during synthesis.

(3) At least three lamellae, with three different specific microfibrillar orientations, can be produced at one and the same time; this is required on account of the observed interweaving between lamellae.

(4) Synthesis may continue even if the capacity for orientation is lost. The model is presented in Fig. 9. This represents parts of three layers of spherical granules, each about 500Å diameter, lying upon the inner face of the wall represented by the plane of the page. The granules are considered to be stacked in cubic close packing, and the microfibrils (three are represented in the figure) are represented each by a set of parallel lines simulating cellulose chains. We may add the further assumption—though this is not strictly necessary—that the granules contain only enzymes capable of forming a 1,4-link between β glucose molecules. When a microfibril abuts on a granule, the granule is stimulated to synthesis. The chains grow forward, kept more or less straight by interchain hydrogen bonding, pass through the granule and come into contact with the next. The process then continues. Clearly, at whatever angle the microfibril "approaches" the set of granules it will thereafter be constrained to proceed through it in a limited number of directions, mainly the four directions represented by the two sides and the two diagonals

of each square in the packing of the granules. The use of only three (or two) of these directions in the Cladophorales may be associated with asymmetries in the internal structure of the granules themselves. In other plants all four may be used; the two possible diagonal directions could, for instance, correspond to the two microfibrillar directions in the S_1 layer of some conifer tracheids. The precise expression of this model in any particular cell type under any particular conditions would depend on the orientation of the files of granules vis à vis the cell axis. The granules must be considered as coextensive with the cytoplasmic surface. This would then allow synthesis to occur either over the whole wall surface of microfibrils with the same orientation or with different orientations from sector to sector of the wall, or to be confined momentarily to any one area such as the center of a cell or its tips, depending upon the starter mechanism. Once a granule has completed its work on one microfibril it may either be destroyed or replaced, or the microfibril, anchored in the wall, may displace the granule inwardly, in place to begin synthesis anew.

The microfibrils in Fig. 9 are shown growing within single layers of granules for the sake of simplicity. They may equally pass from layer to layer, interweaving or not with other microfibrils and branching if individual chains from one microfibril come into contact with two granules. Since the granules are further apart along the diagonals than along the sides of the squares it seems reasonable to suppose that more microfibrils would be deposited in the two directions at right angles than in the diagonal direction, just as observed in the Cladophorales and, indeed in elongated cells of higher plants. On the model as presented here, the incrusting substances would be synthesized independently and the linear chains of those oriented through forces originating at the microfibril surfaces.

Such a model would imply the presence of a special protein at cell surfaces. This is a matter for future inquiry. It is tempting to suggest that the hydroxyproline-containing protein found in growing plant cells by Steward and Pollard (1956, 1957), which does not take part in the protein turnover of the cell metabolism, may be involved (Preston, 1961). Evidence has already been obtained that this protein is closely associated with the wall (D. T. A. Lamporte, private communication).

DISCUSSION

THIMANN: You mentioned the spiraling in *Phycomyces* as an inherent method of wall building, but it is a peculiar fact that, when *Phycomyces* is illuminated and curves toward the light, spiraling ceases. This is associated with some increase in growth rate. Can you explain why this would occur?

PRESTON: Not with any certainty. Frey-Wyssling, Roelofsen, and I have disagreed about the genesis of spiral growth. I think Roelofsen must agree, now that he has himself suggested the multinet growth hypothesis, that he must apply it to *Phycomyces*. The thesis that I put forward is that this wall must be stretched symmetrically; each side must stretch at the same time for the twisting to occur. If, in fact, a stimulus makes a plant grow more on one side than the other, then the mathematics is quite different. I would not expect to get spiraling.

THIMANN: Would it not be an inherent property of the cell wall material?

PRESTON: It is not exactly an inherent property of the cell wall material that is in question; it is an inherent property of the cell with the cell wall as it is laid down around it.

FREY-WYSSLING: I think the most important result is that growth has nothing to do with stretch or strain, but with the production of hemicelluloses. Growth is a secretion of the so-called matrix by the plasmalemma, i.e., it consists of the production of new cell wall material. As a result the width of the elongating wall does not become thinner. This matrix is then reinforced and solidified by cellulose fibrils. Thus the model which has been shown is not only theoretical, but almost a real one. Dr. Moor in our laboratory has obtained with his freeze-etching method electron micrographs of yeast in which these macromolecules, which according to Dr. Preston are involved in cellulose synthesis, can actually be seen (Moor and Mühlethaler, 1963).

One important point has not been touched on by Dr. Preston; in crystalline cellulose the chains are antiparallel. Roelofsen (1959) maintains that this is impossible because two enzymes would be involved, one for the aldehydic and one for the non-aldehydic end of the chain. He considers only one enzyme and thinks that the cellulose fibrils grow at one end only with unidirectionally oriented chains. Dr. Preston's view seems attractive because the globules he has designed could contain an antiparallel system. By negative staining one finds very narrow fibrils ("elementary fibrils"). The smallest fibrils seen by Mühlethaler in the electron microscope have a diameter of only 35 Å (Mühlethaler, 1960). This corresponds to 36 chains which can be considered as antiparallel pairs (Frey-Wyssling and Mühlethaler, 1963). Of the 18 pairs 16 lay in the surface of the crystalline fibrillar core. As a consequence the paracrystalline cortex of the fibril must be produced in antiparallel pairs as well, otherwise there would be no crystallization at all. I think that the organizer under discussion must have an internal structure which allows the production of antiparallel chain pairs.

PRESTON: I tend to like parallel better than antiparallel arrangement for precisely the reasons that Roelofsen gives. I have to say this because I put it into print about five years ago (Preston, 1959). The crystallographic evidence for the antiparallel arrangement is very weak. In fact, the only evidence for the antiparallel arrangement is that it is much easier to make a model with the antiparallel arrangement than with the parallel arrangement. It is, however, at first sight much easier to visualize deposition at an end with the parallel arrangement.

COLVIN: I would like to remind Dr. Preston that there are well-documented instances of orientation in microfibrils, which are remote from the cytoplasm. I am thinking now of collenchyma cells and the epidermal cell walls in coleoptiles. The work of Setterfield and Bayley (1959) shows, it seems to me, that this organizer in the cytoplasm can play no role whatsoever (Setterfield and Bayley, 1959).

PRESTON: The model consists of a series of (as yet hypothetical) spheres each of which can synthesize cellulose. If one sphere appears anywhere in the cell wall at a microfibril end it will synthesize cellulose. If in the bars on the outside of the epidermis of coleoptiles there were cellulose microfibrils parallel to each other, and if we have a synthesizer, then this will synthesize a straight microfibril kept parallel to neighboring microfibrils both because of the internal hydrogen bonding and because it lies between two microfibrils. There would not necessarily be need of an organizer under those circumstances.

FREY-WYSSLING: The parallel-antiparallel controversy is a very important question, and until it is settled all theories on cell wall growth are of no use at all. Parallel arrangement would require hemimorphic fibrils with two chemically and morphologically different ends. Nobody has ever seen such a thing. On the other hand, fibrillar material such as chitin, silk, etc. is antiparallel. I cannot see why cellulose should have a parallel configuration just because we have no explanation for the growth of the antiparallel type.

WARDROP: In comparing tracheids and fibers with *Chaetomorpha*, is there not a point about the symmetry of the disposition of the microfibrils? In the twisting you described, one direction was already at an oblique angle to the cell axis so that, if it grew and the cell twisted, the other would change in unison. But if there were two symmetrically disposed directions about the cell axis, twisting would not follow.

PRESTON: That is not quite true. I have simplified the *Chaetomorpha* story in that I have mentioned *Chaetomorpha* only in the condition when it was growing fast and straight. Later in the year, as it slows down its growth, each cell in the filament bulges into a barrel shape. In that stage the microfibrils have become symmetrically disposed, but the filament still twists around its axis as it grows, now because it is growing laterally. There is here still some asymmetry, as there is also in tracheids and fibers, in the number of microfibrils following each helix.

FREY-WYSSLING: But this requires that the cell expand as a whole. As you have shown, however, there is local growth; it is not the whole wall that expands. One part of the wall is thickening while another part is growing in surface by the secretion of matrix. For the cambial cell this twist hypothesis cannot work, because the tip of a fiber initial is expanding alone while its middle part already displays secondary thickening growth. There is no expansion of the whole wall as in *Chaetomorpha* or *Phycomyces*.

PRESTON: If the tip only is growing, this is growing very much faster than the whole cell would have been growing if the whole cell were stretching. Dr. Wardrop has shown that Roelofsen's multinet growth hypothesis applies at the tips, so some part of the wall is stretching and is stretching more rapidly than would be expected from the over-all change in length of the cell. The top and the bottom must be twisting, but the middle part cannot twist. Something fantastic must happen therefore just where the tips merge into the body of the cell.

ALBERSHEIM: In reference to hemicelluloses as the limiting factor in growth Bonner and co-workers have shown this for some time in the *Avena* coleoptile. They have shown with calcium and potassium the same effects as you have with the algae.

PRESTON: Yes, Bonner was on to this in 1936, although he did not actually say it then.

THIMANN: However, I should like to say that it has been disproved that calcium operates in this way. We should not accept these old data too readily. If plant parts are treated with auxin so that they grow, they should presumably only grow (if this theory is correct) by releasing the calcium which held the two carboxyl groups together. Now if the experiment is done with coleoptiles prelabeled with Ca^{45} there is no significant release of calcium under these conditions, even under conditions where growth is maximally accelerated. I do not see how it is possible to align the function of calcium, therefore, with the theory that polyuronide limits growth in this way.

PRESTON: You are saying that the effect of auxin is not a calcium effect, and I have been careful not to discuss auxin effects. There is still nevertheless an effect of calcium both on growth and on wall creep, however it is mediated.

THIMANN: If growth is being limited by the calcium holding the wall together, and auxin promotes growth, then it should be removing the limitation. But it does not.

PRESTON: *Nitella* slows down growth enormously in the presence of calcium, an effect which is accompanied by the release of potassium, suggesting some site for which these two compete.

THIMANN: Certainly. Calcium slows down growth in everything, but that does not necessarily prove that it is operating in *this* way.

PRESTON: At the same time the creep rate on the wall goes down in the same proportions.

THIMANN: That does not prove that calcium is operating in *this* way.

REFERENCES

Aronson, J. M., and Preston, R. D. (1960a). *J. Biophys. Biochem. Cytol.* **8**, 247.

Aronson, J. M., and Preston, R. D. (1960b). *Proc. Roy. Soc. Ser. B* **152**, 346.

Astbury, W. T., and Preston, R. D. (1940). *Proc. Roy. Soc. Ser. B* **129**, 54.

Belford, D. S., Preston, R. D., Cook, C. D., and Nevard, E. H. (1957). *Nature* **180**, 1081.

Belford, D. S., Myers, A., and Preston, R. D. (1958). *Nature* **181**, 1516.

Belford, D. S., Myers, A., and Preston, R. D. (1959a). *Biochim. Biophys. Acta* **34**, 47.

Belford, D. S., Preston, R. D., Cook, C. D., and Nevard, E. H. (1959b). *J. Appl. Chem.* **9**, 192.

Colvin, J. R., Bayley, S. T., and Beer, M. (1957). *Biochim. Biophys. Acta* **23**, 652.

Cronshaw, J., Myers, A., and Preston, R. D. (1958). *Biochim. Biophys. Acta* **27**, 89.

Dennis, D. T. (1962). "The Fine Structure of Cellulose Microfibrils." Ph.D. Thesis, Leeds Univ., Leeds.

Dennis, D. T., and Preston, R. D. (1961). *Nature* **191**, 667.

Foster, R. C. (1962). "Cell Wall Structure and Growth." Ph.D. Thesis, Leeds Univ., Leeds.

Frei, Eva, and Preston, R. D. (1961a). *Proc. Roy. Soc. London Ser. B* **154**, 70.

Frei, Eva, and Preston, R. D. (1961b). *Proc. Roy. Soc. London Ser. B* **155**, 55.

Frei, Eva, and Preston, R. D. (1961c). *Nature* **192**, 939.

Frei, Eva, and Preston, R. D. (1962). *Nature* **196**, 130.

Frei, Eva, and Preston, R. D. (1963). To be presented to *Proc. Roy. Soc.*

Frey-Wyssling, A. (1959). "Die pflanzliche Zellwand." Springer, Berlin.

Frey-Wyssling, A., and Mühlethaler, K. (1963). *Makromol. Chem.* **62**, 25.

Green, P. B. (1954). *Am. J. Botany* **41**, 403.

Houwink, A. L., and Kreger, D. R. (1953). *Antonie van Leeuwenhoek J. Microbiol. Serol.* **19**, 1.

Liang, C. Y., Bassett, K. H., McGinnes, E. A., and Marchessault, R. H. (1960). *Tappi* **43**, 1017.

Middlebrook, Mavis, and Preston, R. D. (1952). *Biochim. Biophys. Acta* **9**, 32, 115.

Moor, H., and Mühlethaler, K. (1963). *J. Cell Biol.* (in press).

Mühlethaler, K. (1960). *Beih. Z. Schweiz. Forstv.* **30**, 55-64.

Nicolai, E., and Frey-Wyssling, A. (1938). *Protoplasma* **30**, 401.

Preston, R. D. (1948). *Biochim. Biophys. Acta* **2**, 155.

Preston, R. D. (1949). *Forestry* **23**, 48.

Preston, R. D. (1959). *In* "International Review of Cytology." Vol. VIII, pp. 33-60. Academic Press, New York.

Preston, R. D. (1961). "Macromolecular Complexes" (M. V. Edds, Jr., ed.), p. 229, Ronald Press, New York.

Preston, R. D. (1962). *Polymer* **3**, 511.

Preston, R. D., and Astbury, W. T. (1937). *Proc. Roy. Soc.* B **122**, 76.

Preston, R. D., and Cronshaw, J. (1958). *Nature* **181**, 248.

Preston, R. D., and Kuyper, B. (1951). *J. Exptl. Botany* **2**, 247.

Preston, R. D., and Middlebrook, Mavis (1949). *Nature* **164**, 217.

Probine, M. C. (1959). "Molecular Structure and Mechanical Properties of Plant Cell Walls in Relation to Growth." Ph.D. Thesis, Leeds Univ., Leeds.

Probine, M. C. (1963). *J. Exptl. Botany* **14**, 101.

Probine, M. C., and Preston, R. D. (1961). *J. Exptl. Botany* **12**, 261.

Probine, M. C., and Preston, R. D. (1962). *J. Exptl. Botany* **13**, 111.

Roelofsen, P. A. (1951). *Biochim. Biophys. Acta* **6**, 340, 357.

Roelofsen, P. A. (1959). "The Plant Cell Wall." Bornträger, Berlin.

Roelofsen, P. A., and Houwink, A. L. (1951). *Protoplasma* **40, 1.**

Roelofsen, P. A., and Houwink, A. L. (1953). *Acta Botan. Neerl.* **2**, 218.

Setterfield, G., and Bayley, S. T. (1959). *Can. J. Botany* **37**, 861-870.

Steward, F. C., and Pollard, J. K. (1956). *Plant Physiol.* **31**, ix.

Steward, F. C., and Pollard, J. K. (1957). *Plant Physiol.* **32**, lii-liii.

The Biosynthesis of Cellulose

J. Ross Colvin

Division of Applied Biology, National Research Council, Ottawa, Canada

A résumé of work on the biosynthesis of cellulose in a symposium on the formation of wood in forest trees presents some elements of paradox. Cellulose is the major constituent of wood but what we know about the molecular mechanisms of formation of this substance in trees is vanishingly small. Even if we consider all sources of cellulose, the sum of our knowledge is not impressive. In spite of the qualitative importance of cellulose as a skeletal material for most plant cells, the overwhelming amounts produced each year (10^{11} tons; Hess, 1928) and its significance as an industrial raw material (Ott *et al.*, 1954) our understanding of the formation *in vivo* of any kind of cellulose is scanty. An illustration of this fact is that less than a decade ago, a three-volume monograph of about 1500 pages devoted to all aspects of cellulose and technology summarized the results of all studies of cellulose biosynthesis in three-quarters of a page (Ott *et al.*, 1954). This does not reflect adversely upon the reviewer; the paucity of data was correctly and graphically illustrated by the relative pagination. Since then, several reviews have been prepared (Gascoigne, 1963; Neish, 1958a; Roelofsen, 1959; Stone, 1958) which demonstrate a growing interest in this field but each of these admirable summaries except one have dealt with the biosynthesis of cellulose from a restricted viewpoint, i.e., enzymological, cytological, or biochemical. The purpose of the present précis is to try to integrate the scattered fragments of information into a coherent, rational working hypothesis which may be valid generally, even to trees, and to show how wide are the gaps in our understanding of this subject.

At the molecular level, the study of the formation of cellulose microfibrils as physical entities in biological systems may be divided into three categories:

(a) The biochemical pathways leading from glucose or other substrates to the activated monosaccharide residue which is incorporated into a 1→4 β-polyglucosan.

(b) The physical mechanisms whereby the activated precursor is

incorporated into the insoluble microfibril thus forming a distinct addition to a second chemical phase. These mechanisms include those factors
which limit the transverse diameter of the microfibrils to fairly close
limits (Balashov and Preston, 1955).

(c) The mechanisms whereby the growing tip of a microfibril may
have its direction of elongation altered so that the completed microfibril
is oriented as a component of a complex, interlocking system, usually
a plant cell wall. These mechanisms do not include the purely rheo-
logical reorientation of completed microfibrils after deposition, as a
response to strain in the wall (Setterfield and Bayley, 1961).

The above categories are not sharply delineated and merge into each
other. Furthermore, they tend to assume that the general principles of
cellulose biosynthesis are similar in all species. Because most native
cellulose microfibrils are remarkably alike in morphology and general
properties, this is an attractive hypothesis and one which may well be
correct. However, even though we shall make this assumption implicitly
in the remainder of this paper, it is as well to bear in mind that it could
be wrong. Much more work is necessary, however, before the question
can be discussed in detail profitably.

Biochemical Pathways Leading to Cellulose Synthesis

HEXOSE PHOSPHATE HYPOTHESIS

Because of the possible close analogy to the synthesis of starch and
glycogen, the assumption that some form of hexose phosphate was
closely linked to cellulose synthesis has always been attractive and has
been strongly supported by Hestrin and co-workers in Israel. A recent
summary of their point of view has been published (Hestrin, 1961).
They suggest that in the bacterium *Acetobacter xylinum*, which produces
cellulose extracellularly, there exists an intracellular pool of fructose 6-
phosphate, fructose 1,6-diphosphate, glucose 1-phosphate, and glucose
6-phosphate in equilibrium with one another. From this pool, hexose
phosphate molecules (form unspecified) are drained off to be incorporated into cellulose after crossing the bacterial cell membrane. They
postulated masking of the polar phosphate groups to facilitate transfer
to the extracellular phase. The pool is replenished by direct phosphorylation of preformed hexose molecules and by hexose phosphates arising
from operation of a strong pentose cycle. From studies of the distribution of C^{14} along the glucose chain in the cellulose synthesized by the
cultures, they conclude that the carbon skeleton of the glucose molecules
supplied exogenously remained intact prior to incorporation into cellulose and very little breakdown occurred. This result is fully consistent

with the hypothesis of a direct phosphorylation of a hexose molecule and its subsequent use for cellulose formation. However, recent work has indicated that the problem needs reinvestigation. Benziman and Burger-Rachamimov (1962) working in the same laboratory with the same organism have shown that a strong triose recombination pathway must be present at least in cells grown under certain conditions. Likewise White and Wang (1963) also using the same organism have reported that, in addition to the pentose cycle, there is concurrent operation of the Entner-Doudoroff pathway together with a large fraction of recombination of triose phosphate at the aldolase level to yield hexose. The above results are inconsistent with a marked stability of the original hexose skeleton and confirm the early work of Bourne and Weigel (1954) which supported a triose-recombination pathway to cellulose synthesis. A recent conclusion that "the intact glucose carbon skeleton is used directly in some form or other for cellulose synthesis" (Setterfield and Bayley, 1961) may need revision for bacterial cellulose. Aside from the source of the glucose residues entering the cellulose microfibril, an additional reservation concerning the hexose phosphate hypothesis is that so far no one has demonstrated the formation of cellulose from these compounds either by whole cells or in cell-free systems in spite of many attempts (Colvin *et al.*, 1961; Glaser, 1958; Hestrin, 1961). Until this has been demonstrated unequivocally, the hypothesis, while appealing, must be regarded as speculative.

URIDINEDIPHOSPHATE GLUCOSE HYPOTHESIS

The undoubted importance of uridinediphosphate glucose (UDPG) in plant cell wall metabolism (Hassid *et al.*, 1959) in general has stimulated interest in its possible role in cellulose synthesis in particular (Neish, 1958b). Attempts to demonstrate directly participation by UDPG in cellulose synthesis in plants have so far been unsuccessful (Hassid *et al.*, 1959) but working with a particulate fraction from an homogenate of *A. xylinum* Glaser (1958) was able to show the transfer of about 1% of the radioactivity of UDPG, labeled in the glucose portion, to cellulose. Significantly, glucose 1-phosphate was ineffective under the same conditions. Although the amount of transfer was disappointingly small, considering that the reaction is essentially irreversible, Glaser's study does indicate that UDPG probably plays some role in the intracellular phase of the formation of cellulose by this bacterium. This conclusion was strengthened by Klungsöyrs' (1960) observation that the transfer of glucose residues from cellodextrins to an insoluble cellulose-like material by a fraction from the same organism is stimulated by uridinediphosphate. However, the role of UDPG or of related compounds in cellulose synthesis must certainly be intracellular. All attempts to demonstrate the stimulation of cellulose synthesis by this organism using UDPG exogeneously have failed, as might be expected from permeability considerations. As will be made clear later, in the present context the term intracellular means anywhere within the bacterial cell envelope.

EXTRACELLULAR LIPID GLUCOSIDE HYPOTHESIS

As suggested, any role of the polar phosphorylated glucose residues must be intracellular, that is within the bacterial cell wall or the cytoplasmic membrane of higher plants. However, certainly in bacteria the formation of cellulose microfibrils is extracellular and deep in the medium (Colvin and Beer, 1960) and there is good evidence that at least in some plants formation of the cellulose microfibrils is remote from the cytoplasmic membrane (Setterfield and Bayley, 1959) and thus also extracellular in a sense. Clearly, therefore, an intermediate compound capable of crossing the cell membrane must exist and may be isolated. This has proved to be possible with bacteria (Brown and Gascoigne, 1960; Colvin, 1959) and to a much more limited extent with green plants (Colvin, 1961a). A precursor of bacterial cellulose may be extracted from an active culture of A. xylinum or A. acetigenum by 80% ethanol, which is capable of forming typical microfibrils when in an aqueous solution in the presence of an enzyme. Further fractionation of the A. xylinum extract has shown that the active compound contains a lipid, glucose, and possibly an organic base on the basis of its chromatographic behavior (Khan and Colvin, 1961a). Activity of this compound as a precursor of bacterial cellulose has been confirmed using C^{14}-labeled glucose (Khan and Colvin, 1961b). Recent as yet unpublished work indicates that the lipid component is a long chain (about 30 carbons) polyhydroxy alcohol which is preferentially soluble in lipid solvents but also sparingly soluble in water. Identification of the remaining components of the precursor and/or their linkages to one another is now under way, following development of methods for obtaining adequate amounts of the substance. So far, all attempts to fractionate the 80% ethanol extracts from green plants, using similar methods, have failed. This failure with green plant extracts may be attributed to the even lower concentrations of the precursor and the extreme contamination by extraneous compounds.

For the bacterial cellulose system, all the evidence obtained up to the present suggests that the role of the lipid is to act as a carrier of activated glucose across the bacterial cell wall into the extracellular aqueous medium. In this external medium the glucose is transferred to the tips of elongating microfibrils by an extracellular enzyme released from the bacterial cell surface. Since it has been established that the lipid does not accumulate in the external phase, it must either be readsorbed by the cells or be metabolized extracellularly. The point has not been investigated carefully but qualitative assays of the lipid's stability in the cell-free supernatants of active cultures indicate the first alternative is probable. As yet, no role can be assigned to the organic base compound.

As recently suggested by Weigl (1961) the above results and tentative conclusions are not necessarily at variance with the suggestions that the hexose phosphates and/or the uridine nucleotides are implicated in bacterial cellulose synthesis (or the formation of other kinds of cellulose). It is easily conceivable that either or both may be required for the intracellular attachment of glucose to the lipid component and hence for its easy transport across the membrane. In this way, many of the older difficulties with nonpermeability of these polar compounds would be avoided. Nonetheless, it is necessary to stress that so far nothing is known concerning the relationship, if any, of this lipid-glucose compound to either the hexose phosphates or UDPG. Much more work may be required before we can establish any such relationship or describe it explicitly.

In connection with the formation of cellulose outside the cytoplasmic membrane, recent observations of an apparent equilibrium between cellulose and the precursors in a metabolic pool in wheat roots are very interesting (Margarie and Péaud-Lenoël, 1961). The formation of cellulose is usually considered to be essentially irreversible but if this observation can be extended, the conclusion must be modified. If future work supports the general occurrence of such an equilibrium, the above picture will be complicated.

Physical Mechanisms of Microfibril Formation

Any discussion of the physical mechanisms of cellulose microfibril initiation and growth presumes a generally accepted concept of the fine structure of this entity. Unfortunately, at the present time, no such generally accepted structure exists. Therefore, for the sake of clarity in the following, the structure of the cellulose microfibril which is assumed to be most likely correct is that described in general terms by Dennis and Preston (1961). This envisages the cellulose microfibril as a continuous central core of 1→4 β-polyglucosan chains arranged in a crystalline lattice. Surrounding this core is a sheath of paracrystalline polyglucosan chains which may in wood or green plants be encrusted with hemicelluloses. The whole forms a thickish ribbon or flattened rod about 100–250 Å in cross section. For reasons which have been published, (Colvin, 1963) it is believed that recent suggestions (Ohad *et al.*, 1962) that the cross section of native cellulose microfibrils is about 30 Å are not correct.

Intermediate High Polymer Hypothesis

Perhaps because it corresponds more closely with a portion of the mechanism of synthetic fiber formation, the assumption that a soluble polyglucose is intermediate between activated glucose and the insoluble cellulose microfibril has been advocated strongly. It was first clearly stated by Mühlethaler (1949) for bacterial cellulose and has been supported most recently by Ohad et al. (1962). This hypothesis assumes the prior formation of long single chains of 1→4 β-polyglucosan which are soluble in the aqueous external phase. These chains then associate longitudinally by van der Waals forces and later partially crystallize to form the characteristic insoluble cellulose microfibril. The well-known regions of amorphous cellulose in the microfibril are presumed to be areas where the crossing over or entanglement of the previously formed polysaccharide molecules prevents a regular lattice structure. Despite its intrinsic appeal and initial plausibility there are a number of grave difficulties with this hypothesis, some of which have been discussed by Roelofsen (1959). Among the first is the well-known, characteristic insolubility of even short polymers of polyglucose in aqueous solution (Ott et al., 1954). Solubility in water of polyglucose drops so rapidly as chain length increases that it seems most improbable that the postulated long single chains could remain in solution. Since the degree of polymerization of glucose may exceed 10^3 in even degraded cellulose (Ott et al., 1954), the corresponding loss of solubility must argue against the applicability of the above synthesis. Furthermore, this hypothesis offers no explanation of the characteristic limited diameter of cellulose microfibrils. If long polyglucosan chains crystallized from solution to form cellulose microfibrils, this mechanism would predict unlimited transverse growth of the microfibrils which does not occur (Millman and Colvin, 1961). In addition, the above mechanism of formation of microfibrils from long polyglucosan chains would predict splaying or unraveling at the tips of the microfibrils. This too is not observed (Colvin and Beer, 1960; Millman and Colvin, 1961). If microfibrils were formed by crystallization of prior polyglucosan chains, one would also expect anastomosing or cross linking between closely associated microfibrils. Such anastomosing has never been observed even between microfibrils which are closely coiled about one another (Mühlethaler, 1949; Colvin, 1961b) and therefore must have been constructed in close proximity. Finally and most important, as yet there exists no direct unequivocal experimental evidence for the existence of such an intermediate polymer in active bacterial cultures. Attempts to detect soluble oligosaccharides of glucose or soluble polyglucosans in extracts of fresh cultures which were capable of producing cellulose (Colvin, 1959) have failed. Mixtures of such substances have been isolated from older cultures (Jackson and Rama-murti, 1960; Weigl, 1961) but the significance of these observations, from the point of view of cellulose synthesis, is open to question consider-ing the recent work of Husemann and Werner (1963). These investiga-tors have demonstrated the existence of a cellulase in older cultures of *A. xylinum* which is capable of degrading the previously formed cellulose down to cellodextrins. Their work suggests that the oligosaccharides previously isolated may have been simply the products of such a cellulase, which had nothing to do directly with the synthesis of cellulose. The electron microscope evidence for the existence of such an intermediate (Hestrin, 1961; Mühlethaler, 1949; Ohad *et al.*, 1962) is likewise open to question. The amorphous "capsular" material surrounding the cells of *A. xylinum* in the earlier work (Mühlethaler, 1949) may be attributed to insoluble contaminating proteins or other polymers in the beer used as a culture medium. The "abundance of polymeric material in the form of granules, rods and branched processes extending from slimelike regions to parallel mats of polymer" in the later studies on washed cell suspensions (Hestrin, 1961) may also be attributed to nondialyzable protein in these bacterial suspensions. Dr. T. E. Webb working in our laboratory has shown that thoroughly washed cells of *A. xylinum*, when placed in glucose solutions, release substantial amounts of nondialyzable, soluble protein into the extracellular space. The role of this protein in the bacterial suspension is not known but, because it is nondialyzable, it will remain on the films mounted for electron microscopy under the conditions of Ohad *et al.* (1962). Since the "granules, rods and branched processes" formed by this protein cannot be distinguished from a poly-saccharide of similar size, it follows that observations of structures of this kind cannot be considered as valid evidence for an intermediate polysaccharide in cellulose biosynthesis. "Mats" of the type shown (Ohad *et al.*, 1962) have often been observed in our laboratory but there is absolutely no evidence linking them to an intermediate polyglucosan. At the present time definite acceptance of the intermediate high polymer hypothesis in cellulose biosynthesis requires direct experimental evidence for such a series of compounds in the biosynthetic processes for cellulose. Such evidence should preferably include isolation and characterization of these compounds but it has not yet been presented.

HYPOTHESIS OF DIRECT ADDITION OF MONOSACCHARIDE
RESIDUES TO MICROFIBRIL TIPS

An alternative mechanism to that of limited crystallization of polyglucosans is one recently favored by Roelofsen (1959) for synthesis of
cellulose in plant cell walls but which is also applicable to the synthesis
of bacterial cellulose microfibrils (Colvin and Beer, 1960; Millman and
Colvin, 1961). Glucose is transferred from an extracytoplasmic donor,
not to a single chain of 1→4 β-polyglucosan, but to the end of a chain
which is already incorporated into an existing cellulose microfibril. The
microfibril therefore grows at the tip by the addition of single glucose
residues (or, at least, of low polymers of glucose) added successively. No
free soluble polymer is required as an intermediate for this mechanism.
Under this postulate, growth of the microfibrils will be solely at the tips,
as is observed (Colvin and Beer, 1960; Millman and Colvin, 1961) and
because residues are added only to the ends of the preexisting chains
in the microfibril, no tendency to transverse growth of the microfibril
should be detectable, as indeed is the case. For such a mechanism,
polymerization of a glucose residue and crystallization may well be
nearly simultaneous events. Such a mechanism has the advantage that
the final product of the reaction is part of an insoluble second phase and
the glucose residues will therefore be removed effectively from the metabolic system. In other words, the growth of microfibrils is "driven" by
this phase separation and will be essentially irreversible, as is observed,
(with the exception noted above). Furthermore, this mechanism can also
accommodate the occasional chain termination which certainly occurs
as shown by the work of Brown (1962). If, by some defect in polymerization, a particular 1→4 β-polyglucosan chain is terminated at a locus on
the microfibril tip, there seems no valid reason why a new chain may not
be initiated later a few glucose residues along the microfibril length,
in the space left vacant. So far, the above mechanism is consistent with
(but of course is not proved by) the growth of green plant microfibrils
in walls from diffusible nonpolymeric intermediates (Setterfield and
Bayley, 1959) and with sharp alterations of direction of microfibrils
within plant cell walls (Preston, 1959). It is also consistent with the
growth of bacterial cellulose microfibrils *in vitro* from 80% ethanol
soluble precursors which do not lead to oligosaccharides (Colvin, 1959).

However, there are serious difficulties with this mechanism, too, as
discussed by Roelofsen (1959). Depending upon whether the fine
structure of cellulose is parallel or antiparallel, either the rates of growth
of the two tips of a microfibril may differ or two enzymes may be involved
in the final stage of cellulose microfibril formation. Either of these
alternatives has obstacles which will have to be resolved by future work.

The detailed molecular mechanism by which the tip of the microfibril grows is as yet uncertain and will be difficult to study chemically, because of the postulated lack of intermediates, or physically because of the small structures involved. All that can be stated safely at present is that some kind of screw dislocation type of whisker growth may be involved. A growth mechanism of this type can explain the asymmetric twisting of bacterial cellulose microfibrils during elongation (Colvin, 1961) and the limitation to longitudinal growth (Millman and Colvin, 1961). However, acceptance of such a growth mechanism as valid, immediately raises difficult problems about the mechanism of nucleation of new microfibrils which cannot be answered at present.

Mechanisms of Microfibril Orientation

A great deal of careful investigation has established that some of the orientation of cellulose microfibrils can be considered a physical response to some types of strain in the plant cell wall (Roelofsen, 1959). This response takes the form of movement of completed microfibrils during plastic deformation of an extending envelope and may be understood completely in terms of rheology. This type of orientation of cellulose microfibrils is now understood and will not be considered here. In additional examples, however, orientation of cellulose occurs either during or after deposition. A simple example is the mosaic of birefringent areas which appears in the cellulosic pellicle over a static culture of *A. xylinum* or *A. acetigenum*. The birefringence may be pronounced and is clear evidence of the orientation of bacterial cellulose microfibrils in the pellicle. Since the culture was static, the orientation cannot be attributed to strain within the pellicle and must have arisen from preferential orientation of the microfibrils in restricted areas. It is quite a plausible, but as yet unproved, assumption that the orientation of microfibrils completed first may have influenced the direction of deposition of the nuclei of new microfibrils or may have aligned newly formed longer microfibrils, by van der Waals forces. The operation of similar systems in green plants has been suggested (Setterfield and Bayley, 1961). In addition to these relatively easily understood cases, there remains a substantial number of well-documented instances of orientation of cellulose microfibrils which cannot be explained by strain or by lateral association of growing or completed microfibrils. Examples are the intricately coiled microfibrils in sieve plates and the sudden changes in the direction of microfibril orientation in the different layers of the secondary wall of many cells (Roelofsen, 1959) and the previously mentioned changes in direction of single microfibrils (Preston, 1959) within the same layer. Since some of these can be shown to occur deep within the wall and removed from the cytoplasm (Setterfield and Bayley, 1961), any direct physical intervention of the cell contents may be excluded. It is clear, nonetheless, that the often complex sequence of changes of orientation must be under cytoplasmic (and nuclear) control. As yet the mechanism of this control, in either a chemical or physical sense, is completely unknown. A recent suggestion that the orientation of microfibrils in the wall is controlled by the direction of long cytoplasmic elements which have the properties of plant spindle fibers only transposes the difficulty (Green, 1962). This fundamental problem of botany represents an intriguing challenge to physical biologists or biological physicists.

Résumé and Conclusions

The foregoing outlines briefly the divergent viewpoints presently held on various aspects of cellulose biosynthesis. In the following is presented the writer's estimate of the most useful general working hypothesis, based on present knowledge. This is done in the full expectation that future studies will modify not only details but principles.

Glucose molecules, either supplied exogenously or as a product of triose recombination from simpler substrates, are activated intracellularly through G-1-P to UDPG by conventional systems already described (Hassid et al., 1959; Neish, 1958b). The glucose residue is then transferred, still intracellularly (this includes the space within the bacterial cell envelope) to a lipid molecule with at least partial retention of the available free energy in the phosphate-glucose link. The lipid-glucose complex (perhaps with other components) then migrates from the intracellular phase through the bacterial cell wall (or cytoplasmic membrane) to the external medium or into the plant cell wall. Once outside the cell membrane, the glucose is transferred by an extracellular transglucosidase to the end of a 1→4 β-polyglucosan chain already incorporated into the tip of an insoluble cellulose microfibril. Polymerization and crystallization into a lattice may be simultaneous or nearly so. The lipid carrier is then readsorbed by the cell membrane to be reused in the same process, enabling the insoluble cellulose microfibrils to grow extremely long on a molecular scale. In some systems, these long microfibrils may be oriented by purely mechanical strain in the plant cell wall or by lateral association due to van der Waals force. In others, however, the cytoplasm of the cell must exert a directing influence on the local manner of deposition of a glucose residue in such a way that the direction of elongation of a microfibril is changed. How this influence or force is exerted is completely unknown at present.

In conclusion, you can see how far we have come from trees in the above résumé. I hope you will agree, however, that if we could solve some of the problems indicated, we should have a better insight into the manner of formation of at least one of the components of the wood of forest trees, and perhaps into the greater problem of botanical differentiation in general.

DISCUSSION

ALBERSHEIM: Growth at both ends does not necessarily support the idea of anti-parallel arrangement because there still could be two enzymes, one acting on the tail and one on the front end.

COLVIN: True, but let us make the simplest assumption first. This was an attempt to get basic information about the structure of the microfibril, which we cannot get from any other purely physical method. This indicates (not too surprisingly, considering the work on chitin) that the structure of the cellulose microfibril is truly antiparallel. This presents difficulties enzymologically, but we will just have to live with them.

ALBERSHEIM: Are there C_{27} or C_{28} gem-type alcohols in higher plants?

COLVIN: Not that I know of. These are very long alcohols for plants. This type of alcohol is fairly common in bacteria. As a matter of fact, there are reports for bacteria of alcohols with more than 60 carbon atoms in a chain. We do not know that they exist in higher plants; I am just extrapolating.

THIMANN: In the formula of your precursor, you show *two* hydroxyl groups. If it were just functioning as a glucose carrier, one might wonder why there should be a second one. Two years ago W. D. Stein (1961) pointed out that glucose could enter cells much more readily in the form of a dimer than as free glucose; it would be possible for two molecules to have most of their hydroxyl groups facing one another and the hydrogen atoms on the outside. The author adduced some data on the rate of entry of glucose and sorbitol into cells which was thought to support the dimer idea. Could this have any connection?

COLVIN: I do not know.

NEISH: The use of the second hydroxyl may be to provide water solubility.

COLVIN: The long nonpolar chain is preferentially soluble in lipid solvents but this has to work in an aqueous system. The hydroxyls may be necessary to give it sufficient solubility in both phases.

PRESTON: When you talked about lysed cells, did you imply that this is in the cell walls?

COLVIN: Yes.

PRESTON: If lysed bacteria are flattened and stacked and an X-ray photograph is taken with the beam parallel to the flattened faces, one can detect lipid chains lying normal to cell surface. In this way we found a lipid with 34 or 35 carbons, and a hydroxyl one-third of the way down.

COLVIN: We have done this sort of thing. Dr. Dennis has just completed an examination of a compacted mass of these, wet and lyphylized. Neither sample gave any evidence of periodicity.

THIMANN: From the bacterium's point of view this seems to be a rather inefficient use of lipid. How many of those molecules does it ever get back once they have gone out?

COLVIN: I should think most of them. It is a closed system and the question of efficiency does not matter for these bacteria. As you know, *A. xylinum* and *A. aceti-*

genum flourish only under conditions where the energy supply is not the limiting factor; for example, in molasses and sugar factories and in breweries.

WAREING: Crosby and Vlitos (1961) isolated from tobacco plants a growth-promoting substance which stimulated coleoptiles and proved to be l-docosanol. Could this be of some significance in relation to your observation?

COLVIN: We have just completed some work which may be related to this. Dr. Webb and I have a paper in press in which we showed that green plant extracts are able to stimulate the production of cellulose microfibrils from this organism by 300% (Webb and Colvin, 1963). We thought that we had a single factor but a fractionation by column chromatography and other means showed that we were not just dealing with one or two substances; we were dealing with a range of compounds. The evidence is that a number of compounds increase the permeability through the bacterial cell wall. l-docosanol would do this.

REFERENCES

Balashov, V., and Preston, R. D. (1955). *Nature* **176**, 64-65.

Benziman, M., and Burger-Rachamimov, H. (1962). *J. Bacteriol.* **84**, 625-630.

Bourne, E. J., and Weigel, H. (1954). *Chem. Ind. (London)*, p. 132.

Brown, A. M., and Gascoigne, J. A. (1960). *Nature* **187**, 1010-1011.

Brown, A. M. (1962). *J. Polymer Sci.* **59**, 155.

Colvin, J. R. (1959). *Nature* **183**, 1135-1136.

Colvin, J. R. (1961a). *Can. J. Biochem. Physiol.* **39**, 1921-1926.

Colvin, J. R. (1961b). *J. Polymer Sci.* **59**, 473-477.

Colvin, J. R. (1963). *J. Cell Biol.* **17**, 105-109.

Colvin, J. R., and Beer, M. (1960). *Can. J. Microbiol.* **6**, 631-637.

Colvin, J. R., Martin, S. M., and Dearing, G. G. (1961). *Can. J. Biochem. Physiol.* **39**, 493-497.

Crosby, D. G., and Vlitos, A. J. (1961). *In* "Plant Growth Regulation," pp. 57-69. Iowa State Univ. Press, Ames, Iowa.

Dennis, D. T., and Preston, R. D. (1961). *Nature* **191**, 667-668.

Gascoigne, J. A. (1963). *Chem. Ind. (London)*, p. 514.

Glaser, L. (1958). *J. Biol. Chem.* **232**, 627-636.

Green, P. B. (1962). *Science* **138**, 1404-1405.

Hassid, W. Z., Neufeld, E. F., and Feingold, D. S. (1959). *Proc. Natl. Acad. Sci. U.S.* **45**, 905-915.

Hess, K. (1928). "Die Chemie der Zellulose und ihrer Begleiter." Akademische Verlagsgesellschaft, Leipzig.

Hestrin, S. (1961). *Proc. 1st IUB/IUBS Intern. Symp., Stockholm 1960*, p. 317.

Husemann, E., and Werner, R. (1963). *Makromol. Chem.* **59**, 43-60.

Jackson, C. P., and Ramamurti, K. (1960). *Nature* **187**, 942-943.

Khan, A. W., and Colvin, J. R. (1961a). *J. Polymer Sci.* **51**, 1-9.

Khan, A. W., and Colvin, J. R. (1961b). *Science* **133**, 2014-2015.

Klungsöyr, S. (1960). *Nature* **185**, 104-105.

Margarie, C., and Péaud-Lenoël, C. (1961). *Biochim. Biophys. Acta* **47**, 275-287.

Millman, B., and Colvin, J. R. (1961). *Can. J. Microbiol.* **7**, 383-387.

Mühlethaler, K. (1949). *Biochim. Biophys. Acta* **3**, 527-535.

Neish, A. C. (1958a). *Proc. 4th Intern. Congr. Biochem. Vienna 1958*, pp. 82-91.

Neish, A. C. (1958b). *Can. J. Biochem. Physiol.* **36**, 187-193.

Ohad, I., Danon, D., and Hestrin, S. (1962). *J. Cell Biol.* **12**, 31-46.

Ott, E., Spurlin, H. M., and Grafflin, M. W. (1954). "Cellulose and Cellulose Derivatives," 2nd Ed. Wiley (Interscience), New York.
Preston, R. D. (1959). *Intern. Rev. Cytol.* 8, 33-60.
Roelofsen, P. A. (1959). *In* "Encyclopaedia of Plant Anatomy," Part 4, The Plant Cell Wall, 3 (Zimmermann, W., and Ozenda, P. G., eds.), Gebrüder Borntraeger, Berlin.
Setterfield, G., and Bayley, S. T. (1959). *Can. J. Botany* 37, 861-870.
Setterfield, G., and Bayley, S. T. (1961). *Ann. Rev. Plant Physiol.* 12, 35-62.
Stein, W. D. (1961). *Nature* 191, 1277-1280.
Stone, B. A. (1958). *Nature* 182, 687-690.
Webb, T. E., and Colvin, J. R. (1963). *Can. J. Biochem. Physiol.* (in press).
Weigl, J. (1961). *Arkiv. Mikrobiol.* 38, 350-366.
White, G. A., and Wang, C. H. (1963). Dissimulation of glucose and gluconate by *Acetobacter xylinum, Abstracts for 47th Annual Meeting, Federation of American Societies for Experimental Biology.*

The Formation of Lignin in the Tissue and in Vitro

KARL FREUDENBERG

*Forschungsinstitut für die Chemie des Holzes und
der Polysaccharide, Organisch-Chemisches Institut
der Universität Heidelberg, Germany*

What prompted me to attempt to elucidate the constitution of lignin was some early work on cellulose (Freudenberg, 1921). Experiments on the yield of cellobiose, carried out from 1920 onward, convinced me that in the cellulose molecule each individual glucose unit is linked to its neighbors in precisely the same manner as in cellobiose. Staudinger and Haworth later continued research along the same lines. Because cellulose had such an orderly constitution, I argued that the second most abundant individual organic substance in nature, namely lignin, should also exhibit a logical architecture and should not be a random conglomeration.

It took a long time to find the key. Lignin is a highly condensed material, and most degradation experiments were unsuccessful.

Lignin occurs in nature in a proportion to cellulose as 60 to 100.

In the following, unless indicated otherwise, the discussion will be restricted to lignin from spruce, *Picea excelsa* (abies) (Freudenberg, 1962a, b).

In spring the cambium and surrounding tissues become filled with sap; we call it cambial sap. It contains abundant amounts of the glucoside coniferin (IV). Recently, small amounts of *p*-glucocoumaryl alcohol (II) and syringin (VI) were found in accompaniment (Freudenberg and Harkin, 1963). When phenylalanine-β-C^{14} is introduced into 1- or 2-year-old twigs by immersing the trimmed needles of their shoots (Freudenberg *et al.*, 1955) in a solution of the tracer, then a small quantity of glucocoumaryl alcohol (II) and coniferin (IV) can be isolated in radioactive form by extracting the twigs within a day or two (Freudenberg and Torres-Serres, 1963). This does not imply that in the trees

203

the three glucosides must be formed exclusively from phenylalanine, for this is only one representative of a whole group of C_6–C_3 acids which

α   H₂COH

β   CH

γ   CH

R″ ⟋⟍ R′

OR

(I) R, R′, R″ = H: p-Coumaryl alcohol

(II) R = $C_6H_{11}O_5$, R′, R″ = H: Glucocoumaryl alcohol

(III) R, R″ = H, R′ = OCH_3: Coniferyl alcohol

(IV) R = $C_6H_{11}O_5$, R′ = OCH_3; R″ = H: Coniferin

(V) R = H, R′, R″ = OCH_3: Sinapyl alcohol

(VI) R = $C_6H_{11}O_5$, R′, R″ = OCH_3: Syringin

COgluc ‖ CH

(VII) Indican

serve as precursors for p-hydroxycinnamic alcohols. Apart from the three glucosides, small amounts of coniferyl alcohol (III) and of some of its dimeric dehydrogenation products have also been found in cambial sap (Freudenberg and Harkin, 1963). These will be discussed later. The three glucosides, particularly the coniferin, presumably form a reservoir which cannot be attacked by the phenol dehydrogenases which initiate lignification in the layers of cells between the cambium and the mature wood. If radioactive D-coniferin is introduced into young twigs, then radioactive lignin is formed (Freudenberg and Bittner, 1953; Freudenberg et al., 1955). L-Coniferin made from L-glucose and radioactive coniferyl alcohol is not metabolized to form lignin (Freudenberg et al., 1955). Radioactive lignin is also produced when shikimic acid or the C_6–C_3 acids are introduced into spruce in radioactive form (Acerbo et al., 1958; Brown, 1961; Brown and Neish, 1955, 1956; Brown et al., 1953, 1955; Eberhardt and Schubert, 1956; Freudenberg, 1956; Freudenberg and Lehmann, 1963; Freudenberg and Niedercorn, 1956; Freudenberg et al., 1958; Kratzl, 1961a, b; Kratzl and Billeck, 1959; Kratzl et al., 1959). In this case it is necessary to give the plant—here spruce—enough time to go beyond the stage of the p-hydroxycinnamic alcohols or of the glucosides to form lignin. Among the enzymes in cambial sap of spruce (Freudenberg et al., 1958) there is a plentiful supply of laccase and some peroxidase.

These two phenol dehydrogenases appear to permeate the whole of the living tissue in the cambium zone. Although these oxidases do not attack the three glucosides, they can convert the corresponding aglycones into lignin. Hence, a β-glucosidase ought to be encountered somewhere along the route leading to lignin, and has in fact been found (Freudenberg *et al.*, 1955).

Figure 1 shows a photograph of a section through a 1-year-old *Araucaria* stem, the red color indicating staining of lignin by phloroglucinol and hydrochloric acid. It can be seen that the reddening in-

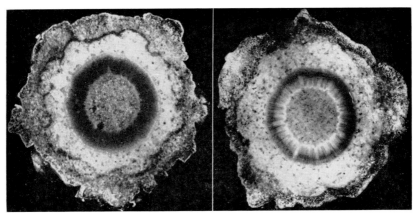

Figs. 1. and 2. Transverse section through a 1-year-old stem of *Araucaria excelsa.* Fig. 1. (*Left*) Stained with phloroglucinol–hydrochloric acid (red). Fig. 2. (*Right*) Treated with indican (blue).

creases gradually from the cambium inwards, attaining its maximum intensity in the mature wood cells. In order to detect the glucosidase, indican (VII) was applied (Freudenberg *et al.*, 1952); this is hydrolyzed into glucose and indoxyl, which is oxidized by air into indigo, indicating the location of glucosidase by its blue coloration (Fig. 2). We see that the main amount of glucosidase is concentrated in the proximity of the cambium, whereas the only glucosidase to be seen in the wood lying further inside is in the medullary rays. The familiar lignified zone in the bark is also to be seen in the red-stained section. A corresponding glucosidase zone is also observable in the blue-stained section.

My botanist friends were so kind as to examine the process more precisely under the microscope and prepared a schematic drawing (Fig. 3) (Freudenberg *et al.*, 1955). The center of the drawing represents the untreated section. The mature wood is on the extreme right, on the left of this are the cells engaged in lignification, and further left are young, nonlignified cells. Then comes the cambium, identifiable by its cell nuclei, and on its left are the cells forming the transition to the bark. The lower drawing is that of the section stained red with phloroglucinol and hydrochloric acid. The upper drawing represents the indigo blue effect showing the position of the glucosidase; it is strongly localized in in the cells. No glucosidase is detectable in the mature wood cells, but there is plenty in the cells undergoing lignification; again, there is none in the youngest cells at the cambium. This makes the process of lignification clear; when the glucosides reach the glucosidase, they are hydrolyzed, and their aglycones, the three p-hydroxycinnamyl alcohols

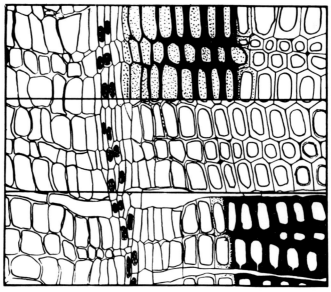

FIG. 3.   Schematic representation of a transverse section through the cambium of a conifer; the cambium is recognizable by the presence of nuclei in the cells. Upper: Blue reaction with indican. Center: Untreated. Lower: stained (red) with phloroglucinol–hydrochloric acid.

(I, III, V), are attacked by the abundant dehydrogenases present, and converted into lignin. When the cell walls become stopped up, the cell dies off.

The radioautogram shown in Fig. 4 indicates how well phenylalanine is transformed into lignin. Radioactive phenylalanine was administered to spruce shoots in early June, after a few layers of cells were already formed, and is incorporated into the lignin of a few rows of cells within the next few days. Afterwards nonradioactive wood continues to grow, displacing the cambium outwards.

Now I want to discuss the phenomenon just mentioned, namely the conversion of p-hydroxycinnamic alcohols into lignin by phenol dehydrogenases. It must not only be proved that they are transformed into lignin but also how this comes about and what the structure of lignin is like.

Nowadays, it is possible to extract from wood lignin preparations that are suitable for chemical investigation. Björkman has shown that extremely fine milling of wood in a liquid which does not cause the wood fibers to swell liberates a large proportion of the lignin in a form that is soluble in aqueous acetone or dioxan. The product is made up of

FIG. 4.   Radioautogram of a transverse section through a young conifer shoot after administration of radioactive L-phenylalanine. From right to left: wood from preceding year; wood formed early in the year of experiment; radioactive deposits; wood formed after experiment; cambium.

fragments of larger lignin molecules which are normally insoluble because of their size and attachment to polysaccharides. As soon as the mechanical degradation reduces the degree of polymerization to about 50 or less, the lignin becomes soluble in these solvents in the cold.

The elemental composition of spruce lignin as the average of numerous analyses is $C_9H_{7.25}O_2[H_2O]_{0.4}[OCH_3]_{0.92}$. The mixture of alcohols on which lignin is based consists of ca. 14 mole % p-coumaryl alcohol I, 80 mole % coniferyl alcohol III, and 6 mole % sinapyl alcohol V (Freudenberg, 1962a, b; Freudenberg *et al.*, 1962); this has the average composition $C_9H_{9.08}O_2[OCH_3]_{0.92}$. It can be seen by subtraction that the lignin has lost about 1.8 atoms of hydrogen and gained about 0.4 molecule of water compared to the hydroxycinnamic alcohol mixture. This will be explained later on.

If this alcohol mixture is oxidized with laccase at room temperature and at pH 5.5 in extremely dilute solution in the presence of air; a flocculent precipitate of a buff-colored substance is formed, which has all the properties of lignin and has the same composition as natural lignin (Freudenberg, 1949, 1962b). The oxidation can also be effected with peroxidase and extremely dilute hydrogen peroxide. Thus, now we have lignin preparations available from natural and synthetic sources for purposes of comparison.

The identity of natural and synthetic lignin covers all of the reactions involving functional groups, such as the content of phenolic and aliphatic hydroxyl groups, the strength of the methoxyl ethers, the extremely low olefinic double bond and aldehyde content, the ketonic carbonyl content, lactone content, etc. Their infrared spectra are superimposable.

Recently, we have succeeded in finding another proof for the basic identity between natural conifer lignin and synthetic lignin (Freudenberg et al., 1962). When either is methylated, treated with hot concentrated alkali to split some of the ether bonds, remethylated, and oxidized, 24 degradation products are obtained (VIII–XXXI). Twenty of these are methoxylated benzenecarboxylic acids (including surprisingly four o-phthalic acids) or biphenyldicarboxylic acids, and at least one is a methoxylated carboxylic derivative of a diphenyl ether. Succinic acid, tricarballylic acid, and benzenepentacarboxylic acid are also found. The weight of identified degradation products is 20% of that of the lignin used.

(VIII) R′, R″, R‴ = H; R = CO₂H   Anisic acid
(IX) R′, R″, R‴ = H; R = CO·CO₂H   Anisoylformic acid
(X) R, R′, R‴ = H; R″ = CO₂H   2-Methoxybenzoic acid
(XI) R″, R‴ = H; R, R′ = CO₂H   4-Methoxyphthalic acid
(XII) R′, R‴ = H; R R″ = CO₂H   4-Methoxyisophthalic acid
(XIII) R′ = H; R, R″, R‴ = CO₂H   Methoxytrimesic acid

(XIV) R, R′, R″, R‴ = H   Veratrole
(XV) R′, R″, R‴ = H; R = CHO   Veratraldehyde
(XVI) R′, R″, R‴ = H; R = COCH₃   Acetoveratrone
(XVII) R′, R″, R‴ = H; R = CO₂H   Veratric acid
(XVIII) R, R′, R″ = H; R‴ = CO₂H   o-Veratric acid
(XIX) R″, R‴ = H; R, R′ = CO₂H   Hemipinic acid
(XX) R′, R‴ = H; R, R″ = CO₂H   Metahemipinic acid
(XXI) R′, R″ = H; R, R‴ = CO₂H   Isohemipinic acid

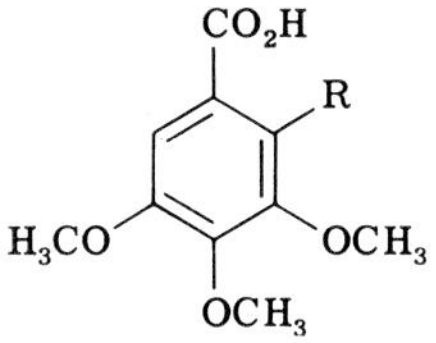

(XXII) R = H   Tri-*O*-methylgallic acid

(XXIII) R = CO_2H Trimethoxyphthalic acid

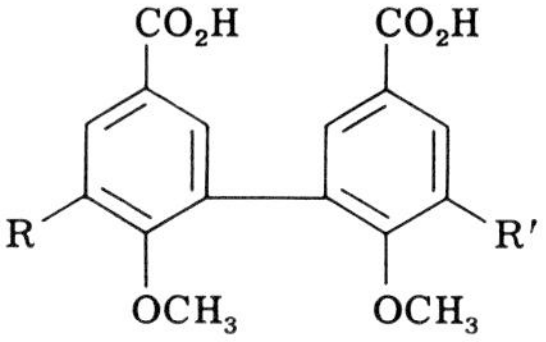

(XXIV) R, R' = H   Dehydrodianisic acid

(XXV) R = H; R' = OCH_3 2,3,2'-Trimethoxybiphenyl-5,5'-dicarboxylic acid

(XXVI) R, R' = OCH_3 Dehydrodiveratric acid

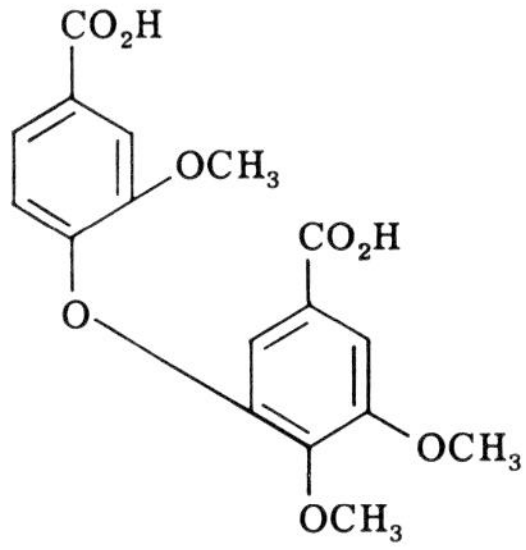

(XXVII)   3,4-Dimethoxy-5-(2-methoxy-4-carboxyphenoxy)-benzoic acid

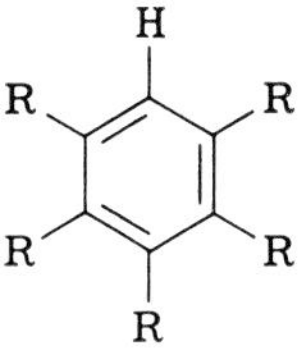

(XXVIII) R = CO_2H Benzenepentacarboxylic acid

(XXIX)   Succinic acid

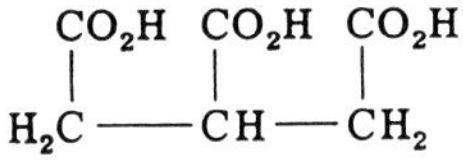

(XXX)   Tricarballylic acid

(XXXI)   Oxalic acid

These acids are derived from a highly complex condensed system, and hence it is not surprising that their yield is low. What is important is the fact that the mixture of acids is exactly the same irrespective of whether natural or synthetic lignin is used. The identity is not only with respect to the nature of the acids—not a single one more or less occurs with synthetic lignin than with natural lignin—but also with respect to the relative yield, which ranges from 9% for veratric acid down to 0.1% or less for many of the other acids. The major amount of degradation compounds comes from coniferyl residues (XIV–XXI, XXV–XXVII). The quantity of acids derived from *p*-coumaryl alcohol (VIII–XIII, XXIV, XXV) is much less, and that from sinapyl alcohol (XXII, XXIII) less again.

Naturally, a constitutional formula for lignin cannot be worked out from the information derived from these acids. This is not even possible with detailed knowledge from estimations of the functional groups in lignin. All these analytical data must of course be reflected in any draft of a formula for lignin, but they do not themselves suffice for constructing a formula of this type.

Comparison of synthetic and natural lignins indicated the manner in which natural lignin is produced in the plant, but not how the coniferyl alcohol units are linked together therein. Once again any pathway for elucidating the constitution of lignin still seemed to be inaccessible.

However, the information about the structure of natural polymers

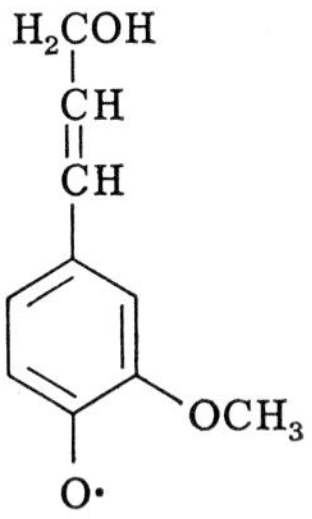

R α

(XXXII)

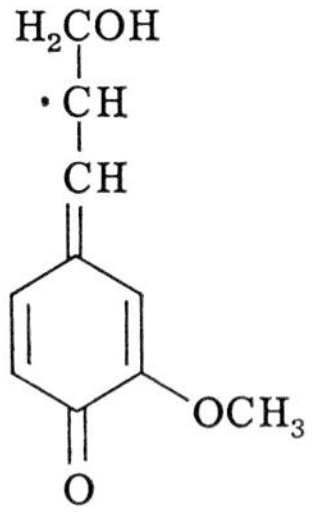

R β

(XXXIII)

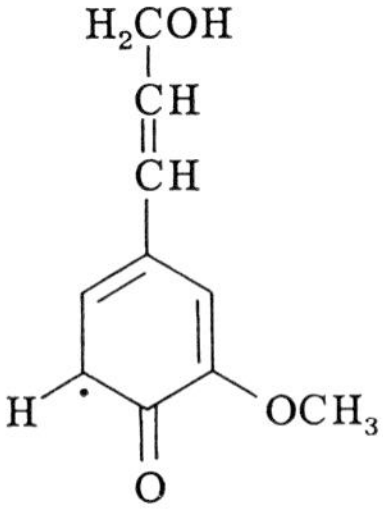

R γ

(XXXIV)

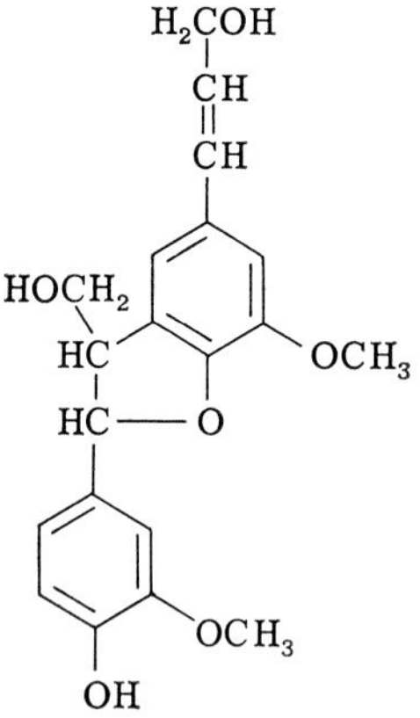

Dehydrodiconi-
feryl alcohol

(XXXV)

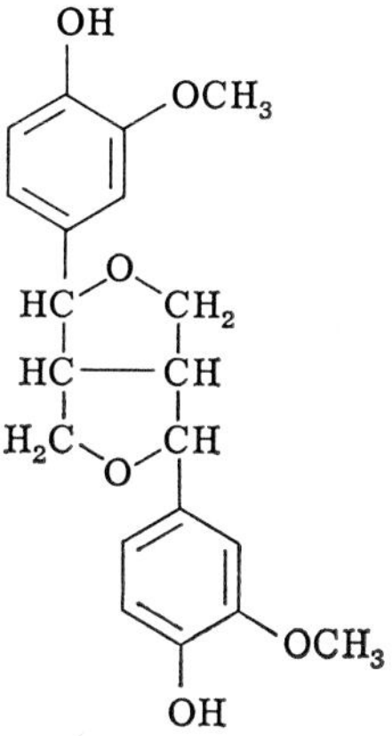

Pino-
resinol

(XXXVI)

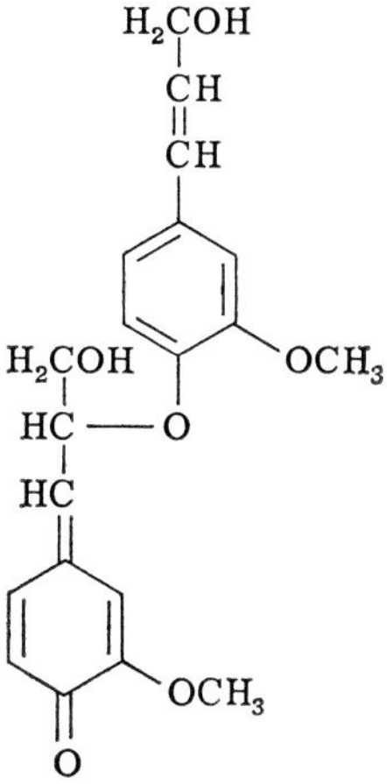

Quinone
methide

(XXXVII)

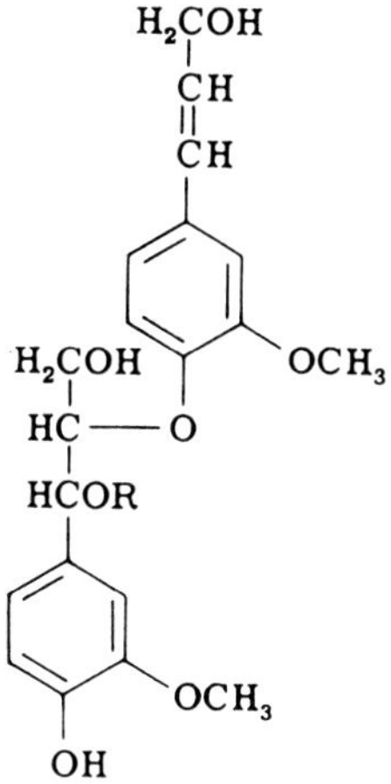

(**XXXVIII**) R = H: Guaiacylglycerolconiferyl ether

(**XXXIX**) R =

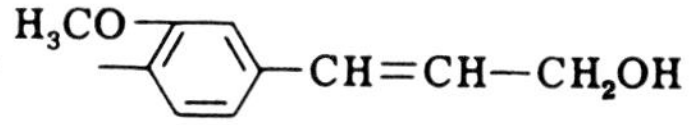

Guaiacylglycerolbisconiferyl ether

(**XXXX**) R = $C_{12}H_{21}O_{10}$
Saccharose ether of (**XXXVIII**)

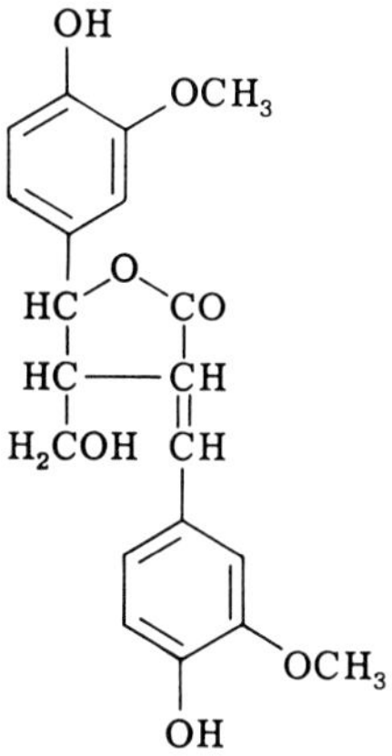

Lignenolide

(**XXXXI**)

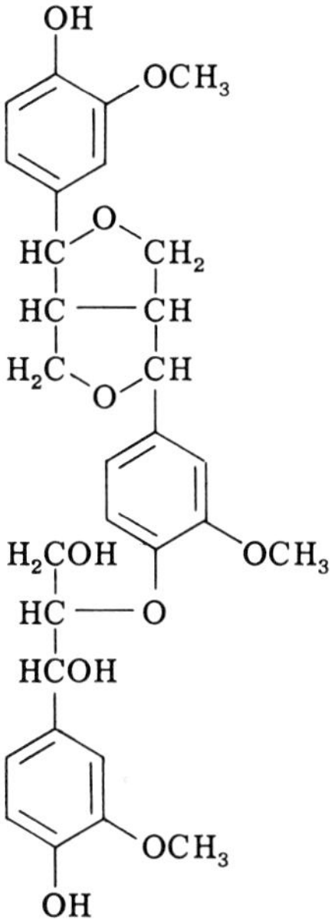

Guaiacylglycerol-
pinoresinol ether

(**XXXXII**)

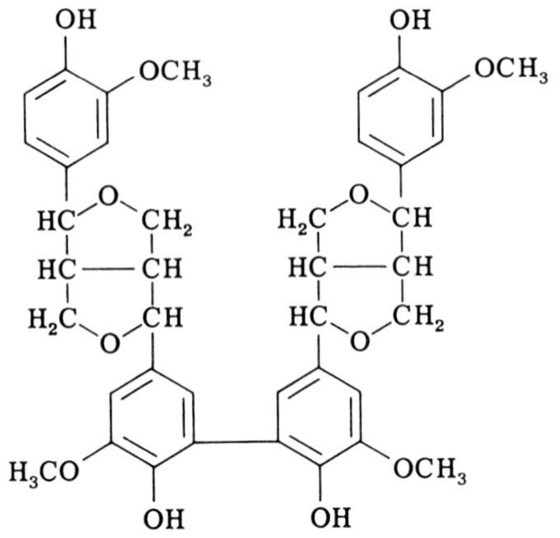

Bisdehydropinoresinol

(XXXXIII)

that is normally obtained by degradation can be gained here by bio-synthesis. In 1952, the first intermediate of the biosynthesis was isolated after carrying out only a partial dehydrogenation (Freudenberg and Hübner, 1952). This was dehydrodiconiferyl alcohol (XXXV). In the following decade, over twenty such intermediates have been identified after separation from the mixture of some 36 products which are formed on dehydrogenation of coniferyl alcohol alone. It would take too long to describe them all. Hence, only the mechanisms of their formation will be discussed. These mechanisms can be deduced from the structures of the intermediates formed.

The coniferyl alcohol is dehydrogenated at the phenolic hydroxyl group. A mesomeric radical is formed with limiting structures such as the aroxyl form R_α (XXXII), the p-quinone methide radical R_β (XXXIII), and the orthoquinonoid form R_γ (XXXIV); these structures can be derived from those of their subsequent products; R_β is strongly favored.

The three mesomeric radicals then intercombine. Combination of R_β and R_γ gives a quinone methide which is stabilized by intramolecular prototropy to give dehydrodiconiferyl alcohol (XXXV). Two R_β units give a double quinone methide which undergoes a double prototropy to give pinoresinol (XXXVI). Two R_γ units combine analogously to give a biphenyl derivative. However, the most important reaction is that between R_β and R_α, which leads to a quinone methide (XXXVII) which cannot react intramolecularly with hydroxyl groups. This quinone methide and others like it are fairly stable. They are yellow and can be identified by their absorptions using a rapidly registering spectrograph. The half-life of (XXXVII) in a 9:1 dioxan/water mixture is 1 hour at 20°. This quinone methide normally reacts preferentially with water to give an adduct, guaiacylglycerol-β-coniferyl ether (XXXVIII). This explains the fact mentioned above that lignin contains more water than the original *p*-hydroxycinnamyl alcohols. Among the other dimers isolated, only the lignenolide (XXXXI) (Freudenberg and Geiger, 1963) might be mentioned here, because it has the important property of being convertible into a cyclolignene. It is the main source of the benzenepentacarboxylic acid among the oxidation products of lignin and may contribute in part to the formation of the *o*-phthalic acids.

In spite of the participation of enzymes, the radicals are symmetrical. All subsequent products including lignin itself are therefore optically inactive.

All the dimeric intermediates formed are phenols, which can also be dehydrogenated by laccase to form radicals, which combine together or with the monomeric radicals. A typical product is then the trimer guaiacylglycerol-β-pinoresinol ether (XXXXII) (Freudenberg and Nimz, 1962). Six trimers have so far been identified. After further dehydrogenation, the dimers can combine to form tetramers, as is proven by the formation of bisdehydropinoresinol (XXXXIII) (Freudenberg and Sakakibara, 1959). Thus, we know that coniferyl alcohol is condensed by dehydrogenation and that the phenolic dimers produced are then also dehydrogenated and condensed. We can call this process of molecular growth "progressive dehydrogenation."

However, anomalous reactions start to occur even during this dehydrogenation stage. It has been indicated how the dehydrogenation constitutes removal of the phenolic hydrogen to form mesomeric radicals. This does not give an adequate explanation for the occurrence of four *o*-phthalic acid derivatives among our degradation acids. Coniferyl alcohol obviously reacts as if some of the radicals are located on carbon atoms 2 or 6 [see numbering in formula (III)]. This can be readily observed by dehydrogenating deuterated coniferyl alcohol. 5-Deuteroconiferyl alcohol loses 45% of its deuterium on dehydrogenative polymerization (Freudenberg *et al.*, 1961; Freudenberg and Jovanović, 1963). 6-Deuteroconiferyl alcohol loses 7%, and the 2-deutero compound loses 4%—just on the borderline of detectability. These results agree with the formation of the phthalic acids. Eugen Müller *et al.* (1960) have discussed mesomeric structures of aroxyl radicals with increased electron concentrations in the *meta* position to the oxygen. Another possible assumption involves a hypothetical radical, which can undergo substitution in the 2 or 6 position via a dienone-to-phenol rearrangement. However, assumption of an inter- or intramolecular radical exchange involving positions 2 and 6 seems more plausible. It is beyond doubt that rapid radical exchange occurs between dehydrogenated phenols and nondehydrogenated ones. No matter what the mechanism may be, structural elements such as (XXXXIV) and (XXXXV) must be assumed from the occurrence of the o-phthalic acids and from the experiments with labeled coniferyl alcohol.

Another condensation, leading to branching, occurs with the quinone methides, which play a central part in the formation of lignin. Two intermediates have been isolated from the dehydrogenation products of coniferyl alcohol that have been formed in no mean amounts by addition of phenols onto the quinone methide (XXXVII) without further loss of hydrogen (Freudenberg and Friedmann, 1960). One is the adduct of coniferyl alcohol itself, namely guaiacylglycerol-β,γ-bisconiferyl ether (XXXIX); the other is the adduct of preformed dehydrodiconiferyl alcohol (XXXV) onto (XXXVII). This reaction forms a new type of

(XXXXIV)   (XXXXV)

bond in lignin, namely γ-aryl ether linkages. The occurrence of such benzylaryl ethers in lignin has recently been confirmed. They explain that, as mentioned above, not quite 2 hydrogen atoms are lost when the p-hydroxycinnamic alcohols are transformed into lignin.

This mode of growth in lignin is particularly important because it can link large preformed blocks together. The adducts are not restricted to phenols; alcohols also add on to quinone methides. The most interesting in this group are the saccharides. If coniferyl alcohol is dehydrogenated enzymically in a concentrated solution of sucrose (Freudenberg and Grion, 1959; Freudenberg and Harkin, 1960), adducts like (XXXX) of the sugar onto the quinone methide (XXXVII) can be isolated. These are not glycosides, but ethers of the sucrose with lignin components. (XXXX) is a readily hydrolyzable γ-sucryl ether of guaiacylglycerol-β-coniferyl ether (XXXVIII). This type of product is also phenolic and would be stabilized by being built into the lignin polymer by further dehydrogenative condensations. The polysaccharides in the cell walls are undoubtedly capable of reacting similarly. This shows the way in which lignin becomes grafted onto the saccharides in the cell wall.

The quinone methides can undergo yet another mode of reaction to increase the molecular size. It has been shown that the quinone methide (XXXVII) and other model substances polymerize readily to give chains of benzylaryl ethers (Freudenberg *et al.*, 1963). It is plausible that, during the long period when the lignin is lying in the wood, the presence of weak acids cause these ethers to rearrange, the benzyl carbon atom being condensed with the position ortho to the phenolic group in the neighboring benzene nucleus. This reaction has also been studied on models. It is the third way in which the lignin molecule grows.

As the structures of our intermediates were identified one after the other over the past few years, and as the principles of lignification were recognized, more or less successful attempts were made by various authors to combine these units together to construct a constitutional formula for lignin. We ourselves also followed their example (Freudenberg, 1962b). We then noticed that the randomness is kept within strict limits when the proportions of the structural units, the elemental composition of lignin, and the quantitative ratios of the functional groups are taken into account. In this work, the method of biosynthesis which was placed in the forefront of the discussion above has been afforded ample support by analyses of lignin, a field in which the Swedish school has been particularly active in the past decades (cf. Adler, 1961).

Hardwood lignin contains more methoxyl than conifer lignin. The proportion of the alcohols from which beech wood lignin is derived is estimated to be (Freudenberg and Sidhu, 1961):

p-Coumaryl alcohol (I) 8%
Coniferyl alcohol (III) 48%
Sinapyl alcohol (V) 44%

Other hardwood lignins seem to have similar compositions; their methoxyl content is generally higher ($> 21\%$) than that of conifers (ca. 14%). In spite of this difference, hardwood lignin is probably built up on the same principles as conifer lignin. The proportions of the three alcohols in lignin from Gramineae is still very uncertain; a mixture of 30% p-coumaryl, 50% coniferyl, and 20% sinapyl alcohol would provide a reasonable figure.

On oxidation with nitrobenzene, conifer lignin yields vanillin, hardwood lignin yields vanillin and syringaldehyde (methoxyvanillin), and Gramineae lignin yields p-hydroxybenzaldehyde, vanillin, and syringaldehyde. Very small amounts of aldehydes were obtained from *Sphagnum fuscum* (Lindberg and Theander, 1952). They consisted of *p*-hydroxybenzaldehyde with a little vanillin and traces of syringaldehyde. However, there are some peculiarities (Creighton *et al.*, 1944; cf. Holmberg, 1934). *Pteridium latiusculum* and *Podocarpus acutifolius* and *Macrophyllus* give results similar to those for conifers, whereas *Podocarpus amarus* and *pedunculatus* and *Tetraclinis articulata* yield both vanillin and syringaldehyde. Vanillin and syringaldehyde have also been obtained in various yields from *Liriodendron tulipifera*, *Trochodendron* sp., *Drimys winteri*, *Belliolum haplopus*, *Zygogynum vieillardi*, *Ephedra trifurca*, *Gnetum indicum*, *Dracaena fragrans* (?), and *Aloe abyssinica*.

Thus, lignin has, as originally supposed, a methodical architecture. Like other polymolecules it is derived from single units, namely the three dehydrogenated *p*-hydroxycinnamyl alcohols, but these combine via mesomeric forms with different types of bonds at different points of attachment and without a definite sequence. The polymolecule grows simultaneously in at least three different ways. In these respects, lignin has a unique position among high polymers.

DISCUSSION

NEISH: Do you think that in angiosperm lignin, polymerization occurs before introduction of methoxyl groups? I have come to that conclusion.

FREUDENBERG: I do not think so. Syringin has been found in a number of hardwoods. In spruce cambium coniferin is present together with small amounts of glucocoumaryl alcohol and syringin.

NEISH: What happens if ferulic acid is added to one of these mixtures when you are making synthetic lignin?

FREUDENBERG: It is incorporated. It is a normal product among the dehydrogenation products. First, coniferyl aldehyde is formed by dehydrogenation of coniferyl alcohol, and from coniferyl aldehyde, ferulic acid. Intermediates like (XXXXI) are formed by dehydrogenation of a mixture of coniferyl alcohol and ferulic acid; they are responsible for the presence of lactone groups in lignin. These dimeric lactones are very closely related to many lignans, such as conidendrin, etc.

THIMANN: Helen Stafford (1960) in her experiments on grasses, found that she got the most natural deposition of lignin by feeding ferulic acid, that is, the lignin most closely resembled the natural lignin of the same plant. Other materials like eugenol gave very abnormal lignin.

FREUDENBERG: A mixture of coniferyl alcohol and ferulic acid gives quite reasonable substances. The ferulic acid content is extremely low in normal lignin.

ZIEGLER: Do you think that the glucosides, coniferin, and syringin are in the cambial initials, or are they synthesized in the undifferentiated xylem cells derived from the cambium? Can coniferin and syringin still be found in the cambium when xylem formation has ceased in autumn, when the fully differentiated xylem cells adjoin the initials?

FREUDENBERG: I only know that syringin is present in the bark of Oleaceae, *Ligustrum*, for instance, or *Syringa* itself, even in the winter. Whereas coniferin is scarcely present in the winter in the bark or in the cambium of spruce.

ZIEGLER: There are some rows of cells between the initials and the cells where the glucosidase begins to be active. Would it be possible for the glucosides to be synthesized from translocation products in these cells rather than in the initials? We are sure that glucosides do not move in the phloem in appreciable amounts.

FREUDENBERG: I am not familiar with the location of the synthesis of the glucosides. Dr. Neish may know more about the transformation of cinnamic acid into coniferin. At least six or seven processes are needed for this transformation. It occurs very quickly.

REFERENCES

Acerbo, S. N., Schubert, W. J., and Nord, F. F. (1958). *J. Am. Chem. Soc.* **80**, 1990-1992.

Adler, E. (1961). *Paperi Puu* **43**, 634-643.

Brown, S. A. (1961). *Science* **134**, 305-313.

Brown, S. A., and Neish, A. C. (1955). *Nature* **175**, 688-689.

Brown, S. A., and Neish, A. C. (1956). *Can. J. Biochem. Physiol.* **34**, 769-778.

Brown, S. A., Tanner, G. K., and Stone, J. E. (1953). *Can. J. Chem.* **31**, 755-760.

Brown, S. A., Neish, A. C., Claire, F. H., and Chisholm, M. D. (1955). *Can. J. Biochem. Physiol.* **33**, 948-962.

Creighton, R. H. J., Gibbs, R. D., and Hibbert, H. (1944). *J. Am. Chem. Soc.* **66**, 32-37.

Eberhardt, G., and Schubert, W. J. (1956). *J. Am. Chem. Soc.* **78**, 2835-2839.

Freudenberg, K. (1921). *Ber. Deut. Chem. Ges.* **54**, 767-772.

Freudenberg, K. (1949). *Sitzber. Heidelberg. Akad. Wiss., Abhandl.* **5**, 151-158.

Freudenberg, K. (1956). *Angew. Chem.* **68**, 508-512.

Freudenberg, K. (1962a). *In* "Advances in the Chemistry of Organic Natural Products" (L. Zechmeister, ed.), Vol. 20, pp. 41-72, Springer, Vienna.

Freudenberg, K. (1962b). *Pure Appl. Chem.* **5**, 9-20.

Freudenberg, K., and Bittner, F. (1953). *Chem. Ber.* **86**, 155-159.

Freudenberg, K., and Friedmann, M. (1960). *Chem. Ber.* **93**, 2138-2148.

Freudenberg, K., and Geiger, H. (1963). *Chem. Ber.* **96**, 1265-1270.

Freudenberg, K., and Grion, G. (1959). *Chem. Ber.* **92**, 1355-1363.

Freudenberg, K., and Harkin, J. M. (1960). *Chem. Ber.* **93**, 2814-2819.

Freudenberg, K., and Harkin, J. M. (1963). *Phytochemistry* **2**, 189-193.

Freudenberg, K., and Hübner, H. H. (1952). *Chem. Ber.* **85**, 1181-1191.

Freudenberg, K., and Jovanović, V. (1963). *Chem. Ber.* **96**, 2178-2181.

Freudenberg, K., and Lehmann, B. (1963). *Chem. Ber.* **96**, 1844-1849.

Freudenberg, K., and Niedercorn, F. (1956). *Chem., Ber.* **89**, 2168-2173.

Freudenberg, K., and Nimz, H. (1962). *Chem. Ber.* **95**, 2057-2062.

Freudenberg, K., and Sakakibara, A. (1959). *Ann. Chem.* **623**, 129-137.

Freudenberg, K., and Sidhu, G. S. (1961). *Holzforschung* **15**, 33-39.

Freudenberg, K., and Torres-Serres, J. (1963). Unpublished.

Freudenberg, K., Reznik, H., Boesenberg, H., and Rasenack, D. (1952). *Chem. Ber.* **85**, 641-647.

Freudenberg, K., Reznik, H., Fuchs, W., and Reichert, M. (1955). *Naturwissenschaften* **42**, 29-35.

Freudenberg, K., Harkin, J. M., Reichert, M., and Fukuzumi, T. (1958). *Chem. Ber.* **91**, 581-590.

Freudenberg, K., Jovanović, V., and Topfmeier, F. (1961). *Chem. Ber.* **94**, 3227-3238.

Freudenberg, K., Chen, C.-L., and Cardinale, G. (1962). *Chem. Ber.* **95**, 2814-2828.

Freudenberg, K., Harkin, J. M., and Werner, H.-K. (1963). Unpublished.

Holmberg, B. (1934). *Ing. Vetenskaps Akad. Handl. N.* **131**, 1-85.

Kratzl, K. (1961a). *Paperi Puu* **43**, 643-653.

Kratzl, K. (1961b). *Holz Roh- Werkstoff* **19**, 219-232.

Kratzl, K., and Billeck, G. (1959). *Monatsh. Chem.* **90**, 536-543.

Kratzl, K., Kisser, K. W., Graf, A., and Hofbauer, G. (1959). *Monatsh. Chem.* **90**, 526-535.

Lindberg, B., and Theander, O. (1952). *Acta Chem. Scand.* **6**, 311-312.

Müller, E., Schick, A., Mayer, R., and Scheffler, K. (1960). *Chem. Ber.* **93**, 2649-2668.

Stafford, H. (1960). *Plant Physiol.* **35**, 108-114.

Cinnamic Acid Derivatives as Intermediates in the Biosynthesis of Lignin and Related Compounds

A. C. NEISH

Atlantic Regional Laboratory, National Research Council of Canada, Halifax, Nova Scotia

Introduction

Development of the isotopic tracer technique has resulted in a considerable amount of research on the biosynthesis of lignin and related compounds during the past decade. An unbiased review of much of this work is to be found in the recent book of Brauns and Brauns (1960). More recent reviews have been contributed by Freudenberg (1959a, b, 1960), Reznik (1960), Neish (1960), Watkin *et al.* (1960), Brown (1961a), and Grisebach and Ollis (1961).

These tracer investigations have shown that the aromatic amino acids (phenylalanine and tyrosine) may function as precursors of compounds such as lignin, flavonoids, coumarins, acetophenones, and aromatic alkaloids. A great deal is known concerning the steps involved in biosynthesis of the aromatic amino acids in microorganisms, mainly because of studies with biochemical mutants (Davis, 1955, 1958). Tracer studies suggest that higher plants and microorganisms synthesize these amino acids in essentially the same manner (McCalla and Neish, 1959a; Gamborg and Neish, 1959; Wightman *et al.*, 1961). Experiments with C^{14}-labeled compounds have also provided support for the theory that cinnamic acid and certain naturally occurring cinnamic acid derivatives (i.e., *p*-coumaric, caffeic, ferulic, and sinapic acids) are intermediates in the conversion of the aromatic amino acids into lignin and related compounds. Studies with newly discovered enzymes by Koukol and Conn (1961) and by Neish (1961) have given support to this concept and have also helped to explain why phenylalanine can be converted readily to

219

lignin in all species tested whereas tyrosine is rapidly utilized, for this purpose, only by certain species.

This paper is concerned primarily with a discussion of evidence supporting the hypothetical scheme shown in Fig. 1. Reznik (1960) has proposed and discussed a similar scheme. The chief point to be empha-

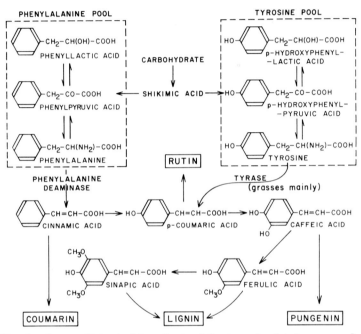

FIG. 1. Intermediates in biosynthesis of lignin and related compounds.

sized is that the cinnamic acid derivatives are derived from the aromatic amino acids and serve as intermediates in the biosynthesis of a number of phenolic metabolites, peculiar to plants; i.e., lignin, flavonoids, coumarins, etc. The actual mechanism for converting the cinnamic acid derivatives to lignin will not be considered in detail here since work on formation of lignin is reviewed elsewhere in this symposium by Professor Freudenberg.

Tracer Experiments

GENERAL

The scheme in Fig. 1 is based mainly on comparison of the efficiencies of a number of C^{14}-labeled compounds as precursors of the end products shown. The labeled compounds which were tested as precursors are listed in Table I. Coniferyl alcohol was not included in these compara-

TABLE I

SOME C[14]-LABELED COMPOUNDS TESTED AS PRECURSORS OF
LIGNIN AND RELATED COMPOUNDS[a]

Nonaromatic compounds	C_6—C_3 compounds
Acetate	D-[c] and L[b]-phenylalanine
Glucose	L-Tyrosine[c]
Shikimic acid[b]	D[c] and L[b] phenyllactic acid
	DL[c]-p-Hydroxyphenyllactic acid
C_6—C_1 compounds	Phenylpyruvic acid[b]
Benzoic acid	p-Hydroxyphenylpyruvic acid[c]
p-Anisic acid	DL-Phenylhydracylic acid
p-Hydroxybenzoic acid	DL-erythro-Phenylglyceric acid
Vanillin	DL-threo-Phenylglyceric acid
Syringaldehyde	Phenylpropionic acid[b]
	Cinnamic acid[b]
C_6—C_2 compounds	m-Methoxycinnamic acid
Phenylacetic acid	p-Coumaric acid[b]
DL-Mandelic acid	Caffeic acid[b]
3,4-Dihydroxyacetophenone	Ferfulic acid[b]
	Sinapic acid[b]

[a] All labeled in the ring, the carbon adjacent to the ring, or generally labeled.
[b] Readily converted to lignin in all species of angiosperms listed.
[c] Readily converted to lignin only by certain species of angiosperms.

tive experiments since it had already been established by the research of the groups associated with Freudenberg (1959b) and Kratzl (1960) that coniferin is readily converted to lignin.

The compounds (Table I) were administered to cuttings of the appropriate plant material. After allowing a short time for metabolic reactions (usually 1 day) the end product was isolated and its specific activity measured. Using this simple approach it was feasible to compare the efficiency of a number of precursors in parallel experiments. It was then reasoned that precursors readily converted to a given end product might be on the same biosynthetic pathway, especially if related structurally. Further tracer experiments, on formation of naturally occurring intermediates, were then carried out. On the basis of this work a scheme was developed (Neish, 1960; Brown *et al.*, 1959) which has since been modified somewhat to give Fig. 1 (Neish, 1961).

EXPERIMENTAL TECHNIQUES

Details of experiments are given in the original papers. However, some general remarks concerning the technique of feeding labeled compounds will be made here.

It is a well-known fact that fresh cuttings such as twigs of trees or shoots of herbaceous plants will remain alive for several days if the cut ends are kept in water. The water is adsorbed into the cutting to make up losses due to transpiration so it is a simple matter to infuse the cutting with a labeled precursor which has been dissolved in the water. If the initial volume is kept small it is feasible to introduce practically all of the precursor in an hour or two. The cuttings can then be transferred to fresh water for the remainder of the metabolic period. This simple infusion technique is the method used for most of the experiments supporting the scheme in Fig. 1. It has been applied successfully in studies on the synthesis of cell wall polysaccharides in wheat (Neish, 1955; Altermatt and Neish, 1956), rutin in buckwheat (Underhill et al., 1957; Watkin and Neish, 1960), pungenin in Colorado spruce (Neish, 1959), aromatic amino acids in several species (McCalla and Neish, 1959a; Gamborg and Neish, 1959; Wightman et al., 1961), and cinnamic acid derivatives in salvia (McCalla and Neish, 1959b), as well as in studies on lignin biosynthesis. Obviously it is not suitable for studies where root tissues are required or for long term experiments, as has been pointed out by Reznik (1960). In such experiments one may use root cultures, tissue cultures, or the precursor may be introduced into the vascular tissue of an intact plant through a wound in the stem, absorbed into cut tips of branches still attached to the tree, or introduced into the cambium by implantation of crystals of the precursor under the bark.

Of all these methods the infusion method is probably the best for the present study. It is the simplest to apply to a wide variety of plants and allows for a rapid, quantitative uptake of precursor. The quick absorption of the precursor minimizes the possibility of its destruction by microorganisms. Although suited best to short-term experiments, it should be emphasized that experiments of short duration are preferable. The purpose of these experiments was to get an indication of the relative rates at which various precursors were converted to the end products. If an experiment is so long that the precursors are nearly all metabolized, appreciable differences in rate between two precursors will not be apparent. Another disadvantage of long experiments is the randomization of labeling which can occur due to recycling. For example when acetate was fed to buckwheat seedlings over a period of 6 days through the roots, the quercetin isolated from the rutin was found to contain only 2–4 times as much C^{14} in ring A as in ring B (Geissmann and Swain, 1957; Shibata and Yamazaki, 1957) whereas in a 1-day experiment using the infusion technique (Watkin et al., 1957) this difference was much greater, ring A having 50–100 times the C^{14} content of ring B. This illustrates how a more clearly defined result may be obtained in a short-term experiment. Another advantage of the infusion method is its economy of time and materials. This is illustrated by comparing an experiment of Kratzl and Faigle (1959, 1960) with a similar experiment of Acerbo *et al.* (1960). Both experiments were designed to see what C^{14} distribution would be obtained in vanillin (from lignin) after feeding glucose-1-C^{14} to spruce twigs. Kratzl and Faigle fed 0.1 mc of labeled glucose to spruce twigs by the infusion method and after 48 hours they isolated vanillin having 382 cpm/mg. Acerbo *et al.* (1960) fed a total of ten times this amount of glucose in four portions, to the upper branches of spruce trees through the cut ends of needles, allowing 7 days for absorption of each portion. Apparently no precautions were taken to prevent possible destruction of the glucose by microorganisms. The vanillin eventually obtained had only 40 cpm/mg, a value so low that the experiment was vitiated by many of the corrected counts being below the background level.

The method of feeding may influence the fate of the precursor. This has been shown by two papers from Kratzl's laboratory. In the first experiment (Kratzl *et al.*, 1957), coniferin-3-C^{14} was fed to spruce branches by implantation of crystals into the cambium. It was found that the vanillin recovered by alkaline nitrobenzene oxidation of the wood residue was about seven times as active as the vanilloyl methyl ketone obtained by ethanolysis. In the second experiment (Kratzl and Faigle, 1958) the coniferin was fed by the infusion method and it was found that the activity of the vanilloyl methyl ketone recovered was now about equal to that of the vanillin. It is probable that a wound reaction was obscuring the results when the implantation technique was used. Kratzl has adopted the infusion method for many of his more recent studies.

The amount of a precursor fed per unit weight of plant material should also be controlled in comparative experiments (Watkin and Neish, 1960). Approximately the same dosage should be maintained in a series of experiments, especially if the results are reported as dilution values. The simplest way to express results is as dilution values, i.e., specific activity of precursor divided by specific activity of the product. This does not require a measurement of the amount of product. If results are expressed as "per cent converted" they are not so sensitive to variation of the dosage, but a quantitative measurement of the product is required and this is difficult to achieve, especially for lignin in herbaceous species.

In conclusion it may be said that there is no method of feeding labeled compounds to living plant tissues which is universally superior to other methods, and which does not involve some departure from "normal" conditions. In general, the best biological system to use in an investigation of biosynthetic pathways is the simplest one that will work, without unnecessary prolongation of the metabolic period.

BIOSYNTHESIS OF AROMATIC AMINO ACIDS

Labeled shikimic acid is converted to the aromatic amino acids in higher plants (McCalla and Neish, 1959a; Gamborg and Neish, 1959; Wightman et al., 1961) so it is likely that the biosynthesis of these amino acids occurs in plants by a route closely similar to that worked out for microorganisms (Davis, 1955, 1958). Quinic acid may also be involved and may play a relatively more important role in plants (Weinstein et al., 1959a, b). Tracer experiments have also shown the existence of two amino acid pools—one for phenylalanine and one for tyrosine (Gamborg and Neish, 1959). These pools contain the corresponding α-keto and α-hydroxy acids, in equilibrium with each other. Each pool arises by an independent route from intermediates of the shikimic pathway, presumably from prephenic acid, as in microorganims (Davis, 1955, 1958; Schwinck and Adams, 1959). Although cinnamic acid derivatives can be formed from these intermediates of the phenylalanine and tyrosine pools, this process is irreversible for all practical purposes (McCalla and Neish, 1959a; Gamborg and Neish, 1959). This finding has an important consequence: it shows that members of the amino acid pools do not function as intermediates in the conversion of the cinnamic acid derivatives to lignin, flavonoids, etc. This helps to establish the sequence of the intermediates in Fig. 1. It is not possible to decide on the basis of tracer experiments which intermediate in the phenylalanine or tyrosine pool forms cinnamic or p-coumaric acid. It has been suggested by Brown et al. (1959) that these unsaturated acids are formed by dehydration of the α-hydroxy acids but the enzyme studies discussed below show they are probably formed by a direct deamination of the corresponding amino acids.

BIOSYNTHESIS OF LIGNIN

In general lignin may be defined as the nonnitrogenous, aromatic material, insoluble in neutral solvents, which is associated with plant cell walls. Since lignin cannot be separated from the cell wall in good yields as a pure, unaltered material, studies on its biosynthesis depend on isolation of some degradation product that can be purified. The technique used in these experiments was to extract the plant material with a polar and then with a nonpolar solvent and to subject the insoluble residue to alkaline nitrobenzene oxidation. The aldehydes obtained (vanillin and syringaldehyde) were taken to represent lignin. Some p-hydroxybenz-aldehyde is frequently found but this may arise either from lignin or tyrosine (Brown *et al.*, 1959). Since the insoluble residues from herbaceous or young plant materials may contain a considerable quantity of denatured protein, it is not advisable to use *p*-hydroxybenzaldehyde as an indicator of lignin. For the experiments discussed here, lignin is the plant material insoluble in neutral polar and nonpolar solvents which gives rise to vanillin and syringaldehyde on alkaline nitrobenzene oxidation. Other definitions of lignin may be made more restrictive but if this practice is carried to extremes there is some danger that the structure of lignin will be arrived at by definition. Most authorities are agreed that lignin has a phenylpropanoid structure, yet the yield of phenylpropanoid breakdown products from lignin rarely exceeds 10%, leaving the constitution of the remaining 90% in doubt. Analyses of lignins, isolated by relatively mild methods, support the C_6—C—C—C structure of lignin but do not prove it, and in any case such analyses have been confined to a few woody species. Alkaline nitrobenzene oxidation has given yields of vanillin and syringaldehyde, accounting for up to 40% of lignin and has been applied to a wide variety of species. When these compounds are used as indicators of lignin it is obvious that a much larger fraction of the lignin is being considered than when only C_6—C_3 products are isolated.

Early tracer experiments by Brown and Neish (1955a) showed that shikimic acid and L-phenylalanine were both good precursors of lignin in wheat and maple. These facts considered in the light of other knowledge suggested that phenylalanine is synthesized by the same route in higher plants as in bacteria and, further, that lignin formation is a ramification of phenylalanine metabolism peculiar to plants. These views follow naturally from a consideration of the principle of "biochemical unity," from the assumption that a biochemical evolution has occurred, and from the belief of chemists that lignin is phenylpropanoid. In a further series of experiments the precursors in Table I were compared (Brown and Neish, 1955b, 1956, 1959; Brown *et al.*, 1959; Wright *et al.*, 1958). Those shown in Fig. 1 were the most efficient. These are all phenylpropanoid in structure. This does not prove lignin has a phenylpropanoid structure but it at least supports this view by showing it can have a phenylpropanoid origin.

Although phenylalanine was a good precursor of lignin in all species tested tyrosine was converted readily to lignin only by certain species (Brown and Neish, 1956; Brown, 1961b). Table II shows the results of feeding phenylalanine and tyrosine to various species in parallel experiments. A high dilution means a precursor is used inefficiently. In species of the Gramineae, tyrosine was about as good as phenylalanine as a precursor of lignin, but most other species used tyrosine less efficiently by about two orders of magnitude except for two species of the Compo-

TABLE II

CONVERSION OF PHENYLALANINE AND TYROSINE
TO LIGNIN BY VARIOUS SPECIES[a]

Family	Species	Dilution of C^{14} in vanillin from lignin[b]		Ratio of dilutions in vanillin (Tyr./Phe)
		Phe. fed[c]	Tyr. fed[c]	
Gramineae	*Triticum vulgare* Vill.	1,100	580	0.53
	Hordeum vulgare L.	6,600	4,100	0.62
	Bromus inermis Leyss.	1,800	1,600	0.89
	Calamagrostis inexpansa (Michx.) Beauv.	1,640	2,600	1.58
Cyperaceae	*Carex laeviconica* Dew.	3,700	240,000	65
Juncaceae	*Juncus bufonius* L.	380	12,000	32
Liliaceae	*Smilacina stellata* (L) Desf.	865	88,000	102
Salicaceae	*Salix amygdaloides* Anders.	1,780	130,000	73
Polygonaceae	*Fagopyrum tataricum* (L) Gaertn.	972	360,000	370
Legumimoseae	*Caragana arborescens* Lam.	445	46,000	104
	Melilotus officinalis (L) Lam.	1,620	160,000	99
Elaeagnaceae	*Elaeagnus commutata* Bernh.	1,890	170,000	90
Compositeae	*Zinnia elegans* Jacq.	328	3,100	9.5
	Lepachys columnifera (Nutt.) Rydb.	525	10,000	19

[a] Data of Brown and Neish (1956) and Brown (1961b).

[b] Vanillin isolated following nitrobenzene oxidation of the extractive-free plant material. The dilution was calculated by dividing the specific activity of the precursor fed by the specific activity of the vanillin isolated.

[c] Phe = L-phenylalanine-C^{14}; Tyr = L-tyrosine-C^{14}

sitae which occupy an intermediate position to this respect. The same conclusions were reached if syringaldehyde was taken as an indicator of lignin.

This interesting taxonomic variation in lignin synthesis extends to other p-hydroxyphenyl compounds of the tyrosine pool, but not to p-coumaric acid, which was converted readily to lignin and related compounds in all systems tested. This is true for formation of quercetin in buckwheat (Underhill *et al.*, 1957), pungenin in spruce leaves (Neish, 1959), or caffeic and ferulic acids in salvia (McCalla and Neish, 1959b). These are all systems where tyrosine does not function readily as a precursor while phenylalanine does. Ibrahim and Towers (1960) have made similar observations regarding synthesis of hydrangenol. The conclusions drawn from Table II can also probably be extended to include sugar cane and spruce. Acerbo *et al.* (1958) have shown that p-hydroxyphenylpyruvic acid is converted efficiently to lignin in sugar cane while Kratzl and Billek (1959) have shown the opposite is true for spruce.

Since sugar cane belongs to the Gramineae, whereas spruce does not, these facts agree with the conclusions drawn from Table II. *p*-Hydroxyphenylpyruvate is easily converted to tyrosine in plants (Gamborg and Neish, 1959) so feeding it is equivalent to feeding tyrosine.

BIOSYNTHESIS OF RUTIN

The biosynthesis of quercetin, the flavonol aglycone of rutin, was investigated using the precursors listed in Table I. Literature pertaining to the biosynthesis of flavonoids has been reviewed recently (Bogorad, 1958; Reznik, 1960; Neish, 1960; Grisebach and Ollis, 1961). It has been established that ring B and the attached three carbons of the heterocyclic ring arise from phenylpropanoid precursors while ring A is derived from acetate. The phenyl intermediates in Fig. 1, and *p*-coumaric acid, were readily converted to quercetin, but intermediates shown after *p*-coumaric acid in this scheme were not.

Bate-Smith (1956) has suggested that lignin and flavonoids come from a common precursor. This suggestion was based on the distribution of both flavonoids and lignin in woody plants. The tracer experiments support this hypothesis and show certain cinnamic acid derivatives are probably the common precursors. These acids are also of widespread occurrence (Bate-Smith, 1956; Kremers, 1957). It is likely that *p*-coumaric acid is the last precursor common to the synthesis of both lignin and quercetin in buckwheat. Another quite distinct line of evidence supporting the idea that *p*-coumaric acid is a central intermediate in the biosynthesis of flavonoids comes from the work of Geissmann and Harborne (1955) on albino mutants of snapdragon. These mutants, which are unable to synthesize flavonoids, were found to accumulate esters of *p*-coumaric acid in unusually large amounts.

BIOSYNTHESIS OF PUNGENIN

This simple glucoside of 3,4-dihydroxyacetophenone constitutes up to 5% of the dry matter in the leaves of certain species of spruce (Neish, 1958). It was first described by Neish (1957) and was rediscovered in Japan by Takahashi *et al.* (1960). A comparison of precursors showed the aglycone was readily formed from phenylalanine, *p*-coumaric acid, or caffeic acid but not from tyrosine or 3,4-dihydroxyphenylalanine (Neish, 1959). These facts are readily interpreted by Fig. 1. The conversion of caffeic acid to 3,4-dihydroxyacetophenone may occur by the route suggested by Robinson (1955) for formation of acetophenone derivatives, i.e., hydration of caffeic acid to the β-hydroxy acid, oxidation to the β-keto acid, then decarboxylation.

Biosynthesis of Coumarins

The fairly extensive literature on biosynthesis of coumarin and its derivatives has been reviewed elsewhere by Reznik (1960), Neish (1960), and Brown (1960), and no attempt will be made here to discuss this field in detail. The evidence of tracer experiments by Kosuge and Conn (1959), Brown et al. (1960), and Brown (1960) strongly suggests that coumarin is derived by a process involving ortho hydroxylation of cinnamic acid (see Fig. 1) and involving o-coumaryl glucoside as an intermediate.

Alkaloids of Phenylpropanoid Origin

Several alkaloids have been shown by tracer experiments to originate from phenylalanine or tyrosine. These include hordenine (Marion, 1958), mescaline (Leete, 1959), morphine (Battersby and Harper, 1958; Leete, 1958), and ephedrine (Imaseki et al., 1958). Recent work in this field has been reviewed by Battersby (1961). There is no reason to believe cinnamic acid derivatives play any part in the synthesis of these compounds. The data suggest rather that an aromatic amino acid may be metabolized by widely divergent pathways. If the initial attack on the amino acid is deamination to a cinnamic acid derivative, then lignin and related compounds may be formed, but if the initial attack is decarboxylation, then alkaloid formation is to be expected.

Formation of Cinnamic Acid Derivatives

Cinnamic acid derivatives are widespread in nature (Bate-Smith, 1956; Kremers, 1957) especially depsides of p-coumaric, caffeic, and ferulic acids. More recently glucose esters have been found by Harborne and Corner (1961). These acids all occur together as esters in the stems of Salvia splendens. In this species the caffeic acid is not bound in chlorogenic acid (McCalla and Neish, 1959b; Herrmann, 1960) as is often the case in other species. Salvia stems were selected as experimental material for a study of the formation of p-coumaric, caffeic, ferulic, and sinapic acids by McCalla and Neish (1959b). All of these acids were readily formed from phenylalanine and time studies agreed with the sequence: phenylalanine → p-coumaric acid → caffeic acid → ferulic acid → sinapic acid. This sequence was further supported by the observation that early members of the sequence are converted to later members more readily than the reverse. It was also shown that cinnamic acid was an excellent precursor of p-coumaric acid. These facts all support the relations shown in Fig. 1.

Enzyme Studies

GENERAL

The scheme in Fig. 1 is based mainly on the results of the tracer experiments reviewed above. However, this kind of evidence is not enough to establish such a scheme, but only serves to develop a working hypothesis. If each of the steps proposed could be demonstrated by separate enzyme reactions, then the scheme would rest on much firmer foundations and more would be known about the actual mechanism.

The scheme shown (Fig. 1) is not quite the same as that originally proposed by Brown *et al.* (1959) but has already been modified as a result of enzyme studies. The reactions shown will now be considered in sequence with respect to present knowledge of the enzymes involved.

ORIGIN OF THE AMINO ACID POOLS

Some of the enzymes involved in the biosynthesis of the aromatic amino acids from carbohydrate are known to be found in higher plants as well as in microorganisms. The presence in higher plants of the enzymes involved in formation of erythrose-4 phosphate and phospho-enolpyruvate is well known. Dehydroquinase was detected in plants by Mitsuhashi and Davis (1954). Dehydroshikimic reductase has also been found in plants by Yaniv and Gilvarg (1955) and Nandy and Ganguli (1961a). Glucose-6-phosphate has been converted to dehydroshikimic acid by a cell free extract of mung bean seedlings (Nandy and Ganguli, 1961b). Enzymes involved in conversion of shikimic acid to prephenic acid have not yet been demonstrated. The conversion of prephenic acid to the α-oxo acids of Fig. 1 requires separate enzymes which are known for microorganisms (Schwinck and Adams, 1959) but not yet found in plants. Transamination of phenylpyruvate to phenylalanine has been shown in plant enzyme systems by Kretovich (1957). The reversible reduction of the α-oxo acids to the α-hydroxy acids can occur under the influence of known enzymes. For example Meister (1950) has shown that crystalline lactic acid dehydrogenase from muscle can carry out this reaction. In addition, it has been found by Gamborg *et al.* (1962) that a crude preparation of glycolic acid oxidase from wheat leaves will carry out oxidation of phenyllactic and *p*-hydroxyphenyllactic acids to the α-oxo acids. It is not certain whether conversion of these α-hydroxy acids to the α-amino acids, as observed in tracer experiments by Gamborg and Neish (1959) and Wightman *et al.* (1961), has any physiological significance or whether it happens because of the low substrate specificity of certain dehydrogenases, already known as enzymes of carbohydrate metabolism.

FORMATION OF CINNAMIC ACID AND ITS DERIVATIVES

In an earlier scheme proposed by Brown *et al.* (1959) it was postulated that cinnamic acid and *p*-coumaric acid were formed by dehydration of phenyllactic acid and *p*-hydroxyphenyllactic acid, respectively. However, the tracer experiments did not distinguish between this possibility and an alternate route, i.e., direct deamination of the amino acids by a reaction analogous to those catalyzed by aspartase (Quastel and Woolf, 1926), β-methylaspartase (Barker *et al.*, 1959), or histidase (Tabor and Mehler, 1955). Recent studies by Koukol and Conn (1961) on phenylalanine and parallel studies by Neish (1961) on tyrosine have shown that plants do contain enzymes which catalyze deamination of these amino acids by the following irreversible reaction:

$$R—CH_2—CH—COO^- \atop \underset{\text{L-isomer}}{\overset{|}{+NH_3}} \rightarrow \underset{\text{Trans isomer}}{R—CH=CH—COO^- + NH_4^+}$$

This appears to be a direct deamination with no demonstrable co-factor requirements. There is no evidence that the α-hydroxy acids are involved. The preparations will not convert *p*-hydroxyphenyllactic acid to *p*-coumaric acid. The enzymes are soluble and have been extracted from acetone-dried plant materials and partially purified by ammonium sulfate precipitation and chromatography on diethylaminoethyl cellulose. In addition to catalyzing the above deaminations, such enzyme preparations also catalyze deamination of *m*-tyrosine to *m*-coumaric acid (Neish, 1961). The physiological significance of this reaction is not clear; neither *m*-tyrosine nor *m*-coumaric acid are of common occurrence in nature. The data indicate that the deaminations of phenylalanine and tyrosine are catalyzed by separate ammonia lyases, which have been given the trivial names phenylalanine deaminase and tyrase respectively. It is likely that a third enzyme is needed to cause deamination of *m*-tyrosine but it has not been conclusively shown that tyrase does not catalyze this deamination also. Further studies are needed to settle this point.

A comparison of the phenylalanine deaminase and tyrase contents of several species of grasses and legumes (Table III) shows that all species have good phenylalanine deaminase activity whereas only the grasses have well-developed tyrase activity. This is significant when compared with the findings of the tracer experiments reviewed above, where it was shown that all the plants tested could utilize phenylalanine for formation of lignin and related compounds whereas only grasses could utilize tyrosine. These facts give strong support for the belief that *p*-

TABLE III

RATE OF DEAMINATION OF PHENYLALANINE AND TYROSINE TO CINNAMIC
AND *p*-COUMARIC ACIDS (RESPECTIVELY), BY ACETONE POWDERS
FROM SEVERAL SPECIES[a]

Source of	μmoles/hour/gm		$\dfrac{\text{cinnamic}}{p\text{-coumaric}}$ ratio
acetone powder	cinnamic acid	*p*-coumaric acid	
Barley seedling shoots	8.0	2.3	3.5
Barley seedling roots	12.2	3.4	3.6
Wheat seedling shoots	9.0	2.5	3.6
Rice seedlings	6.5	1.9	3.4
Rice seedling roots	31.4	10.4	3.0
White sweet clover tops	4.5	0.14	32.
Alfalfa stems	11.0	0.23	48.

[a] Experiment carried out in collaboration with Dr. Jane Koukol; see Neish (1961) for details.

coumaric acid is an obligate intermediate in the conversion of tyrosine to lignin.

It is evident from the tracer experiments that there must be another route to *p*-coumaric acid in addition to the tyrase reaction. Plants which cannot readily convert tyrosine to lignin are still able to synthesize lignin from either phenylalanine or *p*-coumaric acid. Since *Salvia splendens* can form *p*-coumaric acid much more easily from phenylalanine or cinnamic acid (McCalla and Neish, 1959b) than from tyrosine (Brown *et al.*, 1959) it seems likely that para-hydroxylation of cinnamic acid (or some derivative) occurs readily in lignifying plants. So far attempts to demonstrate this hydroxylation in a cell-free system have been unsuccessful. Levy and Zucker (1960) have found that potato slices will convert phenylalanine to *p*-coumarylquinate and to chlorogenic acid (i.e., caffeyl quinate). They suggested that cinnamyl quinate may be the actual substrate for hydroxylation, rather than the free acid. The further hydroxylation of *p*-coumaryl quinate to chlorogenic acid was demonstrated by them in a cell-free system from potatoes. This is probably due to the well-known enzyme tyrosinase. Further conversions would involve methylation of caffeic acid to ferulic acid, a reaction which has been demonstrated with animal enzymes (Pellerin and D'Iorio, 1958). Nothing is known of the conversion of ferulic acid to sinapic acid in cell-free systems. Presumably this is due to further hydroxylation followed by methylation.

Conversion of Cinnamic Acid Derivatives to Lignin
and Related Compounds

The enzyme reactions involved in the conversion of the cinnamic acid derivatives to lignin will not be treated in detail in this paper. Presumably a system exists for the reduction of ferulic acid or a derivative, to coniferyl alcohol, although Stafford (1960) had evidence that grass lignin may be formed from ferulic acid without reduction. Freudenberg (1959a, b 1960) has made extensive studies on the conversion of coniferyl alcohol to a lignin-like dehydrogenation polymer. This reaction is catalyzed by certain oxidases. The properties of the polymer are remarkably like those of spruce milled-wood lignin. The enzymes involved in the biosynthesis of flavonoids, other phenylpropanoid compounds and pungenin are generally unknown, although Kosuge and Conn (1961) have demonstrated several enzymes involved in coumarin metabolism.

General Discussion of Tracer and Enzyme Studies

The scheme in Fig. 1 is a working hypothesis. The reactions cannot be established in any great detail by tracer experiments. When compounds rapidly reach equilibrium with each other in the plant, it is difficult to establish their actual sequence in any biosynthetic scheme. Furthermore, plants have a great capacity to metabolize added precursors; almost any compound can be converted to another to some extent. This means that the possibility of a given compound being a precursor has to be judged on quantitative grounds—not qualitatively. An experiment where a single compound is found to give lignin does not mean much by itself. Comparison of a large number of compounds is required and no matter how many are tried there is always a possibility that a key intermediate has been overlooked. Another problem arises from the low substrate specificity of some enzymes, i.e., a precursor converted efficiently may not be a natural intermediate at all. This may be true for phenyllactic acid, which could be converted to phenylpyruvate (a natural intermediate), due to the action of lactic dehydrogenase, glycolic acid oxidase, or some related enzyme. An additional problem arises in studies on lignin formation due to the general aura of uncertainty concerning the structure of lignin. It is never certain that the lignin formed from a given precursor is identical with the lignin naturally present. This uncertainty can be minimized by isolation of a variety of degradation products, but will not disappear until more is known about the chemistry of lignin in a wide range of species.

In spite of the weaknesses mentioned above, the tracer technique offers a simple method of establishing a working hypothesis. This hypothesis may then be refined and strengthened by the enzyme studies it suggests. For example, enzyme studies have shown that the amino acids are probably the direct precursors of the unsaturated acids and that the hydroxy acids may not be natural intermediates at all. Furthermore, correlation of the taxonomic distribution of tyrase activity with the ability of a plant to use tyrosine for lignin formation helps to establish *p*-coumaric acid as an obligate intermediate in lignin biosynthesis.

More enzyme studies are needed to clarify the reactions involved in interconversion of the cinnamic acid derivatives. The experiments of Levy and Zucker (1960) suggest that the quinate, rather than the free acids are the actual intermediates in the first two aromatic hydroxylations shown in Fig. 1. The first of these reactions (i.e., hydroxylation of cinnamic acid) has not been demonstrated in a cell-free system. This reaction should be much more rapid than any possible hydroxylation of phenylalanine to tyrosine in the plants studied (Gamborg and Neish, 1959). It is possible that the substrate for hydroxylation may be a cinnamic ester such as the quinate or perhaps the coenzyme A derivative. The latter alternative is attractive since if one imagines the sequence involving the unsaturated acids in Fig. 1 to occur with the coenzyme A derivatives (in place of free acids), it would lead to ferulyl-coenzyme A which could be easily reduced because of the high-energy thioester linkage. An analogous reaction is known in mevalonic acid synthesis (Ferguson *et al.*, 1959; Lynen *et al.*, 1959). The quinates which are usually found could easily be formed from the coenzyme A derivatives and in some plants other esters might be formed instead. We have already pointed out above that salvia does not accumulate the quinate of caffeic acid but rather an unknown ester and glucose esters may be found in many species. A study of formation of *p*-coumaric acid from phenylalanine at the enzyme level should answer some of these questions, especially if the hydroxylating system is found to have a high specificity. Introduction of the second hydroxyl is presumably catalyzed by tyrosinase and it has been shown by Levy and Zucker (1960) that an enzyme preparation from potatoes will hydroxylate *p*-coumaryl quinate to chlorogenate. However, this does not prove this is the actual route since tyrosinase will hydroxylate a wide variety of phenolic compounds, and will even convert free *p*-coumaric acid to caffeic acid (Chisholm and Neish, 1960).

Evolution of Lignification

It is interesting to speculate on the origin of lignin and other secondary growth products in relation to the evolution of plants. Lignin is found only in plants more highly evolved than the mosses, i.e., in tracheophytes (Manskaja, 1959). Its presence is correlated with the development of relatively large terrestrial forms, and this is also generally true of other phenylpropanoid compounds such as flavonoids.

Fraenkel (1959) has reviewed some of the ideas on the function of secondary growth substances such as alkaloids, pigments, essential oils, phenolic compounds, etc. The widespread occurrence of such compounds, which are not essential for life itself, is explained in Darwinian terms of survival of the fittest. Suppose a mutant is developed which differs from the parent by having the ability to accumulate an alkaloid. This could make the plant unpalatable to foraging animals or protect it against attack by insects. If the alkaloid is not harmful to the plant the mutant would be expected to gradually replace the parent strain. The same result might be produced if a phenolic compound is formed instead of an alkaloid and protection could be gained against attack by fungi or bacteria, rather than against animal predators. Alternatively, a mutant may acquire pigments or essential oils which attract insects to the flowers and thus aid in pollination. It is significant that very few wild plant species are edible and the majority are pollinated by insects. It is easy to imagine how the development of lignification would give a plant an advantage over competitors. Lignin acts as a water-resistant cement and has made possible the development of fibers and vascular tissue. These strengthening and water-conducting elements have made possible the development of tall forms which compete successfully for light and relegate inferior forms in the same habitat to the humble role of shade plants.

The problem of excretion of "waste" metabolic products by plants has probably been connected with the origin of lignin and other secondary growth substances. Microorganisms can excrete waste or surplus products into the medium, but as more massive forms evolve with low surface/volume ratios, difficulty is experienced. The evolution of large animals has depended on development of a system of organs designed for excretion. Plants do not have well developed organs for this purpose so individual cells depend on "local excretion" either into a central vacuole or into the cell wall, as has been emphasized by Reznik (1960).

Suppose a primitive terrestrial plant developed a single new enzyme (by mutation) and thus acquired the ability to deaminate phenylalanine to cinnamic acid. This reaction is practically irreversible, and due to limited excretory power it may be assumed that the cinnamic acid accumulated in the tissues. The cinnamic acid might have been acted on by other enzymes of broad substrate specificity which were already present for other purposes and thus several simple secondary metabolites (i.e., various esters) could accumulate which might alleviate toxicity of the cinnamic acid and confer some extra survival value on the mutant.

Eventually another mutation might result in production of an enzyme which could act on one or more of the secondary metabolites, formed as a result of the first mutation, and in time a complex biosynthetic sequence could arise leading to lignin, flavonoids, etc.

This view of the origin of biosynthetic pathways is quite different from the hypothesis advanced by Horowitz (1945), but does not clash with it since the situations are not comparable. Horowitz developed his ingenious hypothesis to explain the development of biosynthetic pathways for compounds universally required for life. It applies to a situation where a wide variety of organic compounds are present in a milieu in which simple primitive organisms are evolving from complex organic compounds. Complex biosynthetic pathways of essential metabolites are envisaged as having arisen in a stepwise manner working backwards from the final product. When lignin and related compounds were first developed the primitive earth conditions which favored the origin of life had vanished. The situation was rather that of mutations presenting a complex, efficient, living cell with a product not essential for life and quite often it was probably deleterious. In primitive plants where excretion was difficult, especially in terrestrial forms, such products were ultimately converted to lignin, flavonoids, coumarins, etc., as higher forms evolved. The excretion problem was solved by forming substances of some value to the plant, or else the mutant disappeared. It is philosophically satisfying to speculate that what appears at first sight to be a handicap to the development of a large vegetative body (i.e., a poor excretory system) may have led, through evolution of lignification, to majestic trees, the tallest and most enduring of all organisms.

DISCUSSION

CÔTÉ: Would heartwood formation be a parallel to what you have suggested here for lignification in plants? Do you think that it is a process of excretion which is finally forming heartwood?

NEISH: Yes, I think so. It is not just garbage, of course; it is useful to the tree by preserving it against fungal attack.

TOMLINSON: Your closing ideas recall those of A. H. Church (1919). He considered that a massive woody axis merely represents accumulated waste materials.

ALBERSHEIM: Will any of the other deaminases, such as histidase, react with phenylalanine to give cinnamic acid?

NEISH: I tried β-methyl aspartase and it had no effect at all on tyrosine.

ALBERSHEIM: Histidine would be more analogous in structure.

NEISH: I tried adding histidine to our enzyme preparations, but there was no effect within the limits of our detection. Neither did alanine, aspartic acid, or any other amino acid tested. It only worked on those three. I cannot understand why it is working on m-hydroxytyrosine.

FREUDENBERG: You went directly from shikimic acid to the other C_6—C_3 acids without mentioning prephenic acid. Do you not regard prephenic acid as an intermediate?

NEISH: It has not actually been proven in higher plants, though it probably is there. It might even be converted to lignin precursors without going through the phenylpropanoid amino acids.

FREUDENBERG: Chemically the best way seems to lead from prephenic acid to phenylpyruvic acid, and then to phenylalanine, etc.

NEISH: Nobody has actually fed prephenic acid to a plant.

FREUDENBERG: When does the reduction from the acids to the alcohols occur?

NEISH: I do not know if the ferulic acid is free or in the form of a glucoside; there is no way to tell, but I think that ferulic acid is reduced as a coenzyme A derivative. This is a guess that can be tested.

FREUDENBERG: We have fed it once as a glucoside and it did not work very well.

NEISH: I would think that ferulic coenzyme A is formed and reduced to coniferyl alcohol. Then, if lignification is rapid, you can imagine the coniferyl alcohol being all converted to lignin. I am using your data now. But if for some reason there is an overproduction, such as may occur in spruce cambium, I would imagine that coniferyl alcohol is stabilized as a glucoside, perhaps by reaction with UDP-glucose. Later on, when the glucoside can be moved in from the cambium to the site of action, glucosidase would take the glucose off again. Coniferyl alcohol is so labile that I think it would have to be stabilized for transport.

ALBERSHEIM: What about phosphorylation and reduction of the carboxyl group of aspartic?

NEISH: This could very well be the case. I was just trying to use the derivative which would explain everything.

TORREY: Have you any indication of induced enzyme synthesis if you load it with some of these precursors?

NEISH: I do not know. Phenylalanine and tyrosine are precursors which have to be there according to this theory. If they form their products then they would induce the others. There is not much evidence of inductive enzyme formation in plants, but there is no reason why it should not occur.

WILCOX: The investigators of 50 years ago argued whether the Casparian strip in the endodermis was composed of fat or lignin, because it stains with Sudan in one case and phloroglucinol in the other. Have there been any investigations with these precursors in recent years to see how the fatty acids and the lignin are combined in this region?

NEISH: Not that I know of.

THIMANN: I am puzzled about those plants which are unable to use what look like good precursors—tyrosine and other para-hydroxy derivatives. You mentioned that in one case a 3,4-dihydroxy derivative was not used. This made me wonder if there were competition between two enzyme systems, namely tyrosinase diverting these already hydroxylated products but unable to do anything with the unhydroxylated derivatives. All your tissues contain tyrosinase. I gather from Dr. Freudenberg that his enzyme preparation is essentially tyrosinase. Is that right?

FREUDENBERG: No, I do not think so. Tyrosinase is not present. Laccase and tyrosinase are quite different. We were working with laccase. We have investigated the enzymes of the cambial region; they consist of laccase and peroxidase. They are also difficult to distinguish.

THIMANN: But they would act on the same substrates as tyrosinase.

NEISH: I think the competition that you suggest does occur. For example, if tyrosine is hydroxylated by tyrosinase, it will probably go to melanin; if it is decarboxylated it will probably go to an alkaloid; if it is deaminated it will probably go to lignin and related compounds.

ALBERSHEIM: Are you sure that the 3,4-dihydroxy compounds are taken up? Have you measured this and are they absorbed by the plants in the same amounts as tyrosine or phenylalanine?

NEISH: That was an experiment with an enzyme preparation. The enzyme system which deaminates tyrosine will not deaminate it. I have tried it in some plants and it does not go into lignin at all. I know it is taken up in the twigs, but I do not know where it is found in the cell.

FREY-WYSSLING: It is peculiar that all these secondary compounds should derive from amino acids, whose major function is to make protein for the living cytoplasm (cf. Frey-Wyssling, 1938). One could understand this more easily in an aging cell. But this deamination takes place in a meristematic region. I wonder if this is because the plant is constantly short of nitrogen and tries to recover it by transaminations. It is not easy to understand why these sidelines break away from the main line at the very moment when the amino acids seem to be so important.

NEISH: One would expect rapid production of the amino acids where there is rapid growth. If they are produced more rapidly than required for protein synthesis they would be in excess, and the stage would be set for the formation of lignin.

WAREING: On the other hand, during differentiation of lignified xylem elements, there may well be proteolysis. This could be a source of amino acids.

REFERENCES

Acerbo, S. N., Schubert, W. J., and Nord, F. F. (1958). *J. Am. Chem. Soc.* **80**, 1990-1992.

Acerbo, S. N., Schubert, W. J., and Nord, F. F. (1960). *J. Am. Chem. Soc.* **82**, 735-739.

Altermatt, H., and Neish, A. C. (1956). *Can. J. Biochem. Physiol.* **34**, 405-413.

Barker, H. A., Smyth, R. D., Wilson, R. M., and Weissbach, H. (1959). *J. Biol. Chem.* **234**, 320-328.

Bate-Smith, E. C. (1956). *Sci. Proc. Roy. Dublin Soc.* **27**, 165-176.

Battersby, A. R. (1961). *Quart. Rev.* **15**, 259-286.

Battersby, A. R., and Harper, B. J. T. (1958). *Chem. Ind. London*, p. 364.

Bogorad, L. (1958). *Ann. Rev. Plant Physiol.* **9**, 417-448.

Brauns, F. E., and Brauns, D. A. (1960). "The Chemistry of Lignin" (Supplement Volume), pp. 659-736. Academic Press, New York.

Brown, S. A. (1960). *Z. Naturforsch.* **15b**, 768-769.

Brown, S. A. (1961a). *Science* **134**, 305-313.

Brown, S. A. (1961b). *Can. J. Botany* **39**, 253-258.

Brown, S. A., and Neish, A. C. (1955a). *Nature* **175**, 688-689.

Brown, S. A., and Neish, A. C. (1955b). *Can. J. Biochem. Physiol.* **33**, 948-962.

Brown, S. A., and Neish, A. C. (1956). *Can. J. Biochem. Physiol.* **34**, 769-778.

Brown, S. A., and Neish, A. C. (1959). *J. Am. Chem. Soc.* **81**, 2419-2424.

Brown, S. A., Wright, D., and Neish, A. C. (1959). *Can. J. Biochem. Physiol.* **37**, 25-34.

Brown, S. A., Towers, G. H. N., and Wright, D. (1960). *Can. J. Biochem. Physiol.* **38**, 143-156.

Chisholm, M. D., and Neish, A. C. (1960). Unpublished results.

Church, A. H. (1919). Thalassiophyta and the subaerial transmigration, *Botan. Memoirs No. 3.* Oxford Univ. Press, London and New York.

Davis, B. D.   (1955).   *Advan. Enzymol.* **16**, 247-312.
Davis, B. D.   (1958).   *Arch. Biochem. Biophys.* **78**, 497-509.
Ferguson, J. J., Ourr, I. F., and Rudney, H.   (1959).   *Proc. Natl. Acad. Sci. U.S.* **45**, 499-504.
Fraenkel, G. S.   (1959).   *Science* **129**, 1466-1470.
Freudenberg, K.   (1959a).   *Chem. Ber.* **92**, LXXXXIX.
Freudenberg, K.   (1959b).   *Nature* **183**, 1152-1155.
Freudenberg, K.   (1960).   *Holz Roh-Werkstoff* **18**, 282-287.
Frey-Wyssling, A.   (1938).   *Naturwissenschaften* **26**, 624.
Gamborg, O. L., and Neish, A. C.   (1959).   *Can. J. Biochem. Physiol.* **37**, 1277-1285.
Gamborg, O. L., Wetter, L. R., and Neish, A. C.   (1962).   *Phytochemistry* **1**, 159-168.
Geissmann, T. A., and Harborne, J. B.   (1955).   *Arch. Biochem. Biophys.* **55**, 447-454.
Geissmann, T. A., and Swain, T.   (1957).   *Chem. Ind. London*, p. 948.
Grisebach, H., and Ollis, W. D.   (1961).   *Experientia* **17**, 4-12.
Harborne, J. B., and Corner, J. J.   (1961).   *Biochem. J.* **81**, 242-250.
Herrmann, K.   (1960).   *Arch. Pharm.* **293**, 1043-1048.
Horowitz, N. H.   (1945).   *Proc. Natl. Acad. Sci. U.S.* **31**, 153-157.
Ibrahim, R. K., and Towers, G. H. N.   (1960).   *Can. J. Biochem. Physiol.* **38**, 627-634.
Imaseki, I., Shibata, S., and Yamazaki, M.   (1958).   *Chem. Ind. London*, p. 1625.
Kosuge, T., and Conn, E. E.   (1959).   *J. Biol. Chem.* **234**, 2133-2137.
Kosuge, T., and Conn, E. E.   (1961).   *J. Biol. Chem.* **236**, 1617-1621.
Koukol, J., and Conn, E. E.   (1961).   *J. Biol. Chem.* **236**, 2692-2698.
Kratzl, K.   (1960).   *Tappi* **43**, 650-653.
Kratzl, K., and Billek, G.   (1959).   *Monatsh. Chem.* **90**, 536-543.
Kratzl, K., and Faigle, H.   (1958).   *Monatsh. Chem.* **89**, 708-715.
Kratzl, K., and Faigle, H.   (1959).   *Monatsh. Chem.* **90**, 768-770.
Kratzl, K., and Faigle, H.   (1960).   *Z. Naturforsch.* **15b**, 4-11.
Kratzl, K., Billek, G., Klein, E., and Buchtela, K.   (1957).   *Monatsh. Chem.* **88**, 721-734.
Kremers, R. E.   (1957).   *Tappi* **40**, 262-268.
Kretovich, W. L.   (1957).   *Proc. Intern. Symp. Enzyme Chem. Tokyo Kyoto*, p. 468.
Leete, E.   (1958).   *Chem. Ind. London*, p. 977-978.
Leete, E.   (1959).   *Chem. Ind. London*, p. 604.
Levy, C. C., and Zucker, M.   (1960).   *J. Biol. Chem.* **235**, 2418-2425.
Lynen, F., Knappe, J., Eggerer, H., Henning, U., and Agranoff, B. W.   (1959).   *Federation Proc.* **18**, 278.
Manskaja, S. M.   (1959).   *Proc. Intern. Congr. Biochem. 4th Vienna 1958* **2**, 215.
Marion, L.   (1958).   *Bull. Soc. Chim. France*, pp. 109-115.
McCalla, D. R., and Neish, A. C.   (1959a).   *Can. J. Biochem. Physiol.* **37**, 531-536.
McCalla, D. R., and Neish, A. C.   (1959b).   *Can. J. Biochem. Physiol.* **37**, 537-547.
Meister, A.   (1950).   *J. Biol. Chem.* **184**, 117-129.
Mitsuhashi, S., and Davis, B. D.   (1954).   *Biochim. Biophys. Acta* **15**, 54-61.
Nandy, M., and Ganguli, N. C.   (1961a).   *Arch. Biochim. Biophys.* **92**, 399-408.
Nandy, M., and Ganguli, N. C.   (1961b).   *Biochim. Biophys. Acta* **48**, 608-610.
Neish, A. C.   (1955).   *Can. J. Biochem. Physiol.* **33**, 658-666.
Neish, A. C.   (1957).   *Can. J. Biochem. Physiol.* **35**, 161-167.

Neish, A. C. (1958). *Can. J. Botany* **36**, 649-662.

Neish, A. C. (1959). *Can. J. Botany* **37**, 1085-1100.

Neish, A. C. (1960). *Ann. Rev. Plant Physiol.* **11**, 55-80.

Neish, A. C. (1961). *Phytochemistry* **1**, 1-24.

Pellerin, J., and D'Iorio, A. (1958). *Can. J. Biochem. Physiol.* **36**, 491-497.

Quastel, J. H., and Woolf, B. (1926). *Biochem. J.* **20**, 545-555.

Reznik, H. (1960). *Ergeb. Biol.* **23**, 14-46.

Robinson, R. (1955). "The Structural Relations of Natural Products." Oxford Univ. Press (Clarendon), London.

Schwinck, I., and Adams, E. (1959). *Biochim. Biophys. Acta* **36**, 102-117.

Shibata, S., and Yamazaki, M. (1957). *Pharm. Bull. Tokyo* **5**, 501-502; *Chem. Abstracts* **52**, 13882 (1958).

Stafford, H. (1960). *Plant Physiol.* **35**, 612-618.

Tabor, H., and Mehler, A. H. (1955). *In* "Methods in Enzymology" (S. P. Calowich and N. O. Kaplan, eds.), Vol. II, p. 228. Academic Press, New York.

Takahashi, M., Ito, T., and Mizutani, A. (1960). *J. Pharm. Soc. Japan* **80**, 782-783.

Underhill, E. W., Watkin, J. E., and Neish, A. C. (1957). *Can. J. Biochem. Physiol.* **35**, 219-228.

Watkin, J. E., and Neish, A. C. (1960). *Can. J. Biochem. Physiol.* **38**, 559-567.

Watkin, J. E., Underhill, E. W., and Neish, A. C. (1957). *Can. J. Biochem. Physiol.* **35**, 229-237.

Watkin, J. E., Brown, S. A., and Neish, A. C. (1960). *Chem. Can.* **12** (3), 29-32.

Weinstein, L. H., Porter, C. A., and Laurencot, H. (1959a). *Nature* **183**, 326.

Weinstein, L. H., Porter, C. A., and Laurencot, H. (1959b). *Contrib. Boyce Thompson Inst.* **20**, 121-134.

Wightman, F., Chisholm, M. D., and Neish, A. C. (1961). *Phytochemistry* **1**, 30-38.

Wright, D., Brown, S. A., and Neish, A. C. (1958). *Can. J. Biochem. Physiol.* **36**, 1037-1045.

Yaniv, H., and Gilvarg, C. (1955). *J. Biol. Chem.* **213**, 787-795.

PART III

THE TRANSLOCATION OF PHOTOSYNTHETIC PRODUCTS TO THE CAMBIUM

The Production and Translocation of Photosynthate-C^{14} in Conifers

C. D. Nelson

Biology Department, Queen's University, Kingston, Ontario

The availability of C^{14} and the development of the infrared carbon dioxide analyzer (IRCA) make it possible to observe and correlate photosynthesis, respiration, translocation, and metabolism of photosynthetically assimilated carbon. In our work with young conifers we have combined these techniques of isotope and gas exchange analysis to provide the following information: (1) rate of photosynthesis of the shoot; (2) the nature and amount of the C^{14}-labeled products of photosynthesis; (3) rate of respiration of both shoot and root; (4) the amount of translocation of C^{14} to the roots; (5) an indication of the form in which photosynthate is translocated; and (6) metabolism of translocated C^{14} in roots. The experiments reported here have been done to study the effects on these processes of root development and mycorhiza, of light intensity during growth, of season, and of mineral nutrition, particularly nitrogen and phosphorus.

Experimental Material

Seedlings of *Pinus resinosa* Ait. or *P. strobus* L. were grown in the nursery at Midhurst, Ontario. Some seedlings were brought directly from the nursery to Kingston for use in isotope experiments. Other seedlings were transferred to sand culture and grown in the constant light and temperature chamber at Maple, Ontario. Figure 1 shows a typical *P. strobus* seedling with a well-developed root system and conspicuous mycorhiza. Some *P. resinosa* seedlings were grown by Dr. V. Slankis in sterile culture in the growth chamber. When they were 9 months old they were used in experiments.

Methods

In a typical experiment, the shoot of a plant was sealed into a polyethylene chamber attached to the IRCA (Lister *et al.*, 1961) and allowed to carry on photosynthesis in $C^{14}O_2$ for 1 hour followed by an 8-hour period of photosynthesis in air. During this time translocation of C^{14} took place from the shoot to the root. The light intensity was 2500 ft-c unless otherwise noted. Temperature of the shoot was maintained at $20°$–$25°C$ and that of the root at $16°$–$19°C$. Repiration of the shoot was de-

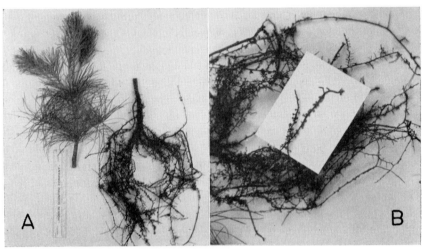

Fig. 1. (A) *P. strobus*, 3 years old, grown in the nursery under full sunlight and without added nutrient. (B) is an enlargement of the roots of the plant to show the well-developed mycorhiza.

termined over two separate 15-minute intervals at 1 and 7.5 hours after $C^{14}O_2$ was first released. At the end of the 9-hour experiment, each seedling was separated into its shoot with needles, roots, and the small piece of stem outside the photosynthesis chamber. After soil was washed from the roots they were sealed into a chamber for the determination of their rate of respiration using the IRCA. The kind of data that was recorded for each plant is shown in Table I.

Plant extracts were prepared by boiling 5–10 gm fresh weight of the shoot or 10–30 gm of the roots in 80% ethanol for 5 minutes. Material was homogenized for 1 minute in a "Virtis" homogenizer. The plant residue was filtered off and reextracted for 5 minutes in boiling 80% ethanol and both extracts were combined. Ethanol was distilled off *in vacuo* at 50°C and the dried extract was taken up in water. It was separated by means of resins into sugar, amino acid, and organic acid fractions. Each fraction was resolved further by two-dimensional paper chromatography (Shiroya *et al.*, 1962).

The total C^{14} content of each fraction was determined by plating and counting aliquots. That of the individual components of each fraction

TABLE I

SUMMARY OF DATA FOR A 3-YEAR-OLD *P. strobus* SEEDLING[a] IN A
TYPICAL TRANSLOCATION EXPERIMENT

Fr wt of shoot (gm)	30
Fr wt of root (gm)	23
Wt of root/wt of shoot	0.74
Apparent rate of photosynthesis	
(mg CO_2 hr^{-1}gm^{-1} fr wt)	0.6
Initial concentration of CO_2 (ppm)	400
Compensation concentration of CO_2 (ppm)	65
Total C^{14} taken up (µc)	300
Rate of respiration (mg CO_2 hr^{-1}gm^{-1} fr wt)	
Shoot	0.1
Root	0.2

[a] Plant illustrated in Fig. 1, grown in the nursery.

was determined by plating and counting eluates from paper chromatograms. Ethanol-insoluble residues were oxidized and counted as $BaC^{14}O_3$ (Nelson and Gorham, 1959).

Translocation to Roots with and without Mycorhiza

It has been suggested that the mycorhizal fungi absorb sugars from the roots of their hosts (Björkman, 1942-43, 1944, 1949). Indeed, Björkman (1949) reported a correlation between the amounts of sugars in pine roots and mycorhizal frequency.

To test the hypothesis that the presence of mycorhiza might influence the amount of material translocated to the roots, plants of *P. resinosa* grown in soil were compared to plants grown in sterile culture. Some of the plants grown in soil and all of the plants grown in sterile culture had no mycorhiza. The pertinent data are summarized in Table II. The first plant is an example of a soil-grown plant without mycorhiza. In 25 hours it translocated only 5% of its radioactive photosynthate while a plant with mycorhiza translocated 54% in the same time. Even after 9 hours a plant with mycorhiza translocated 35% of its fixed carbon. However, the plant without mycorhiza had a root/shoot ratio of 1.1 compared to 3.1 for the plant with mycorhiza. It is possible that the increased metabolic activity generated by a more fully developed root may be responsible for the increase in translocation rather than the presence of mycorhiza. The two experiments with plants grown in sterile culture suggest that this is not so; rather they suggest that there is less translocation of photosynthate in 9 hours to roots of plants grown in sterile culture without mycorhiza.

TABLE II

Translocation of Photosynthate-C^{14} from Shoots to Stems and Roots of
Pinus resinosa with and without Mycorhiza

Mycorhiza	Weight of root / Weight of shoot	Conditions	% Distribution of C^{14}		
			Shoot	Stem	Root
—	1.1^a	1 hr $C^{14}O_2$ light / 12 hr light / 12 hr dark	85	10	5
+	3.1^a	1 hr $C^{14}O_2$ light / 12 hr light / 12 hr dark	43	3	54
+	3.4^a	1 hr $C^{14}O_2$ light / 8 hr light	64	1	35
— (sterile culture)	3.2^b	1 hr $C^{14}O_2$ light / 8 hr light	99	1	0.8
— (sterile culture)	1.1^b	1 hr $C^{14}O_2$ light / 8 hr light	93	2	5

[a] Soil-grown, 3-year-old plants, from the nursery.
[b] Sterile culture, 9-month-old plants, from the growth chamber.

Effect of Mineral Nutrition

The level of mineral nutrition may also affect the physiological activity of the roots and thus influence the amount of photosynthate translocated to the roots (Kursanov, 1956). Three-year-old seedlings of *P. strobus* were transferred in the spring from the nursery to pots where they were grown at a low and a high level of nitrogen (53 and 265 mg per liter, N_1 and N_5 respectively) and at a low, intermediate, and high level of phosphorus (nil, 173, and 692 mg per liter; P_0, P_1, and P_4 respectively). Figure 2 shows typical plants grown for 13 weeks on low and high nitrogen in combination with the intermediate level of phosphorus (N_1P_1 and N_5P_1). Plants grown on high nitrogen had a larger shoot, a thicker stem, and a somewhat better developed root than those grown on low nitrogen. All plants in this experiment had well-developed mycorhiza.

After assimilation of $C^{14}O_2$ by the shoots for 1 hour followed by 8 hours assimilation in air the results shown in Table III were obtained. High levels of either nitrogen or phosphorus nutrition did not result in an increased translocation to the root. In fact, the highest translocation, 13.4%, was observed in the N_1P_0 variant, plants with the lowest level of nutrition. Also, there is an indication that increased phosphorus decreased the amount of material translocated to the roots of the plants grown on either high or low nitrogen. In general, a high translocation did not correlate with a high ratio weight of root/weight of shoot. The rates of photosynthesis were consistent in all the plants except for the higher rate in the N_1P_1 plants and the lower rate in the N_1P_4 plants. Two groups of plants,

N_1P_0 and N_5P_4 with similar rates of photosynthesis of 0.35 and 0.39 mg CO_2 per hour per gram fresh weight had markedly different amounts of photosynthate translocated, 13.4 and 7.7%.

The physiological activity of the roots can be determined by measuring the increase in the number and amount of free amino acids in the roots of plants grown at high nitrogen as compared to plants grown at low nitrogen. Paper chromatography of root extracts showed that there

FIG. 2. *P. strobus*, 3 years old, after growth for 13 weeks in sand culture. (A) Plant N_1P_1 grown on low nitrogen (53 mg/liter) and intermediate phosphorus (173 mg/liter). (B) Plant N_5P_1 grown on high nitrogen (265 mg/liter) and intermediate phosphorus (173 mg/liter).

TABLE III

EFFECT OF NITROGEN AND PHOSPHORUS NUTRITION ON TRANSLOCATION,
PHOTOSYNTHESIS, AND GROWTH OF *P. strobus* SEEDLINGS[a,b]

	P_0	P_1	P_4
	Translocation (C^{14} in root as % of total fixed)		
N_1	13.4	9.0	5.2
N_5	11.2	11.0	7.7
	Apparent Rate of Photosynthesis (mg CO_2 hr^{-1}g^{-1} fr wt)		
N_1	0.35	0.62	0.23
N_5	0.35	0.38	0.39
	Growth (weight of root/weight of shoot)		
N_1	2.2	2.6	1.2
N_5	1.7	1.4	1.1

[a] Each figure is the mean of data from duplicate plants.

[b] Conditions of nutrition expressed as mg per liter were N_1, 53; N_5, 265; P_0, nil; P_1, 173; P_4, 692.

was at least a tenfold increase in free amino acids in the N_5P_1 plants as compared to the N_1P_1 plants. The bulk of this increase was in arginine which could not be detected in the roots of the N_1P_1 plants but made up a large part of the amino acid fraction in the N_5P_1 plants. The rest of the increase in the amino acid fraction was the result of increases in glutamine, asparagine, and alanine. Increases in these compounds are typical of the metabolism of roots of plants grown under high nitrogen (Cocking and Yemm, 1961).

Analysis of the distribution of C^{14} among the compounds of the root also can be used as a measure of physiological activity. Table IV shows that although the bulk of the C^{14} was in the sugars there was an increase of C^{14} in both the amino acid and organic acid fraction in high nitrogen. Together, there was a sixfold increase from 0.51 to 3.0%. Further analysis

TABLE IV

PERCENTAGE DISTRIBUTION OF C^{14} IN THE ETHANOL-SOLUBLE FRACTIONS
FROM THE ROOTS OF *P. strobus* SEEDLINGS[a]

Nutrition[b]	N_1P_1	N_5P_1
Sugars	99.49	97.0
Amino acids	0.06	1.4
Organic acids	0.45	1.6
	0.51	3.0

[a] Plants shown in Fig. 2, grown at two levels of nitrogen.

[b] Conditions of nutrition as in Table III.

of the amino acid fraction showed that a large part of the increase of C^{14} was due to glutamine which contained no C^{14} in the N$_1$P$_1$ plants but 25% of the C^{14} in the N$_5$P$_1$ plants. Most of the remaining increase in this fraction was due to increased C^{14} in alanine, serine, and glycine. Since these amino acids were not translocated there was an active synthesis in the root from translocated photosynthate.

It is surprising that there was not a much larger amount of photosynthate translocated to the roots of the plants that were so actively absorbing nitrogen. Apparently the activity of the roots was not controlling the amount of translocation in these plants.

Effect of Light Intensity

Seedlings of *P. strobus* were grown in the nursery for 2 years under full natural sunlight. Then they were moved to a constant light and temperature chamber for further growth. Some seedlings were grown under full illumination of 2800 ft-c. Other seedlings were covered with Fiberglas screens which reduced the light intensity to 250 ft-c. After 2 months of growth under these conditions of high and low light intensity, the seedlings were brought to the laboratory for use in the experiments shown in Table V. A plant grown at 2800 ft-c (plant 1) and one grown at 250 ft-c (plant 3) were allowed to carry on photosynthesis in C^{14}O$_2$ at 2500 ft-c. Two other plants (plants 2 and 4) grown under high and low light intensity were allowed to carry on photosynthesis in C^{14}O$_2$ at 250 ft-c. About 2.4 mc was taken up by each seedling. Immediately after the C^{14}O$_2$ was taken up the rate of respiration was determined. Following this determination each seedling was illuminated for an additional 7.5 hours with the same light intensity as before. At the end of this time the rate of dark respiration was determined for the second time.

Each seedling was separated into its shoot, stem, and roots. The shoot and stem were extracted immediately with ethanol. The roots were placed in a closed chamber and their rate of respiration was determined prior to extraction with ethanol. Both the ethanol-soluble and insoluble fractions were assayed for C^{14}.

As is seen in Table V, the photosynthetic rates of seedlings 1 and 3 were equally high at 2500 ft-c, and of seedlings 2 and 4 were low at 250 ft-c. Thus, photosynthetic capacity was not affected by low light intensity during the 2-month period of growth prior to the experiment. On the other hand, the rate of respiration of both shoot and roots of the two plants grown under full light intensity was higher than the rate of those grown under low light intensity.

In both the plants grown under high or under low light the specific activity of the respired C^{14}O$_2$ decreased by about half in the 7.5 hours

TABLE V

EFFECT OF LIGHT INTENSITY DURING GROWTH AND DURING TRANSLOCATION ON THE
PHOTOSYNTHESIS AND RESPIRATION OF SHOOTS AND ON THE TRANSLOCATION OF
PHOTOSYNTHATE-C^{14} FROM SHOOTS TO ROOTS OF *Pinus strobus*[a]

Activity	Plant			
	1	2	3	4
Light intensity (ft-c)				
During growth	2800	2800	250	250
During translocation	2500	250	2500	250
Apparent rate of photosynthesis ($mg\ CO_2\ hr^{-1}g^{-1}\ fr\ wt$)	0.64	0.08	0.65	0.14
Rate of respiration ($mg\ CO_2\ hr^{-1}g^{-1}\ fr\ wt$)				
Shoot, 1 hr after $C^{14}O_2$ release	0.40	—	0.32	0.31
Shoot, 7.5 hr after $C^{14}O_2$ release	0.37	0.42	0.27	0.28
Root, 7.5 hr after $C^{14}O_2$ release	0.15	0.20	0.09	0.11
Specific activity of respired $C^{14}O_2$ ($cpm\ mg^{-1}$)				
Shoot, 1 hr after $C^{14}O_2$ release	206	—	380	359
Shoot, 7.5 hr after $C^{14}O_2$ release	104	72	195	201
Root, 7.5 hr after $C^{14}O_2$ release	11	0	0	0
Distribution of C^{14} (%)				
Shoot	84.3	86.0	99.8	100
Stem	3.6	2.9	Trace	0
Root	12.1	11.1	Trace	0

[a] Plants grown in the nursery for 2 years under full natural sunlight. Two months before use plants were potted and transferred to the growth chamber. Two plants were grown at 2800 ft-c, and two at 250 ft-c with the temperature of the shoot 20°–24°C and that of the root 16°–19°C.

between the two measurements. This indicates that as time passed the C^{14} assimilated during the 1-hour photosynthesis period was less available as a substrate for respiration. Also, the plants grown under low light respired $C^{14}O_2$ at a lower rate but with a specific activity two times higher than the plants grown under high light. This means that recently assimilated carbon was the preferred respiratory substrate in the plants grown under low light.

In all seedlings, regardless of their previous growth conditions, about 92% of absorbed carbon dioxide appeared in the ethanol-soluble and 8% in the insoluble fraction at the end of the 9-hour experiment. In all seedlings, the bulk of the absorbed carbon remained in the shoot, although there was a striking difference in the amounts translocated to the roots. Plants 1 and 2, grown under high light intensity, translocated 12 and 11% of the total C^{14} assimilated while plants 3 and 4 grown under low light intensity translocated little or no C^{14} to the roots. Since all of these plants had mycorhiza and root/shoot weight ratios that were comparable it is suggested that the root may not be the controlling factor in translocation but that control over the amount of material translocated may depend on the physiological state of the shoot.

Table VI shows the distribution of C^{14} in the ethanol-soluble fraction

TABLE VI

PERCENTAGE DISTRIBUTION OF C^{14} IN THE ETHANOL-SOLUBLE FRACTION OF A
P. strobus SEEDLING[a] AFTER PHOTOSYNTHESIS AT 2500 FT-C

Compound	Shoot	Stem (bark)	Roots
Amino acids	1	1	0.5
Organic acids	2	1	0.5
Sugars	97	98	99
Sucrose	72	94	94
Glucose	10	1	2
Fructose	11	1	2
Raffinose	1	2	1
Disaccharide	1	—	—
Unknown	2	—	—
Total (μc)	1840	82	283

[a] Plant 1, Table V.

of the shoots, roots, and bark of the stem of a plant after photosynthesis at 2500 ft-c. Since there was only a trace of C^{14} in the woody part of the stem it is not included in the table. The bulk of the radioactivity in all parts of the plant was in the sugar fraction and mainly in sucrose. In all of our experiments with pine, sucrose was always isolated from the stem and in some plants was the only compound detected. This indicates that sucrose is the main form in which the carbon fixed in photosynthesis was translocated. Whether the hexoses and raffinose are translocated or arise in the stem by conversion of translocated sucrose is not known. However, there was much less radioactivity in the hexoses in the stem and roots than in the shoots. Also, the disaccharide and the unknown sugar isolated from the shoots were never detected in the stem or roots. This indicates that assimilation and translocation are not directly coupled. Rather, certain selected products of photosynthetic assimilation are translocated.

Seasonal Variations

Experiments with *P. strobus* illustrate seasonal variations (Fig. 3). Plants, 3 years old, were brought from the nursery each month starting when the ground was still frozen in April. The measure of translocation was the amount of C^{14} recovered from the roots after assimilation of

$C^{14}O_2$ by the shoots for 1 hour followed by 8 hours assimilation in air. The apparent rate of photosynthesis and growth as measured by length of the new leader stem are also shown in the figure.

In April, the plants translocated about 8% of the assimilated C^{14} to the roots. The greatest translocation during the year was in May when

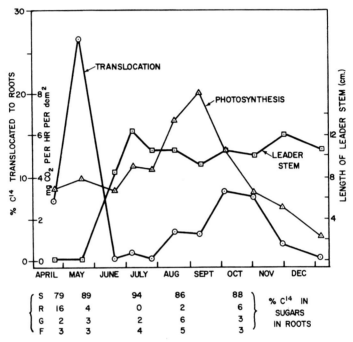

	S	79	89	94	86	88	% C^{14} IN
	R	16	4	0	2	6	SUGARS
	G	2	3	2	6	3	IN ROOTS
	F	3	3	4	5	3	

FIG. 3. Changes with season in the translocation of C^{14} to the roots, the rate of apparent photosynthesis of the shoots, the length of the new leader stem, and the per cent of C^{14} in sugars in the roots. S, sucrose; R, raffinose; G, glucose; F, fructose. Plants were grown for 3 years in the nursery in 8-inch wooden boxes dug into the soil and illuminated by natural sunlight. Each month, starting in April 1961, two plants were moved to the laboratory for the experiment. Each point on the graphs is the mean of data from the duplicate plants.

27% of the assimilated C^{14} was translocated. In April and May the growth of the new leader stem had not yet begun and the apparent rate of photosynthesis was moderate. Translocation to roots stopped completely during June and July, slowly recovered in August, reached a second maximum in October and declined again as winter set in. Elongation of the new leader stem took place entirely during May and June, whereas the apparent rate of photosynthesis steadily rose to the maximum for the year in September. It is interesting to note that the period of most active photosynthesis in September coincided with the time at which there was a low translocation to roots.

The bulk of the C^{14} recovered from the roots was in the sugar fraction. The distribution of C^{14} among the four sugars of this fraction is shown in Fig. 3. Although sucrose was the main radioactive sugar recovered from the roots at all seasons of the year there was a seasonal variation in the amount of C^{14} recovered in raffinose. Raffinose accounted for up to 16% of the C^{14} in the roots in April and up to 6% in October while no radioactivity could be detected in raffinose in July. The high concentration of C^{14} in raffinose coincided with the two peaks of translocation to the root in the spring and fall.

The bimodal curve of translocation may be the result of metabolic activity in the root and correspond to the spring and fall periods of root growth observed in temperate climates (Kramer and Kozlowski, 1960). It may be that increased activity of the roots acts to "pull" assimilates to the roots as Kursanov (1961) suggests. It is possible that water supply may be limiting metabolic activity of the roots during the summer but this problem has not been investigated.

On the other hand, the bimodal curve of translocation can be explained if the phloem was rendered nonfunctional in May. In this case, the initial flow of material in the spring must have occurred through phloem that matured during the previous summer. Translocation to roots began again in late summer after the newly formed phloem had differentiated. There is no anatomical evidence to show that the functional phloem of conifers disappears during the summer. However, the investigations of the sieve tubes of *P. strobus* made in Massachusetts by Abbe and Crafts (1939) indicated that phloem laid down in the spring may not differentiate until late summer or early fall.

Summary

The use of tracers has given an appreciation of the various processes that are involved in translocation of organic material from the site of assimilation or "source" to the place of utilization or "sink." The translocation of a compound may be influenced by the rate of operation of any one or more of the following sequential processes: (a) the assimilation of carbon dioxide; (b) the synthesis of new compounds; (c) mixing of the newly synthesized material with endogenous material; (d) local utilization of the mixed pool; (e) transfer of a compound from the site of synthesis in the mesophyll to the vascular tissue either before or after mixing; (f) longitudinal translocation through the stem; (g) radial translocation of the compound from the conducting elements to the surrounding tissues; (h) accumulation and metabolism of the compound in the conducting and surrounding tissues; (i) physiological activity of the sink; and (j) temporary or permanent immobilization of material in any tissue.

The physiological activity of the sink (process i) has been emphasized as the main factor in controlling translocation. Kursanov (1961) has shown that a high level of ammonium nitrate given to soybeans enhances the translocation of photosynthate to the roots.

In the present work with *P. resinosa* the presence of mycorhiza apparently influences the physiological activity of the root resulting in a large amount of photosynthate-C^{14} being translocated to the root as compared to those plants without mycorhiza. On the other hand, in *P. strobus* with mycorhiza, increased nitrogen nutrition resulted in an increased nitrogen metabolism of the root without an increased translocation of photosynthate-C^{14}. In fact, plants grown at a low level of nitrogen of 2.5 mg per liter translocated as much photosynthate-C^{14} as plants grown at a high level of 265 mg per liter. Apparently in some species or at least under some environmental conditions the physiological state of the root does not control the amount of photosynthate translocated.

Many observations suggest that in *P. strobus* both the kind and amount of material translocated is controlled at the site where material is transferred from the site of synthesis in the mesophyll to the vascular tissue (process e).

The rate of assimilation of CO_2 (process a) did not control translocation as long as there was sufficient photosynthesis to produce sucrose in the leaves. In August and September when the rate of photosynthesis reached its highest levels for the year the amount of photosynthate translocated to the roots was low. In the nutrition experiments there was about the same amount of translocation in plants with an apparent rate of photosynthesis of 0.35 and 0.62 mg CO_2 per hour per gram fresh weight.

Although many compounds including amino acids and sugars became radioactive in the leaves after a period of photosynthesis in $C^{14}O_2$ (process b) only a selected few sugars, sucrose, raffinose, glucose, and fructose were detected in the stem. Of these most of the radioactivity was in sucrose, the main form in which photosynthate was translocated in pine.

Synthesis of sucrose was not inhibited (process c). Also, the utilization of sucrose in the leaves (process e) was not large. In all trees, whether translocation occurred or not, the bulk of the C^{14} fixed in the leaves was recovered as sucrose, the form in which photosynthate is translocated in pine.

In plants grown under low light, translocation to roots was stopped, and recently fixed carbon was preferentially respired in the dark. Apparently there was a block to the transfer of the large pool of sucrose from the photosynthesizing tissue of the mesophyll to the conducting tissue of the veins.

In pine, there is nothing to indicate whether or not the processes of longitudinal translocation and accumulation in the stem (processes f, g, and h) control the flow of photosynthate to the roots. Since the kind of photosynthate translocated is controlled in the leaf and not in the stem, the interpretation is preferred that the amount of photosynthate translocated also is controlled in the leaf at the site of transfer to the vascular tissue.

ACKNOWLEDGMENTS

The author wishes to express his thanks to L. T. White, Department of Forestry, Maple, Ontario, and G. Krotkov, Queen's University, Kingston, Ontario. Without their help in the initiation of this project, continued interest and support during its execution, this work would not have been possible.

Thanks are also due to J. Halpenny, Superintendent at the Provincial Forest Nursery, Midhurst, Ontario, and to V. Slankis, Department of Forestry, Maple, Ontario, for providing the pine seedlings.

The biochemical and gas exchange analyses have been carried out by T. Shiroya and G. R. Lister.

Work on tree physiology at Queen's University has been financed by Extra-Mural Research Grants from the Canada Department of Agriculture and the Canada Department of Forestry.

DISCUSSION

WILCOX: In your graph and figures on translocation, respiration, and photosynthesis in *Pinus strobus,* I was struck by the similarity of the translocation curve to the curve for bimodal root growth. Do you think it is possible that the two peaks in translocation coincide with the two peaks of root growth activity?

NELSON: It is entirely possible, but I have no data for these trees.

ZIEGLER: You had to use different individuals for this study, which means you had to use a statistical approach. How much variation is there in the points on this curve for *Pinus strobus?*

NELSON: Each point on the curve represents data from two plants, grown under high light. In addition, we have used plants grown under low light. These data are for 1961. In 1962 we checked occasionally through the season and found the same thing. There is certainly a summer period of at least a month in which there is little or no translocation to the root.

ZIEGLER: I suppose many more individuals would be needed, to be sure about these peaks.

NELSON: The difficulty here is not to be sure that there are peaks but to be sure when the peaks occur. I think that this changes from year to year. For example, this spring the trees were at first very much behind because of cold weather. The weather turned warm later, and now (April 20) there is good translocation.

So far we have used about fifty trees for experiments in the spring or in the fall, and there was always translocation to the roots. In another twenty plants there was little or no translocation in the summer. I believe that we have analyzed enough individuals to show that there are definitely two peaks, one in the spring and one in the fall.

FREY-WYSSLING: Where do the assimilates go to in the summer when they do not go to the roots? Do they just stay in the leaves? Is there no period when the stream is reversed?

NELSON: I really do not know.

KRAMER: What are the roots living on during this long period in the summer?

WILCOX: My guess would be that they are not growing. An almost complete quiescence of root growth in midseason is common to many species.

KRAMER: Experience shows that this is not true in southern pines. Turner (1936) found in Arkansas that roots of loblolly and shortleaf pine grew continuously during every 8-day observation period for 2 years. Studies of Reed (1939) in the Duke Forest on *Pinus echinata* and *P. taeda* showed that root growth occurred in every month of the year. Decreased rate of growth during the summer seemed to be associated with deficient soil moisture.

Another approach to this might be through actual analysis of carbohydrate content. Hepting (1945) found a relatively high carbohydrate content in the roots of shortleaf pine during the summer and I doubt if there are real deficiencies of carbohydrates in the summer. Is this a difference between a pine which has a well-defined flush or two of growth, and those which may have several flushes?

NELSON: The distribution of C^{14} among the soluble sugars of the roots was different in the summer in that raffinose was lacking. I do not know what relation this might have to water stress. However, I do not believe that water is involved in the seasonal differences in translocation that we observed for the following reason: The data for carbon dioxide uptake indicate that the rate of photosynthesis was not limited by water stress in these plants. Still there was no translocation during the summer.

KRAMER: It would be interesting to measure the carbohydrate content of those roots at the end of the season.

WILCOX: I am dubious about the value of carbohydrate measurements because dormant roots are nearly always full of starch.

WAREING: We find root periodicity in Scots pine and Wight (1933) showed this with field observations. I have also confirmed this using glass-sided boxes where the plants were watered regularly, so it is not just a water effect. I think there is a flush of root growth in the spring until the shoot begins to flush, after which it stops until the shoot stops extending. The difference may lie, as Dr. Kramer said, in different numbers of shoot flushes.

ALVIM: How do you account for the higher rate of photosynthesis in September?

NELSON: All I know is that for 3 years in a row we have observed it. It is interesting that our "sterile-grown" plants have a lower rate of photosynthesis than field-grown plants. The data presented here show the apparent rates of photosynthesis after the plants are brought to the laboratory and before the experiment starts. Under the illumination of 2500 ft-c the rate of photosynthesis remains the same throughout the day, once the period of induction to the new light intensity is over.

THIMANN: Does it have something to do with moving them into the laboratory from outdoors? Suppose you kept them in the lab several days, would they keep up the same rate?

NELSON: We kept two trees in the laboratory for 10 days, and measured the rate of photosynthesis morning, noon, and evening. It was constant for 10 days. At the end of the 10 days these plants started a new flush of growth, which they would not have done if left in the field.

KRAMER: McGregor, in our laboratory, found the highest rate of photosynthesis in loblolly and white pine in July to September, when expressed per unit of needle length or per unit of chlorophyll.

RICHARDSON: Your finding that plants grown under low light intensity do not alter their capacity for photosynthesis is in contrast to quite a lot of work. I wonder if previously reported "adaptation phenomena" could be due to accumulation of photosynthates in the needles. I say this because you also claim that translocation is reduced under low light intensities. These "adaptation phenomena" may be a reduction in photosynthetic potential due to accumulation of photosynthate in the leaves.

NELSON: We have analyzed enough plants now, grown under high and low light, in the growth chamber and in the field, to know that the photosynthetic capacity does not change whether they are grown in high or low light. Of course, this is only for 2 months. The result might be different if the plants were kept under high or low light for 6 months, although 2 months is quite a long period. It seems to me that the high light plants might transfer photosynthate more efficiently from the fixing tissue to the conducting tissue. It is this transfer process that has adapted in these trees. The low light plants respire their recently fixed photosynthates more rapidly than the high light plants. They apparently cannot transfer them readily to the sieve tubes for translocation.

REFERENCES

Abbe, L. B., and Crafts, A. S.   (1939).   *Am. J. Botany* **100**, 695-722.

Björkman, E.   (1942-43).   *Symbolae Botan. Upsaliensis.* **6**, 1-190.

Björkman, E.   (1944).   *Svensk Botan. Tidskr.* **38**, 14.

Björkman, E.   (1949).   *Svensk Botan. Tidskr.* **43**, 223-262.

Cocking, E. C., and Yemm, E. W.   (1961).   *New Phytologist* **60**, 103-116.

Hepting, G. H.   (1945).   *Phytopathology* **35**, 106-110.

Kramer, P. J., and Kozlowski, T. T.   (1960).   "Physiology of Trees," pp. 52-53. McGraw-Hill, New York.

Kursanov, A. L.   (1956).   *Ann. Rev. Plant Physiol.* **7**, 401-406.

Kursanov, A. L.   (1961).   *Endeavour* **20**, 19-25.

Lister, G. R., Krotkov, G., and Nelson, C. D.   (1961).   *Can. J. Botany* **39**, 581-591.

Nelson, C. D., and Gorham, P. R.   (1959).   *Can. J. Botany* **37**, 439-447.

Reed, J. F.   (1939).   *Duke Univ. School of Forestry Bull. No. 4.*

Shiroya, T., Slankis, V., Krotkov, G., and Nelson, C. D.   (1962).   *Can. J. Botany* **40**, 669-676.

Turner, L. M.   (1936).   *J. Agr. Res.* **53**, 145-149.

Wight, W.   (1933).   *New Phytol.* **32**, 77-96.

The Role of Transcellular Streaming in Phloem Transport

R. Thaine and R. D. Preston

Astbury Department of Biophysics, University of Leeds, England

During the past few years ideas on the mechanism of phloem transport have tended to crystallize into two main groups. On the one hand is the school of thought which maintains that the movement concerned is a mass flow, though not necessarily precisely as envisaged by Münch, and that it is inconceivable for the mechanism to be any other than one causing transport of the sieve tube contents, or some part of them, bodily along the stem. On the other hand there is the smaller school, which has maintained that the submicroscopic histology of the phloem is such that mass flow demonstrably can never have occurred and never can occur. These two diametrically opposed conclusions are exemplified by two highly successful lines of investigation, each of which apparently proves its point.

In one of these Weatherley and his colleagues (1959), following the work of Mittler (1957, 1958), and of Kennedy and Mittler (1957) have shown that exudates from aphid stylets piercing the sieve tubes in willow stems must come from a long file of sieve tube elements and must be moving along them at a rate impossible except by mass flow of some kind. He and others have shown, moreover, that if the pores in the sieve element walls are open then the pressures required are not excessive. Similarly Spanner (1962), basing his conclusions on the experimental work of Canny (1960), has shown that while energy requirements cannot be said to favor passive mass flow they are not antagonistic to activated mass flow [such as, for instance, his electroosmotic flow (Spanner, 1958)] through sieve tubes with finely structured sieve pores.

In the other line of investigation a number of workers beginning with Hepton *et al.* (1955) and Hepton and Preston (1960) and, most elegantly, Kollmann (1960) and Kollman and Schumacher (1961) have claimed that sieve pores are filled with cytoplasm which, according to the observations of Kollmann, is permeated by tubules passing from one sieve tube element to the next, possibly a part of the endoplasmic reticulum. These cytoplasmic "plugs" preclude any mass flow through the sieve pores as a whole since continual longitudinal displacement of the sieve tube contents would have left the pores relatively free of contents. Movement along the tubules would require pressures far too high to be conceived as operative in sieve tubes.

The present position can therefore perhaps be summarized as a denial of the possibility of mass flow mediated by a hydrostatic pressure gradient while accepting it that mass flow of some kind is the only transport method which could move the large amount of material involved. Whether in fact mass flow does occur or not, the evidence that the metabolic energy of phloem tissue is involved, recently summarized by Kursanov (1963), seems overwhelming. This view was also reached after a recent Conference on Translocation (Preston, 1963).

In a recent paper one of us (Thaine, 1962) has shown that certain parts of the contents of the sieve tube elements of *Primula obconica* petioles are in streaming motion and has suggested that this gives a visual representation of a particular kind of mass flow involved in phloem translocation. This harks back to the older ideas of Curtis and his school (Curtis, 1929, 1935; Curtis and Clark, 1950), and Canny (1962), who has confirmed the basic observation, has already worked up a theory of translocation based upon this type of streaming. Mason and his co-workers claimed long ago that the energy requirements of a streaming mechanism were far too severe for serious consideration and, though Canny (1960) has claimed that this was based on a faulty argument, it is now clear (Canny, 1962; Spanner, 1962) that the statements made by Mason must stand. Nevertheless, since Mason assumed a velocity of streaming of 336 cm/hour, about 4000 $\times$ greater than that to be envisaged here, the energy requirement (1.6 mg sucrose/ml sieve tube sap/day, with 50 mg available) no longer rules out consideration of streaming (Canny, 1962).

It is the purpose of this article briefly to present, in words, the evidence for the particle streaming observed by Thaine (1962). The movement can be documented only by cine film and no attempt will be made here to reproduce either photomicrographs or stills from the film; a few have already been published (Thaine, 1962). Some preliminary consideration will then be given to the acceptability of streaming as the mechanism underlying rapid mass movement.

Materials and Methods

Although attention in this paper will be largely confined to movement in the sieve tubes of *Primula obconica* petioles, observations have been made on other tissues and other plants and these will also be referred to as far as they are relevant to the main issue.

The observational material consisted normally of fresh hand sections of living phloem tissue mounted in 0.3 *M* sucrose solution. These were examined in transmitted light with a 60 × apochromatic objective, and the observations were recorded on a 16 mm cine film. With *Epilobium hirsutum*, the epidermis and most of the cortex was stripped from the stem, and the phloem and the remnants of the cortex peeled from the stem with forceps. During the whole of this operation the stem was kept wet with 0.3 *M* sucrose solution. With *Cucurbita pepo*, on the other hand, stems were severed under 0.6 *M* sucrose and kept in this solution for 1 hour, by which time the leaves had wilted. Longitudinal hand sections were then mounted in 0.4 *M* sucrose solution. Transverse sections were also examined. Border parenchyma cells were examined in soybean leaves while still attached to the plant and exudate from this plant, collected on glass slides from the cut end of the stem, were also examined. All these methods gave, from time to time, clear evidence of particle movement. The system involved is in most cases very delicate and the highest success was given by the *Primula* petioles.

Results

It is not proposed to reproduce photomicrographs here; they can be found in Thaine (1962). It is found that plant cells are commonly permeated by cytoplasmic threads ranging in diameter up to 7 μ. These have been found in living cortical cells of *Cucurbita*, passing through cell walls and forming lateral links between the vascular bundles in petioles; in stems of *Epilobium hirsutum* where they have been followed longitudinally along files of cortical cells; in cortical cells next to the phloem in *Primula obconica* petioles, in the parietal protoplasm, about 2 μ in diameter and apparently continuous between cells; in sieve tube elements of leaf midribs in soybean, parallel to sieve tube length and passing through sieve pores and similarly, though less frequently, in *Cucurbita* sieve tubes. In many of these tissues particles 2–3 μ in diameter were seen moving along the strands in border parenchyma cells, and have been followed across the end walls of five cells in a longitudinal row.

In *Primula obconica* petioles particles can be seen in motion within transcellular strands in cells which we believe to be sieve tubes, passing longitudinally along the lumina and through sieve pores. The particles occur in close linear order within the strands and are about the size of mitochondria, i.e., about 0.5 μ in diameter. Movement in single strands is always in one direction, but this direction may be upward and downward in strands in the same sieve tube element and even in neighboring strands. The rate of movement is 3–5 cm/hour. Single particles have been followed across ten sieve plates in the same sieve tube (total length 1.0 mm). It is not, of course, known if the particles are the only part of the strand contents to be moving.

In phloem exudates from soybean stems particles are seen in abundance and are then sometimes associated with long, fine fibrils up to 10 mm in length. This recalls an impression given by the transcellular strands of sieve tubes that they contain fine threads. It seems, therefore, possible that the particles within the strands are attached to these fine threads.

Theoretical Considerations

Microscopic structures similar to those described here have been reported from time to time in parenchyma cells, but this is the first time they appear to have been seen in sieve tubes. Toryama (1957, 1958) has described a "threadlike apparatus" in the lacunal cells of *Mimosa pudica* and Scott (1946) earlier suggested that continuity exists between the plasmodesmata and threads in the cytoplasm of differentiating crystalloid cells in a number of plants including *Bohoemeria*. The particulate contents of the strands are well-known cytoplasmic constituents. These were seen almost 40 years ago by Scarth (1927) in transvacuolar cytoplasmic strands of living *Tradescantia* staminal hairs. We believe that both fine threads and particles attached to them may be ubiquitous in plant cells. In assessing the significance to be attached to the particle movements described here it is necessary first to examine both the stature of the strands as real components of the sieve tube contents and the evidence that both they and the particles pass through cross walls. Again we focus attention on the petioles of *Primula obconica*.

The visibility of the strands is certainly enhanced by diffraction effects but the strands are demonstrably not artifacts due to diffraction from side walls, etc. This is demonstrated by the observations that (a) the strands move in and out of focus and are displaced laterally as the microscope body tube is moved vertically, while the cross walls are still in focus; (b) most strands lie parallel to the side walls but some pass along the cells in wavy or spiral paths; (c) the particles always lie in close linear order and move along paths already marked out by the section of the strand lying downstream. The claim that the strands and the particles pass through cross walls rests entirely upon the observation that strands, particles and cross walls are simultaneously in focus when viewed through a 60 × apochromatic objective and whether or not phase contrast is used. The sections are naturally thick but we have no doubt whatever that in each of the very many observations made, the strands lie at the same focal level as parts of the cross wall. Even if, moreover, the particles are to be considered as moving in a cell either above or below the cells separated by an observed cross wall, then the fact still has to be taken into account that single particles have been traced passing ten such cross walls over a length of more than 1 mm. Since there are no cells in the petiole even approaching this length then the particles must pass some cross walls somewhere along the path; these can hardly be other than sieve plates and the cells therefore sieve elements.

Since the transcellular strands show a bulge at each particle and since exuded particles are associated with fine threads, the strands are thought to have four distinguishable constituents: a boundary membrane which separates the tubular strand from the vacuolar fluid, enclosing longitudinally oriented threadlike structures, microscopic (and submicroscopic) particles including mitochondria, and a matrix of fluid endoplasm. Mitochondria are the only constituents large enough to be seen moving in transcellular strands but it is probable that the fluid endoplasm also moves. It will be recalled that Kamiya (1960a, b; see also Kamiya and Kuroda, 1956) has shown in *Nitella* and other members of the Characeae that particles move at a uniform velocity. Kamiya concludes that these particles are carried by the rotating endoplasm which is activated at the interface with the cortical gel. Circulation streaming in higher plants has not been studied in such detail, but on the basis of present evidence the mechanism would seem to be more complex. Adjacent particles of the same size, and particles following identical pathways in the cytoplasm, move at quite different rates and it is difficult to visualize how such pathways can be followed if a fluid flow is the cause of movement. A better understanding of the relationships between moving particles and other mobile constituents in protoplasmic streaming must await future investigations.

The transcellular strand membrane is interpreted to be similar to the tonoplast in structure and physiological properties. Both form boundaries between cytoplasm and vacuolar fluid and the tonoplast in hair cells is apparently continuous with the external surface of transvacuolar strands. On these grounds, it is assumed that the transcellular membrane is differentially permeable and that sugar is actively (and irreversibly in periods of normal growth of the intact plant) secreted across this membrane into the sieve tube vacuolar fluid. When normal supplies of mobile materials are not available from leaves, e.g., in the spring growth or in defoliated cuttings, active uptake will occur with sugar moving in the reverse direction, from storage cells in the stem. In regions of the phloem which are not importing or exporting large amounts of mobile materials a steady level of solute is maintained in the vacuolar fluid. Weatherley *et al.* (1959) described this equilibrium value as "the sucrose potential" which may be the factor controlling the phloem pressure gradient.

These structures give the appearance of a widespread transport system but their evaluation in this respect rests upon demonstration that they can meet the stringent requirements of phloem transport. We visualize the relevant structures in sieve tubes as represented diagrammatically in Fig. 1. The tube contents must presumably be liquid, and this may be moving at a rate which we cannot even guess but which may be

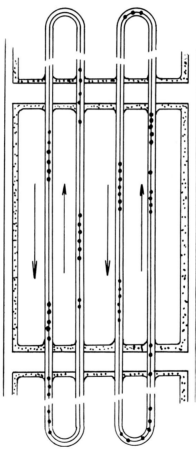

FIG. 1. Diagrammatic representation of the system involved in transcellular streaming in sieve tubes. One element is shown, with two sieve plates, and four transcellular strands joined in pairs at each end. The strands contain particles attached to threads and the arrows show the direction of flow. The parietal cytoplasm is stippled. The details of passage of the strands through the parietal cytoplasm on the sieve plates are uncertain.

very different from that of the particles. The two-way movement can hardly mean that particles either collect in the upper and lower reaches of the plant or are destroyed there. It seems more likely that these flow paths are parts of loops, turning over at least at the apices of the plants presumably in the parietal cytoplasm of terminal sieve tube elements or even in mesophyll cells. Since the movement seen here occurs in isolated strips of phloem, the possibility is not excluded that the strands are interconnected at intervals along the stem, forming relatively short loops. For these reasons, in Fig. 1 the strands are joined above and below.

According to the present concept there are at least three constituents of sieve tube cytoplasm which have both structural and functional importance in phloem transport. These are: (a) the transcellular strands; (b) the vacuolar fluid matrix; and (c) the parietal cytoplasm. Figure 1 illustrates the structural requirements of the theory and interprets cytoplasm structure in a mature *Primula obconica* sieve tube element. It is proposed that transcellular strands form parallel pathways for mobile materials moving across sieve tube lumina and that these strands penetrate the plasmalemma and the sieve plates to pass through sieve pores.

The parietal cytoplasm of sieve tube elements is known to be differentially permeable, and if the membranes which surround the strands and line the sieve pores have the same properties, the vacuoles of adjoining sieve tube elements will be separated by osmotically active membranes. Consequently the turgor pressure within a sieve tube element will depend on the solute concentration of the vacuolar fluid in the single element and not on the concentration of mobile materials. If this is a correct interpretation, concentration and pressure gradients which have been measured experimentally, and related directly to the translocation mechanism, develop outside the pathway of long distance transport and may be regarded as a result of translocation but not its cause. In this concept of phloem transport the solutes of the vacuolar fluid are comparatively immobile in the longitudinal direction while the contents of transcellular strands move rapidly along linear pathways which are not subject to structural or physiological barriers. Some mobile materials within strands may occur in bound form and consequently would not contribute to the osmotic value of the fluid endoplasm.

Canny (1962) has published an alternative model for phloem transport in which the relationship between mobile materials and transcellular streaming is quite different. In contrast to the above proposals, Canny assumes that sucrose in the vacuolar fluid is mobile and in the direct pathway of longitudinal movement. If the sucrose solution in the vacuolar fluid is mobile then the strand membrane constitutes a barrier to rapid cell to cell movement. In Canny's model this problem is overcome by the assumption that the strand membrane is more permeable than the plasmalemma. However, it is difficult to reconcile an unusually permeable strand membrane, introduced to give rapid exchange of sucrose between the strand and its fluid matrix, with the maintenance of three separate concentration gradients along sieve tubes: in the fluid matrix, in the strands moving in the same direction as the gradient in the fluid matrix and, most difficult to visualize, a gradient in opposite direction to the first two in strands streaming from "sink" to "source." Another objection to Canny's model is that it involves a stepwise pathway (strand–vacuolar fluid–strand) which is likely to be less efficient than movement along a linear flow pathway readily available through the strand. The issue to be decided is whether mobile materials passing longitudinally through the phloem move in and out of the vacuolar fluid in response to concentration gradients as Canny suggests, or whether longitudinal movement is through the strand by the mechanism of protoplasmic streaming which could, if necessary, operate against a concentration gradient. To resolve these different views more information is needed about the distribution of mobile materials within undamaged sieve tube elements.

If concentration gradients and pressure gradients demonstrated in the phloem are not *directly* involved in the transport mechanism then it can be assumed that the sucrose in this fluid is secreted across a normal membrane boundary which separates the strand cytoplasm from the vacuolar fluid. In this interpretation, concentration gradients in phloem tissue and exudate, either from cut phloem or aphid stylets, develop in the vacuolar fluid and are not part of the transcellular transporting system. What then is the role of concentration gradients in this concept of phloem transport? Since mass transfer occurs predominantly in the direction of the concentration gradient, that is, from the sites of synthesis to the sites of utilization, this gradient may have an indirect effect on transport. Presumably more energy is required for transport in the direction of greatest mass transfer than is required for transport in the opposite direction. The pressure gradient between "source" and "sink" may serve to reduce the motive-force energy requirement in the direction of larger mass transfer. A source of motive-force energy is readily available in the form of ATP synthesized by the mitochondria moving along transcellular strands and Canny (1960) has already suggested that the constant proportional breakdown of transported sucrose which he revealed in vine petioles may be due to strand mitochondria.

Lateral movement in and out of the phloem is thought to occur via the vacuolar fluid and parietal cytoplasm of cells involved in long distance transport. Mobile materials may move between parenchyma cells and sieve tubes through the "symplasm" of parietal cytoplasm linked by plasmodesmata and sieve field connections. The connection between the transcellular strands and parenchyma cell cytoplasm in the terminal regions of the vacuolar system could follow the structural arrangement in hair cells where transvacuolar strands merge with parietal cytoplasm. The external membrance of the vacuolar strand is apparently continuous with the tonoplast, and particles moving within the vacuolar strand pass unimpeded into the parietal cytoplasm. In the region of the stem apex, the linear file of mature sieve tube elements is joined to progressively less differentiated cells which finally results in undifferentiated cells being "in file" with the sieve tube. It is suggested that, during differentiation, the cytoplasm of the sieve tube element is oriented in parallel strands which at one stage join up across the sieve plate. It is conceivable that particles moving along transcellular strands change direction when the strand merges with parietal cytoplasm in the region of differentiation. In leaf veins, border parenchyma cells, which are thought to be involved in accumulation of mobile products from the lamina, could similarly be "in file" with mature sieve tubes of larger veins.

The whole concept of transcellular streaming as a long-distance transport mechanism must, however, stand or fall by its capacity to explain mass transfer along stems at the known rates. The observed linear rate of movement, 3–5 cm/hour, lies far below the observed rates of 100 cm/hour and this is undoubtedly the weakest part of the whole argument.

It is to be remembered, however, that the rates of particle streaming have been measured only in isolated petiole phloem strips severed at each end and it could be that the rates are higher in intact tissue. Moreover, it is commonly observed that in streaming in higher plants smaller particles move faster than larger particles and the same may be true here. If the fluid matrix in the strands is also moving the rate could be far higher. The figure of 3–5 cm/hour is therefore certainly a minimal figure.

Linear rates of movement are, however, of somewhat doubtful significance and it is perhaps of more critical importance to examine the position with regard to rates of mass transfer. This can at the moment be done only in a provisional, perhaps even trivial way. Let us consider two possibilities: (a) that the fluid matrix of the strands contains the mobile material, considered moving at the same rate as the particles, and (b) that the particles themselves contain the mobile material. In either case we may then deduce how extensively, if at all, the rate of movement, or some other factor, needs to be changed in order to meet known requirements. In either case it is taken that the transport mechanism will need to move sucrose along a petiole at a rate of 2 gm/cm² sieve tube per hour.

Taking first the alternative of liquid movement, it is possible to determine how many strands will be necessary per sieve tube to carry this amount of sugar per hour. Suppose there are n strands per sieve tube, each 3 μ diameter, transporting a 10% solution of sucrose. The rate of mass transfer per sieve tube assuming a linear rate of 5 cm/hour will then be

$$n \cdot \pi \, (1.5 \times 10^{-4})^2 \cdot 5 \; ml/hour$$

$$= \frac{n \cdot 2.25 \cdot \pi}{2} \times 10^{-8} \; gm \; sucrose \; per \; hour$$

Taking the radius of the sieve tube lumina as 10 μ, this amounts to

$$\frac{2.25 \; n}{200} \; gm/cm^2 \; sieve \; tube \; per \; hour$$

$$= 2$$

$$\therefore n = 170$$

The total cross-sectional area of these strands is equivalent to the area of a circular capillary about 20 μ in radius, larger therefore than the sieve tube itself, which is impossible. If the total flow path is to have, say 10% of the cross-sectional area of the sieve tube, the product (velocity of transport × concentration of sucrose solution moved) will need to be increased by a factor of about 40. If the maximum conceivable concentration of mobile sucrose solution is 20%, the velocity of movement will therefore need to be about 20 × that of the particles.

If, on the other extreme, the particles in movement were to be regarded as solid, available polysaccharides, then the number of particles required per unit length of flow path can be calculated. Taking the particles as 0.25 μ radius, the weight of each, assuming a density of 1.5, is about 10^{-13} gm. If there are N of these per centimeter length of path in each strand, with n strands per sieve tube, then the transport rate is

$$\frac{5 \; Nn}{\pi} \cdot 10^{-5} = 2 \; gm/cm^2 \; sieve \; tube \; per \; hour$$

If $n = 10$ (the barely possible limit), then

$$N = 12,000$$

giving 12 particles in a 10 μ length of strand. This is quantitatively an acceptable answer. Particle involvement, however, raises a new set of questions on the fate of the particles at the sink and their production at the source.

These preliminary calculations seem to show, however, that the present concept should not be discounted on rates of movement alone, for the modifications required to meet the rates of flow are not quite inconceivable. Much more experimental work is necessary before a final decision can be reached.

DISCUSSION

ESAU: We have made some pertinent observations at Davis on the species used by Dr. Thaine, *Primula obconica*. The "transcellular strands" depicted in the cine film are lines resulting from diffraction of light from walls at various depths in the section. When the sections are treated with NaOH, 95% alcohol, or papain, and the cytoplasm is removed or severely shrunken, the lines are not affected. Moreover, the cells interpreted as sieve elements in this film are parenchyma cells; the sieve elements are much narrower. The streaming seen in the film occurred in the long parenchyma cells of the older phloem. Underlying shorter cells provided views of transverse walls that were incorrectly interpreted as sieve plates. [The comment was illustrated by means of lantern slides depicting diffraction lines in material treated as mentioned above. This study, including the illustrations, is to be published; see Esau *et al.*, 1963.]

PRESTON: Dr. Thaine is well aware that there is streaming in parenchyma cells. He has been scrupulously careful to take this into account, to ensure that the movement he has seen was, in fact, in sieve tubes. This is a subjective judgement, and many more people must look into this to make the case convincing. Thaine has followed a particle moving along what appears to be a strand for a distance of 1 mm, passing on the way 10 cross walls. This seems to rule out streaming in parenchyma cells.

ESAU: The outside parenchyma cells can easily be a millimeter long. These are the first cells to appear in the phloem and as new phloem is formed, they elongate.

PRESTON: In Thaine's preparations the parenchyma cells which might be confused with sieve tubes are nothing like so long. It is in a sense immaterial whether the particles are moving in the parenchyma or in the sieve tubes. If they are moving in the parenchyma, this is still long-distance transport. Concerning Prof. Esau's illustrations of sections treated with proteinase and NaOH, I would make this remark: If one looks at the living nucleus one sees chromosomes vaguely; one sees them better in phase contrast, better still if stained, better still if treated with proteinase, and one still sees them if they are treated with NaOH. That is to say, there is something there which condenses. I think the same thing is happening here. If we have oriented cytoplasm, in this particular sense, then unless the proteinase is one which will digest both the strand wall and the threads, and of course proteinases vary widely and commonly and do not take all of the cytoplasm, then there will be something left. Moreover, it must be remembered that proteinases do not enter cells readily. If the original was oriented, then what is left will be oriented. The same thing is true of NaOH. So even these things that Dr. Esau is seeing may not be diffraction phenomena. I am completely convinced that whatever these things are that we are calling strands, they are *not* diffraction phenomena. Diffraction phenomena can be very easily recognized.

THIMANN: What are Dr. Thaine's criteria for deciding that he is dealing with sieve tubes?

PRESTON: His criteria rest largely on the dimensions of the cell. He did not photograph any single cell which was larger than the common diameter of the sieve tube. It is not possible to see the sieve pores in these very thick sections.

THIMANN: But according to Dr. Esau the sieve tubes are very small.

PRESTON: The cells you have seen on the film are small, but there are more important points than that. First, these particles move over long distances. Second, when the particles come to what we have interpreted as a sieve plate they halt and wriggle through, and when they are through they move away. This does not suggest that they are moving under the cross wall, but that they are moving through a hole, in whatever this wall is.

ZIEGLER: But this hesitation at the "sieve plate" could be explained in another way as well. At the sieve plate the diameter of the sieve element is slightly greater, so that the wall of the parenchyma cell would be somewhat curved around it. A particle moving along this wall may give the illusion of a hesitation, if seen in longitudinal section, because it moves along the wall around the sieve plate.

PRESTON: I think the curve around the sieve plate would have to be exaggerated a great deal to get enough hesitation. Moreover, many of the strands observed lie well away from the wall, in the center of the cell.

ZIMMERMANN: I do not think that a curve is necessary. The apparent hesitation of the particle could well be caused by mere diffraction of the transverse wall.

FREY-WYSSLING: Dr. Preston, I cannot understand how you can say that there is no diffraction. The sections are very thick and the objective of the microscope has a very short focal depth. It is impossible to obtain a picture of such an object without also getting diffraction lines. In the *Tradescantia* hair some of the particles were white, some were black, and some had a black margin around a white center, all Fresnel fringes of refraction. Diffraction phenomena are unavoidable with your method.

PRESTON: Of course; I agree that we are seeing these strands by diffraction; we are not seeing the strands themselves. If we were to photometer across these strands the strand would appear as two profiles with two Fresnel fringes on each side. There is no doubt that the appearance of this strand is due to diffraction phenomena. But it is a diffraction phenomenon produced by something real at the position of the strand, not by something else lower down. Thaine interprets the two bright strands with the dark center as a tube; this could be wrong. Until it can be verified in the electron microscope, if it ever can be, one cannot be sure what the structure of the body causing the stranded appearance is.

FREY-WYSSLING: In *Tradescantia* Dr. Thaine suggests that the particles cross the wall between the hair cells. Diffraction makes those walls appear twice as wide and the particle diameter twice as great as they are in reality, so that the particles appear to move within the wall.

PRESTON: Dr. Thaine does not say that particles do go through the wall in *Tradescantia* hairs, even though sometimes it looks a bit like it.

BAILEY: I think it is quite clear that the first part of the film, on *Tradescantia*, shows a type of cyclosis which is characteristic, carrying globules of a fatty substance. Vital staining shows them to be of a fatty nature. Possibly if you used vital stains on the *Primula* you could determine whether you were dealing with the circulation of particles of a fatty nature in the adjacent cells, or whether you were dealing with polysaccharides within the sieve tube.

PRESTON: These particles mostly stain with Janus green, suggesting that they are mitochondria. They are about the size of mitochondria.

ZIMMERMANN: Did you include in your calculation the fact that one half of the cytoplasm is moving one way and the other half the other way? This would cut your calculated rate in half.

PRESTON: No, the calculations deal only with the strands moving downwards. Since the rates were already far too high I did not worry about the strands moving upwards. I agree that the rate of movement is completely wrong here, by a factor of at least 10. This is at the moment the weakness of the whole theory.

ZIMMERMANN: You showed a model of a sieve element. If an aphid stylet bundle is sticking in such a sieve element, we can measure the rate of exudation from the cut end. If this rate is compared with the volume of the sieve element, we find that the sieve element is being refilled at least 3 to 10 times per second. How would you explain this rapid refilling with the proposed mechanism of transport?

PRESTON: I would not at the moment.

TOMLINSON: How wide are the sieve pores in the plant Dr. Thaine used?

PRESTON: The particles, 0.3–0.5 μ.

ESAU: I doubt very much that the pores are large enough to let these particles pass through.

PRESTON: The size of these particles is an estimate; obviously there is a diffraction enlargement. In any case it is now well documented that cell organelles, including mitochondria, can be reversibly deformed.

TOMLINSON: Why can these strands not be seen in fixed material?

PRESTON: In freeze-dried material they can be seen quite easily. What you see then is the strand with bulges containing bright, refractive particles.

TOMLINSON: Could you watch the cells as they were being fixed and see what changes occurred?

PRESTON: That should be done. I think we should try to see this movement in an intact stem and I think there are now ways of achieving this. Until such observations are made, arguments based on rates of movement, for instance, are irrelevant.

TOMLINSON: How long are these pieces of petiole you photographed.

PRESTON: The actual section was about 4 mm long.

TOMLINSON: If it is not connected at either end, I do not see how this proves that Münch's hypothesis of mass flow is false. In this section there is neither source nor sink for mass flow to work.

PRESTON: I think that if there is bidirectional movement in severed phloem at any stage, you can no longer assume mass flow in the sense originally used by Münch.

TOMLINSON: It seems to me that you have a system that is quite artificial, and you are assuming that it functions like an undisturbed natural system.

PRESTON: One can see this type of movement in the terminal sieve elements in the green leaves of an intact plant.

NELSON: If the logarithm of radioactivity per centimeter of stem is plotted against translocation distance down the stem of a plant, after application of $C^{14}O_2$ to a leaf, a straight line of decreasing radioactivity with increasing distance is obtained. The curve reaches the level of background radiation at a certain point. Beyond that, further away from the leaves, there is an advancing front of irregular intensity. This results in a discontinuous profile. Radioactivity is in sucrose in the phloem tissue (Nelson *et al.*, 1959). This phenomenon is quite general and must be taken into account when one sets up a theory for a translocation mechanism. I cannot rationalize this with any long-distance transport mechanism based on strands.

PRESTON: There are presumably two components moving, the particles and the liquid contents of the strands. If these move at different rates, as I believe they must, it is possible to conceive that the same compound or two different compounds could be separated between these both in space and time. It would be a bit difficult at the moment to account for the discontinuity just before the advancing front. It might be both sucrose absorbed on particles and sucrose in the liquid.

REFERENCES

Canny, M. J. (1960). *Ann. Botany London* **24**, 330.
Canny, M. J. (1962). *Ann. Botany London* **26**, 603.
Curtis, O. F. (1929). *Am. J. Botany* **16**, 154.
Curtis, O. F. (1935). "Translocation of Solutes in Plants." McGraw-Hill, New York.
Curtis, O. F., and Clark, D. G. (1950). "An Introduction to Plant Physiology," McGraw-Hill, New York.
Esau, K., Engleman, E. M., and Bisalputra, T. (1963). *Planta* **59**, 617.
Hepton, C. E. L., and Preston, R. D. (1960). *J. Exptl. Botany* **11**, 381.
Hepton, C. E. L., Preston, R. D., and Ripley, G. W. (1955). *Nature* **176**, 868.
Kamiya, N. (1960a). *Ann. Rep. Scient. Works. Fac. Sci. Osaka Univ.* **8**, 13.
Kamiya, N. (1960b). *Ann. Rev. Plant Physiol.* **11**, 323.
Kamiya, N., and Kuroda, K. (1956). *Botan. Mag. Tokyo* **69**, 544.
Kennedy, J. S., and Mittler, T. E. (1957). *Nature* **171**, 528.
Kollmann, R. (1960). *Planta* **55**, 67.
Kollmann, R., and Schumacher, W. (1961). *Planta* **57**, 583.
Kursanov, A. L. (1963). *Advan. Botan. Res.* **1**, 209.
Mittler, T. E. (1957). *J. Exptl. Biol.* **34**, 334.
Mittler, T. E. (1958). *J. Exptl. Biol.* **35**, 74.
Nelson, C. D., Perkins, H. J., and Gorham, P. R. (1959). *Can. J. Botany* **37**, 1181-1189.
Preston, R. D. (1963). *Progr. Biophys. Biophys. Chem.* (in press).
Scarth, G. W. (1927). *Protoplasma* **2**, 189.
Scott, F. M. (1946). *Botan. Gaz.* **107**, 372.
Spanner, D. C. (1958). *J. Exptl. Botany* **9**, 332.
Spanner, D. C. (1962). *Ann. Botany London* **26**, 511.
Thaine, R. (1962). *J. Exptl. Botany* **13**, 152.
Toryama, H. (1957). *Cytologia* **22**, 60.
Toryama, H. (1958). *Botan. Mag.* **71**, 309.
Weatherley, P. E., Peel, A. J., and Hill, G. P. (1959). *J. Exptl. Botany* **10**, 1.

Effects of Water Stress on the Translocation of Photosyntheti- cally Assimilated Carbon-14 in Yellow Poplar[1]

Bruce R. Roberts[2,3]

School of Forestry, Duke University, Durham, North Carolina

Introduction

A great amount of time and effort has been expended in research on translocation of organic substances in plants. Surprisingly, however, little work has been done on the effects of plant water stress on translocation, in spite of the fact that the internal water balance must have a significant influence on translocation, regardless of the mechanism involved.

Gates (1955a,b) concluded that changes in stem to leaf weight ratios which occurred in young tomato plants subjected to water stress were caused by changes in the normal patterns of translocation. Pallas (1959) and Pallas and Williams (1962) reported a marked decrease in movement of P^{32} and C^{14}-labeled 2,4-D in red kidney beans subjected to water stress. Wilson and McKell (1961) found that less than half as much P^{32} was translocated out of the leaves of sunflower plants in soil at a soil moisture tension of 15 atm as from leaves of plants in soil at a tension of 0.3 atm. Several other workers have reported decreased translocation out of leaves of plants subjected to water stress (Petinov and Malysheva, 1960; Crafts, 1956; Zholkevich *et al.*, 1958).

In most experiments plant water stress was not measured quantitatively. However, Wiebe and Wihrheim (1962) reported that translocation of C^{14}-labeled photosynthate out of sunflower leaves was re-

[1] The research reported in this paper was supported by National Science Foundation Grant No. G-6151 made to Dr. Paul J. Kramer, Department of Botany, Duke University.
[2] This paper was presented by P. J. Kramer.
[3] Present address: U.S. Department of Agriculture, Delaware, Ohio.

duced about one-third as diffusion pressure deficit increased from 1–2 atm to 10–12 atm. Basler *et al.* (1961) found that both absorption and translocation of C^{14}-labeled 2,4-D by bean seedlings was greatly decreased as the relative turgidity of the leaves fell below 80%.

Very little information is available concerning the effect of water stress on translocation in woody species. A series of experiments therefore was performed to measure the effects of known levels of water stress on translocation of photosynthate out of the leaves of yellow poplar (*Liriodendron tulipifera* L.). This species was used because the long, slender petioles and large orbicular leaves are convenient for experiments in which leaves are enclosed in a container.

Methods and Materials

Three-year-old potted seedlings were used. They had been grown for a year in the greenhouse and were kept well supplied with water and mineral nutrients. The seedlings selected for study in any one experiment were moved to the laboratory and grown for a week at $25 \pm 2°C$ under a 14-hour photoperiod with 1500 ft-c of light. The pots were covered with aluminum foil and transpiration was measured by daily weighing. Some of the seedlings were subjected to drought by withholding water while the others were kept well watered as controls. When the decrease in transpiration rate of droughted seedlings indicated the desired level of water stress they were exposed to radiocarbon.

The blade of a young, fully developed yellow poplar leaf was inserted into a modified 3-liter boiling flask which served as a photosynthesis chamber and the mouth was sealed with a split rubber stopper fitted around the petiole. The photosynthesis chamber was lighted with a 300-watt inside reflector lamp mounted above a water filter which maintained a light intensity of 2550 ft-c. The temperature was maintained at $26 \pm 1°C$. All experiments were started at the same time of day to prevent any effect from diurnal variations in rate of photosynthesis, sugar concentration, or translocation. A closed system similar to that of Swanson and El-Shishiny (1958) was used to supply $C^{14}O_2$ to the exposed leaf. After an exposure period of 1 hour, the excess $C^{14}O_2$ was cleared from the system by absorption in 0.1 N NaOH and the leaf was removed from the photosynthesis chamber. Each seedling was then placed under a light intensity of 2200 ft-c for an additional 4 hours to allow time for translocation of the labeled photosynthate. Care was taken to avoid injury to leaves or petioles because injured plants often show anomalous translocation (Koontz and Biddulph, 1957).

At the time of removal from the photosynthesis chamber a leaf immediately above or below the leaf exposed to $C^{14}O_2$ was detached for measurement of water deficit. Water deficit measurements were made by a modification of the Stocker (1929) method. To obtain the turgid or saturated weight, the basal portion of the leaf was cut off and the leaf placed in a closed container with the cut surface in 1 cm of water for 12 hours. Whole leaves rather than leaf discs were used since punching out discs probably results in absorption of water through cut surfaces and affects the accuracy of the measurement (Hewlett and Kramer, 1963).

After 4 hours under light, the stem of each seedling was cut into 5-cm segments and the bark (phloem) and xylem separated. The fresh weight and the outline of cross-sectional area for each bark section were obtained and the sections were then extracted in boiling 80% ethanol. After boiling, the volume of extract was recorded and the bark sections dried in an oven at 105°C for 12 hours. A 250 λ aliquot from each extract was pipetted onto a stainless steel planchet and dried under infrared light.

The C^{14} activity in each aliquot was counted in a windowless gas flow counter and the appropriate conversion factor applied to those samples having a significant net count rate in order to obtain the radioactivity in the total volume of extract.

Results

EFFECT OF WATER STRESS ON TOTAL C^{14} ACTIVITY

The effect of water stress on the total quantity of radiocarbon in a seedling is shown in Fig. 1. Above a water deficit of about 5% there is a steep reduction in the amount of radioactivity absorbed and translocated. As water stress increases from 5 to 20% the amount of radioactivity decreases 93%. Minimum quantities of C^{14} occur at water deficits of approximately 35%, above which a very slight increase in radiocarbon occurs.

The results shown in Fig. 1 raise an important question. Is the reduction in amount of radioactivity present in a stressed seedling the result of decreased absorption of the isotope by the leaf or of decreased translocation after it becomes fixed in the leaf? In an attempt to answer this question calculations were made of the effects of water stress on $C^{14}O_2$ absorption per unit of leaf area and on the percentage of radiocarbon translocated from the exposed leaf. The results of these calculations are presented in Fig. 2, 3 and 4.

As shown in Fig. 2, the absorption of radiocarbon decreases with increased plant water stress. The amount of $C^{14}O_2$ absorbed per unit of leaf area was reduced by 95% as plant water stress increased from

5 to 20%. The lowest absorption occurred at a water deficit of 25%, above which the quantity of radiocarbon absorbed increased slightly (2%) to a peak at a water deficit of 40%.

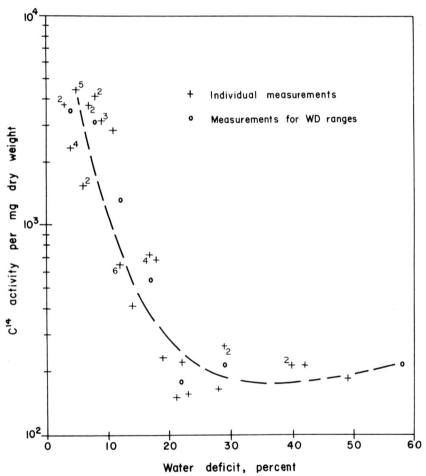

FIG. 1.   Effect of water stress on the total quantity of C^{14} in yellow poplar seedlings 5 hours after initial exposure to $C^{14}O_2$. Results are expressed as the counts per minute per milligram dry weight of leaf and bark tissue sampled. Plotted points are the total number of observations recorded at each water deficit. Averages for the following water deficit ranges are also plotted: 5% and less; 6–10%; 11–15%; 16–20%; 21–25%; 26–30%; 36–40%; 41% and higher.

Wilson and McKell (1961) and Pallas and Williams (1962) reported that increased soil moisture stress caused decreased absorption of radiophosphorus applied to the leaves, but there was no mention of increased absorption with further increase in soil moisture tension. On the other hand, Pallas (1959) and Basler *et al.* (1961) concluded that changes in water stress had little effect on absorption of C^{14}-labeled 2,4-D in bean seedlings. Probably, foliar absorption and translocation are

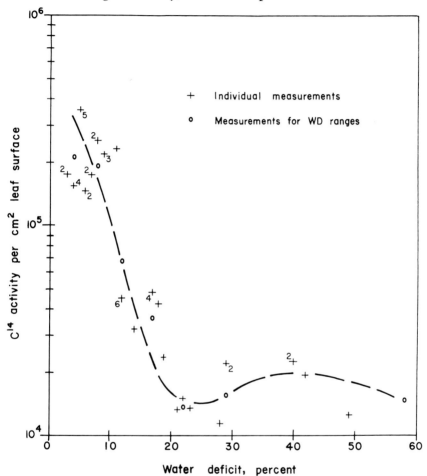

Fig. 2. Effect of water stress on the absorption of radiocarbon by the leaves of yellow poplar during 1 hour exposure to $C^{14}O_2$. Results are expressed as the counts per minute of C^{14} in each plant per unit area of leaf surface. Plotted points are the total number of observations recorded at each water deficit. Averages for the following water deficit ranges also are plotted; 5% and less; 6–10%; 11–15%; 16–20%; 21–25%; 26–30%; 36–40%; 41% and higher.

affected by the nature of the compound and the form in which it is supplied, as well as by the water stress of the plant.

From the shape of the curve in Fig. 2 it is believed that as plant water stress increases, the stomates begin to close thus decreasing the inward diffusion of $C^{14}O_2$ and resulting in decreased absorption of the radioisotope. At the point of lowest $C^{14}O_2$ absorption (water deficit of 25%) maximum resistance is offered to entrance of radiocarbon dioxide through stomates. It is suggested that the subsequent increase in radio-activity with further increase in plant water stress might result from mechanical injury to the epidermal cells of the exposed leaf which makes it possible for radiocarbon dioxide to enter through the epidermis. Macroscopic observations made during this study indicate that such a mode of entry is possible. At the higher water tensions leaf surfaces exhibited dried, cracked areas which would readily permit entry of gaseous radiocarbon. If the isotope entered through cracks in the cuticle and epidermis the only limiting factor in determining the quantity of $C^{14}O_2$ absorbed would be the ability of the leaf to fix the radio-carbon after it had gained entrance.

If it is assumed that net photosynthesis is very low at high plant water stress, there are two explanations for the increase in radiocarbon absorption. First, it is possible that the shape of the curve for C^{14} activity between water deficits of 25–55% is affected by an increase in respiration, as was observed by Brix (1962) for loblolly pine. It is not unreasonable to assume existence of a similar relationship for yellow poplar. Second, it is possible that the small increase in C^{14} activity observed at a water deficit of 40% represents an increase in nonphoto-synthetic fixation of $C^{14}O_2$. Wood and Werkman (1936) have shown that the condensation of pyruvic acid with carbon dioxide results in the formation of oxaloacetic acid in certain bacteria. This and other similar reactions show that carbon dioxide can be fixed in organic form in a variety of normally occurring biological reactions which take place in most living organisms.

Effect of Water Stress on Translocation of C^{14}

Figures 3 and 4 show the influence of increased water stress on the transport of radiocarbon out of the exposed leaf. Figure 3 shows the percentage of labeled photosynthate translocated from the treated leaf. As in the previous curves (Fig. 1 and 2) there was a large decrease in the quantity of C^{14} translocated as plant water stress increased from a water deficit of 5% to a water deficit of 20%. This represents a reduction in radioactivity of more than 86%. After reaching an apparent minimum at a water deficit of approximately 23%, the total amount of C^{14} transported increased slightly.

The distribution of radiocarbon in the bark as influenced by five different water regimes is shown in Fig. 4. The results are expressed as the logarithm of the C^{14} activity per unit area of bark tissue. There

is very little difference in the slope of the curve for those seedlings subjected to water deficits of 5% or less and those at water deficits of
6 to 10%. In fact a slightly higher amount of activity was found in
the upper stem segment of those seedlings under a slightly higher water
tension. This probably reflects a condition of optimum stomatal opening

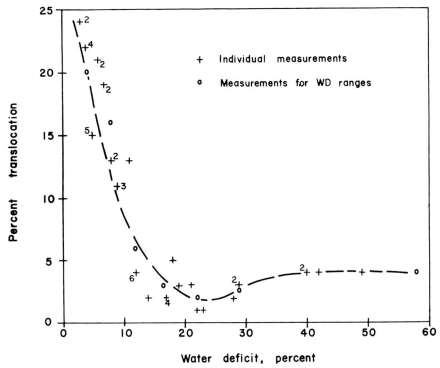

Fig. 3. Effect of water stress on the percentage of radiocarbon translocated out
of the leaves of yellow poplar 5 hours after initial exposure to $C^{14}O_2$. Results represent the percent of the total C^{14} activity in counts per minute which occurred outside
the exposed leaf. Plotted points are the averages of the total number of observations
recorded at each water deficit. Averages for the following water deficit ranges are
also plotted: 5% and less; 6–10%; 11–15%; 16–20%; 21–25%; 26–30%; 36–40%;
41% and higher.

and thus optimum diffusion of radiocarbon dioxide into the leaf. As
the plant water deficit increased to 11–15% there was a reduction in the
quantity of C^{14} activity in the bark as well as a reduction in the total
distance of translocation. The slope at the end of this curve shows a
sharper decrease than was evident from the preceding curves. This
indicates a steeper activity gradient in the last 2 or 3 stem segments. As
the water deficit increased to 16–20% the portion of the curve which

was relatively flat for seedlings subjected to only moderate water stress, became very steep. The reduction in both quantity and distance of C^{14} transport is very pronounced at the higher plant water stress. This condition becomes increasingly obvious as water stress is increased to 21% and higher. Using the 5% deficit as a basis for computation,

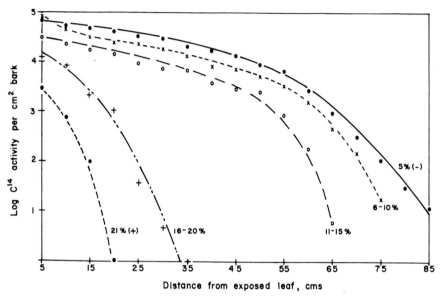

Fig. 4. Effect of water stress on the distribution of radiocarbon in the bark of yellow poplar 5 hours after initial exposure to $C^{14}O_2$. Results are expressed as the logarithm of the C^{14} activity per unit area of bark. Each plotted point represents the total radioactivity in one 5-cm segment of bark.

the reduction in translocation distance with increased plant water stress is 12%, 24%, 59%, and 76% for water deficits of 6–10%, 11–15%, 16–20%, and 21+% respectively. The same trends are evident when the data are expressed on either a fresh or a dry weight basis.

It would appear from the data collected in this study that increased plant water stress indirectly affects translocation of organic solutes in yellow poplar by decreasing the quantity of photosynthate available for transport (Fig. 2) and directly by reducing the amount of translocation (Fig. 3).

Effect of Water Stress on the Rate of C^{14} Movement

The effect of increasing plant water stress on rate of translocation can be seen in Fig. 5. As the water deficit increased from 5 to 20%, the rate of movement of labeled photosynthate decreased 86%. This general trend is in agreement with most other research conducted on the effects of water stress on translocation (Pallas, 1959; Wiebe and Wihrheim, 1962; Wilson and McKell, 1961; Basler *et al.*, 1961; Petinov and Malysheva, 1960; Zholkevich *et al.*, 1958).

It is difficult to compare the rates of C[14] movement in this experiment

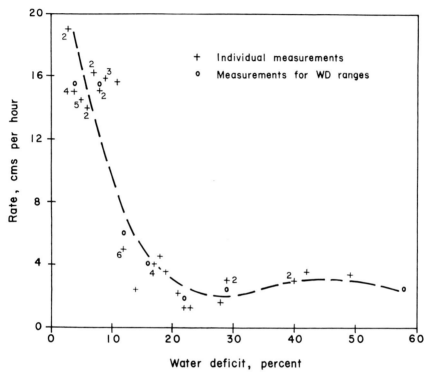

FIG. 5.   Effect of water stress on the rate of C[14] movement in yellow poplar seedlings. Results are expressed in centimeters per hour. Rates are based on 5-hour periods of translocation, including time for absorption and migration of radiocarbon to the conducting elements of the phloem. Plotted points are the averages of the total number of observations recorded at each water deficit. Averages for the following water deficit ranges are also plotted: 5% and less; 6–10%; 11–15%; 16–20%; 21–25%; 26–30%; 36–40%; 41% and higher.

with translocation rates reported by other investigators working with different plant material. Values range all the way from 5040 cm/hour in soybean (Nelson *et al.*, 1959) to 10 cm/hour in kidney bean (Day, 1952), with the average rate falling somewhere around 75–100 cm/hour for most herbaceous species studied. The highest rate observed in yellow poplar was 19.4 cm/hour while the average for all control seedlings was 15.6 cm/hour. Although the rates reported here appear rather low in comparison with those of most herbaceous plants, it is possible that these slower rates of organic solute movement may be characteristic of woody plant species.

Two important factors should be considered in analyzing the rates obtained in translocation studies. First, computing rates by the method used in this study is not strictly valid, since practically nothing is known about the true "front" of radioactivity. Even though it is assumed that the radioactive front occurs at the intercept of the plotted curve (Fig. 5) there is really no evidence to support such an assumption (Vernon and Aronoff, 1952). In fact, Nelson et al. (1958), working with soybeans which had been exposed to radiocarbon dioxide, could not locate the true "front" of radioactivity even after allowing only short periods of time for translocation. A comprehensive review of the problems associated with determining rates of translocation has been presented by Canny (1960b).

The second factor which merits consideration is the presence of a time lag between entrance of the radioisotope into the leaf and its eventual transport through the conducting elements. During the course of preliminary studies on optimum periods for C^{14} exposure it was noted that a time lag existed between absorption of $C^{14}O_2$ and eventual translocation of activity down the stem. Similar observations have been reported by Wilson and McKell (1961), using radiophosphorus in the study of translocation in sunflower and by Crafts (1956). Crafts reported a time lag of 1–2 hours for absorption and migration of 2,4-D-C^{14} to the conducting elements of the phloem. The time lags observed in this study were approximately 3 hours. It should be noted that the rates of C^{14} translocation recorded in Fig. 5 include the total time from introduction of $C^{14}O_2$ into the photosynthesis chamber until sectioning and extraction of the stem. If the time required for fixation of the radiocarbon and migration of the labeled photosynthate to the conducting elements could be recorded accurately it would then be possible to obtain a more precise calculation of the rate of C^{14} translocation in the phloem.

Effect of Water Stress on Direction of C^{14} Translocation

There is very little reference made in the literature to the influence of water stress on direction of translocation in plants and the few observations have been made on herbaceous species. Wilson and McKell (1961) reported finding more radioactivity in the growing regions of sunflower plants in the absence of soil water stress than when water was limiting. From the data of Wiebe and Wihrheim (1962) one might conclude that there is a slight increase in upward translocation of C^{14}

in sunflowers subjected to $C^{14}O_2$ for 1 hour at relative turgidities of 80–85% as compared with values obtained at relative turgidities of 86–93%. However, the authors make no assumption concerning upward movement of the isotope. In the only other study in which direction was noted, Nelson and Gorham (1957) reported that translocation of glu-

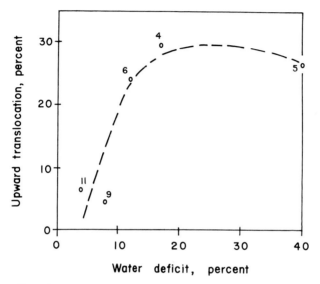

FIG. 6. Effect of water stress on the direction of C^{14} translocation in the bark of yellow poplar 5 hours after initial exposure to $C^{14}O_2$. Results are expressed as the percentage of radioactivity moving up the stem from the exposed leaf. Only those seedlings having C^{14} activity in the stems are included. Plotted points are the averages of the total number of observations within the following water deficit ranges: 5% and less; 6–10%; 11–15%; 16–20%; 21% and higher.

cose-C^{14}, fructose-C^{14}, and sucrose-C^{14} introduced through the cut petiole of the primary leaf of bean seedlings was primarily downward from the point of isotopic introduction. Very small amounts of radioactivity were moved up to the stem tip. Although water stress was not a factor in their study, the results are important as an aid in evaluation of data obtained under conditions of limited water.

Figure 6 shows the percentage of C^{14} activity transported up the stem as a function of water deficit. Only those seedlings which had activity in the stem were included in this graph. The curve indicates that increased plant water stress resulted in a larger percentage of material moving upward in the stem. Such a phenomenon probably is the result of strong competition by the apical meristem for the products of photosynthesis. The young, actively growing meristematic tissue has a greater demand for photosynthetic products than other parts of the plant and the net result is increased upward translocation of C^{14}. It is interesting to note that the curve levels off at the higher water stresses. This may well represent the point at which meristematic activity finally ceases. Reduced growth would not consume the quantity of photosynthate used in the absence of water stress.

As observed in previous data from this experiment, a water deficit of approximately 5 to 20% seems to be critical for translocation of sugars in yellow poplar. Changes in the predominant direction of C^{14} movement also occur in this general water stress range. As water deficit is increased from 5 to 20% there is a corresponding 85% increase in the radiocarbon activity in stem sections above the exposed leaf.

General Remarks

Every effort was made in this study to insure that movement of radiocarbon occurred in the phloem. This was accomplished by supplying the radioisotope in the gaseous form and by keeping the seedlings under environmental conditions which were favorable for normal translocation. Despite precautions, losses in C^{14} activity probably occurred as a result of the following: (a) lateral movement of radioactivity from phloem to xylem (Biddulph and Cory, 1957; Biddulph et al., 1958); (b) loss of activity during separation of wood and bark (Zimmermann, 1961); (c) loss of C^{14} activity during transport of labeled solutes through the phloem (Canny, 1960a).

The results obtained during this study are consistent with the conditions required for operation of the pressure-flow theory of organic solute translocation. This theory, formulated by Münch (1927), postulates the movement of organic solutes and water through the phloem as a direct result of differences in turgor pressure between the leaf and the roots or stem tip. The critical factor necessary for flow through the sieve elements is establishment of a turgor pressure gradient. By imposing a water stress on the plant, one would expect the turgor pressure of the leaves to decrease ($DPD = OP - TP$), resulting in reduced solute movement. The results of this study certainly indicate a marked decrease in rate and amount of translocation with decrease in plant turgor. However, it seems that almost any possible mechanism of translocation would be affected by reduction in cell turgor.

Summary

The effects of water stress on translocation of photosynthetically assimilated C^{14} in yellow poplar seedlings were studied. Three-year-old seedlings were subjected to various degrees of water stress up to a water deficit of 60% prior to exposure of a single leaf to $C^{14}O_2$ in a closed system. After exposure to radiocarbon dioxide for 1 hour at 2550 ft-c and 26 $\pm$ 1°C, the leaf was removed from the photosynthesis chamber and the water deficit of an adjacent leaf was measured. After an additional 4 hours under a light intensity of 2200 ft-c to allow translocation of labeled photosynthate out of the treated leaf, the stem of each seedling was sectioned into 5-cm segments and boiled in 80% ethanol for 5 minutes. The C^{14} activity in a 250 λ aliquot of the extract was recorded and the results expressed on a fresh weight, dry weight, and area basis for each bark segment.

Increasing plant water stress decreased both the uptake of radiocarbon by leaves and the amount translocated out of the leaves. The decreased uptake of C^{14} appears to result from stomatal closure, since translocation was reduced to the same extent as carbon dioxide uptake by increased water stress. The amount of radiocarbon translocated out of the leaves, the rate of translocation, and the distance to which it was translocated were drastically reduced as leaf water stress increased from a water deficit of 5 to 20% as measured by the Stocker method. High water stress resulted in a larger percentage of the radiocarbon translocated upward than in plants subjected to low water stress.

DISCUSSION

NELSON: If one waters the plants, pines for example, during a tracer experiment, one almost always finds that the rate of photosynthesis increases slightly. In order to keep photosynthesis stable during an experiment we have therefore always tried to have the plants sufficiently watered before we start.

KRAMER: The uptake of CO_2 is exceedingly sensitive to water stress. In some species a slight increase in water stress results in an increase in CO_2 uptake. We have good statistical evidence for this. However, if water stress is increased further, CO_2 uptake drops off very rapidly. Brix (1962) found that a relatively low DPD, 6 or 7 atm, will greatly reduce photosynthesis in pine. It practically stops at 10 atm. That does not seem like a very high water stress.

Dr. Zimmermann, what happens to phloem pressure in your trees on a hot summer day?

ZIMMERMANN: Probably the turgor of the sieve tubes goes down and the concentration goes up. Weatherley *et al.* (1959) found this when they perfused xylem with mannitol solutions. In a more recent study, Peel and Weatherley (1962) gave willow cuttings repeated light-dark cycles. In the light, sieve-tube turgor went down and the concentration of stylet exudate went up. They interpreted this in terms of water stress during light periods when the stomata were open. I found a similar phenomenon in my ash trees during temperature experiments. When the stem was frozen at a height of 6 meters above ground, a sharp concentration increase developed in the sieve tubes above freezing. This happened even at about −1°C, where the phloem does not freeze and will recover later. I ascribe this concentration increase to water stress above the place of freezing; the frozen point at 6 meters height is a barrier in the water-conducting system and causes tensions in the xylem above.

PRESTON: Does not xylem sap freeze only well below 0°C? I would say that the low temperature you used was precisely the same temperature which stops cyclosis.

ZIMMERMANN: The concentration of sieve-tube exudate increases all along the stem above the point of freezing, at places where the temperature is normal. We did these experiments during the night when the transpiration stream moves with minimum velocity. It does take very low temperatures to freeze the *moving* xylem water. I am quite certain that we are dealing here with water stress. Of course, I am not saying that *all* the xylem water freezes, just enough to cause a marked resistance to the flow of water. If we lower the temperature more to cause more extensive freezing, the tree wilts and dies.

PRESTON: When a stem is chilled the leaves wilt, but it is fairly clear that the xylem sap does not freeze. This has been observed by Curtis and others. Handley, for instance, showed that if the stem is cooled to 2.5°C, the leaves do not wilt. If it is cooled to 2°C, then they wilt. If the temperature is raised back to 2.5°C, then the leaves recover (Handley, 1939).

ZIMMERMANN: One must be very cautious about drawing conclusions from these experiments because it is almost impossible to measure phloem temperature accurately. The transpiration stream constantly changes the temperature of the phloem, so that all the temperature experiments that have been reported in the literature so far are untrustworthy. Even in the cases where leaves were bagged, the transpiration stream was kept going by root pressure.

PRESTON: Even so, the experiments of Curtis and others were carried out above the freezing point so the xylem sap was certainly not frozen; nevertheless, the tree wilts.

NELSON: I would like to offer an explanation for this effect of wilting. Water stress affects photosynthesis as has been shown. Whether water stress affects the translocation mechanism in the sieve tubes we do not know. However, sugar beet petioles will translocate labeled photosynthate when the blades are quite wilted, indicating that the transfer from photosynthesizing cells to conducting cells is resistant to water stress, as well as translocation in the sieve tubes.

HELLMERS: The closing stomata seem to mask the results of these experiments. Would it be possible to keep the stomata open by blocking them with small crystals so that CO_2 could get into the leaves, even if they wilt?

ZIEGLER: One could do this with a hypostomatal plant such as spinach or *Valerianella olitoria* where the lower epidermis is naturally separated from the chlorenchyma and can be removed.

BAILEY: The *Winteraceae* are characterized by having the stomata blocked by an alveolar form of cutin so that they cannot close.

KRAMER: Figure 3 shows that about 25% of what was in the leaves moved out in fully turgid plants, but only 2–3% under high water stress.

THIMANN: Could not this be interpreted in terms of mass flow? Water is actually entering the phloem from the adjacent cells and participating in flow.

KRAMER: Dr. Roberts said that his data are not inconsistent with the mass-flow theory.

THIMANN: It is interesting to see, however, that translocation does continue even under water stress. This may be due to the maintenance of withdrawal at the other end.

NELSON: We may assume that the rate of translocation is reflected by the slope of the logarithmic profiles in Fig. 4. It is very interesting that the rate is not changing at water stresses from 11% up to 5%. Certainly at 16% the rate changes drastically. But this does not help with your other question.

KRAMER: I am afraid that our data do not support any particular hypothesis of translocation.

NELSON: Is there any way to introduce a constant amount of C^{14} to the leaf and then induce a water stress?

KRAMER: It could be done by growing the plants in water culture and increasing the salt concentration around the roots, but I am afraid this would cause side effects.

BROWN: You could transfer the root system to a very cool environment, and wilt the leaves.

KRAMER: Temperature introduces another complication that I would prefer to avoid.

ALVIM: Would it be possible to feed labeled sugar to the leaves? This works quite well with potatoes and coffee.

KRAMER: Nearly all studies on translocation as affected by water stress have been done using herbicides. We wanted to introduce carbon in a more "natural" fashion. Though sugar works with the tomato, I doubt that we could get it into yellow poplar very easily.

NELSON: As you increased the water stress, more material went up. In soybean we have done the same experiment as you, but darkened the rest of the plant except the photosynthesizing leaves. Then the direction of flow is changed upwards. I wonder whether this is a water-stress effect or a light effect.

KRAMER: Wiebe and Wihrheim (1962) measured the water stress and the translocation; they found that water stresses of 5 atm DPD or more caused a reduction in translocation. Their data also suggest increased upward translocation at high water stress. It might be possible to demonstrate it in the sunflower under their experimental conditions, for the stem tip may be less affected by water stress at that time and so could compete successfully with the other tissues and thus act as a sink even under high water stress.

RICHARDSON: What happens in the root tips?

KRAMER: They should also be competing, but unfortunately we do not know what happens to root tips under water stress.

ZIMMERMANN: Perhaps this problem of more translocation to the tops could be approached by measuring turgor in the sieve tubes under different conditions with aphid stylets.

WILCOX: The fact that apical meristems have a pretty good competitive basis is borne out by the early work on the shrinkage of lemon fruit, is it not?

ZIMMERMANN: It is also one of the expressions of apical dominance. The leader of a tree attracts relatively more photosynthetic products and produces more secondary vascular tissue than the rest of the tree. This was shown by Huber (1928).

KRAMER: I should think that water stress would interfere not only with translocation within the sieve tubes but also with the transfer of substances from supplying cells into the sieve tubes; this must be a very vulnerable step.

NELSON: Certainly, because different species differ drastically in the amount of C^{14}-photosynthate they will transfer. Burr's work with sugar cane shows that if $C^{14}O_2$ is fixed in the light the plant makes labeled sucrose; in time all of this sucrose will move out of the leaves (Burr *et al.*, 1958). Jones *et al.* (1959) showed that in tobacco only 20% is moved out of the leaves. We have shown that soybean leaves retain their labeled sucrose for a week. The only other plant which, like sugar cane, will transport most of the labeled sucrose is sugar beet.

REFERENCES

Basler, E., Todd, G. W., and Meyer, R. E. (1961). *Plant Physiol.* **36**, 573-576.
Biddulph, O., and Cory, R. (1957). *Plant Physiol.* **32**, 608-619.
Biddulph, S., Biddulph, O., and Cory, R. (1958). *Am. J. Botany* **45**, 648-652.
Brix, H. (1962). *Physiol. Plantarum* **15**, 10-20.
Burr, G. O., Hartt, C. E., Tanimoto, T., Takahashi, D., and Drodie, H. W. (1958). *Proc. 1st (UNESCO) Intern. Conf. Sci. Res.* **4**, 351-368.
Canny, M. J. (1960a). *Ann. Botany* **24**, 330-344.
Canny, M. J. (1960b). *Biol. Rev.* **35**, 507-532.
Crafts, A. S. (1956). *Hilgardia* **26**, 287-334.
Day, B. E. (1952). *Plant Physiol.* **27**, 143-152.
Gates, C. T. (1955a). *Australian J. Biol. Sci.* **8**, 196-214.
Gates, C. T. (1955b). *Australian J. Biol. Sci.* **8**, 215-230.
Handley, W. R. C. (1939). *Ann. Botany* **3**, 803-813.
Hewlett, J. D., and Kramer, P. J. (1963). *Protoplasma* **57**, 381-391.
Huber, B. (1928). *Jahrb. wiss. Botanik* **67**, 877-959.
Jones, H., Martin, R. V., and Porter, H. K. (1959). *Ann. Botany* **23**, 493-508.
Koontz, H., and Biddulph, O. (1957). *Plant Physiol.* **32**, 463-470.
Münch, E. (1927). *Ber. Deut. Botan. Ges.* **45**, 340-356.
Nelson, C. D., and Gorham, P. R. (1957). *Can. J. Bot.* **35**, 703-713.
Nelson, C. D., Perkins, H. J., and Gorham, P. R. (1958). *Can. J. Biochem. Physiol.* **36**, 1277-1279.
Nelson, C. D., Perkins, H. J., and Gorham, P. R. (1959). *Can. J. Bot.* **37**, 1181-1189.
Pallas, J. E. (1959). *Plant Physiol.* **34**, suppl. xxi.
Pallas, J. E., and Williams, G. G. (1962). *Botan. Gaz.* **123**, 175-180.
Peel, A. J., and Weatherley, P. E. (1962). *Ann. Botany* **26**, 633-646.
Petinov, N. S., and Malysheva, K. M. (1960). *Plant Physiol.* **7**, 455-458.
Stocker, O. (1929). *Planta* **7**, 382-387.
Swanson, C. A., and El-Shishiny, E. D. H. (1958). *Plant Physiol.* **33**, 33-37.
Vernon, L. P., and Aronoff, S. (1952). *Arch. Biochem. Biophys.* **36**, 383-398.
Weatherley, P. E., Peel, A. J., and Hill, G. P. (1959). *J. Exptl. Botany* **10**, 1-16.
Wiebe, H. H., and Wihrheim, S. E. (1962). "Radioisotopes in Soil—Plant Nutrition Studies," pp. 279-287. International Atomic Energy Agency, Vienna.
Wilson, A. M., and McKell, C. M. (1961). *Plant Physiol.* **36**, 762-765.
Wood, H. G., and Werkman, C. H. (1936). *Biochem. J.* **30**, 48-53.
Zholkevich, V. N., Prusakova, L. D., and Lizandr, A. A. (1958). *Plant Physiol.* **5**, 333-340.
Zimmermann, M. H. (1961). *Science* **133**, 73-79.

The Relation of Transport to Growth in Dicotyle-donous Trees

MARTIN H. ZIMMERMANN

Maria Moors Cabot Foundation for Botanical Research, Harvard University, Petersham, Massachusetts

Forest botanists of the past century were very interested in the question whether annual growth rings of trees are produced from stored photosynthetic material of the previous year or from material produced by the photosynthetic activity of leaves during the current year. In some cases the question was answered quite clearly (Hartig, 1856), but other experiments led to confusing misunderstandings (Wieler, 1896). One of the main difficulties was that growth hormones were unknown at the time; consequently experimental results showing reduced growth were often ascribed to lack of photosynthetic products when they were caused by lack of hormonal stimulation.

In spite of our present-day knowledge of hormonal activities, we are not much better informed about the exact origin of the material that goes into primary and secondary growth than were the forest botanists of the late nineteenth century. The situation is a complex one and there seem to be considerable differences among species. In principle, there are three possible transport-growth relations in trees:

1. Material is translocated directly from active leaves to places of growth via phloem.

2. Material is retranslocated from places of storage to places of growth, either via phloem or via xylem.

3. Material is stored very near the place of growth, mobilization thus involving a minimum of long-distance transport; the phloem may not be involved.

There are a number of reports in the literature dealing with these problems either directly or indirectly. The major difficulty with such reports is that they all concern different species and very different methods of investigation. The present article is an attempt to review some of these papers and to outline a hypothesis of phloem activity throughout the year. This outline is largely hypothetical but it may prove to be a helpful guideline for future work.

Seasonal Phloem Activity

An annual growth ring is formed not only in the xylem but also in the phloem (Fig. 1). This newest layer of phloem functions as a long-distance transport tissue during midsummer and early autumn when trees have fully mature leaves. Sugars and other substances are manufactured in the leaves and exported via the phloem. The exported sugars go into latewood formation and into storage in the form of starch throughout the twigs, the branches, the main stem, and the roots. Places of storage include mainly xylem and phloem parenchyma of both the axial tissues and the rays. In autumn chlorophyll and other substances are broken down. Some of these breakdown products are exported out of the leaves together with the last photosynthates. This is the time when the color of the leaves changes from green to yellow or red. Leaf abscission follows, and some 2 weeks later heavy callose masses are formed on the sieve plates of the current year's phloem. The tree has entered its dormant stage. During January, February, or March, dormancy is broken and the deposited callose is partially or totally dissolved. The phloem is now reactivated and essentially ready for translocation. Buds start to grow as soon as weather conditions permit, in the Petersham area about May 1. When the buds open, storage materials move upward into the growing shoots via reactivated phloem. During the period of leaf development upward movement is reduced as the storage materials become depleted. The leaves, however, become increasingly self-sufficient as they develop, and a short period of no phloem transport may follow. Transport begins again when the new leaves are fully developed and ready to export photosynthetic products. The direction of transport is now reversed (i.e., out of the leaves) and movement takes place in new phloem tissue formed during the early period of growth. The new leaves are exporting via new phloem and the cycle is closed. This stage is reached during the last days of June in the Petersham area.

Let us now go through the whole cycle once more and discuss the individual stages in the light of available evidence.

Export Transport via Phloem during the Summer

Most of the experimental transport work reported in the literature has been carried out during the summer, the time during which export material is translocated out of mature leaves. The anatomical situation is fairly clear during this time: transverse sections of the bark of most species of dicotyledonous trees of our north temperate zone show fairly clear annual phloem growth rings (Fig. 1). This was already well known to the forest botanists of the nineteenth century. The youngest

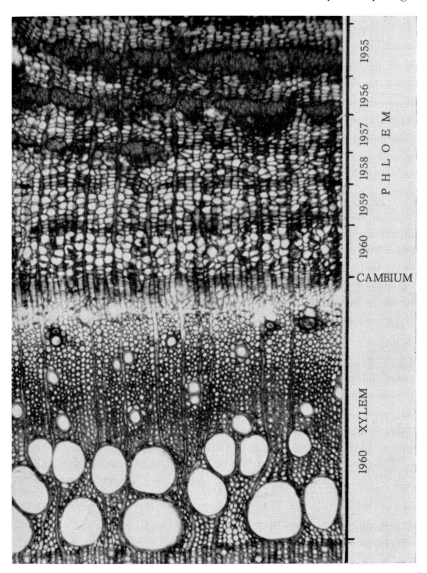

FIG. 1. Transverse section through the bark of white ash (*Fraxinus americana* L.) showing growth rings in the phloem. The tree was cut on July 11, 1960. The 1960 growth ring of the xylem and several growth rings of the phloem are shown.

of these growth rings can be recognized as the conducting tissue; it contains the fully developed and functioning sieve tubes. In contrast to this, the sieve tubes of the older growth rings appear dead; they are often completely crushed (Holdheide, 1951; Huber, 1958; see also the paper by Esau on p. 37 of this volume).

Exudation studies confirmed these anatomical findings. Huber and Rouschal (1938) reported that incisions into the phloem of dicotyledonous trees yield exudate only if the incision is deep enough to reach the youngest growth ring of the phloem. By making sections through a number of bark incisions we were able to confirm the observations of Huber and Rouschal.

Anatomical investigations of the location of aphid stylet bundles also indicate that phloem transport takes place in the innermost portion of the phloem. Mittler's method of obtaining sieve tube exudate is well known: bark-feeding aphids are anesthetized with carbon dioxide and cut from their mouth parts. Sieve tube turgor maintains a steady flow of exudate from the stylet stumps at a high rate and for up to several days (Mittler, 1957, 1958). During the summers of 1960 and 1961 serial sections were cut through a number of barks containing exuding or nonexuding stylet bundles to find their exact location within the bark tissue. Thirty-nine bark blocks which contained the stylet bundles of *Longistigma caryae* Harr. were sectioned from the following tree species: *Tilia americana* L. (25 blocks), *Populus tremuloides* Michx. and *P. grandidentata* Michx. (5 blocks), *Castanea* sp., *Carya ovata* (Mill.) K. Koch, and *Fraxinus americana* L. (3 blocks each). In addition, 27 bark blocks of *Salix babylonica* L. containing stylet bundles of a willow aphid were sectioned. The sample number (66), though representing a considerable amount of work, is statistically small. Whenever the cut stylet bundle was exuding, its end portion was located in the innermost phloem, the region of functioning sieve tubes. The very tips of the stylets were found undisturbed in only about one out of five cases in *Tilia;* in the remaining four cases the tips had been disturbed by the microtome knife. But whenever the tips were undisturbed, they were found in an individual sieve element, provided the stylet bundle had been exuding prior to preparation (illustrations in Zimmermann, 1961, 1963).

Our best information on the location of aphid stylet tips was from *Tilia americana* L. Linden is often cited as an example of a tree having phloem that functions for more than 1 year. We could not confirm this. The stylet tips were never found in phloem tissue older than the current year's growth ring. However, it must be noted that our sample is small.

Anatomical sections of bark not only show the stylet bundles present in the tissue, but also the tracks of stylet bundles that had been with-drawn by the aphids prior to preparation of the bark block for sectioning. These tracks consist of solidified yellowish saliva secreted by the aphid during the penetration of the mouthparts through the bark. The presence and shape of saliva tracks is always an interesting indicator of aphid behavior and phloem condition. If the continuity of the sieve tubes is interrupted by wound or dormancy callose, the aphids have great difficulty in feeding. They wander around and probe the bark repeatedly with their stylets. This searching for food results in many branched saliva tracks.

Leaf Senescence and Dormancy

Leaf senescence is marked by a change in color of the foliage. It oc-curs naturally in autumn and consists essentially of a breakdown of leaf pigments and other large molecules into smaller units and their return, via phloem, back into the tree. Thus, valuable material is salvaged prior to leaf abscission. Sieve tube exudates from bark incisions and aphid sty-lets, very low in nitrogenous substances and phosphorus compounds dur-ing the summer, contain a relatively high percentage of these substances during the time of leaf senescence. (Mittler, 1958; Ziegler, 1956; Zim-mermann, 1958a).

The onset of dormancy in autumn is marked by the formation of callose on the sieve plates of the conducting phloem. Callose stains a brilliant blue with resorcin blue. Thus, stained radial sections show a blue band just outside the cambium (Fig. 2). In white ash (*Fraxinus americana* L.) of our region dormancy callose is formed about 2 weeks after abscission. Simultaneously exudation from bark incisions stops (Zimmermann, 1958b). Aphids cannot feed on the phloem when dormancy callose is formed. Greenhouse colonies are extremely difficult to maintain during this period (Hill, 1962).

The onset of dormancy in many of our temperate-zone woody plants is governed by an internal mechanism. These species cannot be prevented from going dormant even if summer temperatures and long daylengths are provided in the greenhouse. It may be that the formation of dor-mancy callose is an integral part of the whole change of the organism into the dormant condition. However, it is equally possible that dormancy callose formation is some sort of wound reaction going out from the points of leaf abscission. Let us briefly look at this possibility.

It has been found that interruption of phloem tissue causes the forma-tion of callose over appreciable axial distances. In some trees like *Salix* or *Tilia* callose formation is incomplete, and aphids can feed on cut branches of these trees (Weatherley *et al.*, 1959; Hill, 1962). In other trees like *Carya* or *Castanea* the sieve tubes are blocked completely when injured. Aphids are unable to feed on branches cut from such a tree, even if the foliage can be maintained in a healthy condition (Zimmermann, 1961). We are entirely ignorant of the nature of the "message" ("the

Fig. 2. Diagrammatic view of a radial section through the bark of white ash (*Fraxinus americana* L.) cut on October 18, 1958. Several growth rings can be recognized in the phloem. The callose seals in the 1958 growth ring, blue in the original microslide, are shown in black.

phloem leaks seal the sieve plates") that is carried away from the point of injury and causes callose formation. We do know that the turgor release is propagated both up and down from the point of injury (Münch, 1930) and we may perhaps speculate that this turgor release is actually the "message." Returning now to the dormancy callose, we can only point out the possibility that its formation is triggered by leaf abscission. The phloem would probably not leak at the leaf base after abscission, but continued sugar removal from the sieve tubes in the stem and lack of supply from the leaves may lower the turgor enough to simulate injury.

There is one important difference between callose induced by injury and that due to dormancy. Injury-induced callose formation does not in all species completely close the sieve plates, whereas dormancy callose formation always, as far as we know, results in a fairly complete seal.

Chemically, callose is a polysaccharide consisting of 1–3 linked glucose units (Kessler, 1958). Preliminary experiments on callose synthesis have been reported by Eschrich (1961), but the few results he obtained were not based on sieve tube callose.

The Break of Dormancy and Phloem Reactivation

Our knowledge of the relation of callose dissolution to the break of dormancy of the plant organism as a whole is as incomplete as our knowledge of callose formation in autumn at the onset of dormancy. We know nothing about the mechanisms involved. The "message" might come from the buds and descend basipetally together with the beginning of cambial activity. We know that in diffuse-porous trees the beginning of cambial activity descends from the buds at a velocity roughly comparable to that of auxin transport. We could speculate that the message is a hormone. On the other hand, dormancy is broken weeks or even months before cambial activity begins. We can hardly expect a photoperiodic response behind the thick bark at the base of the tree. The message, in this case, could be cold treatment, but this is again only a speculation.

Anatomists have given us a detailed description of callose dissolution (Esau, 1948; Kollmann and Schumacher, 1962; see also the two papers by Esau in this volume, pp. 37, 51). Furthermore, studies like those of Curtis (1925) suggest that there is reactivation of the old phloem, at least near the growing buds. Little is known about phloem exudation during late winter and early spring from reactivated phloem (Fig. 3). Eschrich (1961) reported exudation from a few species from February 26 on. He found that phloem exudate is slightly acid (pH 5–6) during early spring, in contrast to the condition during summer and autumn when it has a pH of around 7.5. Eschrich also discovered callase activity in commercial papain preparations. Optimal activity of these was at 36–38°C and pH

4–5. From this he concluded that the low pH of early-spring phloem exudate favors the dissolution of callose from the sieve pores.

Exudation from aphid stylets after the break of dormancy was reported by Mittler (1958). Hill (1962) devoted a detailed study to stylet exudation during dormancy and phloem reactivation. One of Mittler's signifi-

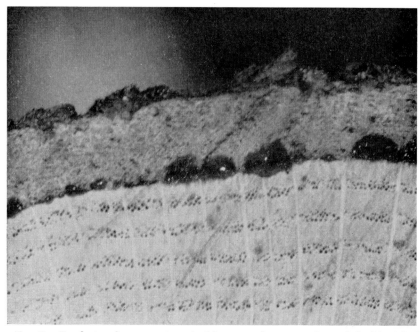

Fig. 3. Exudation from reactivated phloem on the cut surface of freshly felled red oak (*Quercus rubra* L.). Photographed at the Harvard Forest on March 20, 1961, a warm, sunny day. There was still snow on the ground and bud burst was many weeks away.

cant observations was that relatively large amounts of nitrogenous substances were present in stylet exudate at bud burst. One cannot help thinking that these were the very same substances that had been salvaged from aging leaves at the end of the previous season and remained in the phloem during the winter. In other words, the salvaged material from aging leaves is stored in the phloem and then used again for the growth of new shoots and leaves.

In Hill's study aphid behavior was an excellent indicator for phloem activity. Hill (1962) writes: "During physiological dormancy branches brought from the woods into greenhouse or laboratory conditions of warmth and extended daylength did not break bud within 2 months. The aphids on such branches produced a little honeydew (far less than that produced after physiological dormancy had ended) for about a week. They changed position frequently, probed extensively, and reproduced very slowly, all indications of unfavorable conditions. In fact, at this time the greenhouse colonies were in danger of dying off. Evidently they could obtain very little sap from the sieve tubes. Physiological dormancy ended near the close of December and branches brought in subsequently broke bud in 2 to 4 weeks at first, the period decreasing until it was about 12 days in the middle of March. The aphids thrived on these branches, producing copious honeydew and reproducing rapidly." Unfortunately this study was not followed by an anatomical inspection of callose dissolution, but there is little doubt that there must be a correlation between the two observations: aphids have great difficulties in feeding when sieve tubes are closed by callose during the dormant period, but they can easily feed as soon as callose is dissolved.

A Possible Period of "No Transport" and New Phloem Formation

Hill (1962) did most of his experiments with detached branches of *Tilia*. Although one has to be aware of the effects of phloem interruption on transport, there are certain advantages to this method; the timing of events can be determined rather precisely. When dormancy is broken and a branch is brought from the cold forest to the warm greenhouse, events take place at well-defined times after transfer of the branch. In Hill's experiments, for example, the sugar concentration of stylet exudate of two different branches, collected on March 22 and 29, respectively, was plotted in the same graph, with zero as the time of collection. This graph shows that the exudate concentration changed little during the first 2 weeks, but dropped drastically during the 3rd and 4th week when buds began to grow. Stylet exudation declined further when leaves began to expand, and aphid colonies began to show signs of starvation at this time.

Hill's interpretation of the drop of concentration of stylet exudate during bud growth and the difficulty aphids had in feeding during leaf expansion is based primarily on a theory of competition of two sinks (the aphid stylet bundle and the growing shoot), although he left room for other explanations. It seems more likely that the prime reason for the concentration drop is exhaustion of reserve material and increasing self-sufficiency of the young leaves. Whether or not additional factors are involved in causing the concentration drop, new leaves must reach a stage of self-sufficiency before they mature. When this stage is reached, last year's reactivated sieve tubes are no longer needed, and go out of function.

During the period of extension growth, cambial activity produces new sieve tubes which become functional at the time of leaf maturity. This is true at least for the region of the shoot tips in many tree species. This export translocation from mature leaves closes our cycle.

Possible Variations in Different Species

The present discussion appears to contradict Huber's statement that in some trees the sieve tubes collapse about 2 weeks after leaf fall (Huber, 1958; Huber in the discussion following the paper by Zimmermann, 1958a). However, he does not say that the collapse occurs throughout the whole tree. Phloem transport through reactivated phloem is only a requirement near the shoot tips. The reserve material near the shoot tips may be adequate to supply growing buds until the young leaves become self-sufficient. Movement through reactivated phloem may thus be quite local. Sieve-tube reactivation in shoot tips would then not be in contradiction to autumnal sieve tube collapse in the stem. Thus, the difference between species would not rest on whether or not the sieve tubes are reactivated after the dormant period, rather it would be a difference in how far basipetally this reactivation reaches. The phenomenon of reactivation may be very local in some species, while in others, like *Quercus rubra* L., reactivation seems to extend all the way down the main stem. In still others collapse may be restricted in the stem to older layers of the growth ring, while reactivation is confined to younger ones located near the cambium, as found by Schneider (1945) in *Prunus avium* L.

There is little information about phloem activity cycles in tropical trees, but again we can make certain speculations. The situation is probably similar to trees of temperate zones in those species that go through a dormancy period, be it externally induced (by a dry season, for example) or internally governed in all or part of the tree at any one time. In the latter case we may assume that, if one branch is dormant, the phloem underneath it and belonging to it is also dormant, even if neighboring tissue is active.

So far our discussion has dealt with woody plants in which extension growth consists only of the expansion of shoot and leaves preformed in the bud. *Fraxinus* is a good example of this growth type. However, there are other trees that continue to grow after the bud leaves have expanded, *Populus* for example. Continued growth can be recognized by the resulting leaf dimorphism; the bud leaves are different in shape from the additional leaves produced spontaneously later (Critchfield, 1960). The translocation pattern in continuously growing shoots is somewhat complicated, because movement from mature leaves is both upward into the shoot tips and down toward the roots. This means that phloem transport in internodes between mature leaves is bidirectional in a wider sense. This pattern of translocation is to be expected in continuously growing shoots of both tropical and temperate woody species (for example in green-house-grown grapevines; Swanson and El-Shishiny, 1958; Hale and Weaver, 1962); it is also common in seedlings. Biddulph and Cory (1960) worked on this problem with beans. They found transport in different directions to take place mostly in different conducting bundles. In a few cases, however, their data indicate bidirectional transport within single bundles. They interpreted their results as showing that movement occurs in one direction in one layer of the phloem bundle and bidirectionally in another layer. However, a much simpler interpretation would be movement in one direction in one layer and movement in the other direction in another layer of the phloem tissue within the bundle.

In summary we can say that it is somewhat misleading to speak about sieve tubes of deciduous species functioning for more than 1 year if there is reactivation in early spring. The functional stages are distributed over two vegetation periods, but they do not seem to overlap. In other words, the total functional period, including the dormancy period during the winter, is not more than 12 months.

One feature of past research is growth-translocation relations stands out very clearly: investigations have been carried out with different methods separately on all kinds of different plants. It is obvious that we would learn a great deal more if we used these methods simultaneously on one or more species.

DISCUSSION

WILCOX: Do you distinguish between phloem reactivation and differentiation of elements brought over from the previous season?

ZIMMERMANN: Precocious elements are known in conifers; I do not know whether they play a role in dicotyledons. Immature elements which mature in the spring do, of course, represent some sort of reactivation, possibly an important one.

WAREING: It is tempting to suggest that the removal of callose is a chilling effect, because it seems to correlate with the removal of dormancy. We know that starch hydrolyzes during chilling, as in potato tubers. It would be interesting to see whether there is no disappearance of callose if the plants are kept warm.

ZIEGLER: The tree species you mentioned with sieve tube reactivation are ring-porous species. Ring-porous trees really need functioning phloem early in the spring because they have to form the new xylem very early. Since the diffuse-porous trees do not depend so much on new xylem, they can form the new phloem first. I believe ring-porous trees always have either reserve sieve tubes or reactivation of phloem in the spring. In diffuse-porous trees the sieve tubes are completely closed in the winter, and in the spring the new sieve tubes are formed before the buds begin to grow. Xylem is formed later because the old xylem is still functioning. We must distinguish between ring- and diffuse-porous species when we consider the activity of the cambium and of the phloem in early spring. I am not surprised that oak phloem is functioning in March.

TORREY: In the case of the wound callose, could there be a chemical signal? Does it occur simultaneously in all the sieve tubes?

ZIMMERMANN: I do not know.

BROWN: I am glad to hear that the sieve tubes do not become plugged in all species. If one separates a downward-pointing bark strip from the bole wood in *Populus* and encloses it in a polyethylene bag, one can collect, over a period of ten days, at least a liter of solution from this bark strip. This liquid seems to come down through the sieve tubes.

ZIMMERMANN: I do not believe that what you collect in the polyethylene bag is sieve tube exudate, at least not all of it. It looks to me more like the phenomenon Münch (1930) has described. If there is cambial activity in the downward-pointing bark strip you describe (cf. the paper of Brown on p. 389 of this volume), carbohydrates would be removed from the sieve tubes and this removal of osmotically active molecules causes a loss of water. Münch estimated that a small percentage of the transpiration stream consists of this phloem water. This experiment is actually one of the crucial ones supporting his mass-flow hypothesis.

In *Populus* species, indeed, the sieve plates are not completely plugged upon injury. Aphids will feed on cut branches. The sieve plates near the cut end must get sealed, or else they could not build up turgor. They might be sealed by slime plugs. This should be investigated anatomically.

Chestnut is interesting. When cut chestnut branches are brought to the lab they can be maintained in an apparently healthy condition for a long time, but aphids cannot feed on them, although they do feed easily on the intact tree. The aphids wander around on the cut branches, fall off, and die. Sections show heavy masses of callose. If one keeps putting new aphids on, eventually they begin to feed quite well. Sections show that there is now a little newly differentiated phloem. It would be interesting to see if the stylet tips really do end in this new phloem.

ZIEGLER: A species like willow will grow all winter long if kept in the greenhouse. There are always growing buds and there is always functioning phloem, and aphids can easily be maintained on such a species during the winter. One cannot feed aphids during the winter on a species which becomes dormant.

ZIMMERMANN: It can be done, but it is not easy. Hill (1962) actually did it. Dormant branches may contain a very few odd sieve tubes that are more or less open. If one starts with a large population of aphids and a good supply of branches, one can succeed in bringing some aphids through the dormant period. But there is a second problem here; once the aphids are triggered into the sexual cycle they will produce eggs and then die off. We lost our aphid colonies during two autumns in that way.

WAREING: Is the life history of the aphids not controlled by daylength?

ZIMMERMANN: It might be. We did give them long days, but in the cases where we failed we may have started too late. The life history of *Longistigma* is very poorly known. Entomologists are not interested in it because it is not a pest.

ZIEGLER: There are aphids which feed on trees in the spring when the nitrogenous content of the phloem is high. Then they spend the summer on herbs in which the nitrogenous content is always high, and in the autumn when the nitrogenous content of the trees has gone up again, they return to the trees. We have such a species in Europe on *Acer platanoides* (*Aphis platanoides*). We tried to keep these aphids on maple during the summer by adding urea to the leaves, but we have not yet been successful.

REFERENCES

Biddulph, O., and Cory, R. (1960). *Plant Physiol.* **35**, 689-695.

Critchfield, W. B. (1960). *Amer. J. Botany* **47**, 699-711.

Curtis, O. F. (1925). *Ann. Botany* **39**, 573-585.

Esau, K. (1948). *Hilgardia* **18**, 217-296.

Eschrich, W. (1961). *Z. Botanik* **49**, 153-218.

Hale, C. R., and Weaver, R. J. (1962). *Hilgardia* **33**, 89-131.

Hartig, Th. (1856). *Allgem. Forst- Jagdz.* **22**, 361-372.

Hill, G. P. (1962). *J. Exptl. Botany* **13**, 144-151.

Holdheide, W. (1951). *In* "Handbuch der Mikroskopie in der Technik" (H. Freund, ed.), Vol. V. pp. 195-367. Umschau, Frankfurt.

Huber, B. (1958). *In* "The Physiology of Forest Trees" (K. V. Thimann, ed.), pp. 367-379. Ronald Press, New York.

Huber, B., and Rouschal, E. (1938). *Ber. Deut. Botan. Ges.* **56**, 380-391.

Kessler, G. (1958). *Ber. schweiz. bot. Ges.* **68**, 5-43.

Kollmann, R., and Schumacher, W. (1962). *Planta* **59**, 195-221.

Mittler, T. E. (1957). *J. Exptl. Biol.* **34**, 334-341.

Mittler, T. E. (1958). *J. Exptl. Biol.* **35**, 74-84.

Münch, E. (1930). "Die Stoffbewegungen in der Pflanze." Fischer, Jena.

Schneider, H. (1945). *Bull. Torr. Bot. Club* **72**, 137-156.

Swanson, C. A., and E. D. H. El-Shishiny (1958). *Plant Physiol.* **33**, 33-37.

Weatherley, P. E., Peel, A. J., and Hill, G. P. (1959). *J. Exptl. Botany* **10**, 1-16.

Wieler, A. (1896). *Forstwiss. Zentr.* **18**, 361-374.

Ziegler, H. (1956). *Planta* **47**, 447-500.

Zimmermann, M. H. (1958a). *In* "The Physiology of Forest Trees" (K. V. Thimann, ed.), pp. 381-400. Ronald Press, New York.

Zimmermann, M. H. (1958b). *Plant Physiol.* **33**, 213-217.

Zimmermann, M. H. (1961). *Science* **133**, 73-79.

Zimmermann, M. H. (1963). *Scientific American* **208** (3), 133-142.

Storage, Mobilization and Distribution of Reserve Material in Trees

HUBERT ZIEGLER

Botanisches Institut, Technische Hochschule, Darmstadt, Germany

I. The Storage Cells

The cells in the stems and roots of woody plants able to accumulate reserve material are living cells of parenchymatic nature. When a cell dies during its normal differentiation (for example, in the development of lignified cells or during heartwood formation) its reserve material is always consumed or withdrawn. As a rule all storage cells are at least temporarily capable of storing starch. They therefore contain numerous leucoplasts, which can be developed into chloroplasts in the outer bark zone.

Not all the living cells in the stem and root are able to accumulate reserve material to a great extent. A number of elements have physiological functions which could be disturbed by an enrichment with reserve substances. To these cells belong the sieve tube members, respectively, the sieve cells, the companion cells and the functionally corresponding "albuminous cells" (*Strasburger* cells) in the Gymnospermae, a part of the ray cells (the upright cells at the margin of the heterogeneous rays), a part of the xylem parenchyma (*Belegzellen*), the meristematic cells, the root endodermis, the epithelial cells of the resin ducts, and the idioblasts.

II. The Arrangement of the Storage Cells in Wood and Bark

1. STORAGE TISSUE IN THE XYLEM

Quite frequently the cells of the pith remain alive for a long time and are able to store reserve material. This applies to many Gymnospermae and to a number of Angiospermae, viz., *Castanea, Fagus, Betula, Alnus, Quercus,* and *Tilia.* In other species the cells of the central medullary zone die, but the medullary sheath remains alive for some time and is capable of storage; for example, in *Populus, Acer, Robinia, Sambucus* (cf. review by Braun, 1961).

303

In these, as in all other cases, the living cells must remain in contact with each other, as well as with the assimilate translocation system. Should one of the living cells lose this connection, it dies unresistingly. An instructive example of this statement is the "stretched" rays (*gedehnte*

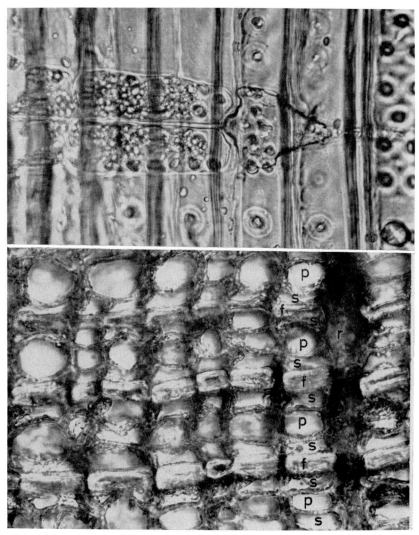

Fig. 1 (Top). *Taxodium distichum*, radial section through the stem wood. "Stretched" ray: One ray cell on the inside has no more connection with the living and starch-storing ray cells. The isolated cell is dead and empty. × 600.

Fig. 2 (Bottom). *Taxodium distichum*, cross section through the bark. Regular sequence of fiber (f), sieve cell (s), parenchyma cell (p), sieve cell, and so on. r = ray. × 600.

Markstrahlen) found by Strasburger (1891) in some Gymnospermae: single cells on the inside of secondary rays become isolated, lose their cell substances and die (Fig. 1).

For the living pith cells this rule means an undisturbed ray connection with the phloem. It is remarkable that this connection lasts for many years even in ring-porous species, although the water-conducting system is confined to a few growth rings.

The arrangement of the other storage tissues in the xylem shows varying characteristics, which are conditional partly on the taxonomic position of the species and partly on the biological properties (especially the duration of the foliage). The most striking feature is the possibility of mutual replacement of the different storage tissues.

For example, summergreen Gymnospermae are found which develop no xylem parenchyma in spite of considerable storage demands; they have a much denser ray system than evergreens without xylem parenchyma (e.g., *Pinus*). Such summergreens are *Ginkgo biloba* and *Larix*. Other summergreen species have xylem parenchyma (e.g., *Taxodium*), which also occurs in evergreen species like *Taxus* and *Cephalotaxus*.

In the Gymnospermae with xylem parenchyma there is a tendency to localize the storage cells at the end of the growth rings. The advantage of this arrangement is the short distance the migrating substances travel during the filling and clearance of the storage tissues. In the Angiospermae this "terminal parenchyma" is developed in many species, including *Fraxinus, Populus, Alnus, Betula, Salix*, and *Tilia*. Another tendency in the arrangement of xylem parenchyma in the Angiospermae is the complete or partial bordering of vessels or of vessel groups ("paratracheal parenchyma"). I will not discuss the physiological significance of these parenchyma sheaths.

2. Storage Tissues in the Bark

The storage parenchyma in the bark is often concentrated in tangential layers of characteristic arrangement and forms an undisrupted network with the storing and translocating ray cells.

According to their phloem structure the Gymnospermae can be divided into three groups:

(a) Species in which the cambium forms in an endogenous "four-cycle" rhythm a regular sequence of tangential layers consisting of fibers, sieve cells, phloem parenchyma, sieve cells, etc. Single cells of the parenchyma (but not ray cells) are distinguished from the other parenchyma cells by lack of reserve material and by pits to sieve cells and to ray cells ("albuminous cells," *Strasburger* cells). Another distinct feature is their simultaneous disorganization with the sieve cells. To this group belong, for instance, *Ginkgo, Taxus,* and *Cephalotaxus.*

(b) In the second group species are found with "albuminous cells" in the phloem parenchyma and in the rays. The phloem shows also the "four-cycle" rhythm. In this group we find among others *Taxodium* (Fig. 2) and *Thuja.*

(c) A number of species in which the phloem is not constructed according to the fixed rhythm. The "albuminous cells" are only found on the margin of the rays. To this third group belong, for example, the Abietaceae.

The representatives of this last structural type show a great variation of parenchyma arrangement. In *Picea excelsa,* for instance, one tangential band of parenchyma cells is formed every year. This parenchyma formation occurs in middle Europe, according to Huber (1961) between June 20th and July 10th (presumably photoperiodically controlled). The phloem of spruce is otherwise composed of radial rows of sieve cells.

Huber (1961) pointed out that in Cupressaceae the first band of sieve cells can consist of two or three layers before the regular "four-cycle" rhythm begins. Therefore he considers it more likely that the Abietaceae type developed from the Cupressaceae type ("four-cycle" type) than vice versa. This conception corresponds to the degree of specialization of the albuminous cells, which are certainly more highly organized in the Abietaceae. Furthermore we also found deviations of the normal "four-cycle" structure in the Taxaceae and Cephalotaxaceae which are regarded as particularly inflexible. In *Cephalotaxus,* for example, the regular order can be interrupted by a "two-cycle" structure of sieve cells, parenchyma cells, sieve cells, parenchyma cells (Fig. 3).

In the Angiospermae the arrangement of the storage cells in the wood as well as in the bark is much more manifold than in the Gymnospermae.

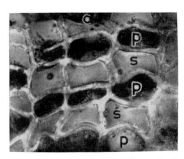

FIG. 3.   *Cephalotaxus drupacea,* cross section through the phloem. Special case of a sequence of parenchyma cell (p), sieve cell (s), parenchyma cell, sieve cell ("two-cycle" rhythm), which was inserted in a normal "four-cycle" rhythm. c = Cristal cell. × 360.

However, a definite, species-specific order of the different cell types is also recognizable. In some species (e.g., *Ribes*) even a "four-cycle" rhythm is developed (for a detailed review cf. Holdheide, 1951).

III. The Storage Material in Trees

The most important reserve substances in the stems and roots of trees are starch, fat (or fatty oils), and nitrogen compounds. According to the most conspicuous reserve material we distinguish between "starch trees" and "fat trees" (cf. review by Kramer and Kozlowski, 1960). This classification is based primarily on histochemical analysis, the evidence of which is not always without doubt (see also Büsgen and Münch, 1927). There is no question about the significance of *starch* as reserve material for numerous species of the Gymnospermae as well as for the Angiospermae. This starch is formed in the leucoplasts of the storage cells, probably from transport sucrose (or from other transport carbohydrates). Indeed, it is common experience, although at present not fully understood biochemically, that the transformation sucrose $\rightleftharpoons$ starch proceeds extremely easily.

The significance of *fat* as reserve material as well as the time and extent of the starch $\rightleftharpoons$ fat transformation are in many cases not well defined. The material from which the fat is built up (acetyl coenzyme A or fatty acids and glycerol) moves in the translocation tissues—if at all—only in such a small amount that these translocated substances are not important for the balance of the fat synthesis. The lipides in the storage cells therefore must be formed either from transport sugars or from starch.

In any way, during the transformation of carbohydrates into fat, oxygen must be released. As a consequence of the smaller requirement of exogenous oxygen, the respiratory quotient CO_2/O_2 must increase. Reciprocally, the transformation of fat into carbohydrates requires additional exogenous oxygen. This results in a decrease of the RQ value below 1.0. A determination of the respiratory quotient, which can easily be done by manometric methods, therefore gives information about the extent of the transformation in the storage tissues.

Such measurements were taken (in collaboration with H. Bräu) at different times of the year in "starch" trees (*Acer platanoides* and *Fagus sylvatica*) as well as in "fat" trees (*Picea excelsa, Pinus sylvestris, Tilia vulgaris, Populus deltoides, Aesculus hippocastanum*) separately for wood and bark. At the same time the fat content was determined by means of ether extraction. Only the most typical results will be discussed here.

The measured RQ values corresponded with the theoretical expectations: In the "starch" trees we obtained at every time of the year values of

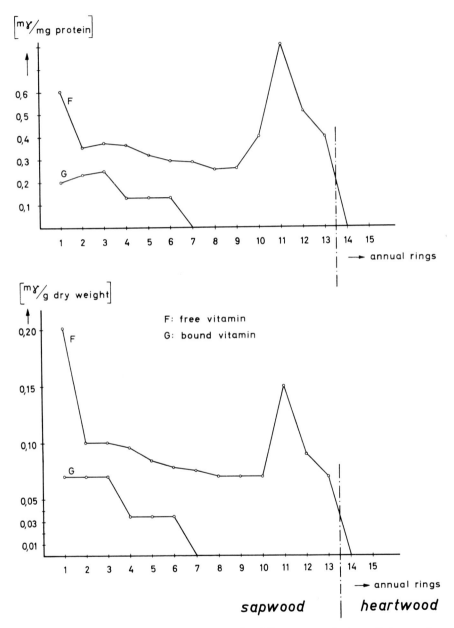

FIG. 4. *Pinus strobus*, biotin content in the different annual rings of the trunk-wood. Determination microbiologically (cf. Ziegler and Ziegler, 1962). Note also the high vitamin concentration in the transition zone near the sapwood/heartwood border.

about 1.0. The "fat" trees on the contrary showed an increased value during the autumn and a decreased value at time of fat respiration in the winter and during the fat mobilization period in spring. The branch wood of *Pinus silvestris*, for example, showed on November 12th (outside day temperature at this time 3–8°C, with light frost at night) at 20°C an RQ value of 1.792, at 10°C of 1.804, and at 2°C of 2.697, thus a tendency to

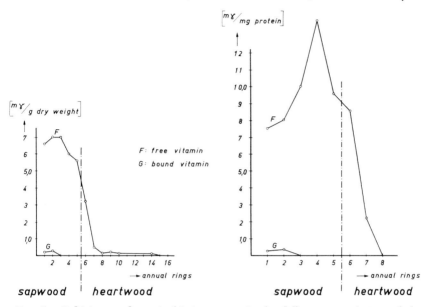

Fig. 5. *Robinia pseudoacacia*, biotin content in the different annual rings of the trunk-wood.

increase fat production at lowering of temperature. (For comparison: a goose being fattened has an RQ value of 1.38.)

In the spring (March 7th, 1963) a 2-year-old part of the stem of a little pine tree, which stood in the open during the winter, showed in the wood a fat content of 2.58% of the dry weight and an RQ value of 0.7. In the bark the values were 10.9% and also 0.7. In a pine stem of the same age and from the same site, which stood in a glasshouse during the winter (with temperatures between 15 and 20°C), the fat content of the wood was 2.42% and that of the bark 6%. The RQ value for both tissues was 0.8. Also here the fat production is favored by low temperatures and the respiratory quotient agrees with the theoretical expectations.

It is a well-known fact that generally in the *roots* of trees—even in "fat" trees—almost no fat is produced and that starch is accumulated as reserve material. Kramer and Kozlowski (1960, p. 148) stated that "several investigators have emphasized that roots contain little or no fat, but none have explained why stems are much more efficient than roots in their ability to produce and accumulate fats."

Two reasons for the present observation are possible: (1) The roots are biochemically not able to synthesize large amounts of reserve fats. (2) The roots are not exposed to the same environmental influences which cause extensive fat production.

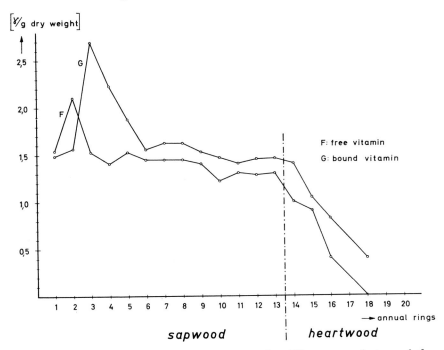

FIG. 6. *Pinus strobus*, pyridoxine content in the different annual rings of the trunk-wood. Determination microbiologically (cf. Ziegler and Ziegler, 1962).

Let us see whether a decision in favor of one of these alternatives is possible.

(1) The biochemical reactions transforming carbohydrates into fat use substances arising from the normal carbohydrate metabolism: glycerol is synthesized by reduction of the glycerolaldehyde; the fatty acids are formed from acetyl coenzyme A in the presence of biotin, partly also of pyridoxal phosphate as coenzymes (cf. Wakil *et al.*, 1960).

In connection with quantitative determinations of water-soluble vitamins in the wood of some Gymnospermae as well as of ring- and diffuse-porous species of Angiospermae (together with H. Bräu) we also determined biotin and the pyridoxine group in the stems and roots of "starch" and "fat" trees (with *Lactobacillus arabinosus* 17–5 ATCC 8014 and

Neurospora sitophila 299 ATCC 9276, respectively, as test organisms).
There are great differences between different species and between organs.
For instance, the biotin content in the stem of the fat-storing *Pinus strobus* (Fig. 4) is lower than in the stem of the "starch" tree *Robinia* (Fig.
5). The pyridoxine content in the stem of *Pinus strobus* (Fig. 6), on the
other hand, is higher than in the stem of *Robinia* (Fig. 7).

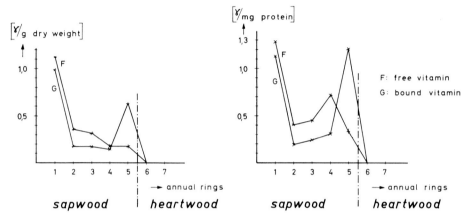

FIG. 7. *Robinia pseudoacacia,* pyridoxine content in the different annual rings of
the trunk-wood.

The biotin content in the wood of the stem of *Tilia vulgaris* ("fat" tree)
was indeed considerably higher (3.295 mµg/gm dry weight) than in the
wood (0.875 mµg/gm) and in the bark (1.400 mµg/gm) of the root.

The meaning of these results is not completely clear; the occurrence
of these vitamins is not at all restricted to fat-accumulating cells.

Specific differences rather are to be expected in the enzyme set
involved in the transformation of the fat into the carbohydrates. According to the results of Beevers (1961) obtained with fat-accumulating seeds,
acetyl coenzyme A, arising from the oxidative breakdown of the fatty
acids, is transformed into oxalacetic acid (and further into sucrose) via
the glyoxylic acid cycle (Fig. 8). Two specific enzymes, isocitratase and
malate synthetase, are involved in these processes. These enzymes occur
in higher plants only in fat-accumulating organs and are especially active
during the mobilization of the reserve material.

Determinations of the activity of the isocitricase in the wood and in
the bark of stem and root in *Tilia vulgaris* (in spring) according to the
method of Dixon and Kornberg (1959) indicated that this reaction
scheme is also followed in the fat-accumulating trees. There were, however, no differences in the activity between the stem and the root.

As the result, we must state that we could not find sufficient bio-chemical differences between root and stem to explain the striking differences in the kind of reserve matrial.

(2) Therefore the significant factor remains the difference in environment, especially in temperature, to which the stems and roots are exposed.

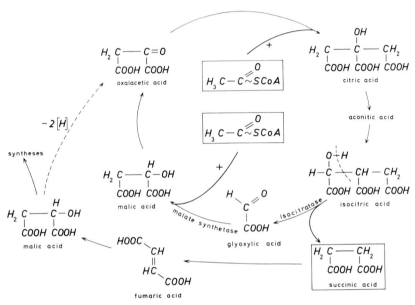

FIG. 8.   Glyoxylic acid cycle.

During the long-lasting, severe frost of last winter (1962-63), when the soil was deeply and continuously frozen, it was possible to examine roots that had been exposed for many months to temperatures below 0°C. Under these conditions the roots of *Tilia vulgaris* (ca. 4 cm diameter from approximately 20 cm soil depth) showed the same extensive and exclusive fat accumulation (Fig. 9) as the above-ground organs (Fig. 10). This was confirmed by histochemical reactions, by the determination of the extractable fat (10.9% of the dry weight in the bark, 5.38% in the wood) and by the RQ value of the root in spring (always values below 1.0).

Therefore, we must conclude that the roots of the "fat" trees are able to synthesize fat as reserve material like the stems. Normally, however, the roots are not exposed to sufficient low temperatures to induce this fat synthesis.

Another interesting problem concerning the nature of the reserve material has been pointed out by Sinnott (1918): The diffuse-porous species usually are "fat" trees or have an abundance of fat in winter-time while ring-porous species have almost starch as reserve material. For this rule also no explanation could hitherto be given.

Considering that in ring-porous species the radial extension of the

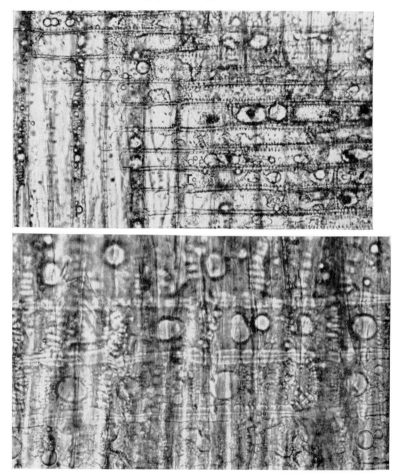

Fig. 9. (Top.) *Tilia vulgaris*, radial section through the root-wood. Lipoid droplets in the ray cells (r) and in the xylem parenchyma (p). × 225.

Fig. 10. (Bottom.) *Tilia vulgaris*, radial section through the trunk-wood. Lipoid droplets in the ray cells. × 600.

storage tissue in wood is generally more limited than in diffuse-porous species (even when they are not covered by the water-conducting area as mentioned before), we would like to assume that in the ring-porous species the material with the highest energy content is accumulated. It is well known that the energy content per unit weight of fat (9.3 kcal/

gm) is considerably higher than that of carbohydrates (4.1 kcal/gm). In the present situation we are not interested in the energy content per unit of weight—it is not important for a tree whether the storage tissue is a little heavier or lighter—but whether the present volume of storage tissue can take up more energy in the case of fat or of starch accumulation.

From the specific weight of the fats (tripalmitine, for example, 0.8657; cf. Rauen, 1956) and their energy content, it can be calculated that in fat storage an energy capacity of about 8 kcal/cm³ can be obtained, provided that the space is completely filled. For the starch the order of the specific weight can be calculated from the data of Kreger (1946), according to which, in B-starch, 8 glucose residues occupy a volume of 1783 Å³; we get a value of 1.2 for the specific weight. If all the space were completely filled 4.9 kcal/cm³ of starch could therefore be stored. It is clear that neither fat nor starch can completely fill the volume of the storage cells; according to the cytological picture it seems that the starch is packed more tightly than the fat, but this advantage certainly cannot fully compensate the lower energy capacity described.

The starch accumulation of the ring-porous species is therefore not profitable energetically.

A selection advantage of fat accumulation in diffuse-porous species may be based on the fact that the transformation of reserve fats into carbohydrates in spring needs a considerable amount of oxygen. At this time the water-conducting elements must be liberated from the gas bubbles appearing during the cold period and it is just the oxygen which causes particular difficulties because of its low solubility in water.

This view is at present, of course, hypothetical, but it should be taken into consideration.

IV. The Filling and Clearance of the Storage Tissues

All variations in the amount and in the nature of the reserve substances in wood and bark normally start in the region of the cambium or the functioning phloem and proceed from here to the inside or the outside. In this way the storage tissues are filled during the accumulation period, the carbohydrates are transformed into fat and reverse in the "fat" trees, and the reserve material is mobilized. Only the heartwood formation proceeds from inside to the outside.

The material for the synthesis of the reserve substances is translocated through the phloem and in radial direction certainly through the rays to the storage cells. The water-conducting elements are involved only as acceptors for the water released by the condensation reactions (and eventually as donors for a part of the inorganic ions which are needed for the enzymic processes).

The processes for the distribution of the mobilized reserve material are more complicated. The substances can be used for three main purposes: (1) for the formation of young shoots; (2) for the diameter growth, that is, for the cambium activity, and (3) for fruit and seed formation.

All experimental results show that the growing buds are more active centers of attraction for the mobilized reserve material than the cambium. The latter only receives the "surplus" of the reserves. According to experiments by Lutz (cf. Büsgen and Münch, 1927), the continued removal of developing buds from young beech trees during the whole growing period, results in a continued new sprouting of reserve buds, but no diameter growth takes place. After removing the crown from 100-year-old beeches, R. Hartig and Weber (1888), on the other hand, obtained a complete, although small, growth ring in the first year, at the expense of the reserve substances. Here no resting buds were present.

Also in pines, from which the needles and the buds have been removed, the reserve material can be utilized for the cambial growth, when the plants lack resting buds (Lutz). It is remarkable that the newly formed xylem elements in this case showed the characteristics of earlywood, although the needles were removed at a time when latewood normally is formed.

In intact trees, the stock of the reserve material is by no means always completely consumed in the spring. Especially in the trunk and to a lesser extent in the roots, considerable quantities remain accumulated normally. Only by ample fruit formation are these reserves completely consumed; this applies particularly to nitrogen compounds.

In deciduous trees the building material for shoot development (e.g., starch) comes almost completely from the reserve material. In evergreens, on the contrary, a large part of the building material is supplied by the organs of photosynthesis, the mature leaves or needles (cf. Büsgen and Münch, 1927). The developing buds obtain the mobilized material mainly via the phloem, partly also via the transpiration stream. The relative participation of the two translocation systems will not be discussed here (cf. Zimmermann's chapter, p. 289).

V. Radial Transport in the Rays

The experimental data on transport in the rays are so poor that the word "ray" is generally not found in the index of translocation monographs. Our conceptions are therefore based mainly on anatomical evidence and need experimental proof.

1. THE MIGRATING SUBSTANCES

a. Minerals and Water. It is not necessary for the cambium and the phloem to be provided with water and minerals from the sapwood. They can also be supplied by the phloem. This is especially evident when bark strips separated from the wood or parts of bark above destroyed wood remain alive and even show normal growth (cf. Brown, p. 389). The well-known fact that the tracheid cells at the margin of the wood rays in some Gymnospermae are not continued in the bark agrees with this statement.

Probably the rays are also important for supplying the inner parts of the wood, the vessels of which are blocked up by air or tyloses, with water and salts. As we have previously mentioned, the living tissue with requirements of these substances extends much further to the inside than the water-conducting sapwood. The ray tracheids in various Abietaceae consequently contain water also in the inner region of the wood and keep their bordered pits open for a long time.

The well-known fact that tangential pits in the latewood tracheids are found more frequently in species in which the ray tracheids are not well developed is also in accord with the view that these tracheidal ray cells are really radial water channels. For example, *Pinus sylvestris* normally has no tangential pits at all.

In the "heterogenous" rays (for instance in *Salix*, Fig. 11) the upright cells at the ray margin probably also serve for water conduction; they show numerous pits to the vessels and contain relatively small amounts of reserve material.

The rays are also the path of centripetal salt transport from the phloem to the inner parts of the wood. Mason and Maskell (1928) found that in girdled *Gossypium* plants phosphate accumulated transitorily in the wood above the girdling zone.

b. Assimilates. There is no doubt, even though there is no direct proof,

---

FIG. 11. (Top.)   *Salix alba.* Heterogeneous rays. The upright cells at the margin with large pits and almost no reserve material. The procumbent cells with lipoid droplets. × 300.

FIG. 12. (Center.)   *Picea excelsa*, radial section through the trunk-wood. Air-filled intercellulares (dark lines) in the middle part of the ray, but not on the margin. Note also the interrupted ray tracheid border on the underside of the ray. × 600.

FIG. 13. (Bottom.)   *Picea excelsa*, radial section through the branch wood. Intercellulares in the ray in bark (b) and wood (w), but not in the cambium zone (c). × 225.

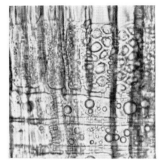

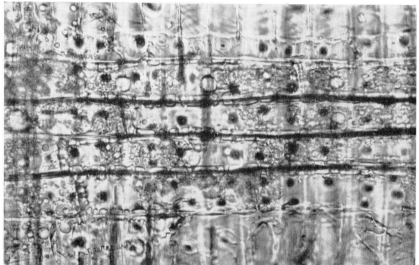

that assimilates are translocated in the rays from the phloem through the cambium into the wood. We have at present no knowledge of the nature of the migrating substances. A centrifugal transport of organic material in the wood rays is also probable. The finding that in special cases wood formation stops under a girdle even if the rays in this area contain large amounts of reserve material seemingly contradicts this assumption. Presumably the cambium activity ceases here, not because of a lack of organic material, but because of the absence of leaf-born growth substances, which migrate in the phloem and cannot be stored.

There is evidence that the assimilates in the sieve elements do not enter the ray cells directly, but pass through the companion cells (in the Angiospermae) or the albuminous cells (in the Gymnospermae). These cells have a common cytologic and enzymic nature (dense cytoplasm, numerous mitochondria, large nuclei, lack of reserve substances; active phosphatase, cf. Ziegler and Huber, 1960), are connected by pits with the sieve tubes and with the ray cells, and disintegrate simultaneously with the sieve tubes.

The albuminous cells are not developed in the wood rays of the Gymnospermae; therefore they are not involved in the ray transport itself.

It seems that the cambium is supplied predominantly via the rays with the assimilates and growth substances of the phloem. This can be concluded mainly from the data on Cupressaceae given by Bannan (1951, 1953); he stated that the fate of the excessively formed cambium cells depends mainly on the number of the ray contacts. The cells with the least contacts always die or form new ray initials. This is an effective feed-back regulative system, which provides for an equidistant arrangement of the rays.

The ray initials are in a unique physiological situation: they are meristematic cells through which passes a permanent intensive substance flow.

c. Gases. The rays have radial intercellular spaces, serving for the gas exchange of the inner tissues. These intercellular spaces are normally absent in uniseriate rays and are localized in the multiseriate rays in the middle part, between the living cells (Figs. 12, 13). In this way the danger of a gas transgression to the water-conducting xylem elements is greatly diminished.

The main resistance to gas transport is located in the cambium (Fig. 13). It can grow to such an extent that the central parts of the tree trunk can be subjected to anaerobic conditions (Ziegler, 1957).

2. The Mechanism of the Ray Transport[1]

The translocation of water and salts in dead cells of the rays, for instance, in the ray tracheids, certainly can be explained by the cohesion theory. The more interesting question is that of the velocity and the mechanism of assimilate transport in the living ray cells: Is the efficiency of a normal diffusion sufficient for this?

Experiments which dealt with the centripetal transport of C[14] glucose in the girdled stems of different species showed that this radial translocation exceeds normal diffusion. Therefore, we have to assume some kind of acceleration. It is probably of the same nature as the metabolically driven parenchyma transport.

Discussion

WILCOX: I do not know much about the secondary tissues of the root, but in the primary tissues the pericycle and the root cap seem to store a great deal of starch, although the root cap seems an unlikely spot for storage.

ZIEGLER: I think in root caps the starch is a very important cell constituent, because it functions here as a statolith apparatus.

WILCOX: In dormant roots the pericycle is filled with starch.

ZIEGLER: In this condition the pericycle is not a functioning meristematic tissue.

WARDROP: Have you observed the rate or sequence of fat removal from pine stems after they have had low temperature treatments?

ZIEGLER: When fat is removed there is in general an RQ below 1; with the help of this value the amount of metabolized fat can roughly be estimated. It seems that part is immediately metabolized and part is transformed into starch. There is also a transformation of starch to fat in the autumn. Thus, starch is also found in the fat trees at certain times of the year.

ZIMMERMANN: Are the upright ray cells of beech and willow living or dead?

ZIEGLER: They are living because they sometimes store reserve material.

ZIMMERMANN: Do you think that the resistance to water movement through the protoplast is less than through the cell walls?

ZIEGLER: This seems very unlikely. We certainly have to restrict the validity of the cohesion theory to the dead tracheids of the gymnosperm rays.

ZIMMERMANN: The cohesion mechanism of water movement could still work through the walls.

ZIEGLER: But then the margin cells would not be better pathways for the water than the inner parts of the rays.

BROWN: Ray cells are one of the most neglected areas in the physiology of woody plants. I have cultured ray cells *in vitro;* there are indications that these cells are polar in a vertical, rather than horizontal, direction to auxin transport. Inverted xylem pieces show very poor ray-cell proliferation; however, if the acropetal end is placed in the medium there is good proliferation. It seems to me that auxin is transported preferentially in a vertical plane. But the direction of auxin transport may be quite different from the transport of carbohydrates.

ZIEGLER: Centrifugal transport of reserve material is also very poor in many cases. The rays may be filled with reserve material in the wood, but this material cannot

---

[1] Cf. Ziegler (1961).

serve for the functioning of the bark when the connection with the leaves is interrupted, perhaps because of lack of hormone supply. In the heartwood, on the other hand, there must be a substantial amount of transport from the outside to the inside, because much more material is consumed in the heartwood-forming region than is present there.

WARDROP: Have you observed any relation between the disappearance of starch or fat and the formation of phenolic substances?

ZIEGLER: I did not study the metabolism of phenols. Phenols might certainly also be formed at the expense of reserve substances.

REFERENCES

Bannan, M. W. (1951). *Can. J. Botany* **29**, 421-437.
Bannan, M. W. (1953). *Can. J. Botany* **31**, 63-74.
Beevers, H. (1961). *Nature* **191**, 433-436.
Braun, H. (1961). "Der histologische Aufbau und das Hydrosystem des Stammholzes der Bäume," Habilitationsschrift. Freiburg i. Br.
Büsgen, M., and Münch, E. (1927). "Bau und Leben unserer Waldbäume." Fischer, Jena.
Dixon, G. H., and Kornberg, H. L. (1959). *Biochem. J.* **72**, 3P.
Hartig, R., and Weber, R. (1888). "Das Holz der Rotbuche in anatomisch-physiologischer, chemischer und forstlicher Richtung." Berlin.
Holdheide, W. (1951). *In* "Handbuch der Mikroskopie in der Technik" (H. Freund, ed.), Vol. V, pp. 193-367. Umschau, Frankfurt a.M.
Huber, B. (1961). "Grundzüge der Pflanzenanatomie." Springer, Berlin.
Kramer, P. J., and Kozlowski, T. T. (1960). "Physiology of Trees." McGraw-Hill, New York.
Kreger, D. (1946). *Nature* **158**, 199.
Mason, T. G., and Maskell, E. J. (1928). *Ann. Botany (London)* **42**, 189-253.
Rauen, H. M. (1956). "Biochemisches Taschenbuch." Springer, Berlin.
Sinnott, E. W. (1918). *Botan. Gaz.* **66**, 162-175.
Strasburger, E. (1891). "Über den Bau und die Verrichtung der Leitungsbahnen in den Pflanzen," Histologische Beiträge, Vol. III. Fischer, Jena.
Wakil, S. J. (1960). *J. Biol. Chem.* **235**, PC 31-32.
Ziegler, H. (1957). *Flora (Jena)* **144**, 229-250.
Ziegler, H. (1961). *In* "Recent Advances in Botany," pp. 1229-1232. Univ. of Toronto Press, Toronto.
Ziegler, H., and Huber, F. (1960). *Naturwissenschaften* **47**, 305.
Ziegler, H., and Ziegler, I. (1962). *Flora (Jena)* **152**, 257-278.

PART IV

INTERNAL AND EXTERNAL
CONTROL OF WOOD
FORMATION

The Role of Endogenous Hormones in Cambial Activity and Xylem Differentiation

P. F. WAREING, C. E. A. HANNEY, and J. DIGBY

Botany Department, University College of Wales, Aberystwyth, Wales

The Roles of Auxin and Gibberellin in Cambial Activity and Xylem Differentiation

There is now a considerable body of evidence suggesting that endogenous auxin arising in the apical regions of growing shoots stimulates cambial division and xylem differentiation in the stem below. This evidence has been discussed recently by several authors (Larson, 1962a; Wareing, 1958a; Wilcox, 1962; Wort, 1962) and may be summarized as follows:

(1) The initiation of cambial activity in the spring is dependent upon the presence of expanding buds, at least in deciduous species.

(2) Cambial divisions commence beneath the expanding buds, and a wave of cambial division spreads downwards from there to the branches and trunk, i.e., the cambial stimulus appears to travel basipetally only.

(3) Young expanding leaves are known to be rich sources for production of auxin, which is transported in a predominantly basipetal direction ("polar transport").

(4) Application of auxin to disbudded twigs of woody plants in the spring results in some cambial division and the formation of new xylem elements, at least for a short distance below the point of application.

Nevertheless, the new xylem formed below the point of application of indoleacetic acid (IAA) to decapitated and disbudded shoots of woody plants was found to extend only a relatively short distance, and only in chilled shoots of *Poplar* was it possible to obtain cambial activity over several centimeters in response to applied IAA (Reinders-Gouwentak, 1941). These and other observations led certain authors to postulate that, in addition to IAA, some other factor, such as vitamins, must be necessary for cambial activity. With the discovery of natural gibberellins in higher plants and the availability of pure samples of gibberellic acid (GA), it was natural to test the effect of this new class of growth substances on cambial activity. It had been observed that spurs of apricot sprayed with GA showed increased cambial activity and xylem development (Bradley and Crane, 1957). This latter experiment was carried out with leafy shoots and the observations on cambial activity were somewhat incidental to the main object of the investigation. It was therefore decided to study the effects of applying IAA and GA, both separately and in combination, to disbudded winter shoots of various woody species. In the first series of experiments (Wareing, 1958b) the "diffuse porous" species *Acer pseudoplatanus* and *Populus robusta* and the ring-porous species *Fraxinus excelsior* were used. The shoots were collected from out of doors in March and disbudded, cut into uniform lengths, and stood with the basal ends in water; they were maintained at 20–25°C. IAA at 500 and 100 ppm and GA at 1000 and 500 ppm in lanolin were applied separately and together. The lanolin preparations were replaced at intervals of 3–5 days. After 10–14 days from the time of application of the hormones, the shoots were sectioned by hand at various distances, in the range 1–5 cm, from below the upper end, and observations were made on the cambial regions.

It was found (Fig. 1) that, with lanolin only, there had been no detectable cambial division, and no new tissue had been added to the face of the xylem of the previous year. Where IAA alone had been applied, new xylem elements could clearly be discerned on the periphery of the old wood. However, the new elements did not form a continuous ring around the stem, but isolated groups of vessels occurred at intervals, with very little differentiation of the intervening tissue between the adjacent groups. Moreover, the width of the new xylem was comparatively narrow. In the shoots to which GA alone had been applied, active division of the cambium had evidently occurred and a distinct zone of new tissue could be discerned on the inner side of the cambium. This tissue was not differentiated, however, and consisted of very thin-walled fusiform cells which still retained their protoplasmic contents. These cells were clearly cambial derivatives which had not undergone any further differentiation into normal xylem tissue.

In the shoots to which both IAA and GA had been applied there was a wide zone of new xylem, consisting of apparently "normally" differentiated vessels, fibers, and other wood elements with thickened and lignified walls. Thus, the application of GA plus IAA, in comparison with IAA alone, had resulted in far greater cambial division and much more normal

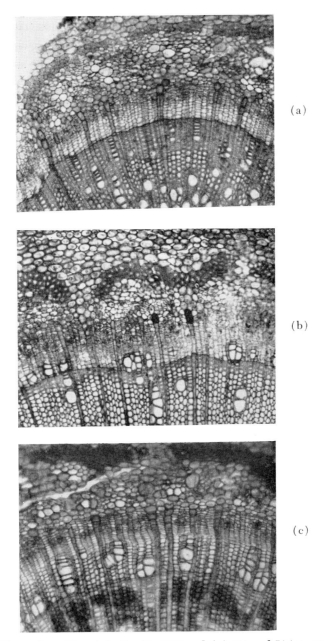

Fig. 1.   Effects of applying (a) GA, (b) IAA and (c) GA and IAA together, to disbudded shoots of *Acer pseudoplatanus*.

differentiation of the derivative cells; whereas only small groups of cells (as seen in transverse sections) had differentiated with IAA alone, a whole band of differentiated tissue was formed with the application of both IAA and GA. It was difficult to ascertain whether new phloem had been formed in response to the treatments, since there is no clear annual ring in the phloem of the species investigated. There was evidence, however, from the apparently increased total width of the phloem in the shoots treated with GA + IAA, that some new phloem tissue had been formed. This matter was further investigated in the following experiments.

An attempt was made to determine the effects of various concentrations of IAA and GA on xylem and phloem differentiation in poplar. IAA and GA were each supplied at four different levels in all combinations and the shoots were examined after 18 days. It was found that considerable cambial activity had occurred with most treatments, and in order to obtain quantitative data, the widths of (a) the new xylem and (b) total phloem tissue from the cambium to the primary phloem fibers, were measured, ten measurements being made for each of ten shoots in each treatment. Any increase in width of the phloem was determined by subtracting the mean width of phloem in the lanolin controls from the mean width for any given treatment. The results are summarized in Fig. 2.

Considering first the effects on xylem development [Fig. 2(a)], it is seen that a small amount of xylem was formed in the presence of IAA alone, but that this did not increase appreciably at concentrations above 100 ppm. A small amount of undifferentiated xylem tissue was formed with GA alone, but this also showed little effect of increasing GA concentration. In the presence of both IAA and GA there was a great increase in cambial activity, maximum xylem development occurring with IAA and GA each at 100 ppm, but with only a small decrease at higher concentrations of each substance.

No phloem formation occurred with IAA alone at any concentration, but considerable amounts of phloem were formed with GA alone at 100 ppm [Fig. 2(b)]. As with xylem development, maximum phloem was formed with IAA at 100 ppm in combination with GA at 100 or 500 ppm.

Although the widest zone of new xylem was formed with IAA and GA each at 100 ppm, with this treatment much of the xylem was undifferentiated and unlignified. The most "normal"-looking xylem was formed with IAA at 500 ppm and GA at 100 ppm.

From the foregoing results it is clear that IAA in the absence of GA results only in xylem development. Phloem development can occur with GA alone, but both xylem and phloem development reach their maximum in the presence of IAA and GA together. GA causes the formation of

MEAN XYLEM WIDTH e.p.u.

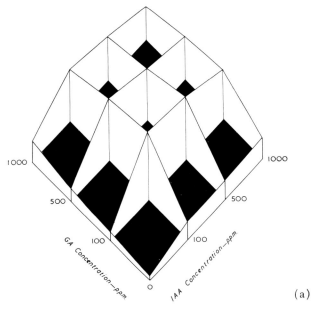

(a)

MEAN PHLOEM WIDTH e.p.u.

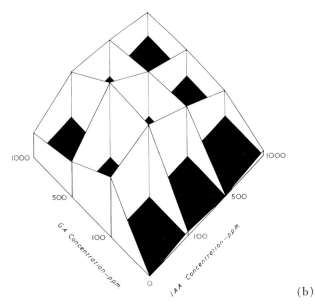

(b)

Fig. 2. Effects of various concentrations of GA and IAA on (a) xylem and (b) phloem development in *Populus robusta* as measured by width of new tissue formed. Note: The hormone concentrations shown are those in the lanolin, and give no indication of the concentrations present in the tissues.

cambial derivatives on the internal (xylem) side of the cambium, but these remain undifferentiated in the absence of IAA.

A careful study of the new phloem formed in response to applied IAA + GA, or GA alone, has so far revealed no sieve tubes or companion cells, all new tissue apparently being entirely parenchyma. A study has also been carried out on phloem production in grapevine (*Vitis vinifera*). In this species, the late-season phloem shows smaller-celled parenchyma and sieve tubes than the spring phloem, so that a distinct "annual ring" can be recognised (Esau, 1953). The advantage of this species for the present purpose, therefore, is that any new phloem formed in response to hormone treatment can be clearly recognized. Application of IAA + GA to isolated pieces of grapevine stems produces both new xylem and new phloem, but so far only parenchyma has been observed in the latter, although some evidence of sieve plates has been obtained and the disposition of certain cells suggests sieve tubes and companion cells.

Further experiments were carried out with a coniferous species (*Larix decidua*) and with the herbaceous species *Coleus blumei* and *Phaseolus multiflorus* (Hanney, 1960). One-year seedlings of *L. decidua*, planted in pots, were disbudded and the hormones (both at a concentration of 500 ppm) were applied to the decapitated main axis. The seedlings were sampled after 20 days and the cambium examined by transverse sections as before. There was no evidence of cambial activity where lanolin alone had been applied, but where IAA was applied a narrow zone of tracheids with partially thickened walls was present. With GA alone a zone of un-differentiated cambial derivatives was present, as in the experiments with broad-leaved species. Where IAA and GA were applied together a broad zone of wide-lumened, thick-walled tracheids was present.

With the *Coleus* a number of lateral shoots, and in *Phaseolus* the main axis, were decapitated, and the growth hormones applied in lanolin to the top of the decapitated internodes. After 2–3 weeks, the treated inter-nodes were sectioned at various distances below the cut surface. Although no annual ring was present to serve as a reference point, with all treat-ments there was a marked change in the diameter and other character-istics of the cells formed subsequent to decapitation, and hence it was relatively easy to distinguish the new tissue. Once again, IAA alone resulted in the formation of a limited number of xylem cells with thickened, lignified walls (Fig. 3), but these possessed a very much nar-rower lumen than the wide vessels formed before decapitation. In the plants to which GA alone had been applied the cambial derivatives were undifferentiated, whereas in the plants receiving both IAA and GA a wide zone of apparently "normal" xylem had been formed in all species. It was difficult to determine whether any new phloem had been formed in the herbaceous species, but in *Coleus* it appeared that there had been little, if any, phloem formation. However, in view of the effects of IAA and GA concentration on the relative development of xylem and phloem in poplar (p. 326), it would seem necessary to test a range of concentrations with herbaceous species before drawing any firm conclusions.

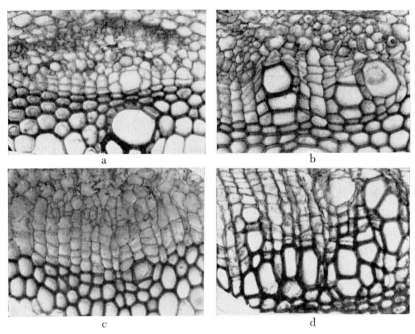

Fig. 3. Effects of hormones on cambial activity in *Phaseolus multiflorus*. (a) Lanolin control, (b) IAA alone, (c) GA alone, and (d) GA and IAA together.

The foregoing experiments thus gave essentially similar results for xylem development, whether broad-leaved woody species, conifers, or herbaceous dicotyledons were used. In all cases, some cambial division occurred with either IAA or GA alone, and in the case of IAA there was also some differentiation of the cambial derivatives to form vessels; in the case of GA alone the cambial derivatives remained undifferentiated. With IAA and GA together there was a great stimulation in the division of the cambium and in the degree of differentiation which occurred.

The effects of kinetin, alone and in combination with IAA, were tested on shoots of *Acer pseudoplatanus* and *Populus*, but it appeared to have no promotive effect upon cambial division, and indeed it appeared to be slightly inhibitory in combination with IAA. It is possible, however, that the concentration used (1000 ppm) was supraoptimal. Sorokin *et al.* (1962) have recently reported that kinetin in combination with auxin causes more normal xylem differentiation in pea internodes than auxin alone.

The results of the experiments reported have given confirmation of earlier reports that IAA alone applied to disbudded woody shoots will cause cambial division (Söding, 1937; Reinders-Gouwentak, 1941). It is also known from tissue culture studies that exogenous IAA or 2,4-D is essential for the cell division and growth of callus cultures of certain species, e.g., Jerusalem artichoke, *Ampelopsis, Salix, Crataegus*, etc. (Gautheret, 1959).

Although there is no doubt that IAA will act as a cell division factor for certain types of tissue, it is now also well established that gibberellins also stimulate cell division, for example, in internode extension (Sachs *et al.*, 1959). It has now been shown that gibberellic acid will also stimulate cell division in the cambium, but that the derivative xylem cells appear to undergo little or no further differentiation. Thus, two very different types of growth substance are both able to stimulate cambial division when applied independently to woody shoots. On the other hand, when they are applied together there is a marked synergistic effect, so that the rate of cambial division is greatly increased. This latter observation suggests that both auxin and endogenous gibberellins are necessary for cambial division in the intact plant. On this hypothesis, however, it becomes necessary to explain how it is that either of these growth substances alone will also stimulate cambial division. It has been found that disbudded woody stems contain small amounts of auxins (Digby, unpublished) and it is possible that they also contain small quantities of gibberellins, at levels below the threshold necessary for cambial division; the addition of either growth substance in greatly increased amounts may be sufficient to bring about division in the presence of small amounts of the other.

Whereas both IAA and GA can promote cambial division, apparently only IAA can stimulate the further differentiation of the derivative xylem cells. The differentiation of vessel elements in the xylem involves vacuolation and considerable increase in size, and similarly the formation of tracheids and fibers involves cell growth. In all the latter types of cell, differentiation involves development of a relatively complex secondary wall and lignification of both primary and, often, secondary walls. The vacuolation of xylem cells during differentiation is, of course, simply another aspect of the processes involved in cell extension stimulated by IAA in parenchymatous cells, such as those of the *Avena* coleoptile. Moreover, the stimulation of cell wall synthesis during differentiation of vascular tissue is in agreement with the current view that the role of auxin in promoting cell extension is closely connected with its effect upon the properties of the cell wall. The incorporation of C^{14} into the cell wall has been shown to be stimulated by auxin in *Avena* coleoptiles (Ray, 1961; Ray and Baker, 1962).

The lignification of the cell wall occurring during the later stages of differentiation of vascular tissue can be regarded as yet another manifestation of the process of differentiation occurring in response to IAA. Certain workers, however, have argued that IAA has a rather more specific effect on lignin synthesis. Thus, it is known that the biosynthesis of "lignin" from eugenol is dependent upon the presence of peroxidase, and it has been found that IAA stimulates the production of peroxidase (Siegel, 1956). On the other hand, the antioxidant properties of IAA cause it to inhibit lignin synthesis, so that the possible role of IAA in lignification is complex.

Apart from the probable role of endogenous IAA in stimulating the differentiation of cambial derivatives already destined to become xylem tissue, there is considerable evidence that auxin may actually control the *initiation* of vascular tissue. Thus Jacobs (1952) has shown that auxin passing basipetally from leaves in the upper part of the plant plays an important role in determining the regeneration of vascular tissue in the pith. Similarly, several authors (Camus, 1949; Wetmore and Sorokin, 1955; Clutter, 1960) have shown that exogenous auxin may induce xylem in callus cultures.

From the foregoing evidence, the role of auxin in xylem differentiation seems to be well established. The possible hormonal control of phloem development has been little studied previously. The results of the present experiments suggest that in the presence of auxin alone the cambium divides to give only or predominantly xylem tissue, and in the presence of GA alone mainly phloem tissue is formed; in the presence of IAA and GA together, both xylem and phloem may be formed concurrently. It appears that the normal activity of the cambium in poplar, involving the formation of both fully differentiated xylem and phloem, depends upon a balance between the concentrations of IAA and gibberellin.

In shoots of poplar to which GA was applied, the zone of cambial division seemed much more diffuse than in a normal cambium, in which a quite sharply defined cambium is usually located between the differentiating xylem and phloem. Studies of vascularization in callus cultures suggest that the polarization into xylem and phloem, separated by a cambium, is determined by concentration gradients of auxin (Gautheret, 1957). Thus, the sharp polarization into xylem and phloem in a normal shoot may depend upon the supply of auxin from the apical region.

From the foregoing discussion, there seems little doubt that normal cambial activity and differentiation into xylem and phloem depend upon both auxin and gibberellins. The question thus arises as to how far the seasonal periodicity of the cambium can be related to changes in levels of endogenous auxins and gibberellins, and how far these substances can be said to "control" cambial activity. Since the initiation of cambial activity in woody plants in the spring depends upon the presence of expanding buds, which are known to produce high concentrations of auxin, it seems that the cambium is not able to supply its own auxin requirements, but that it is supplied from expanding leaves. On the other hand, in ring-porous tree species, the initiation of cambial division in the spring spreads extremely rapidly—much faster than the known rates of auxin movement—and it has been postulated (Wareing, 1951) that there may be a reserve of auxin precursor in the stems of such species. It is of interest, therefore, that in the ring-porous species *Fraxinus excelsior* the bark appears to act as a reservoir of tryptophan, a known auxin precursor (Szalai and Gracza, 1958).

The cessation of cambial activity with the termination of extension growth in diffuse-porous trees is no doubt due to the fact that auxin production in the shoot apical region falls sharply when extension growth ceases. On the other hand, in ring-porous species the production of summer wood may continue long after extension growth has ceased, and it has been shown for *Robinia pseudacacia* that summer wood formation is dependent upon some stimulus coming from the mature leaves (Wareing and Roberts, 1956). Although auxin production by mature leaves is much lower than that by expanding leaves, nevertheless detectable amounts can be extracted from the latter, and presumably there may be sufficient export of auxin from mature leaves of ring-porous species to maintain cambial division and xylem differentiation after extension growth has ceased. Thus, there seems sufficient evidence to support the view that the seasonal periodicity of cambial activity and xylem differentiation is controlled by auxin coming from expanding buds, or from mature leaves.

The role of endogenous gibberellins in cambial activity has not yet been elucidated. Little is known regarding the site of gibberellin synthesis in the plant, and in woody species in particular. Nevertheless, it has been shown that appreciable quantities of material with gibberellin activity are present in buds of *Acer pseudoplatanus* in the spring (Eagles, 1962). Thus, the expanding buds may also supply gibberellins, as well as auxins, to the cambium. The available evidence suggests that gibberellins are very mobile in the plant and do not show "polar transport." Thus, although the cambium probably has to be supplied with both these types of growth substance, if gibberellin moves readily through the plant whereas auxin is transported from the localized centers in a strictly polar manner, it seems that auxin is more likely to play a regulatory role than gibberellins. Of course, any essential factor, such as water, which becomes limiting may be regarded as controlling cambial activity, but assuming that external factors such as water, light, and temperature are not limiting, then the *internal* regulation of cambial activity would seem to be determined primarily by auxin. Indeed, it is quite possible that the effect of such external factors as water deficiency on cambial activity may be exerted indirectly through their effects on auxin production.

We know considerably less regarding regulation of phloem development in trees. Indeed, there is remarkably little information regarding the seasonal pattern of the phloem formation in trees. There is no doubt that in herbaceous plants xylem and phloem development proceed simultaneously, but apparently this is not always the case in woody plants. Thus, according to Elliott (1935), in *Acer pseudoplatanus* there is little phloem formation during the period of active xylem development up to July, but as extension growth ceases phloem development commences and proceeds actively until leaf fall. On the other hand, Evert (1960) found that in pear, under California conditions, one or two rows of the cambial zone differentiate into sieve elements and companion cells in March. Cambial activity starts at approximately the same time and the production of phloem initials continues (parallel with xylem development) until the middle of June, when almost all sieve-element differentiation has taken place. The available literature on seasonal periodicity in the phloem is summarized by Evert (1960) and Bannan (1962). Since cambial division can occur with gibberellins alone, but auxin is essential for xylem differentiation, the observation that xylem development in *Acer pseudoplatanus* ceases with extension growth (i.e., when auxin production falls), but phloem development continues, raises the question as to whether the differentiation of phloem occurs in the presence of gibberellins associated with low levels of auxins. Thus, it is possible that, while auxin production falls sharply with cessation of extension growth, the production of gibberellins may be maintained by leaves, roots, or other parts of the plant. That is to say, the change from xylem to phloem production in *Acer pseudoplatanus* may be controlled by a change in the auxin: gibberellin balance.

Effects of Gravity on Response of the Cambium to IAA

It is well known that horizontal shoots of both angiospermous and coniferous trees show differential cambial activity on the upper and lower sides, leading to the formation of "reaction" wood. In angiospermous trees greater cambial division occurs on the upper side of a horizontal branch, giving rise to the so-called "tension wood," which has certain abnormal characteristics, the fibers having gelatinous walls and the size and number of vessels being reduced. In horizontal shoots of coniferous trees, on the other hand, greater cambial activity occurs on the *lower* side and gives rise to "compression" wood, in which the tracheids appear rounded in transverse section and the walls have a slightly higher lignin content and lower cellulose content than in normal wood. (See also the article by Wardrop, this volume, p. 405).

Since there seems little doubt that endogenous auxin and gibberellin play important roles in cambial activity and xylem differentiation in normal erect shoots, the question arises as to whether the differential cambial activity and abnormal xylem development observed in tension wood and compression wood of horizontal shoots arises from some redistribution of hormones within the shoot. It has long been held, of course, that the geotropic curvatures of shoots and roots involve the redistribution of auxin on the upper and lower sides of horizontal organs, with apparently greater amounts of auxin accumulating on the lower side. The occurrence of wider growth rings on the lower side of horizontal coniferous stems is consistent with the hypothesis that greater amounts of auxin accumulate on this side. Moreover, Wershing and Bailey (1942) were able to induce compression wood in pine seedlings by applying high concentrations of exogenous auxin. Nečesaný (1958) has argued that greater amounts of auxin accumulate on the lower side of horizontal stems of angiospermous trees also. He reported that he was able to extract higher amounts of auxin from the lower side of horizontal shoots of *Populus alba*. Moreover, he was able to suppress the formation of tension wood on the upper side of horizontal shoots of poplar by applying higher concentrations of IAA to that side. He concluded, therefore, that the formation of tension wood on the upper side of horizontal angiospermous shoots is due to the low levels of auxin on that side. It is difficult, however, to explain on this hypothesis why greater cambial division occurs on the upper side of such shoots. The technique of using isolated pieces of stem to study cambial activity described in the first section of this article would seem to afford a convenient means of studying the effects of gravity in relation to hormone redistribution.

The following experiments were carried out to investigate the effects of gravity on the responses of isolated stem pieces of poplar to applied auxin and gibberellin (Hanney, 1960). Strongly growing, erect shoots of *Populus robusta* were collected in January and stored in a damp atmosphere at 0°C until required. For experimental purposes, the shoots were cut into 10-cm lengths and disbudded. A slit approximately 0.6 cm deep was cut at the apical end of each shoot, and a coverslip was inserted, dividing it into an upper and a lower half. IAA and GA, alone and in combination, were applied in lanolin, each at a concentration of 500 ppm. The experiments described here were carried out at 25°C under continuous illumination from fluorescent tubes, but certain experiments were repeated in darkness and gave similar results. The lanolin preparations were replaced every 5 days.

In the first experiment, shoots of poplar were prepared as described and the basal end of each shoot was attached by means of polythene tubing to a length of glass tube bent at right angles, which was filled with water and dipped into a trough of water. In this way it was possible to hold the shoots in a horizontal position while maintaining the basal end in water.

Six experimental treatments were applied as follows:

Upper half:	Lan	Lan	IAA	GA	IAA + GA	Lan
Lower half:	Lan	IAA	Lan	IAA + GA	GA	IAA + GA

Gibberellic acid was used, since it had been found in the earlier experiments to act synergistically with IAA in cambial activity.

At the end of 3 weeks, sections were cut at 1, 3, and 5 cm from the treated apical ends, and the widths of the new xylem zones formed on the upper and lower sides of the shoots were measured. The results are summarized in Fig. 4.

It is seen that at 1 cm from the treated end there was more cambial activity on the upper or lower sides, depending on whether the IAA was applied above or below the coverslips, respectively. However, at 3 and 5 cm more xylem was formed on the upper side of all the shoots, the differences being highly significant. In a similar experiment with ash (*Fraxinus excelsior*), when the bark of a shoot receiving the treatment Lan/(IAA + GA) was removed and the wood left to dry, it was possible to trace the new xylem elements (formed in response to the treatment) passing from the lower side to the upper side of the shoot, as illustrated in Fig. 5.

Thus, in a horizontal shoot treated with auxin there is greater cambial activity on the upper side at 5 cm from the apical end, independently of whether the IAA was applied to the upper or lower halves of the apical region. Furthermore, although the application of GA in combination with IAA produced a greater response than IAA alone, this effect seemed to be independent of whether GA was applied to the upper or lower halves of the apical region. Since the same pattern of results was obtained with IAA alone as with IAA plus GA, it seems likely that it is IAA rather than GA which becomes redistributed in relation to gravity.

The absence of cambial division on the lower side at 5 cm from the

apical end of horizontal shoots of Poplar might be due to lack of auxin
or to supraoptimal (inhibitory) levels of auxin there. An attempt was
made to obtain evidence bearing on this problem in the following experiment. IAA alone was applied to the lower halves of the apical ends of
4 horizontal shoots. To the remaining 4 shoots, GA + IAA were applied

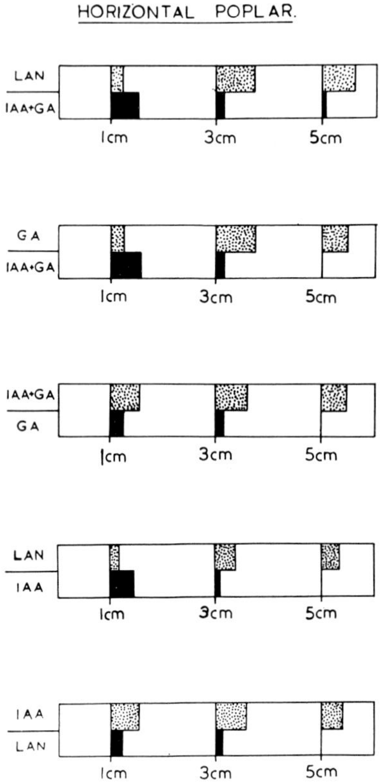

HORIZONTAL   POPLAR.

FIG. 4.   Effect of applying IAA and/or GA to the apical ends of horizontal poplar
shoots. The stippled and black areas indicate the mean width of new xylem tissue on
the upper and lower sides, respectively, at various distances from the point of application.

FIG. 5.   Diagram indicating pattern of "spring" vessels in horizontal shoots of
Fraxinus excelsior (from which the bark has been removed) in response to IAA and
GA applied to the lower half of the apical end.

to the lower halves, but in both cases IAA alone was also applied to the
lower side of the shoot at 5 cm from the apical ends. The outer layers of
the cortex were first removed from the lower side of each shoot before
the auxin was applied. After 14 days, transverse sections were cut at
various intervals from the apical ends, and the extent of new xylem

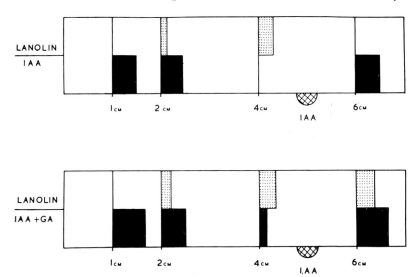

FIG. 6. Effect of making a second application of IAA to the lower side of horizontal poplar shoots at a point 5 cm from the apical end (see text for details).

formation measured. It may be seen (Fig. 6) that at 4 cm from the point
of application there was no new xylem on the lower side where IAA
alone had been applied at the apical end and very little with IAA + GA.
At 6 cm (i.e., 1 cm basal to the second point of application of IAA),
however, cambial activity was again present on the lower side (Fig. 6).
Thus, it would seem that the absence of xylem development on the lower
side of the shoots at 5 cm from the treated ends is not due to inhibitory
concentrations of auxin on the lower side of horizontal shoots, but rather
to deficiency of auxin there. The fact that there is greater cambial activity
at 1 cm from the second point of application of IAA when IAA + GA are
applied to the apical end than when IAA alone is applied there suggests
that GA is present on the lower side of the shoots even at 6 cm from the
apical end.

An experiment was carried out to determine the minimum angle from
the vertical at which a difference in cambial activity on the upper and
lower sides could be detected. This was done by arranging shoots at
various angles from the vertical, and applying IAA alone in lanolin to

the lower sides. After 14 days, sections were cut at various distances from the point of application, and the amount of cambial activity on the upper and lower side was determined, the results being summarized in Fig. 7. It is seen that for angles of greater than 18° from the vertical

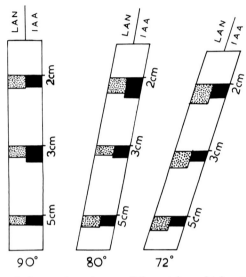

Fɪɢ. 7.   Effect of shoot orientation on differential cambial activity on upper and lower sides of poplar shoots, in response to applied IAA.

significant differences in cambial activity between the upper and lower sides could be detected.

It would seem that the differential cambial activity in horizontal shoots must involve the lateral redistribution of auxin by some mechanism other than the normal "polar" transport. In horizontal shoots, the two mechanisms are apparently working at right angles to each other, but it seemed possible that, in a normally orientated vertical shoot, the two mechanisms may operate in the same direction, whereas in an inverted shoot the two mechanisms may operate in opposite directions. Although there is good evidence that the transport of the cambial activity stimulus is strictly polar (Priestley, 1930), it was investigated whether this was true for the isolated stem pieces with exogenously applied IAA used in the present experiments, independently of whether they were in their normal erect position or inverted. IAA in lanolin was applied to the apical ends of 10 shoots, 5 of which were inverted. To the remaining 10 shoots, the IAA was applied to the basal ends, and 5 of the shoots were placed erect and the remaining 5 were inverted. Transverse sections were cut after 2 weeks and indicated that, when IAA was applied to the apical ends of erect and inverted shoots, the cambial activity extended the whole length of the shoots, but, when IAA was applied to the morphologically basal ends of erect and inverted shoots, cambial activity did not extend more than 2–3 cm from the treated ends, and there was little difference between the erect and inverted shoots. From these results it would seem that, in isolated poplar shoots, the IAA moves in a polar manner independently of the orientation of the shoots.

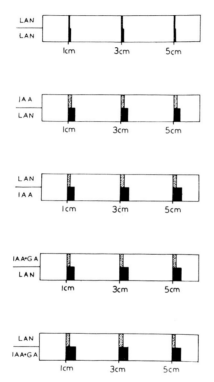

Fig. 8. Effect of applying IAA and/or GA to disbudded, horizontal shoots of *Pseudosuga taxifolia*.

Since inclined and horizontal shoots of conifers form compression wood on the *lower* side, an experiment was carried out to determine whether exogenously applied IAA results in differential cambial activity between the upper and lower sides of horizontal shoots of *Pseudotsuga taxifolia*. Since difficulty was experienced in obtaining cambial activity in response to exogenously applied IAA with isolated shoots of conifers, the experiments were carried out in the spring with intact shoots of *P. taxifolia* on trees growing in the open. Strongly growing erect laterals were tied into a horizontal position. The shoots were decapitated, and the cut ends divided into upper and lower halves with a coverslip, as previously. IAA and GA, each at a concentration of 500 ppm, were applied in lanolin as follows:

Upper:	Lan	IAA	Lan	IAA + GA	Lan
Lower:	Lan	Lan	IAA	Lan	IAA + GA

The treatments were continued for 3 weeks, the lanolin preparations being renewed every 4 days. At the end of this time the shoots were sectioned at 1, 3, and 5 cm from the apical end.

The results are shown in Fig. 8. It is apparent that a small amount of cambial activity had occurred even in the lanolin-treated controls, and that the latter had formed a slightly wider zone of new wood on the lower side. Nevertheless, treatment with IAA alone, or with IAA + GA, increased the amount of new wood formed, and the width of the latter was significantly greater on the *lower* side in all cases, regardless of whether the hormones were applied to the upper or lower halves. Thus, exogenously applied IAA resulted in increased cambial divisions on the lower side of horizontal shoots of *P. taxifolia*, just as occurs in such shoots naturally. Similar results were obtained with dormant seedlings of European larch (*Larix decidua*) growing in pots and placed horizontally. These were disbudded and IAA was applied to the decapitated main axis. A much wider zone of wood was again formed on the lower side.

The foregoing results are in agreement with the observations that in naturally occurring horizontal stems greater cambial activity occurs on the upper side in angiospermous species, whereas in coniferous species there is greater activity on the lower side. In view of the known activity of auxin in stimulating cambial division, the anatomical observations suggest that in angiospermous trees auxin is redistributed in horizontal shoots so that there are greater concentrations on the upper side, whereas in coniferous species the reverse is true. On the other hand, there is considerable evidence that in herbaceous dicotyledons and monocotyledons there are greater amounts of auxin on the lower sides of the shoots, at least over the short periods necessary to produce geotropic curvatures. Westing (1960) has observed greater quantities of a substance which reacts with ferric chloride, possibly an indole compound, in the lower halves of horizontal shoots of *Pinus strobus*. Similarly, as already stated, Nečesaný (1958) found greater amounts of growth substances in the lower halves of horizontal shoots of both poplar and pine. On the other hand, we ourselves have been unable to confirm the latter results and could obtain no consistent differences in the content of either growth promoters or growth inhibitors in extracts from the upper and lower sides of horizontal poplar and willow shoots. Moreover, we were unable to obtain any lateral redistribution of C^{14}-labelled IAA applied to horizontal stems of poplar. It is possible, however, that differences might have been detected if we had assayed the amount of *transported* IAA, since Gillespie and Thimann (1961, 1963) found the greatest differences in C^{14}-labeled auxin between the upper and lower halves of horizontal coleoptiles when they determined the amount of IAA transported within the tissues.

If Nečesaný's claim that greater quantities of auxin accumulate on the lower side of horizontal shoots of poplar is substantiated, then it will be necessary to explain why greater cambial activity occurs on the upper side, both in the intact tree and in isolated shoots, with exogenously applied auxin. The results of the latter experiments suggest that the reduced cambial activity on the lower side is due to the lack of auxin on that side rather than to inhibition resulting from supraoptimal concentrations of auxin, since a second application to the lower side at 5 cm from the apical end resulted in cambial division (p. 337).

On the other hand, it is possible that the differential cambial activity between the upper and lower halves is not due primarily to redistribution of auxin, but to differential sensitivity of the cambium on the two sides; thus it is possible that cambial division is inhibited in some manner on the lower side, so that division occurs only on the upper side. This hypothesis is consistent with the fact that bud outgrowth is inhibited on the lower side of horizontal poplar and willow shoots, this inhibition apparently not being due to supraoptimal auxin concentrations (Smith, 1962). The suggestion that auxin moves in opposite senses in dicotyledons and conifers may not at first appear very plausible, but this idea becomes more acceptable when it is remembered that Sinnott (1952) found that compression wood may occur on either the lower or the upper side in pine shoots. If pine branches were pulled downwards they produced compression wood on the lower side and tended to undergo compensating movements which restored them to their original position. On the other hand, if pine branches were displaced upwards, compression wood was formed on the *upper* side and the branches underwent compensating movements again tending to restore them to their original position. Thus, if the formation of compression wood in pine is due to the differential redistribution of auxin, we must postulate that the auxin accumulates in opposite directions, depending on whether the shoot is displaced upwards or downwards. In similar experiments with eucalyptus, Wardrop (1956) observed that in shoots displaced upwards tension wood developed on the lower side. Thus, the normal occurrence of tension and compression wood on opposite sides of dicotyledonous and coniferous shoots need not disturb us, since both types of reaction wood may be formed on either side of the shoot, depending upon the direction in which the displacement occurs.

DISCUSSION

ESAU: How did you attempt to determine whether or not sieve elements were present?

WAREING: We cut longitudinal sections and tried to see sieve plates. We did not identify callose.

WARDROP: Asymmetric stimulation of cambial activity is one thing in relation to reaction wood formation, but there is the point Wershing and Bailey (1942) made that if IAA is added to conifer stems reaction wood is formed even if the stem is vertical. I know of nothing which will induce tension wood in vertical stems. You have demonstrated the relation of IAA and GA to cambial activity, but this is not quite the same thing as saying they induce reaction wood formation.

WAREING: I agree. Nečesaný (1958) and ourselves have really been talking about different things. We dealt with the increased cambial division on the upper side. Nečesaný dealt with the anatomical features associated with reaction wood.

WARDROP: Eccentric stem development in gymnosperms or angiosperms is a phenomenon distinctly different from reaction wood formation. Angiosperms can have a noneccentric stem with reaction wood on one side. The two phenomena are not necessarily causally connected.

WAREING: It is usually stated that the tension wood formed on the upper side is associated with wider rings. But can you get a horizontal shoot forming symmetrical rings?

WARDROP: Usually it is the association you mentioned. On the other hand, eccentricity may occur toward the lower side of an angiosperm stem, but the reaction wood toward the upper side.

LARSON: This type of eccentricity is frequently found in the same branch in angiosperms. One annual ring may have the ellipse on the top, the next one on the bottom. It seldom occurs in this fashion in conifers.

BAILEY: Years ago I repeated the classical experiments of Robert Hartig (1901) with upside-down spruce trees which had some of their branches pulled up and some down. It was questioned at the time whether light could have had any effect on his results. I therefore put a black cover over the plants and put mirrors underneath which directed the light upwards. Gravity, of course, was pulling downwards. Then I applied pulleys. Using a spruce with perfectly horizontal branches, it did not matter whether the branches were pulled down or up; the compression wood always formed on the under side of the branches in relation to gravity.

WAREING: We did our poplar experiments in the light, but to eliminate the light effects we ran parallel experiments in the dark; the results were exactly the same. Whether we were getting reaction wood is another matter.

BAILEY: There is another useful phenomenon in this connection; the vigor of growth in the gymnosperms is correlated with the amount of reaction wood induced. In southern pines, erect, very vigorously growing trees may at times form compression wood all around the bole for quite a distance below the crown.

FREUDENBERG: Perhaps you could obtain additional information by using indican. Phloroglucinol indicates the lignin present. Indican localizes the tissue where lignin formation is still in progress. There is difficulty in the literature about the synthesis of indican. We have revised the synthesis (Freudenberg *et al.*, 1952). I can provide small samples to anybody who needs indican.

MEIER: Professor Wareing, you said that in coniferous wood, when you bend a branch upwards the auxin is redistributed toward the upper side, and downwards when you bend the branch down. How could such a redistribution take place?

WAREING: I cannot say how the auxin can be redistributed, but it seems to me that the fact that one gets differential cambial activity and reaction wood formed on the upper or lower side, depending on which way the branch has been displaced, is merely part of the same problem.

PRESTON: In all these redistributions the problem is really: What is the underlying mechanism? In one of your poplar stems you had evidence for an anatomical reason that there was redistribution. Did you literally get spiraling of the wood elements from below upwards?

WAREING: Yes, but I would say that the anatomical effects were probably the results of the auxin redistribution. From the recent work of Gillespie and Thimann (1961, 1963) we can be sure that there is redistribution of auxin in lateral organs, but we are not in a position to say how this is brought about.

THIMANN: I think the most likely solution is the ancient one proposed by Nemeč and by Haberlandt, that is, the movement of heavy bodies such as plastids packed with starch. It is easy to show in the coleoptile that the time it takes the plastids to roll down onto the lateral wall coincides nicely with the presentation time for gravity.

WAREING: There are movable starch grains in twigs, but we want to accumulate statistical evidence on the accumulation of these grains on the lower side.

PRESTON: Is the concept that auxin is absorbed on some heavy particles?

THIMANN: No, the concept is that auxin moves from cell to cell by a metabolically powered transport system. This transport system is fairly nearly saturated in many plants under natural conditions. The movement of auxin through the membrane depends on the state of the membrane at that point. When the particles press on the membrane they so modify it that the auxin is now able to move through the membrane. We have shown that auxin does move laterally from cell to cell across the tissue (Gillespie and Thimann, 1963). A permeability which normally would not allow much lateral movement when the plant is vertical becomes changed to allow such movement when the plant is horizontal.

PRESTON: Does this redistribution always involve changes in anatomy as exemplified by your poplar twig? I was thinking of the observation that when a tree is "swastika"-ringed the vessels under the horizontal phloem bar become oriented horizontally. Presumably the theory would be that the auxin passing along the swastika orients the vessels in some way.

WAREING: That auxin can determine initiation of vascular tissue is evident from the work of Wetmore and Sorokin (1955) and of Camus (1949) with callus cultures. They could induce the differentiation of vascular tissue in callus by grafting in buds or by introducing auxin. Vascular differentiation is also found in *Coleus* across the pith if a bundle is interrupted. Jacobs (1952) has shown that this is dependent on auxin coming from above. I would explain your results in terms of auxin movement.

REFERENCES

Bannan, M. W. (1962). *In* "Tree Growth" (T. T. Kozlowski, ed.), pp. 3-21. Ronald Press, New York.
Bradley, M. V., and Crane, J. C. (1957). *Science* **126**, 972.
Camus, G. (1949). *Rev. Cytol. Biol. Vegetales* **11**, 1-195.

Clutter, M. E. (1960). *Science* **132**, 548-549.
Eagles, C. F. (1962). Ph.D. Thesis, University College of Wales.
Elliott, J. H. (1935). *Proc. Leeds Phil. Lit. Soc., Sci. Sect.* **3**, 55-67.
Esau, K. (1953). "Plant Anatomy." Wiley, New York.
Evert, R. F. (1960). *Univ. Calif. (Berkeley) Publ. Botany* **32**, 127-194.
Freudenberg, K., Reznik, H., Boesenberg, H., and Rasenack, D. (1952). *Chem. Ber.* **85**, 641-647.
Gautheret, R. J. (1957). *J. Natl. Cancer Inst.* **19**, 555-590.
Gautheret, R. J. (1959). "La Culture des Tissus Végétaux." Masson, Paris.
Gillespie, B., and Thimann, K. V. (1961). *Experientia* **17**, 126-129.
Gillespie, B., and Thimann, K. V. (1963). *Plant Physiol.* **38**, 214-225.
Hanney, C. E. A. (1960). M.Sc. Thesis, Univ. of Wales.
Hartig, R. (1901). "Holzuntersuchungen. Altes und Neues." Springer, Berlin.
Jacobs, W. (1952). *Am. J. Botany* **39**, 301-309.
Larson, P. R. (1960). *Forest Sci.* **6**, 110-122.
Larson, P. R. (1962a). *In* "Tree Growth" (T. T. Kozlowski, ed.), pp. 97-117. Ronald Press, New York.
Larson, P. R. (1962b). *Am. J. Botany* **42**, 132-137.
Nečesaný, V. (1958). *Phyton (Buenos Aires)* **11**, 117-127.
Priestley, J. M. (1930). *New Phytologist* **29**, 316-354.
Ray, P. M. (1961). *Plant Physiol.* **36**, Suppl. XIV.
Ray, P. M., and D. B. Baker (1962). *Nature* **195**, 1322.
Reinders-Gouwentak, C. A. (1941). *Koninkl. Ned. Akad. Wetenschap. Proc.* **44**, 654-662.
Sachs, R. M., Bretz, C., and Lang, A. (1959). *Exptl. Cell Res.* **18**, 230-244.
Siegel, S. M. (1956). *Quart. Rev. Biol.* **31**, 1-18.
Sinnott, E. W. (1952). *Am. J. Botany* **39**, 69-78.
Smith, H. (1962). Ph. D. Thesis, Univ. of Wales, Aberystwyth, Wales.
Söding, H. (1937). *Jahrb. Wiss. Botan.* **84**, 639-670.
Sorokin, H. P., Mathur, S. N., and Thimann, K. V. (1962). *Am. J. Botany* **49**, 444-454.
Szalai, I., and Gracza, L. (1958). *Phyton (Buenos Aires)* **11**, 111-114. 18-28.
Wardrop, A. B. (1956). *Australian J. Botany* **4**, 152-166.
Wareing, P. F. (1951). *Physiol. Plantarum* **4**, 546-562.
Wareing, P. F. (1958a). *J. Inst. Wood Sci.* **1**, 34-42.
Wareing, P. F. (1958b). *Nature* **181**, 1744-1745.
Wareing, P. F., and Roberts, D. L. (1956). *New Phytologist* **55**, 289-388.
Wershing, H. F., and Bailey, I. W. (1942). *J. Forestry* **40**, 411-414.
Westing, A. H. (1960). *Forest Sci.* **6**, 240-245.
Wetmore, R. H., and Sorokin, S. (1955). *J. Arnold Arboretum (Harvard Univ.)* **36**, 305.
Wilcox, H. (1962). *In* "Tree Growth" (T. T. Kozlowski, ed.), pp. 57-88. Ronald Press, New York.
Wort, D. J. (1962). *In* "Tree Growth" (T. T. Kozlowski, ed.), pp. 89-95. Ronald Press, New York.

Some Indirect Effects
of Environment on
Wood Formation

Philip R. Larson

Lake States Forest Experiment Station, Forest Service, U. S. Department of Agriculture, Rhinelander, Wisconsin

Environment traditionally has been accepted as a direct rather than an indirect determinant of wood formation. Most generally, this view has been fostered by investigators attempting to relate environment or some factor of environment to over-all wood formation, or radial growth. Such investigations have met with varying degrees of success or failure, success being determined most frequently by the predominating influence of a particular environmental factor in the locale or during the season in which the study was conducted.

In recent years, greater emphasis has been given to isolating factors of the environment and to segregating components of radial growth. The most readily recognized features of wood are the growth rings and, within the growth rings, the zones of earlywood and latewood. In conifers, formation of these growth zones closely parallels the seasonal development of the foliage organs of the crown. Environment induces either temporary fluctuations or long-term modifications in the growth and development of these foliar organs, and each fluctuation is accompanied by a commensurate alteration in the developing tracheids comprising the wood in some part of the tree. Thus, factors of the environment exert their influence directly on the crown and only indirectly on the formation of wood.

The environment acting on a tree is complex and constantly changing and the response of the tree to the environment is equally complex and similarly changing. Nevertheless, by controlling the environment so that one factor predominates, the influence of this factor on the growth of the crown, and consequently on the formation of wood, may be evaluated. In this paper, we will consider two of the most prominent features of growth ring development, tracheid diameter and wall thickness, and a few of the environmental factors that influence them.

Tracheid Diameter

The decrease in tracheid diameter accompanying the normal transition from earlywood to latewood has been a subject of investigation for many years. Among the numerous theories advanced to account for this phenomenon, the hormonal theory currently appears most plausible since it is the only one that can satisfactorily explain the distributional patterns of variation in tracheid diameter.

Some of the first clues to the hormonal control of growth ring development may be found in the early work of Jost (1891, 1893) who correlated certain aspects of wood formation with a "stimulus" originating in the terminal growth centers. Actual discovery of the plant hormones in the late 1920's was soon followed by evidence that cambial activity was among the many plant processes influenced by these growth-regulating substances (Snow, 1935; Söding, 1936; Zimmermann, 1936). During this same period, Priestley's (1930, 1932, 1935) classical investigations reemphasized and greatly clarified the relationship between extension growth and wood development. In the ensuing years, the results of these and many other similarly oriented investigations were gradually synthesized into a hypothesis or concept to explain at first the initiation of cambial activity and at a later date growth ring development per se. It is difficult to determine when the hormonal theory of growth ring development was actually conceived, and it is not the intention of this paper to do so, for the contributions of many researchers are involved and the interpretations of these researches extremely varied. The subject has been reviewed from a number of viewpoints (Wareing, 1958; Larson, 1962b; Wilcox, 1962) and it is patently obvious from these reviews and from more recent publications that the theory is still undergoing a rapid evolution.

In recent years, new-found knowledge of other plant growth mechanisms and information from other areas of plant science have been used to study wood development and quite naturally interpretations concerning these growth processes have been interwoven into the hormonal theory. One of these allied areas of knowledge, photoperiodic control, although not new in itself, has proven to be among the most useful research techniques for studying wood formation. Physiological drought, long associated with latewood formation in trees, has also provided valuable information. By controlling these environmental factors, photoperiodism and drought, it has been possible to determine their influence on tracheid diameter and the relationship existing between crown development and wood formation in trees.

Photoperiod

Photoperiod has been shown to exert a decisive influence on cambial activity (Wareing, 1951). The evidence indicates, however, that the response in terms of wood formation is indirectly related to the photoperiodic response of the foliar organs (Larson, 1962a).

We have pursued this subject in some detail and found that most variations in wood formation so far investigated could be interpreted in terms of the attendant changes in foliar development brought about by photoperiodic exposure. In all of our experiments photoperiod has been used simply to control vegetative growth of the crowns in young (5- to 6-year-old) *Pinus resinosa* trees, and no attempt has been made either to duplicate a photoperiodic regime in nature or to determine the precise photoperiodic requirements of the species. Photoperiodic exposure in all cases has been of 18 hours duration for long days and 8 hours duration for short days; these photoperiods have been found entirely adequate to prolong and to inhibit, respectively, the foliar development of young red pine trees.

From experiments with young red pines grown under both natural and artificially controlled daylengths, it has been concluded that the transition from earlywood to latewood approximately coincides with the cessation of terminal elongation. It is essential to emphasize the *approximate* cessation of terminal growth, for measurable evidence of the transition will depend upon such factors as sampling position in the stem, vigor of the tree, and abruptness of the terminal growth cessation. Although anatomical data are obtained for each internode of every tree in our experiments, it invariably has been found that the current year's internode is by far the most sensitive and provides the most useful index for evaluating environmental influences.

Under natural photoperiods earlywood formation coincides with the extension growth of the buds or shoots. Immediately following the termination of internode extension, the preformed needles of the new shoot begin vigorous elongation. At about this time narrow diameter tracheids, distinctive of latewood, are evident first at the base of the tree and then at successively higher levels. Position of sampling and vigor of the tree are of primary importance at this stage, particularly in larger trees, for the earliness and the abruptness of the transition increase as the length of the clear bole increases and as tree vigor declines. The critical importance of sampling position is also evident from the fact that, within the crown and to varying distances down the stem, earlywood formation continues throughout most of the growing season under the regulating influence of the elongating needles and the meristems of the developing buds.

Short photoperiods are known to inhibit terminal growth and are, therefore, extremely useful in studying the series of events culminating in the earlywood-to-latewood transition. Some investigators (Molski and Zelawski, 1958; Zelawski and Wodzicki, 1960) have questioned whether the process of latewood differentiation is actually related to the photoperiodic reactions of the terminal meristems. We have found, however, that the response of plants to photoperiod is not necessarily uniform throughout the season, and exposure of young red pines to short-day conditions evokes changes in tracheid diameter that vary with the stage of vegetative development. A short day imposed upon the tree during the period of axial extension growth curtails internodal elongation[1] to some extent. But the strong growth potential of the determinate-type buds prevails and considerable internodal as well as subsequent needle elongation occurs even when trees are grown in continuous darkness. So long as meristematic activity remains vigorous within the internode, large diameter, earlywood cell production continues regardless of the photoperiod.

Following the termination of internodal extension, needle elongation becomes more vigorous. During this early period, the growth potential of the needles persists to some degree, but the sensitivity to short photoperiods gradually increases as the needles approach maturity. Short-day treatment imposed on trees during the stage of most active needle elongation effectively reduces both needle growth and tracheid diameter although a minimum of 20 to 24 short days is required. At a later stage of foliar development, when the needles have attained greater lengths, a minimum of 7 to 10 short days suffices to reduce needle elongation and consequently tracheid diameter. In all cases, the influence of the shortened photoperiod is analogous to an advancement of seasonal maturity of the needles which normally occurs with the declining photoperiod of late summer.

Photoperiodic manipulation provides a highly versatile and efficient technique for growth control and the study of xylem development. Short days induce first a reduction and finally a cessation of needle growth which is reflected in a concomitant diminution of tracheid diameter and eventually complete cessation of cambial activity. However, the reduction in xylem cell diameter associated with short-day exposure is qualita-

---

[1] Internodal elongation refers to the extension growth of the tree as measured between branches or branch whorls on the main axis and not, in the strict botanical sense, between needles or individual foliar organs.

tive and the transition to latewood is by no means consistently abrupt or entirely unequivocal. Generally, the transition parallels the pattern of needle elongation. When needle growth declines gradually, as in the case of short days imposed during the vigorous growth stage, the transition to narrow-diameter cells occurs gradually and continues over an extended period. Contrarily, when conditions are opportune for the abrupt reduction of needle elongation, the initiation of narrow-diameter cell formation also occurs abruptly and within a relatively short time interval.

As in normal latewood development, the latewood tracheids induced by short days are not only evident earlier near the base of the tree but they are also narrower in diameter than farther up the stem. The tendency for the persistent formation of large-diameter cells in the upper stem, particularly in the internodes retaining active needles, is consistent with the concepts of juvenile wood (Zobel *et al.*, 1959; Rendle, 1960) and crown-formed wood (Trendelenburg, 1935; Wandt, 1937). Nevertheless, continued short-day treatment over an extended period does result in the formation of a very wide band of typical latewood cells throughout the entire tree. Although latewood cell production can be prolonged by favorable growth conditions in spite of the complete cessation of needle elongation under the influence of short days, cambial dormancy will eventually set in.

In contrast to the reduction and inhibition of growth brought about by short photoperiods, growth can be maintained and prolonged by exposure to long photoperiods. The needles of trees grown on long days continue to elongate, although at a decreased rate later in the season, and young red pine needles readily attain lengths 100% to 150% above normal. As in the case of short-day trees, tracheid diameters approximately parallel the patterns of needle elongation in long-day trees and large-diameter, earlywood cell production continues with prolonged needle growth. In spite of the long photoperiod, however, needle growth eventually ceases and cell diameter decreases accordingly, although the decrease is not as striking as in short-day trees.

Continued exposure to long days throughout the growing season may induce the premature flushing of summer buds and the elongation of new needles. This resurgence of apical activity is usually accompanied by a resumption of earlywood production and the formation of a false ring, providing the growth pause preceding the second flush was of sufficient duration to result in latewood development. Some trees can be forced to flush several times during a growing season and each renewal of apical growth can be associated with the formation of a false ring in the stem. Similarly, the transference of trees from short-day to long-day conditions

can promote renewed needle or bud growth and large-diameter cell production, providing the trees have not attained a state of dormancy
wherein long photoperiods are no longer effective. Short-day plants
exposed to a 30-minute, low-intensity, light break at midnight also

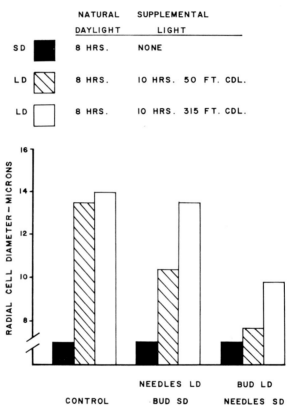

Fig. 1.   Tracheid diameters of young red pines with the terminal bud and the
needles exposed to different photoperiodic conditions. Photoperiodic treatments were
given following the termination of internodal extension growth when the needles
were actively elongating.

respond by renewed bud growth and increased cell diameter indicating
that the terminal growth response is a true photoperiodic phenomenon.
   It is evident that the foliar organs exert a profound influence on the
development of the wood cells in the stem. Nevertheless, under long-day
conditions the continued activity of both buds and needles makes it difficult to determine the relative contribution of either organ to xylem cell
diameter. By experimentally isolating the buds and the needles, however, and exposing each to different photoperiodic conditions, it has been

possible to distinguish their independent contribution to tracheid diameter (Fig. 1). This approach suggests that the bud or apical meristem exerts a decisive regulatory influence on cell diameter during the period of active extension growth of the shoot. When extension growth terminates

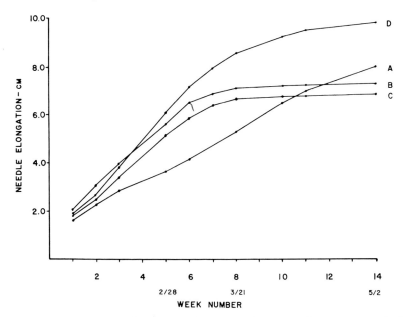

FIG. 2. Cumulative weekly needle elongation of young red pine trees with different-aged needles exposed alone to daylight. (A) Current-year needles exposed. (B) 2nd-year needles exposed. (C) 3rd-year needles exposed. (D) Control trees. The periodic harvesting dates for wood evaluation are indicated on the abscissa.

and primordia are being laid down in the formation of a new bud, the influence of the bud declines and the elongating needles become the principal source of the stimulus contributing to cell diameter (Larson, 1962a).

In a similar manner, the relative contribution of needles of different ages to wood formation has been tested by the simple device of covering, for a growing season, all needles on a tree except those of the desired age class (Larson, 1963b). When all mature needles were covered and the apical bud alone remained exposed, the new shoot developed over a normal growth period, although the resulting internode was considerably shorter and less vigorous than normal. Needle elongation from this shoot was slow but remarkably consistent and maintained a linear growth pattern throughout the season (Fig. 2). When only the second-year (previous season) or the third-year needles were exposed to the light, the

current-year needles exhibited a normal growth curve but ceased elongation relatively early in the season in spite of the long-day conditions; the
needles of red pine do not elongate after the first season of growth.

Tracheid development followed a predictable pattern on the basis of
needle elongation data obtained from previous experiments. When only
the current-year shoot remained exposed, large-diameter cell production
continued throughout the season as needle elongation continued. Although a considerable proportion of latewood occurred at the base of
the current internode, this was due to an increase in wall thickness and
not to a decrease in tracheid diameter; wall thickness will be discussed
later. On the contrary, when either the second- or third-year needles were
exposed alone, latewood formation occurred throughout the tree, beginning at the base, as needle elongation subsided and ceased. However, in
the latter instances, latewood was due to a marked decrease in tracheid
diameter with only a slight accompanying increase in wall thickness.

From these photoperiodic studies a definite pattern emerges and a
common thread of continuity is evident throughout, namely, that tracheid
diameter closely parallels the variations in terminal growth, primarily the
elongation growth of the current-year needles. Thus, when terminal
growth declines or ceases, tracheid diameter decreases, and if conditions
permit a resumption of terminal growth it will be reflected by an increase
in tracheid diameter. The effect of photoperiod is only indirectly on the
activity and development of the cambium and differentiating xylem cells.
The direct effect is on the vegetative organs of the tree, and the stimulus
arising from the photoperiodically induced activity within these organs
is transmitted to the differentiating xylem cells.

Drought

The effects of drought on wood development are very similar to those
attributable to photoperiod (Larson, 1963a). Young red pine trees subjected to drought periods of varying duration produced tracheids that
decreased in diameter in accordance with the decline in needle elongation
induced by the drought. Rewatering of the trees brought about a vigorous resumption of needle growth and a commensurate increase in
tracheid diameter resulting in the formation of a conspicuous false ring
in the stem. When two drought periods were interposed in the growing
season, two false rings were produced and each could be readily correlated with the drought-induced variations in needle elongation.

As in the case of photoperiod, the effect of drought on tracheid
diameter was found to be indirect. The direct effect was on foliar development and the decrease in tracheid diameter was a reflection of the foliar
response. A test of this indirect influence was achieved by suppressing

terminal growth by short-day exposures. As a result, there was no response to watering in terms of increased tracheid diameter when needle elongation failed to occur; latewood cells continued to form. Similarly, removal of the current-year needles at the time of rewatering prevented the resumption of large-diameter cell formation in trees exposed to both long and short photoperiods although cambial activity continued under the influence of the remaining mature needles. Thus, rewatering following a drought cannot elicit an increase in the tracheid diameter unless preceded by an appropriate response in apical or foliar activity.

The Hormonal Theory

The influence of both photoperiod and drought on tracheid diameter can be interpreted in terms of the hormonal theory and, in fact, adds substantiation to the theory. In both cases, the direct effect is on terminal growth which, in turn, presumably creates changes in the synthesis of auxin. The auxin emanating from the environmentally influenced foliar organs is, therefore, believed to be the direct regulator of tracheid diameter in the stem.

Evidence implicating auxin with the regulation of tracheid diameter may be obtained by exogenous applications of synthetic growth regulators and by auxin chromatography and bioassay. Applications of indole-3-acetic acid (IAA) to the cut surface of decapitated young red pines growing on short days induces the formation of a new zone of earlywood following the normal short-day latewood (Larson, 1960). When the decapitated tip is bisected by inserting a glass coverslip into an incision and IAA applied unilaterally to one of the halves, then large-diameter cells are produced immediately beneath the point of application. With increasing distance around the periphery, however, cell diameter gradually decreases until normal latewood is encountered on the untreated half. Vertically, a similar gradient of cell size from true earlywood to true latewood may be observed beneath the point of application. This latter gradient is relatively steep and is a characteristic response of all decapitation experiments, for without an intact bud the basipetal translocation of exogenous auxin is severely restricted.

A contrary response may be evoked by the exogenous application of the auxin-antagonist 2,3,5-tri-iodobenzoic acid (TIBA). In this case, narrow-diameter cells can be induced in trees growing on long photoperiods and normally producing earlywood (Fig. 3). Again, vertical gradients of cell size, and peripheral gradients in the case of unilateral applications, can be observed emanating from the point of application. Physiologically active concentrations of both IAA and TIBA that will evoke morphologically normal cell responses are relatively short lived and tracheid diameter reverts rather soon to that produced prior to treatment. Supraoptimal concentrations of IAA applied to short-day trees, however, result in vigorous cambial activity and the formation of typical reaction wood encircling the entire periphery. Gradients of cell size and cell type are again evident and there is an almost imperceptible gradation from reaction

FIG. 3. A false ring consisting of narrow diameter tracheids (arrow) produced in response to a tip application of TIBA (2,3,5-triiodobenzoic acid) to a young red pine growing on long days. The effect of TIBA was short lived and the tree soon reverted to the production of large-diameter tracheids.

wood to typical earlywood and finally to short-day latewood. These gradients, occurring transversally and peripherally on the cross section as well as vertically in the stem, are very similar in all respects to those found in stems containing naturally formed reaction wood. On a grand scale, these gradients are comparable to the transition in tracheid dimensions across an annual growth ring and vertically within an annual increment from stem apex to base.

Auxin bioassays, based on the chromatographic separation of extracted auxins, have shown that trees grown on the regime of long day → short day → long day exhibit a high auxin activity on long days that is reduced on short days and partially restored by return to long-day conditions (Larson, 1962b). It has been previously demonstrated that short-day exposure was correlated with a decline in both foliar growth and tracheid diameter, and transference back to long-day conditions with renewed foliar growth and an increase in tracheid diameter. An almost identical pattern of auxin activity, foliar growth, and tracheid diameter can be obtained by the treatment sequence of water → drought → water (Larson, 1963a). Although the auxin activity curves obtained by these procedures are strictly relative, they do provide corroborative evidence of an auxin-mediated link between apical growth and cell formation.

Indirect evidence in support of the hormonal theory may be obtained from the distributional patterns of tracheid size throughout the seasonal growth increment of a tree. The apical shoot with its developing needles appears to be the principal source of auxin for tracheid enlargement. Furthermore, the seasonal gradients of auxin activity appear to parallel the gradients of tracheid diameter not only temporally across the growth ring but spatially down the stem (Larson, 1962b). Reference has been made previously to the seasonal gradients that occur at a particular level in the stem and a few examples may suffice to illustrate the vertical gradients. For example, under normal conditions of terminal growth cessation, or the inhibition of foliar growth by manipulation of the environment, latewood will be initiated at the stem base and narrow-diameter cells will subsequently appear at progressively higher levels. This acropetal trend of latewood formation is presumably due to the waning auxin production of the terminal organs. With increasing proximity to the auxin source, however, the latewood becomes more transitional, and true earlywood production continues within the upper crown throughout most of the growing season. On the contrary, the abrupt removal of the auxin source by decapitation will reverse the auxin gradient, and narrow-diameter cells will be apparent first at the apex. Renewal of the auxin gradient by the flushing of a summer bud after latewood formation has been initiated throughout the stem will regenerate a new zone of earlywood. But, the distance that this new band of earlywood is propagated down the stem will depend on the intensity of the apical growth stimulus; in many cases the resulting false ring will be evident only within the confines of the crown.

It is clear that the crown of the tree exerts a definite regulatory influence over tracheid formation in the bole. From this it may be proposed that any factor that alters or influences the growth or activity of the terminal organs, consequently auxin synthesis, will be reflected by a concomitant change in tracheid diameter and perhaps wood formation in general. The pronounced gradients in tracheid diameter that occur both temporally and spatially throughout a growth increment during its formation suggest further that the auxin requirements for tracheid development are of an increasing order from latewood to earlywood to reaction wood and that all intergradations can exist. As a corollary, it may also be suggested that the diameter an individual tracheid attains will depend primarily upon the quantity of auxin reaching that tracheid during its critical stage of enlargement. Assuming the correctness of these suggestions, for which there is considerable evidence, one thus has an indirect "bioassay" within the tree itself. Within limits, the relative diameter of a tracheid at any position in a tree provides a relative index of the auxin reaching that tracheid. Although based on broad assumptions, this approach provides a working hypothesis whereby one can interpret essentially all the variations in tracheid diameter occurring within a tree in terms of the conditions that alter terminal growth and presumably auxin synthesis.

Quantitative relationships between attributes of terminal growth and tracheid diameter can seldom be established in spite of the demonstrable regulatory control of the crown on wood formation; this becomes increasingly difficult with larger trees. Although correlative evidence links the gradients of auxin activity and tracheid diameter within the woody stem, experiments demonstrating causality are unfortunately lacking. Similar gradients of auxin activity, however, have been found to occur in the stems of herbaceous plants and various proposals have been offered in explanation (Goldsmith and Thimann, 1962). In particular, interference with auxin transport or differences in the ability of tissues to transport auxin appear to play a decisive role in establishing these vertical stem gradients (Leopold and Lam, 1962; Scott and Briggs, 1962). Discussion of these specific problems of auxin metabolism are beyond the scope of the present paper. Nevertheless, there is reason to believe that the interpretations derived from experiments with non-tree species will prove to be generally applicable to trees, since very pronounced changes in xylem anatomy have also been induced in the former species by conditions that alter vegetative growth (Roberts and Struckmeyer, 1948) and presumably auxin synthesis.

Cell Wall Thickness

In normal latewood development the decrease in tracheid diameter is generally accompanied by a simultaneous increase in secondary wall thickening. These two processes, however, appear to be fortuitously correlated and not necessarily under the control of the same physiological mechanisms (Larson, 1960; Richardson and Dinwoodie, 1960; Wodzicki, 1960). The early German physiologists recognized this distinction (see

André, 1920) and recent work has, indeed, shown that cell diameter and wall thickness can be altered independently and often by quite different growth conditions.

Secondary wall thickening typical of latewood most generally begins at the base of the stem and progresses upward in much the same manner as the decrease in tracheid diameter. A further similarity of the two processes is the occurrence of gradients in wall thickness that frequently, although not invariably, inversely parallel the gradients of cell diameter. The initiation of latewood wall thickening usually occurs subsequent to the cessation of elongation growth, sometimes preceding and sometimes following the decrease in cell diameter. In the current-year internode of young red pines grown under natural conditions, the excessive wall growth of typical latewood is commonly absent or restricted to the last-formed tracheids. However, this internode and the one immediately beneath it produce wide bands of thick-walled tracheids when subjected to suitably controlled environments.

The measurable changes in wall thickness are by no means as amenable to environmental manipulation as cell diameter. A definite time lag is usually evident and in the case of short-day exposure during earlywood production the first narrow-diameter cells will be thin walled. Only after extended short-day treatment will wall thickness increase. On the other hand, once latewood formation has become established considerable fluctuations in tracheid diameter may occur with little change in wall thickness. Pronounced decreases in wall thickness can only be brought about by vigorous flushes of growth that actually renew earlywood formation. Mutilations such as decapitation or defoliation that interfere with photosynthetic ability evoke almost immediate alterations in wall development and cells with extremely tenuous walls can be produced. Although the ultimate source of the constituents that govern both tracheid diameter and wall thickness is the vegetative growth of the crown, it is possible to force the production of a desired cell type for limited periods by appropriate control of the conditions of growth that favor either auxin synthesis or photosynthesis (Fig. 4).

It is clear from a number of lines of evidence that the marked changes in wall thickness accompanying latewood development may be ascribed to a complex of factors related primarily to photosynthesis and net assimilation. Net assimilation alone, however, cannot satisfactorily account for these variations in wall development unless one also considers the differential translocation or availability of assimilates to other growing points in the tree with which the wood cells are, in a sense, competing. The wood cells are also actively competing among themselves, and this competition increases with increasing activity of the cambial zone. Competition is particularly severe during the periods of internodal extension and needle elongation when the reserve as well as the current assimilates are being channeled to these new growth centers. Studies of photosynthetic efficiency have shown that in young pines several weeks may elapse after bud break before the new growth contributes positively to dry matter

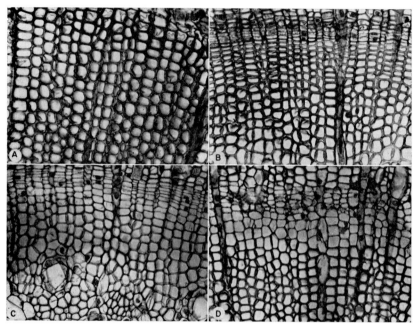

FIG. 4. Tracheid diameter and wall thickness can be altered independently for limited periods by appropriate growth control. Under favorable growing conditions, tracheids with normal wall thickness are produced, but radial diameter varies with photoperiodic exposure. (A) Long days. (B) Short days. Defoliation of the current-year internode results in an immediate decrease in tracheid wall thickness, but radial diameter again varies with photoperiodic exposure and activity of the terminal bud. (C) Short days, terminal bud dormant. (D) Long days, terminal bud flushing. Although nuclei are visible in the differentiating tracheids of (C), these cells eventually mature with little further increase in either diameter or wall thickness.

production (Bourdeau, 1959; Neuwirth, 1959), and it is reasonable to assume that the initial photosynthetic contribution of these new needles would be utilized in their own elongation growth. Kursanov (1961) has, in fact, found that although partially developed young leaves are able to photosynthesize they do not yield their assimilates to other parts of the plant, but continue for a long time to receive photosynthates from the nearest mature leaves. As the current-year needles approach maturity, however, their rate of photosynthesis rapidly rises (Freeland, 1952; Clark,

1961), and they shift from the consumption to the net production of assimilates. Thereafter, the contribution of the new needles to the over-all net assimilation of the tree for stem growth and wood formation increases (Rutter, 1957). There is no doubt regarding the twofold effect of needle maturity—decreased consumption and increased contribution of assimilates—on net assimilation of the stem, and presumptive evidence strongly suggests a correlative relationship between needle maturity and the latewood type of wall development. Indirect evidence of this relationship may be obtained from controlled-growth experiments.

As mentioned previously, a definite time lag exists between appearance of the first narrow-diameter cells and the visible cell wall thickening in young red pines exposed to short days during the early stages of needle elongation. Exposure to short photoperiods at a later period of needle development, however, reduces the time lag considerably and, in fact, both components of the latewood cell may be simultaneously altered. These growth patterns suggest that the reduction of needle elongation under the influence of short days permits the shunting of assimilates from foliar growth to wall development. The reduction of the time lag as the season advances appears related to the greater photosynthetic contribution of the more mature current-year needles. Similar photoperiodically induced changes in wall thickness were observed in *Larix* by Wodzicki (1961a,b) but, other than photoperiod, no causal explanation was offered.

A quite different pattern of tracheid wall development may be attained by growing trees on long-day conditions for extended periods. In this case, large-diameter tracheid production continues for many months as a result of the prolongation of needle growth and the sporadic flushing of summer buds. But once the current-year needles have achieved a certain stage of maturation, then secondary wall thickening increases rapidly throughout the entire tree irrespective of tracheid diameter. Under these extremely favorable growing conditions, it is very probable that the current-year needles are the main contributors to wood formation in spite of their continued elongation growth. The wood formed by these extremely thick-walled, large-diameter tracheids presents an unusual appearance microscopically, and has been referred to as "long-day latewood" (Larson, 1960).

A somewhat similar situation was observed in the experiment testing the influence of different-aged needles on wood formation. When light was continuously excluded from the older needles and only the current-year internode exposed, the needles of this internode continued to elongate throughout the course of the experiment. Again, large-diameter cell production continued but wall thickness gradually increased, presumably as the net photosynthetic contribution of the elongating needles increased.

From such controlled-environment studies it may be suggested that any condition that promotes maturation of the terminal meristems will result in a concomitant increase in wall thickening, providing photosynthesis remains at an optimal level. Maturation as used in this sense refers to a

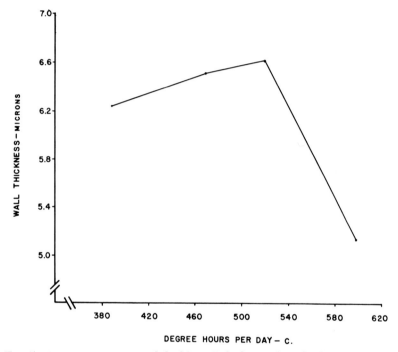

Fig. 5. Variation in tangential double-wall thickness of tracheids in terms of total degree hours per day (degrees centigrade). The young red pine trees were all grown under a seasonal photoperiodic regime comparable to 45° N latitude but different temperature conditions.

developmental stage in which the new needles are contributing positively to wood formation, and it may be attained either by premature cessation of needle growth as in the case of short days or by exceptional needle development as in the case of prolonged long days. Cessation of needle elongation alone, however, will not necessarily be accompanied by an increase in wall thickness, particularly if photosynthesis is limiting or if respiration is excessive. Thus, the narrow-diameter tracheids induced by drought in our experiments were relatively thin walled, possibly owing to the curtailment of photosynthesis associated with internal moisture stress (Kramer, 1958). Most generally the physiological processes contributing to tracheid diameter and wall development are fairly well synchronized in normal tree growth, and recognizable earlywood and late-wood will occur in the usual sequence during the growing season. None-theless, the almost constant variation in cell dimensions throughout a growth increment are undoubtedly reflections of the environmentally induced fluctuations in growth and metabolic activity of the foliar organs.

When net assimilation in relation to wall development is considered, other environmental factors must also be taken into account. Light in-tensity is most certainly involved (Tronchet and Roussel, 1954; Din-woodie and Richardson, 1961). Similarly, temperature is vitally important since it is intimately associated with photosynthesis, respiration, and as-similation; temperature may also exert a direct physiological effect on cambial activity and tracheid development. In young red pine, wall thick-ness was found to increase with temperature to a maximum at about 520 degree hours per day and then drop rapidly (Fig. 5). Richardson and Dinwoodie (1960) attempted to evaluate a similar response in Douglas fir and redwood and obtained a good correlation between cell wall thick-ness and night temperature but no consistent variation with day tempera-ture. These results may be associated with the suggestions that shoot growth is directly related to temperature through its effect on respiration (Dahl and Mork, 1959), and that under optimum conditions most shoot growth occurs at night (Kienholz, 1934; Wilhelmi, 1959). Considerable research is certainly needed, however, to clarify the subtle interactions of these growth processes.

Conclusion

From this brief résumé, it is apparent that environment plays a decisive role in wood formation by its effect on tracheid diameter and wall thick-ness, to name but two of the attributes comprising wood. Nevertheless, the effect of environment on these cell properties is believed to be pri-marily indirect. The direct effect is on the vegetative growth of the crown, the production site of the auxins that regulate tracheid diameter and the photosynthates that contribute to wall development. Much has been written concerning the variability in these cell dimensions within trees and between trees grown under a host of environmental conditions, and there is reason to assume that all of these variations can be inter-preted in terms of crown growth and development. Under suitably con-trolled-growth conditions, certain environmental factors can be reason-ably well isolated and their influence on vegetative growth and wood formation studied and evaluated. Although the physiological processes through which environment operates are by no means clearly understood at the present time, progress is being made in this direction.

DISCUSSION

ZIMMERMANN: When you cover part of the tree with a black bag to keep the light from some of the needles, do you do anything to avoid the effect of excess temperature and humidity in the bag? I wonder if you could construct some sort of a box in which the light-covered space is more open for air circulation? It seems to me this point is fairly important.

LARSON: We have considered the effect of temperature within the cloth bags. In our area, almost all of our greenhouse work is done during the winter; winter time is almost exclusively cloudy. I have measured temperature periodically in these bags on days that were fairly sunny; there was very little increase. Later in the spring, however, when the sun's rays are more direct, temperature can become excessive.

Under our greenhouse conditions in the winter, humidity is generally about 20 to 30%, except during the morning and evening periods of watering. The coverings were double layers of porous cloth. There was CO_2 exchange, but I am quite sure that there were variations in both CO_2 and humidity within the bag. This was a preliminary experiment attempting to get away from the conventional defoliation experiments. One cannot defoliate a current-year internode until it has fully elongated, and defoliation of older internodes introduces side effects. We intend to follow up this work, perhaps with tracer experiments.

THIMANN: When one is interpreting these effects, both Dr. Larson's and Dr. Richardson's, in terms of auxin production, there are certain difficulties about the auxin-producing zone in these plants. We came across this in Ginkgo, but I believe the results would apply to these conifers. The auxin content of the long shoot of Ginkgo increases down the shoot; this is free diffusible auxin, and therefore no doubt physiologically active. If one decapitates the terminal bud, there is no difference; furthermore, the terminal bud itself yields very little auxin in diffusion-type experiments. If the shoot is defoliated, the auxin content goes very markedly down after several days. Thus although the leaves do not seem to be contributing detectable auxin (and indeed the terminal bud also very little) they evidently control the auxin in a more indirect way. I feel very strongly that in shoots of this type the terminal bud makes only a very minor contribution. This may explain the apparent transfer from the buds to the needles, or *vice versa*, described by Dr. Larson. The leaves supply something which the cortical tissue itself converts to auxin, i.e., the actual auxin production system is in the stem tissue. This makes it more complicated but, I believe, makes it possible to understand many of these rather curious auxin phenomena.

BROWN: What you said about Ginkgo essentially holds true for some of the southern pines. The auxin content at the base of the shoot is always higher than in the rapidly elongating part of the shoot. If, however, the first two millimeters of the shoot apex are cut off, the auxin content in pine drops to zero within 24 hours in that shoot. Removing the needles causes the same reduction. Apparently there may be two sources of precursors, one the apical meristem and one the leaves.

LARSON: I have always been fascinated by the very pronounced gradients in cell development from the apical internode downward throughout the tree. In most instances, these gradients are so regular that one can follow them readily; this suggests that some stimulus controlling cell diameter also exhibits a gradient down the stem.

RICHARDSON: We ought to determine whether there is any gradient in root wood. Have you ever given short-day treatment, then transferred to long-day and at the same time increased the light intensity? This might answer the question about the nature of your long-day latewood.

LARSON: Most of the extremely thick-walled "long-day latewood" has been produced in trees that were grown under long days in summer. The trees, which had been previously cold-exposed, were started in early spring and most of their normal wood was laid down during the spring. The needles continued to elongate under the influence of the longer days of summer when light intensity was high. Photoperiod was still maintained at 18 hours, but during the summer this is primarily high-intensity normal sunlight. When the supplemental light is of low intensity, for example 8 hours of normal day and 10 hours of artificial light, the response in terms of needle elongation is similar but not quite as dramatic. Thick-walled "long-day latewood" is also produced, but wall thickness is not as excessive as that produced under high-intensity light.

RICHARDSON: This does emphasize the importance of net assimilation in producing wall thickness. Why is there so much inconsistency in the literature on this point? Some people have found no correlation between net assimilation and the level of photosynthesis.

WAREING: Recently Dr. T. Wodzicki, working in our laboratory, has investigated the possible role of endogenous growth substances in the control of cell wall thickness. It had previously been shown by Zelawski (1957) that thick-walled tracheids, characteristic of latewood, were formed under short days, which resulted in the development of a resting bud. When low-intensity illumination was given during the dark period, however, extension growth of the shoot was maintained but thick-walled tracheids were still produced (Molski and Zelawski, 1958). On the other hand, when only the apical part of the shoot is subjected to short days and the leaves are exposed to long photoperiods at high intensity a resting bud develops, but *thin-walled* tracheids are formed (Wodzicki, 1961a). Thus, whereas there seems to be a close correlation between shoot elongation and tracheid diameter, as Dr. Larson has shown, the thickness of the cell wall appears not to be directly affected by shoot elongation, but depends upon the light conditions to which the mature leaves are exposed.

Dr. Wodzicki has now studied the effects of light intensity and daylength on the levels of growth promoters and growth inhibitors in larch, and has attempted to correlate these observations with the associated changes in cell wall thickness. One-year plants of European larch were grown under the following conditions:

(1) Continuous light, with 8 hours of daylight supplemented by high-intensity illumination at 800–1000 ft-c from high-pressure, fluorescent-coated, mercury vapor lamps for 16 hours.

(2) Continuous light as for (1), but with low-intensity (1–3 ft-c) supplementary illumination.

(3) Short photoperiods (8-hour day).

After 21 days of these treatments the plants were all placed under high-intensity continuous light for a further 28 days. Sample plants were taken from each treatment at 7- or 14-day intervals and extracted with aqueous methanol. The reduced methanolic extracts were partitioned to give ether and aqueous fractions which were subjected to paper chromatography and the growth activity was assayed. The ether extracts contained growth-promoting substances which showed greater activity in the two continuous light treatments than under short day. The ether extracts also contained large amounts of growth-inhibiting activity, which appeared to be due to resins, and which did not show any marked variation with daylength conditions.

The aqueous fractions also contained growth-promoting zones but the activity did not vary with the different treatments. On the other hand, the inhibitory zones in the aqueous extracts varied markedly with the treatment, there being much greater growth-inhibitory activity in the shoot apices and cortical tissues in the plants receiving continuous light at high intensity. Moreover, the two treatments which gave high levels of the water-soluble inhibitor also resulted in thick-walled tracheids. Thus, there was a marked correlation between the accumulation of this water-soluble inhibitor in the apices and cortical tissues and the production of thick-walled tracheids. Whether this correlation implies a causal relationship, however, requires further investigation.

REFERENCES

André, H. (1920). *Z. Botan.* **12**, 177-218.

Bourdeau, P. F. (1959). *Ecology* **40**, 63-67.

Clark, J. (1961). *N. Y. State Coll. Forestry, Syracuse Univ., Bull.* **85**, 72 pp.

Dahl, E., and Mork, E. (1959.) *Medd. Norske Skogforsøksv.* **16**, 81-93 (Norwegian with English summary).

Dinwoodie, J. M., and Richardson, S. D. (1961). *J. Inst. Wood Sci.* **7**, 34-47.

Freeland, R. O. (1952). *Plant Physiol.* **27**, 685-690.

Goldsmith, M. H. M., and Thimann, K. V. (1962). *Plant Physiol.* **37**, 492-505.

Jost, L. (1891). *Botan. Ztg.* **49**, 485-495; 501-510; 525-531; 541-547; 557-563; 573-579; 589-596; 605-611; 625-630.

Jost, L. (1893). *Botan. Ztg.* **51**, 89-138.

Kienholz, R. (1934). *Botan. Gaz.* **96**, 73-92.

Kramer, P. J. (1958). *In* "Physiology of Forest Trees" (K. V. Thimann, ed.), pp. 157-186. Ronald Press, New York.

Kursanov, A. L. (1961). *Endeavour* **20**, 19-25.

Larson, P. R. (1960). *Forest Sci.* **6**, 110-122.

Larson, P. R. (1962a). *Am. J. Botany* **49**, 132-137.

Larson, P. R. (1962b). *In* "Tree Growth" (T. T. Kozlowski, ed.), pp. 97-117. Ronald Press, New York.

Larson, P. R. (1963a). *Forest Sci.* **9**, 52-62.

Larson, P. R. (1963b). *Forest Sci.* (in press).

Leopold, A. C., and Lam, S. L. (1962). *Physiol. Plantarum* **15**, 631-638.

Molski, B., and Zelawski, W. (1958). *Acta Soc. Botan. Polon.* **27**, 83-102 (Polish with English summary).

Neuwirth, G. (1959). *Biol. Zentr.* **78**, 559-584.

Priestley, J. H. (1930). *New Phytologist* **29**, 316-354.

Priestley, J. H. (1932). *Forestry* **6**, 105-112.

Priestley, J. H. (1935). *Forestry* **9**, 84-95.

Rendle, B. J. (1960). *J. Inst. Wood Sci.* **5**, 58-61.

Richardson, S. D., and Dinwoodie, J. M. (1960). *J. Inst. Wood Sci.* **6**, 3-13.

Roberts, R. H., and Struckmeyer, B. E. (1948). *In* "Vernalization and Photoperiodism" (A. E. Murneek and R. O. Whyte, eds.), pp. 91-100. Chronica Botanica, Waltham, Massachusetts.

Rutter, A. J. (1957). *Ann. Botany* **21**, 399-426.

Scott, T. K., and Briggs, W. R. (1962). *Am. J. Botany* **49**, 1056-1063.

Snow, R. (1935). *New Phytologist* **34**, 347-360.

Söding, H. (1936). *Ber. Deut. Botan. Ges.* **54**, 291-304.

Trendelenburg, R. (1935). *Z. Ver. Deut. Ingr.* **79**, 85-89.

Tronchet, A., and Roussel, L. (1954). *Ann. Sci. Univ. Besançon, Botan.* **1**, 25-30.

Wandt, R. (1937). *Mitt. Forstwirtsch. Forstwiss.* **8**, 343-369.

Wareing, P. F. (1951). *Physiol. Plantarum* **4**, 41-56.

Wareing, P. F. (1958). *J. Inst. Wood Sci.* **1**, 34-42.

Wilcox, H. (1962). *In* "Tree Growth" (T. T. Kozlowski, ed.), pp. 57-88. Ronald Press, New York.

Wilhelmi, T. (1959). *Allgem. Forst-u. Jadgztg.* **130**, 204-209.

Wodzicki, T. (1960). *Acta Soc. Botan. Polon.* **29**, 713-720.

Wodzicki, T. (1961a). *Acta Soc. Botan. Polon.* **30**, 111-131.

Wodzicki, T. (1961b). *Acta Soc. Botan. Polon.* **30**, 293-306.

Zelawski, W. (1957). *Acta Soc. Bot. Pol.* **26**, 79-103.

Zelawski, W., and Wodzicki, T. (1960). *Folia Forest. Polon.* **2**, 113-121 (Polish with English summary).

Zimmermann, W. A. (1936). *Z. Botan.* **30**, 209-252.

Zobel, B. J., Webb, C., and Henson, F. (1959). *Tappi* **42**, 345-356.

The External Environment and Tracheid Size in Conifers

S. D. RICHARDSON

Forest Research Institute, Rotorua, New Zealand

Introduction

The concern of the forester with wood anatomy stems from the realization that variability in anatomical characteristics affects the properties of wood as a raw material (see, e.g., *14, 53*) and that such variability may be both intra- and interspecific. Features of interest in this connection include cell size, the proportion and arrangement of the different elements, the relative amounts of early- and latewood, the orientation of tracheid fibrils, and the occurrence of so-called "juvenile" and reaction wood. In part, intraspecific anatomical variation may be controlled genetically (*12, 15, 17, 22, 38, 39, 46, 58, 82*) and attempts to select or breed strains of tree species with desirable wood properties feature prominently on the research programs of forest geneticists (*13, 16, 22, 23, 25, 37, 64, 84, 85*). At the same time, wood anatomy is markedly influenced by growing conditions, silvicultural treatment, climate, etc. (see, e.g., *13, 19, 44*), though the significance of these environmental determinants has yet to be evaluated satisfactorily. The purpose of the present paper is to review, briefly and selectively, literature relating to the causes of variability in tracheid size and to present data on some effects of temperature, light intensity, and daylength on cell length, wall thickness, and lumen diameter.

Tracheid Length

The general pattern of variation in tracheid length within the secondary xylem of conifers was established by Sanio (*63*) for *Pinus sylvestris* and most subsequent work has simply added refinements to his conclusions. Since recent reviews are available (*19, 61, 62*) the subject will not be treated in detail here. Within any one growth ring, the average length of latewood cells is greater than that of the early wood elements—though Gerry (*27, 28*) and Wardrop (*74*) have reported exceptions to this

367

trend—but the increase is linear only in rings immediately adjacent to the pith (*18*). In older tissue, cells in the middle of the growth ring may be shorter (*9*) or longer (*72*) than the average earlywood length. Between growth rings, mean tracheid length increases rapidly from the pith outwards until a maximum length is attained at a position varying from 10 rings from the pith in *Pinus radiata* (*10, 55*) to over 200 rings from

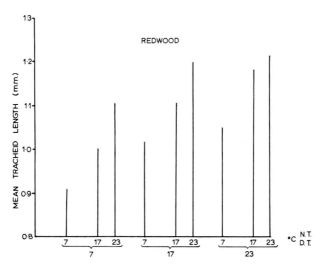

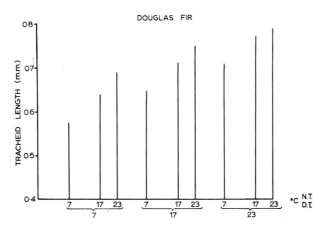

Fig. 1.   The effects of day and night temperatures on tracheid length in seedlings of redwood and Douglas fir. N.T. = night temperature; D.T. = day temperature. Means of 6 seedlings.

the pith in *Sequoia sempervirens* (3). With increasing height up the stem, within a growth ring, tracheid length increases from the base to about one-third stem height and then decreases. Thus, the point of maximum length is located at progressively higher levels as successive rings are formed. In the ring nearest the pith, however, tracheid length remains relatively constant with increasing height (33, 36).

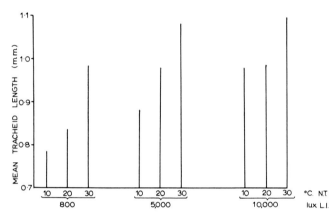

FIG. 2. The effects of night temperature and light intensity on tracheid length in Sitka spruce seedlings. N.T. = night temperature; L.I. = light intensity. Means of 4 seedlings.

Numerous attempts have been made to relate tracheid length variation to the rate of stem diameter growth (5, 8, 10, 11, 18, 22, 24, 28, 33, 34, 41, 49, 51–53, 66, 70, 72) and cambial increment (1, 2, 4, 6, 7, 46, 57). Correlations have been positive, negative or nonexistent—indicating that, while there may be an association between tracheid length and the environmental factors which determine stem increment, there is no direct causal relationship between them. Specific studies of environmental factors have been rare; gross effects of site (30, 40, 69), position in the forest canopy (40, 48, 65), and nutrition (e.g., 32) have been reported, but, apart from a few incidental observations (18, 23, 47), practically nothing is known about the influence of climatic variables.

In Figs. 1–4, some effects of temperature, daylength, and light intensity on tracheid length in various conifer seedlings are illustrated.

For initial experiments (62) seedlings of Douglas fir [*Pseudotsuga menziesii* (Mirb.) Franco] and redwood [*Sequoia sempervirens* (Lamb) Endl.] were grown at constant light intensity and daylength but under a range of day and night temperatures (7, 17, and 23°C day temperatures and 7, 17, and 23°C night temperatures in all possible combinations). Figure 1 demonstrates a clear relation between tracheid length and temperature, but the effect of night temperature is rather greater than that of day temperature. Temperature coefficients over a 100 degree-hour interval in night temperature are 1.14 for redwood and 1.13 for Douglas fir; over the same interval in day temperature they are, respectively, 1.06 and 1.07.

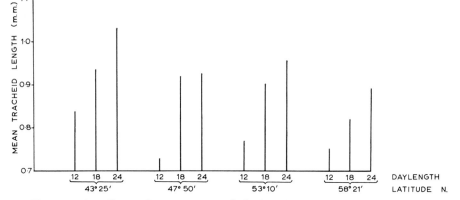

FIG. 3. The effects of provenance and daylength on tracheid length in Sitka spruce seedlings. Means of 9 seedlings.

Other experiments (20) were carried out with seedlings of Sitka spruce [*Picea sitchensis* (Bong.) Carr.]; in one, the effects of light intensity and night temperature on material grown at a constant day temperature (20°C) and daylength (16 hours) were examined; in another, seedlings from four different provenances ranging from latitude 58° 21′ N to 43° 25′ N) were grown at a constant temperature (20° day and night) under three daylength regimes (12, 16, and 24 hours light per 24-hour cycle). Tracheid length increased with night temperature and light intensity (Fig. 2) and, also, with daylength (Fig. 3); but decreased with increasing latitude of origin (Fig. 3). The interpretation of these results is complicated by a highly significant linear relationship between tracheid length and height increment (Fig. 4). Height increment could account for the majority of the variation associated with photoperiod and part of that associated with light intensity. After adjusting for the influence of height growth, however, tracheid length was still significantly correlated with light intensity and night temperature.

In another experiment, daylength and night temperature treatments were combined. Seedlings of *Pinus radiata* D. Don. were raised in soil to a height of about 8 inches and then transferred to growth cabinets. Three daylengths (8, 12, and 16 hours per 24-hour cycle) and three night temperatures (10, 20, and 30°C) were employed. All plants received 8

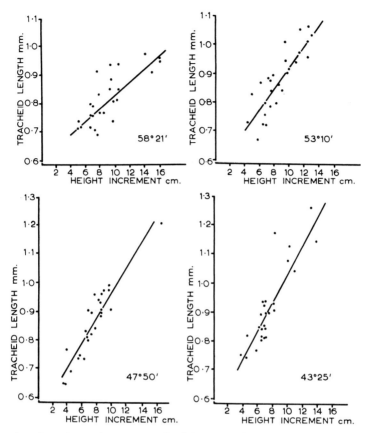

FIG. 4. The relation between tracheid length and stem height increment in 4 provenances of Sitka spruce.

hours light at 5000 lux, supplemented for 12- and 16-hour daylength treatments by fluorescent light at about 200 lux. After 6 weeks growth, tracheid length was measured at the midpoint of the new stem growth (i.e., that formed under the experimental treatments). Table I illustrates the effects of daylength and night temperature on tracheid length and height increment.

Again, tracheid length tends to increase with night temperature but in this case there is no consistent relation with daylength. Height increment, on the other hand, increases with daylength at all night temperatures but is inversely related with night temperature.

An analysis of covariance for this experiment is summarized in Table II.

After the effect of height increment has been removed, tracheid length

TABLE I

THE EFFECT OF NIGHT TEMPERATURE AND DAYLENGTH ON TRACHEID
LENGTH (MM) AND HEIGHT INCREMENT (CM) IN *Pinus radiata*.
MEANS OF 6 SEEDLINGS.

Night Temperature (°C)	Daylength (hours)			
	8	12	16	Mean
	Tracheid Length			
10	0.865	1.074	1.045	0.995
20	1.259	1.077	1.054	1.130
30	1.142	1.340	1.236	1.239
Mean	1.089	1.164	1.112	—
	Height Increment			
10	4.4	7.2	8.0	6.5
20	3.2	6.0	7.2	5.5
30	3.7	4.4	5.5	4.4
Mean	3.8	5.9	6.9	—

TABLE II

ANALYSIS OF COVARIANCE (TRACHEID LENGTH AND
HEIGHT) FOR *Pinus radiata*

Source of variation	D.F.	S.S. length	F.	S.S. height	F.	S.S. length after reg. on ht.	D.F.	F.
Daylength	2	0.053933	< 1	91.77	11.89[a]	0.241924	2	4.12[b]
Night temperature	2	0.540007	5.72[a]	35.20	4.56[b]	1.091137	2	18.59[a]
Interaction	4	0.370273	1.96	10.85	< 1	0.542485	4	4.62[b]
Error	45	2.124493		173.77	—	1.291220	44	—

[a] Significant at 1% level.
[b] Significant at 5% level.

is significantly correlated with night temperature at the 1% level; but, in addition, there is now a significant (5%) *inverse* correlation with daylength and a significant (5%) interaction between daylength and night temperature. This unexpected and, in the light of previous experiments, anomalous result appears to be largely due to the abnormal behavior of the short-day, 30°C night temperature series, in which the regression of tracheid length on height increment has a significantly higher coefficient than the other series. Further experimental analysis is required to confirm this behavior and, in view of the low level of significance attaching to the tracheid length: daylength relationship, undue weight should not be placed on it.

Within treatments, tracheid length was linearly related to height increment but could not be associated with stem or leaf dry weight. Thus, while dry weight decreased with increasing night temperature, photoperiod had no effect, in spite of the marked influence on height increment. Total dry weight data are presented in Table III.

TABLE III
THE EFFECT OF NIGHT TEMPERATURE AND DAYLENGTH ON TOTAL DRY
WEIGHT (GM) OF *Pinus radiata*. MEANS OF 6 SEEDLINGS.

Night temp. (°C)	Daylength (hours)			
	8	12	16	Mean
10	3.7196	3.4346	3.1997	3.4513
20	3.6373	3.1947	3.3710	3.4010
30	3.4948	3.0128	3.1363	3.2148
Mean	3.6172	3.2140	3.2358	—

Further evidence of the role of temperature as a determinant of tracheid length has been obtained from "temperature bridge" experiments, in which small stem segments of seedlings were enclosed and subjected to temperatures higher than the remainder of the plant. In one of these, a temperature of 25°C (5°C above ambient) was used; after 6 weeks, stems were sampled within the temperature bridge and immediately above and below it. Lengths of the last-formed tracheids (means of 30 tracheids per sample) are presented in Table IV. They demonstrate a consistent direct effect of temperature on tracheid length.

TABLE IV
MEAN TRACHEID LENGTHS (MM) OF SITKA SPRUCE SEEDLINGS
SAMPLED BELOW, WITHIN AND ABOVE
A TEMPERATURE BRIDGE

Seedling no.	Below (20°C)	Within (25°C)	Above (20°C)
1	0.74	0.97	0.76
2	0.96	1.13	1.02
3	0.99	1.61	0.90
4	0.73	1.04	0.99
Mean	0.86	1.19	0.92

Experiments have also been carried out in which stems have been girdled by removing all tissues exterior to fully differentiated xylem elements over a distance of 5 mm. The object here was to test the hypothesis that tracheid length may be influenced by the local accumulation of carbohydrates in the phloem and ray parenchyma, in an attempt to analyze further the role of light intensity. If the observed effects of light intensity were mediated by carbohydrate availability, an increase in tracheid length above the girdle might be expected. In fact, tracheid length immediately above the girdle showed a significant *decrease*.

A possible explanation of this unexpected result lies in the work of Bannan (6). He has shown that anticlinal division of fusiform initials occurs at relatively high rates of frequency and that the overproduction of new cells is accompanied by extensive cell loss. There is a tendency for the longest cells (i.e., those having the greatest number of contacts with rays) to survive and produce tracheids. It is possible, therefore, that an increase in the carbohydrate content of ray cells (as would occur after stem girdling) enables a greater survival of shorter cells, resulting in a decrease in mean tracheid length. It is clear, at any rate, that increases in cell length associated with increased light intensity are not explainable in terms of local carbohydrate accumulation.

The evidence of all these experiments taken together emphasizes the complex nature of light and temperature effects on tracheid length. The influence of temperature may be relatively direct, acting on cell development, while that of light may be both direct and indirect. Thus, the relation between tracheid length and daylength is not consistent for all species and, where it exists, is associated with photoperiodic effects on stem height growth. Similarly, a major part of the effect of light intensity is correlated with height increment and, although there is evidence also of a more direct influence of light intensity, it does not operate through increasing carbohydrate availability. These observations provide further evidence of interaction between terminal meristematic activity and the dividing cambium.

Cell Wall Thickness

Apart from the fact that latewood tracheids have thicker walls than earlywood cells, and that, in both early- and latewood, wall thickness tends to increase from the pith to the cambium (65), little is known about variation in cell wall thickness within trees. From a practical point of view, interest centers upon wood density, of which wall thickness is but one component. The considerable literature dealing with variation in density within and between trees (e.g., 29, 68, 82) will not be reviewed here. Of more relevance to the present discussion are studies of annual ring differentiation in which attempts have been made to analyze the role of climate in the transition from early- to latewood formation.

Numerous studies have been made of the gross effects of climate and site on early- and latewood differentiation (see, e.g., 26, 29, 35, 44, 56, 73, 80) and, in general, it has been found that features which promote growth of the tree crown favor earlywood production. In few investigations, however, has a distinction been made between effects on cell wall thickness and determinants of tracheid diameter; yet there is now clear evidence that these variables are not necessarily related. For example, Wareing (75) and Larson (42) postulated that latewood formation is correlated with the cessation of terminal elongation and the setting of new buds through an auxin-mediated system. Working with 4-year-old plants of *Pinus resinosa*, Larson (42) examined the effects of daylength, disbudding, IAA, and gibberellic acid treatments on differentiation at various levels in the stem; he found that changes in cell wall thickness were not always correlated with changes in cell diameter, and surmised that the two processes are subject to separate physiological control. In older stem sections, under long-day treatment, cell wall thickness increased immediately following the termination of height growth, whereas, in sections directly below the apical meristem, changes in wall thickness occurred later and were less consistent. In seedlings with intact buds, short days for periods longer than 3 weeks gave rise to thick-walled cells; following decapitation or disbudding, however, wall thickness always decreased. Larson concluded that while auxin may perform a role in cell wall thickening, "the products of photosynthesis are more likely to be involved in this phase of summerwood development."

Similar experiments have been carried out by Zelawski (81), Molski and Zelawski (50), and Wodzicki (76–79), but with somewhat different results. In 1-year seedlings of *Larix polonica* Rac. and 3-year plants of *Picea abies* (L) Karst., short days induced both resting bud formation and cell wall thickening; the imposition of short-day treatment on the stem apex only, however, while it brought about the formation of a resting bud, did not affect cell wall thickening. Similarly, during uninterrupted extension growth under continuous light (natural days, supplemented by low-intensity illumination) thick-walled tracheids could be laid down. With decapitated or ringed seedlings short days induced cell wall thickening, while long days had no effect. Wodzicki concluded that both extension growth and cell wall thickness are photoperiodically controlled but that the two phenomena are quite distinct; the locus of perception of the photoperiodic stimulus controlling extension growth is in the stem apex; while that of the reaction which determines cell wall thickness is in mature leaves.

Wodzicki failed to find any correlation between cell wall thickness and dry weight or number of needles. He also carried out stem ringing experiments in which seedlings were double ringed, above and below a well-developed lateral shoot. Cell wall thickness within the ringed portion of the stem was affected by photoperiod as before. These observations led him to reject, tentatively, any quantitative influence of carbohydrate supply on cell wall thickening. The fact that thick-walled tracheids were

formed under conditions of water deficit, however, did not allow him
completely to discount climatic factors other than photoperiod.

Van Buijtenen (71), on the other hand, working with *Pinus taeda* L.,
recorded a reduction in tracheid wall thickness with increasing temperature, while variations in photoperiod or soil moisture had no effect.

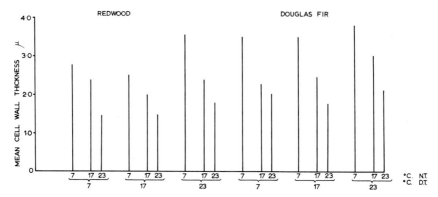

Fig. 5.   The effects of day and night temperatures on cell wall thickness in seedlings of redwood and Douglas fir. N.T. = night temperature; D.T. = day temperature.
Means of 6 seedlings.

It is apparent, therefore, that there is some disagreement as to the influence of climatic factors on cell wall thickness. On *a priori* grounds, a
relation with carbohydrate synthesis might be expected (31, 54, 57) but
it has not always been found. It appeared to the writer that confusion
might be avoided by examining material in which there is no apparent
differentiation across the growth ring. In the experiments reported earlier
with Douglas fir and redwood, 6 months growth in constant environments produced no apparent variation in cell wall thickness or lumen
diameter across the stem sections. Cell wall thickness was measured on a
series of traverses running radially across sections cut at the midpoint of
each stem. Lumen diameters (radial) were measured for each cell in the
traverse and totaled for every five cells covered. These values were sub-
tracted from the total radial width of the relevant five-cell group and
divided by 10 (since each cell has two tangential walls) to give mean
cell wall thickness. In Fig. 5, mean wall thicknesses of the 15 last-
formed cells are presented by day and night temperature. There is a
clear inverse relation between cell wall thickness and night temperature
but the effect of day temperature is inconsistent.

It was argued that the decrease with night temperature reflects the
level of available carbohydrates in the seedlings. This conclusion has
since been confirmed by work with Sitka spruce and *Pinus radiata*. In the

former species, close correlations between stem density and leaf weight have been established under a range of environmental conditions (20), and stem density in turn correlated with cell wall thickness. Figures 6 and 7 illustrate the effects of light intensity and daylength. Cell wall thickness (again, of the last-formed cells) increases with light intensity (Fig. 6)

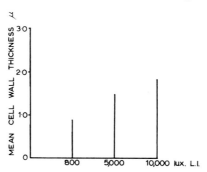

FIG. 6. The effect of light intensity on cell wall thickness in seedlings of Sitka spruce. L.I. = light intensity. Means of 4 seedlings.

and daylength (Fig. 7). The daylength effect, however, may operate partly via an effect on leaf weight. Within each daylength treatment, cell wall thickness increased linearly with leaf weight but the coefficients for the regression of leaf weight on cell wall thickness decreased with increasing daylengths from 0.983 (short days) to 0.516 (long days); thus there would seem to be a relatively direct influence of photoperiod also.

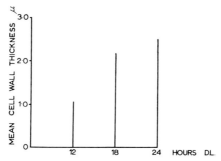

FIG. 7. The effect of daylength on cell wall thickness in seedlings of Sitka spruce. D.L. = daylength. Means of 27 seedlings.

In *Pinus radiata* (see Table V), cell wall thickness again decreased with increasing night temperature and increased with photoperiod. In this experiment, daylength did not affect leaf weight and this result might be taken as a further indication that the photoperiodic effect on cell wall thickness is not mediated by carbohydrate synthesis. However, stem height growth was markedly increased by increasing daylength (see Table I) and needle internodes were consequently longer. It is possible, therefore, that under long days the disposition of needles on the stem is conducive to a higher level of photosynthesis.

TABLE V

The Effect of Night Temperature and Photoperiod on Cell Wall Thickness in *Pinus radiata*. Means of Measurements on 4 Radii on Transverse Sections of 6 Seedlings, μ

Night Temp. (°C)	Daylength (hours)			
	8	12	16	Mean
10	1.92	2.06	2.42	2.13
20	1.68	1.83	1.97	1.83
30	1.56	1.62	1.49	1.56
Mean	1.72	1.84	1.96	—

Further information has been derived from the ringing experiments already referred to, and from experiments involving various degrees of defoliation. In Sitka spruce, stem ringing, in spite of a local accumulation of carbohydrates above the girdle, produced no measurable effect on cell wall thickness. Defoliation, on the other hand, resulted in the formation of thin-walled cells, but there was no association between thin-walled tracheids and the defoliated area of the stem. Figure 8

```
     -1·9  } - 2·8  1·7  1·9  2·0 }         1·4  1·6  1·5  1·4   1·1
                                    - 1·7  1·9 -
     -2·2  - } 2·0  1·9  2·2  1·7              1·7       1·4
                                                   } 1·4
     -1·8  -   2·2  } 2·6  2·1  1·8 - } 2·6  1·3     1·6 } 1·2
                                                             } 1·3
     -2·4  -   2·7   2·2 } 2·9  1·6 - 2·5 } 1·4  - } 1·6  1·3
     -2·3  -   2·9   2·3  2·8 } 2·3              1·4  1·6       1·3

MEAN     2·1  -  2·5  2·1  2·4  1·9  - 2·3  1·5  - 1·4  1·5  1·5  1·3  1·2
```

Fig. 8. The effects of defoliation over various lengths of the stem on cell wall thickness in Sitka spruce seedlings. Means of 4 seedlings. For explanation, see text.

illustrates this point. The first column (left) shows the mean wall thickness of the 5 last-formed cells at various positions in the stem of 2-year seedlings grown for 2 months in a constant environment (daylength, 16 hours; light intensity, 5000 lux; temperature, 20°C); The remaining columns illustrate the effects of removing the primary needles over various distances (indicated by brackets) from these positions. Defoliation of the apical region suppressed cambial activity and, with one exception, less than five new cells were formed. Apical dominance was also destroyed by this treatment. Over the remainder of the stem, increasing the defoliated length reduced cell wall thickness through the entire stem. Similar results have also been obtained with *Pinus radiata.*

In these experiments, cell wall thickness was measured as before on five-cell groups by subtracting the sum of lumen diameters from the sum of cell diameters and dividing by 10. It must be recognized that the measure so obtained is not a very precise one. The results are sufficiently consistent, however, to add support to the old hypothesis that cell wall thickness is largely determined by the level of photosynthesis.

Lumen Diameter

As with cell wall thickness, evidence of climatic effects on cell diameter is best adduced from studies designed specifically to investigate differentiation within the growth ring. In a recent attempt to relate environmental effects on wood anatomy to crown development, Larson (44) has reviewed evidence of variability in the transition from large-diameter "earlywood" tracheids to narrow "latewood" cells. He points out that while correlations have been demonstrated between latewood formation and various environmental factors (stand structure, climate, site, silvicultural treatment, etc.) these influences are probably secondary and, of themselves, unpredictable. For example, latewood formation may be prematurely induced by drought early in the season (21) while, in autumn, the same conditions can suppress it. Pruning can have similar effects (59).

A more direct influence on cellular development is exercized by the terminal meristem. Under long days, cambial activity in 4-year-old *Pinus resinosa* is continuous, producing large-diameter cells; on the other hand, short days or decapitation induce the formation of narrow-diameter tracheids (42). Furthermore, substitution of the terminal meristem by IAA in seedlings under short days, leads to a temporary reversion to large-diameter cell formation. These photoperiodic reactions have been confirmed for 1-year plants of *Larix polonica* (77) though not for first-year seedlings of either *Larix polonica* or *Picea abies* (79). Van Buijtenen (71), working with both seedlings and mature trees of *Pinus taeda,* failed to find any consistent effect of photoperiod or temperature on tracheid diameter, though an increase in soil moisture increased this variable. More recently, Larson (45) investigated the separate influences of buds and needles on tracheid diameter and concluded that the response to photoperiod varies with development stage. During active extension growth, the bud exerts a regulatory influence, but when extension growth stops, the needles provide the main source of the stimulus. Larson suggests that these effects are associated with auxin production.

The influence of temperature on cell diameter in first-year seedlings of redwood and Douglas fir is essentially similar to that on tracheid

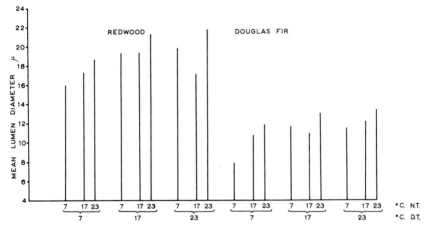

FIG. 9. The effects of day and night temperatures on lumen diameter (radial) in seedlings of redwood and Douglas fir. N.T. = night temperature; D.T. = day temperature. Means of 6 seedlings.

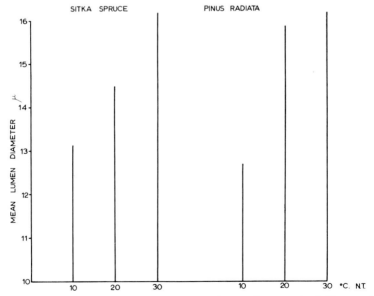

FIG. 10. The effects of night temperature on lumen diameter (radial) in seedlings of Sitka spruce and *Pinus radiata*. N.T. = night temperature. Means of 12 (Sitka spruce) and 18 (*Pinus radiata*) seedlings.

length (*62*) in that night temperature is more effective than day temperature in increasing cell size (Fig. 9). With Sitka spruce and *Pinus radiata*, too, increasing night temperature increases tracheid diameter more or less linearly (Fig. 10) and, within a 25°C temperature bridge, cell diameter increases over that at 20°C (Table VI).

TABLE VI

MEAN LUMEN DIAMETER (μ) OF SITKA SPRUCE SEEDLINGS, MEASURED ON THE 5 LAST-FORMED MATURE CELLS AT 4 POINTS AROUND EACH STEM. STEMS SAMPLED BELOW, WITHIN, AND ABOVE A TEMPERATURE BRIDGE.

Seedling no.	Below (20°C)	Within (25°C)	Above (20°C)
1	18.8	20.7	16.2
2	15.9	20.8	19.3
3	19.3	22.5	16.5
4	19.3	18.8	17.1
5	18.6	22.7	19.6
6	18.4	22.0	17.7
Mean	18.4	21.3	17.7

Variations in light intensity, however, have no direct effect on cell diameter though defoliation (Fig. 11) and stem girdling (Table VII) lead to the production of narrow tracheids. Neither is there any correlation between cell diameter and height increment. This provides further evidence that tracheid length and cell diameter are not subject to the same control mechanism.

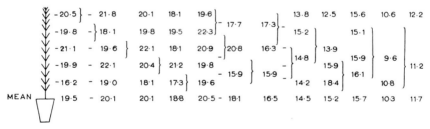

FIG. 11. The effects of defoliation over various lengths of the stem on lumen diameter (radial) in Sitka spruce seedlings. Means of 4 seedlings. For explanation, see text accompanying Fig. 8, p. 378.

In experiments with first-year seedlings, no consistent effect of daylength on tracheid diameter has been noted; with 2-year-old Sitka spruce, on the other hand, short days (8 hours) reduce cell diameter though there is no significant difference between 18- and 24-hour treatments (see Fig. 12).

TABLE VII

THE EFFECT OF STEM GIRDLING ON LUMEN DIAMETER IN SITKA SPRUCE
AND DOUGLAS FIR. MEANS OF MEASUREMENTS ON 4 RADII, μ

Seedling no.	Sitka spruce		Douglas fir	
	Above	Below	Above	Below
1	19.4	14.4	11.0	7.2
2	18.9	13.5	11.9	9.2
3	19.5	12.6	12.1	7.0
4	18.7	19.6	10.1	6.1
5	20.8	12.2	11.6	7.0
6	23.8	15.5	15.2	6.4
Mean	20.2	14.6	12.0	7.1

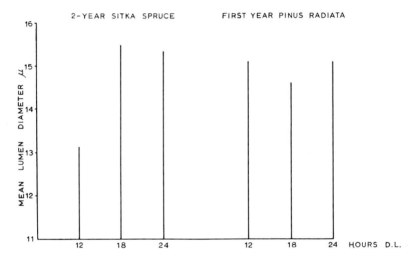

FIG. 12.   The effect of daylength on lumen diameter (radial) in seedlings of Sitka spruce and *Pinus radiata*. D.L. = daylength. Means of 12 (Sitka spruce) and 18 (*Pinus radiata*) seedlings.

Conclusion

The components of tracheid size discussed in this paper—length, cell wall thickness, and lumen diameter—are influenced in varying degree by temperature, light intensity, and daylength. Cell length increases with increasing temperature, but the effect of night temperature is greater than that of day temperature, indicating an interaction with a process that is photosensitive. It has been suggested elsewhere that this process may be stem elongation (20). Tracheid length also increases with increasing light intensity, but part of this effect is again correlated with stem height growth. In addition, however, there is a significant effect of light intensity after adjusting for height growth, though it does not appear to be related to carbohydrate accumulation in the stem. The influence of daylength on tracheid length is also confused by effects on height growth and, after adjustment for height increment, the effect is not consistent among species.

Thus, while the temperature effect is partially direct, the others appear to be mediated by activity within the apical meristem. Hypotheses to explain the mechanism of this system would, at this stage, be purely speculative and must await further analysis. In particular, it is necessary to consider at what point in the chain of events between the pseudo-transverse division of a fusiform initial in the cambium and the ultimate maturation of the tracheids derived from it these influences may act. Clearly, there are several possibilities. Changes in the frequency of pseudotransverse division in the cambium (fusiform initials or xylem mother cells), the rate of elongation of the fusiform initials between multiplicative cycles, and the extent of intrusive growth in the maturing tracheids, may all affect the ultimate tracheid length. With a view to analyzing further the effect of temperature on cell length, material from the experiment with *Pinus radiata* described above is being examined in transverse section and by means of serial tangential sections from bark to pith. This examination is not yet complete, but, from transverse sections, there are indications that, with increasing temperature, the number of periclinal divisions relative to that of anticlinal divisions decreases. At the same time, cell survival (and maturation) is enhanced at the higher temperatures. It may be, therefore, that temperature operates primarily by influencing the rate of cell division rather than through any direct effect on cell enlargement. Studies of transverse sections are, however, clearly inadequate to permit any conclusion on this point; precise measurements of changes in cell length derived from the serial tangential sections are necessary.

It is also necessary to consider whether the variations in tracheid length occurring within and between annual growth increments are explainable in terms of responses to climatic factors. The range of variation within a growth ring of 30-year-old *Pinus radiata*, for example, may be of the order 2.5–4.5 mm (55); within the tree, between growth rings, the mean tracheid length may vary from < 1 mm to 5.0 mm (52, 55). The variations induced by environmental changes reported in the present paper are of a much lower order; for example, the effect of a rise in night temperature from 10°C to 30°C is to increase mean tracheid length by about 30%. On present evidence, therefore, it is doubtful whether climatic effects are of major significance in the determination of tracheid length. However, cell length variation in growth rings near the pith and in seedlings is always much less than in older material (18) and it is possible that the role of climatic variables increases with age. If, in fact, tracheid length is primarily a function of cell division rate, this might be expected. The effects of controlled environmental changes on cell length variation in large trees need to be examined in order to resolve this problem.

The relation between cell length and height increment in seedlings confirms a tentative conclusion of Hartley (32) with respect to *Pinus radiata*. It could have important practical implications if it is of general validity. Bisset *et al.* (10) have presented evidence that the average tracheid length in the so-called juvenile zone is directly related to that in mature wood; in other words, individual stems with long tracheids initially will continue to produce long tracheids throughout their life. It might be possible, therefore, to select potentially long fibered trees in the nursery, simply on the basis of initial height growth. Alternatively, increasing height growth in the first year by, for example, fertilizer treatments could result in the continued production of long-fibered material, with obvious advantages for the pulp and paper industry. It should be pointed out, however, that recent work with *Pinus radiata* in New Zealand (55) and Australia (52) has failed to confirm the reported relationship between initial and ultimate tracheid lengths. More detailed work on material of known seedling height for which annual measurements of height growth have been made over a period of years, is presently underway.

Variations in cell wall thickness effected by temperature, light intensity, and daylength can, for the most part, be attributed to changes in carbohydrate synthesis, though there may also be an effect of daylength which is independent of carbohydrate availability. It is not clear why some investigators (77, 78) have consistently failed to find any relation between factors affecting photosynthesis and cell wall thickness; nor is it apparent why stem ringing should have no measurable effect on wall thickness. Studies involving continuous recording of carbon dioxide assimilation under different daylength treatments, combined with cell wall thickness measurements on the same plant material, are necessary to settle the first of these problems; the second requires investigation of the influence of stem ringing on the distribution of photosynthates within the stem. There is little doubt that the role of external environmental factors as determinants of cell wall thickness is more complex than postulated originally (60).

As with tracheid length, the major variations within a growth ring in radial lumen diameter are not primarily determined by temperature or light intensity. The magnitude of the change from large-diameter earlywood cells to narrow latewood cells is normally greater than the responses recorded in seedling material in the experiments reported here. On available evidence, daylength acting through an auxin system determines gross seasonal changes. Within this framework, however, temperature has a positive effect on lumen diameter, though light intensity has no direct influence. The absence of any correlation between cell diameter and height increment underlines the separate control of diameter and tracheid length.

In summary, therefore, it appears that direct effects of climatic variables are of little significance in determining ultimate cell size in conifers. Indirect influences may be important with respect to wall thickness and lumen diameter but the major determinants of tracheid length are unknown. Further work, involving environmental control of larger trees (or parts of them), is a prerequisite for the successful analysis of limiting factors, and a confident assessment of the genotypic component of the phenotype.

DISCUSSION

LARSON: Dr. Richardson, you have shown a good relationship between internode length and tracheid length in young seedlings. Do you think this same relationship will continue in older internodes?

RICHARDSON: It is probably not the same. The only work we have done on this was done by a student of mine in Aberdeen. He wanted to find tracheid length variation within the terminal shoot of a 20-year-old Sitka spruce. He measured the tracheid length throughout the terminal shoot, as well as the intervals between the leaf scars on the terminal shoot, in an attempt to get a measure of its rate of elongation. He found a close relationship between tracheid length and the interval between leaf initials and concluded that the faster the rate of elongation of the terminal shoot the longer were the tracheids. That relationship still holds in the terminal shoot of a mature stem, but further down in the same growth ring it does not hold at all. Outside the pith there seems to be no relationship between internode length and tracheid length. There is a marked difference between the first ring from the pith and subsequently formed rings. Recent unpublished work by Ladell at Oxford correlates the pattern of tracheid length variation within the shoot with needle density. Tracheids below leaf traces tend to be shorter than average. The denser the needles, therefore, the shorter the mean tracheid length. I do not have details of this work, but it could be a more important correlation, causally, than that with rate of height increment.

WAREING: Have you investigated the relationship between length and wall thickness? Do the longer cells have thinner walls?

RICHARDSON: I do not think one can generalize. In some cases there is a correlation, but I am sure that it is not causal, because wall thickness can be controlled independently of length.

THIMANN: Would there be some industrial advantage in having thin-walled as opposed to thick-walled cells?

RICHARDSON: There could be advantages in either case. For some types of paper thin-walled cells are preferred, for other types long cells, for still other types thick-walled cells.

HELLMERS: You showed an effect of temperature on tracheid length. Does the sunny side of a tree have longer tracheids?

RICHARDSON: Liese and Dadswell (1959) found that tracheids are longer on the sunny side of the tree than on the shady side.

BAILEY: I think it is high time that someone investigated tracheid length in roots.

RICHARDSON: I agree. If we accept hormonal theories of the control of early- and latewood differentiation, this should extend to the roots. There should be daylength effects in root wood. I do not believe that there are.

TORREY: We have been puzzled by the fact that isolated roots in culture seldom produce secondary tissue. There are reports in the literature that the formation of secondary tissues in the root is under photoperiodic control by the shoot system, for instance in the original papers of W. W. Garner and H. A. Allard (*J. Agr. Res.* **23**, 871-920, 1923). We are now feeding auxins and sugars through the basal ends of isolated roots in culture. We can produce secondary tissues in such unlikely experimental objects as pea roots, by feeding sucrose and indoleacetic acid.

RICHARDSON: Can you control differentiation?

TORREY: We have not yet investigated the IAA-GA relationship. As long as we feed indoleacetic acid we can get quite good secondary xylem, but much more limited secondary phloem. There are great variations in vessel length, diameter, etc. We do not know enough about it yet to tell if it is early- or latewood. Most of our experiments last about 1 month.

LARSON: A big problem in the development of root wood in trees is the terrific length of the translocation channels. There are many things that can happen to auxins and other stimuli originating in the apical meristems on the way down to the roots.

TORREY: We are working on the general idea that the whole secondary tissue system of the root is a shoot-induced system. Many of the hormonal stimulations which reach it originate in the shoot and are imposed on the root.

RICHARDSON: A long time ago I carried out some daylength experiments, looking for starch in root and shoot. In our sections we found no differentiation into early- and latewood in the root.

TORREY: We are now studying this in radish where one would expect more extensive development. There the derivatives of the cambium are almost all parenchyma. If this is photoperiodically controlled it could well be via a balance of IAA, GA, and other factors in a situation comparable to Wareing's (cf. Wareing's paper in this volume). You seldom get a woody radish root unless it is given the wrong temperature and daylength conditions.

REFERENCES

1. Bailey, I. W. (1920). *Am. J. Botany* **7**, 355-367.
2. Bailey, I. W. (1923). *Am. J. Botany* **10**, 499-509.
3. Bailey, I. W., and Faull, A. F. (1934). *J. Arnold Arboretum* (Harvard) **15**, 233-254.
4. Bannan, M. W. (1950). *Am. J. Botany* **37**, 511-519.
5. Bannan, M. W. (1954). *Can. J. Botany* **32**, 466-479.
6. Bannan, M. W. (1956). *Can. J. Botany* **34**, 769-776.
7. Bannan, M. W. (1957). *Can. J. Botany* **35**, 425-434.
8. Bannan, M. W. (1960). *Can. J. Botany* **38**, 177-183.
9. Bisset, I. J. W., and Dadswell, H. E. (1950). *Australian Forestry* **14**, 17-29.
10. Bisset, I. J. W., Dadswell, H. E., and Wardrop, A. B. (1951). *Australian Forestry* **15**(1), 17-30.
11. Chalk, L. (1930). *Forestry* **4**, 7-14.
12. Champion, H. G. (1933). *Indian Forest Records,* **17**(5), 1-76.
13. Dadswell, H. E. (1958a). *Proc. 7th British Commonwealth Forestry Conf., Canberra, 1957,* p. 161.

14. Dadswell, H. E. (1958b). *J. Inst. Wood Sci.* **1**, 11-33.
15 Dadswell, H. E., and Wardrop, A.B. (1959). *APPITA* **12**(4), 129-136.
16. Dadswell, H. E., and Nicholls, J. W. P. (1959). *C.S.I.R.O. Forest Prod. Tech. Paper* **4**, 1-16.
17. Dadswell, H. E., Fielding, J. M., Nicholls, J. W. P., and Brown, A. G. (1961). *Tappi* **44**, 174-179.
18. Dinwoodie, J. M. (1960). Variation in Tracheid Length in *Picea sitchensis*. Ph.D. Thesis, Univ. of Aberdeen.
19. Dinwoodie, J. M. (1961). *Forestry* **34**(2), 125-144.
20. Dinwoodie, J. M., and Richardson, S. D. (1961). *J. Inst. Wood Sci.* **7**, 34-47.
21. Dobbs, C. G. (1951). *Forestry* **24**, 22-35; **25**, 104-125; **26**, 97-110.
22. Echols, R. M. (1955). *Trop. Woods* **102**, 11-22.
23. Echols, R. M. (1958). *Yale Univ. School Forestry Bull.* **64**, 1-52.
24. Elliott, G. K. (1960). *J. Inst. Wood Sci.* **5**, 38-47.
25. Fielding, J. M., and Brown, A. G. (1960). *Commonwealth Australia Forestry and Timber Bur. Leaflet* **77**.
26. Foil, R. R. (1961). *Louisiana State Univ. Forestry Notes*, **44**.
27. Gerry, E. (1915). *Science* **41**, 179.
28. Gerry, E. (1916). *Science* **43**, 360.
29. Goggans, J. F. (1962). *Forest Tree Improvement Program.* (*N. Carolina State Coll. School Forestry*) *Tech. Rept.* **14**.
30. Harlow, W. M. (1927). *Ecology* **8**, 453-470.
31. Harper, A. G. (1933). *Ann. Botany (London)* **27**(108), 621-642.
32. Hartley, W. R. (1960). *Empire Forestry Rev.* **39**(4), 474-482.
33. Hata, K. (1949). *Kawaga-Ken. Agr. Coll. Tech. Bull.* **1**, 1-35; also in *Forestry Abstr.* **15**, 629.
34. Helander, A. B. (1933). *Found. Forest Prod. Res. Finland, Publ.* **14**, 75 pp. (Engl. summary).
35. Hildebrandt, G. (1962). *Proc. 5th World Forestry Congr., Seattle, 1960*, **3**, 1348-1353.
36. Jackson, L. W. R. (1959). *J. Forestry* **42**, 336-367.
37. Jackson, L. W. R., and Greene, J. T. (1958). *Forest Sci.* **4**(4), 316-318.
38. Kennedy, R. W., and Smith, J. H. G. (1959). *Forestry, Faculty Univ. B.C. Res. Note* **19**.
39. Kennedy, R. W., and Wilson, J. W. (1954). *Pulp Paper Mag. Can.* **55**(7), 130-132; **55**(8), 119-121.
40. Kienholz, R. (1931). *Am. J. Botany* **17**, 739-764.
41. Kramer, P. R. (1957). *Texas Forest Serv. Tech. Rept.* **10**, 1-22.
42. Larson, P. R. (1960a). *Forest Sci.* **6**(2), 110-122.
43. Larson, P. R. (1960b). *In* "Tree Growth" (T. T. Kozlowski, ed.), pp. 97-117. Ronald Press, New York.
44. Larson, P. R. (1962a). *Tappi* **45**(6), 443-448.
45. Larson, P. R. (1962b). *Am. J. Botany* **49**(2), 132-137.
46. Liang, S.-C. (1948). *Forestry* **22**(2), 222-237.
47. Liese, W., and Dadswell, H. E. (1959). *Holz Roh- Werkstoff* **17**(11), 421-427.
48. MacMillan, W. B. (1925). *J. Forestry* **23**, 34-42.
49. Misra, P. (1939). *Forestry* **13**, 118-133.
50. Molski, B., and Zelawski, W. (1958). *Acta Soc. Botan. Polon.* **27**(1), 83-102.
51. Mork, E. (1928). *Papier-Fabrikant* **26**, 48.

52. Nicholls, J. W. P., and Dadswell, H. E. (1962). *C.S.I.R.O., Div. Forest Prod. Technol. Paper* **24**, 1-19.
53. Nylinder, P., and Hägglund, E. (1954). *Medd. Statens Skogsforskningsinst.*, Stockholm **44**, 11. (In Swedish; English summary.)
54. Oppenheimer, H. R. (1945). *Polish J. Botany* **5**(1), 22-51.
55. Orman, H. R. (1959). Unpublished data.
56. Paul, B. H., and Marts, R. O. (1954). *U.S. Forest Serv. Forest Prod. Lab. Rept.*, 1988.
57. Priestley, J. H. (1930). *New Phytologist* **29**, 56-73, 96-140, 316-354.
58. Rees, L. W., and Brown, R. M. (1954). *J. Forestry* **52**(9), 662-665.
59. Richardson, S. D. (1959a). Unpublished data.
60. Richardson, S. D. (1959b). *Proc. 9th Intern. Botan. Congr. Montreal* **2**, 326.
61. Richardson, S. D. (1961). *Tappi* **44**(3), 170-173.
62. Richardson, S. D., and Dinwoodie, J. M. (1960). *J. Inst. Wood Sci.* **6**, 3-13.
63. Sanio, K. (1872). *Jahrb. Wiss. Botan.* **8**, 401-420.
64. Schreiner, E. J. (1958). *Silvae Genet.* **7**(4), 109-136.
65. Schultze-Dewitz, G. (1959). *Holz Roh- Werkstoff* **17**(8), 319-326; C.S.I.R.O. *Translation No.* **4800**.
66. Shepard, H. B., and Bailey, I. W. (1914). *Proc. Soc. Am. Foresters* **9**, 522-525.
67. Spurr, S. H., and Hyvärinen, M. J. (1954). *Botan. Rev.* **20**(9), 561-575.
68. Spurr, S. H., and Hsuing, W.-Y. (1954). *J. Forestry* **52**, 191-200.
69. Susmel, L. (1951). *Ital. Forest. Mont.* **6**(2), 67-75; also in *Forestry Abstr.* **13**, 607.
70. Trendelenburg, R. (1939). "Das Holz als Rohstoff." J. F. Lehmann, München, Berlin.
71. Van Buijtenen, J. P. (1958). *Tappi* **41**(4), 175-177.
72. Vasiljevic, S. (1955). *Univ. Belgrade Bull. Coll. For.*, **10**(5), 161-190 (Engl. summary).
73. Voegeli, H., and Reinhart, O. (1956). *Schweiz. Z. Forstw.* **107**, 407-415.
74. Wardrop, A. B. (1948). *Proc. Leeds Phil. Lit. Soc. Sci. Sect.* **5**, 128-135.
75. Wareing, P. F. (1958). *J. Inst. Wood Sci.* **1**, 34-42.
76. Wodzicki, T. (1960). *Acta Soc. Botan. Polon.* **29**(4), 713-730.
77. Wodzicki, T. (1961a). *Acta Soc. Botan. Polon.* **30**(1), 111-131.
78. Wodzicki, T. (1961b). *Acta Soc. Botan. Polon.* **30**(2), 293-306.
79. Wodzicki, T., and Witkowska, L. (1961). *Acta Soc. Botan. Polon.* **30**(3-4), 755-764.
80. Zahner, R. (1962). *Forest Sci.* **8**(4), 345-352.
81. Zelawski, W. (1957). *Acta Soc. Botan. Polon.* **26**(1), 80-103.
82. Zobel, B. J. (1956). *For. Prods. J.* **6**(10), 442-447.
83. Zobel, B. J. (1961). *Silvae Genet.* **10**(3), 65-70.
84. Zobel, B. J., and Rhodes, R. R. (1957). *Tappi* **41**(4), 167-170.
85. Zobel, B. J., Cole, D., and Stonecypher, R. (1962). Paper presented at Soc. Am. Foresters Tree Imp. Meeting, Georgia, 1962.

The Influence of External Pressure on the Differentiation of Cells and Tissues Cultured in Vitro

CLAUD L. BROWN

Department of Botany and School of Forestry, University of Georgia, Athens, Georgia[1]

Tissue culture techniques have become a valuable tool in studies of growth and differentiation in vascular plants. Today, with our increased knowledge of plant nutrition, it is possible to culture cells, tissues, and organs of diverse species for indefinite periods. The tissues of some plants are easily maintained on culture media of known chemical consistency, whereas tissues from other species require complex organic supplements, and still others are cultured with extreme difficulty or not at all.

Tissue cultures of woody plants are usually established by aseptically transferring small fragments of tissue from the pith, phloem, or cambial zone to a synthetic medium containing a carbon source, essential inorganic nutrients, and various organic supplements or growth factors. Usually when the parenchymatous cells of the excised tissue are placed in culture they undergo rapid proliferation resulting in the formation of a typical unorganized callus. Pieces of this initial callus may then be successively subcultured to study specific phases of growth and development.

In many instances, the increase in size of the callus culture is accompanied by the differentiation and maturation of specialized cells, occurring singly or in isolated groups, scattered throughout the callus parenchyma. These highly differentiated cells more often appear as modified tracheids or vessel segments, although isolated phloem elements

---

[1] This work was sponsored, in part, by the Georgia Forest Research Council, Macon, Georgia.

389

may also arise *de novo* as pointed out by Gautheret (1957, 1959). Following the formation of these specialized cells, it is not at all uncommon to find a meristematic zone, resembling cambial elements developing in the form of a ring, or spherical sheath, and enclosing the central mass of differentiated cells. These localized areas of development may later give rise to root or shoot primordia as demonstrated by Steward *et al.* (1958).

In callus cultures obtained from the cambia of woody plants, Gautheret (1953) and Jacquiot (1955a,b) point out that elm (*Ulmus campestris*), birch (*Betula verrucosa*), and basswood (*Tilia parvifolia*) cultures grown on standard nutrient media show various types of differentiation, ranging from undifferentiated callus cells to apparently normal shoots and roots. Ball (1950) also finds that cultures of redwood callus (*Sequoia sempervirens*) retain the ability to form masses of tracheids even after numerous transfers.

Other cambial cultures may behave differently from the patterns described above in that they tend to lose the potentiality for forming specialized cells, thereby becoming less differentiated in successive subcultures. This pattern of development has been observed by Gautheret (1953) in callus cultures of willow (*Salix caprea*) and hawthorn (*Crataegus* spp.). Geissbühler and Skoog (1957) also noted the complete disappearance of tracheids in callus cultures of Jack pine (*Pinus banksiana*) by the end of the eighth transfer. These and other studies show that different species and various types of tissue explants may react completely differently on nutrient media of essentially the same consistency.

Other experiments in recent years have been directed more specifically to testing the specific roles of various growth factors in an attempt to learn more of the mechanisms controlling differentiation. Wetmore and Sorokin (1955) have demonstrated the role of auxin in stimulating the formation of tracheids in callus cultures of lilac (*Syringa vulgaris*) without modifying any other aspect of the cellular environment. Skoog and Miller (1957) and Das *et al.* (1956) have also demonstrated the effects of auxin (indole-3-acetic acid) and kinetin, alone and in combination at varying ratios, in bringing about different patterns of organ formation in tobacco callus cultured on media of known consistency.

From the limited number of studies mentioned here, and from numerous others found in the literature, it is obvious that tissue culture techniques have greatly extended our knowledge of factors affecting differentiation, but by no means have the endogenous mechanisms controlling differentiation at the cellular or tissue level been elucidated. Although one may, by the specific manipulation of certain growth factors such as auxins and kinins, modify patterns of differentiation leading to shoot and root formation, it is not yet possible to produce organized xylem and phloem at will from undifferentiated tissues. This limitation no doubt reflects many complex interactions between the physical and chemical environment of cell aggregates. Spatial relationships, involving tensile and compressive forces resulting from mutual cell growth, directly bear upon gas exchange, transport of metabolites, and the accumulation of metabolic by-products. It is this aspect, the influence of pressure on differentiation of cells and tissues, which stimulated the present study.

Whenever the cambium of woody plants is separated from the bole wood and left attached to the parent tree or excised and planted on a nutrient medium, the exposed cells proliferate to form initially an unorganized callus tissue which differs greatly from the organized layers of xylem and phloem in the intact plant. The pattern of cambial proliferation and the subsequent differentiation of cell types *in vitro* differ markedly, however, from that of similar segments released from apparent pressure but left attached to the parent tree. These differences are sufficiently distinct to warrant a discussion of the histological observations.

Brown and Sax (1962) described the sequence of events following separation of the cambial zone from the bole wood in which the cambial cells on the inner surface of the bark were (1) left freely suspended in a humid atmosphere, and (2) subjected to different amounts of externally applied pressure.

In these experiments, longitudinal bark strips of cottonwood (*Populus trichocarpa*) and white pine (*Pinus strobus*) were lifted away from the bole, and enclosed with polyethylene plastic film to prevent desiccation (Figs. 1 and 2). Whenever a piece of bark is separated from the bole of a tree during active springwood formation, the separation takes place primarily in the zone of newly formed xylary derivatives, leaving the cambium intact along an irregular and undulating inner surface (Fig. 3). The cells thus exposed on the inner surface are chiefly xylem mother cells still capable of cell division although some may have partially undergone early differentiation as xylem components. Proliferation of these exposed cells rapidly follows, and in most cases the derivatives from the ray initials are the first to show cellular enlargement and active divisions. Although some of the fusiform derivatives do septate and undergo repeated divisions, they contribute relatively little to the formation of callus in comparison with the rapidly proliferating ray cell derivatives (Figs. 4 and 5).

During the early stages of proliferation, cell divisions occur at random resulting in haphazard planes of cell plate formation and the develop-

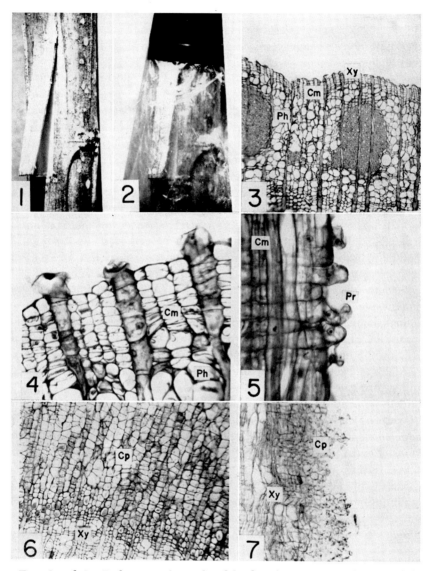

Figs. 1 and 2.   Bark strips of *Populus deltoides* after separation from the bole. × ½.

Fig. 3.   Transverse section of bark strip showing irregular separation in xylem mother cell zone. × 60. Xy, Xylem mother cells; Cm, cambium; Ph, phloem.

Figs. 4 and 5.   Proliferation of ray cells on bark strips of *Populus* 24 hours after separation from bole, transverse and longitudinal sections, respectively. × 250. Pr, proliferating ray cells; Cm, cambium.

Fig. 6.   Transverse section of callus pad on *Populus* bark strip 21 days after

ment of a typical unorganized callus. However, with continued cell division and enlargement, the callus pad rapidly increases in radial thickness, forming a rather compact mass of parenchyma cells by the end of the second or third week. The influence of mutual cell pressures gradually becomes apparent and rather distinct rows of radially aligned cells are formed, resulting from a preponderance of periclinal divisions and tangential wall formation (Fig. 6). It should be pointed out that, during this active stage of callus formation, the original cambial initials have retained their identity and continue to function in setting aside xylem and phloem derivatives. The first differentiated xylem vessels and tracheids mature as shortened elements, obliquely oriented in many instances, thus giving the first-formed mature xylem tissue a contorted, malformed appearance. The later-formed xylary derivatives, only 3–4 cells removed, differentiate into apparently normal elongate elements, restoring the organized pattern of xylem formation (Fig. 7).

Usually by the end of the third week the callus pad has reached several millimeters in radial thickness, and a new phellogen begins to differentiate in the callus parenchyma in close proximity to the original phellogen, extending tangentially from both radial margins of the bark segment around the outer periphery of the callus pad until continuity is established on the abaxial side. Prior to this extension of the phellogen the outer 2–3 layers of exposed cells have usually undergone various histological changes, some of the cell walls have apparently become suberized, and the cell contents vary in intensity of staining along the outer periphery.

Concomitant with the differentiation and extension of the phellogen, a new cambium begins to differentiate at the radial margins of the existing vascular cambium and rapidly extends around the inner periphery of the callus until continuity is also established on the abaxial side of the callus pad (Fig. 8). After peripheral continuity of the newly differentiated cambium is established in the callus, the original bark strip becomes "stem-like" in form and function (Fig. 9).

It is interesting to speculate on the nature of the stimulus which mediates this preferential path of cambial differentiation. Wilson and Wilson (1961), in examining the regeneration and union of cambia in callus wound tissues, oppose the idea of a growth hormone diffusing laterally in front of the extending cambium. Rather they suggest that

separation from bole. × 60. Cp, callus pad; Xy, first-formed xylem from original cambium.

FIG. 7. Longitudinal section of bark strip 7 days after release from pressure showing orientation of new xylem. × 50. Cp, callus; Xy, shortened and contorted vessel segments.

cambial formation is restricted to a particular distance beneath the surface, the distance factor being essentially a physiological gradient from the outer callus inward, until at a given position some factor reaches the threshold level for cambial initiation. The orientation with regard to phloem and xylem formation would then be determined by the direction

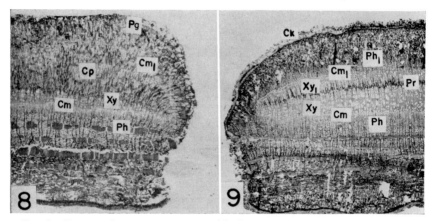

Fig. 8. Portion of transverse section of bark strip at 21 days showing lateral extension of phellogen and cambium in the callus pad. × 15. Pg, phellogen; Cm$_1$, regenerating cambium; Cm, original cambium; Cp, callus pad; Xy, xylem; Ph, phloem.

Fig. 9. Transverse section of a portion of *Populus* bark strip 60 days following release from pressure. × 10. Ck, cork; Cm and Cm$_1$, original and newly differentiated cambium; Ph, Ph$_1$ and Xy, Xy$_1$, phloem and xylem respectively produced by the original and newly formed cambium; Pr, "pith" area of original callus.

of the gradient. Undoubtedly, physiological gradients do exist from the outer exposed callus inward and these physiological differences probably result from many physical aspects of the cellular environment, including gas exchange and accumulation of food reserves and waste products, in addition to mutual pressures and tensions from growth. The causal factor controlling cambial formation at any given position could still be a hormonal one, in which the stimulus moves laterally from the pre-existing cambium as the regenerating cambium is blocked out in the undifferentiated wound callus.

The role of physical forces in maintaining normal differentiation of xylem and phloem in intact plants cannot be overlooked as pointed out by Brown and Sax (1962). Whenever longitudinal bark strips are released from their spatial environment and separated from the bole wood by a layer a polyethylene plastic film, then returned to the initial slot and held under external pressures of only 0.25 atm, the cambium continues to produce essentially normal xylem and phloem characteristic of the species (Fig. 10).

The specific influence of applied pressure was further demonstrated by placing the callus of freely proliferating bark segments under pressure for varying periods. When this is done, proliferation of the callus pad ceases almost immediately, accompanied by an appreciable increase in cell wall thickness which proceeds inward from the outer confined cells

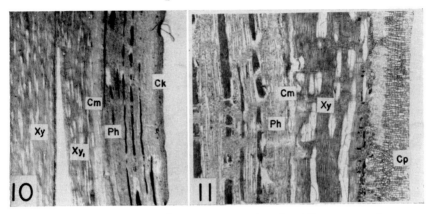

Fig. 10. Longisection of bark strip maintained under 0.5 atm external pressure for 30 days following release. × 15. Polyethylene plastic film initially inserted at zone between Xy and Xy_1 separating bole wood xylem from xylem formed after treatment. Cm, cambium; Ph, phloem; Ck, cork.

Fig. 11. Longitudinal section of *Populus* bark strip released from pressure for 14 days, followed by application of pressure for an additional 30-day period. × 30. Cp, thickened walls of callus pad; Xy, xylem; Cm, cambium; Ph, phloem.

of the callus. Parenchyma cells of the callus pad, when confined in this manner, lay down pitted secondary walls showing varying degrees of lignification (Fig. 11). Because of the apparent influence of pressure in changing the patterns of cell and tissue differentiation, studies of a similar nature have been carried out with cambial explants *in vitro*.

Methods: *in Vitro* Studies

The synthetic medium used in these experiments consisted of Knop's major and minor elements; 2% sucrose; ferric citrate, 5.0 ppm; thiamin hydrochloride, 0.1 ppm; pyridoxin, 0.5 ppm; nicotinic acid, 0.5 ppm; indole-3-acetic acid, 2.0 ppm; kinetin, 0.2 ppm; and 0.8% agar. The pH of the medium was adjusted to 5.5 and autoclaved for 20 minutes under 15-lb pressure.

Two-year-old stem segments of eastern cottonwood (*Populus deltoides*) were used to obtain cambium explants. The outer bark was removed aseptically and inner phloem explants averaging approximately 6 × 25 × 2 mm in size were planted horizontally in 35-mm culture tubes. The acropetal end of the exised segment was submerged in the nutrient agar with the cambial side oriented upward, so that the phloem side rested upon the top surface of a neoprene rubber stopper (Fig. 12). External pressure could then be applied to specific portions of the excised tissue by raising a column of mercury in specially designed glass tubes. For

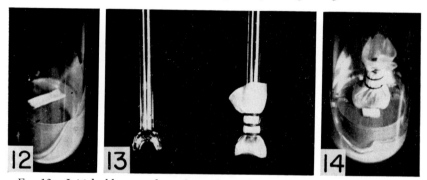

FIG. 12.   Initial phloem explant of *Populus* without applied pressure. × ½.

FIG. 13.   Barometric tubing and mercury reservoir used for applying pressure to explants *in vitro*. × ½.

FIG. 14.   Method of applying external pressure to phloem explants. × ½.

this purpose, the basal portion of standard barometric tubing was formed into a concave reservoir and covered with two layers of thin latex rubber (Fig. 13). The assembly was placed over the bark segments in such a manner that the weight of the tube was supported by the lips of the reservoir resting on the neoprene stopper so that only the rubber membrane came in contact with the plant tissue (Fig. 14). The tubes were held securely in place by a tightly seated rubber stopper at the upper end of the 35-mm tube.

In these experiments 3 dozen cultures were initially established for each treatment. The treatments were (1) control, without external pressure, (2) external pressure of 0.1 atm, and (3) external pressure of 0.05 atm.

Six excised segments in each of the three treatments were collected at 7, 14, 21, and 30 days for histological observations. These were killed and fixed in formalin–glacial acetic acid–50% ethyl alcohol (5:5:90 ml), dehydrated through a series of tertiary butyl alcohol, infiltrated with paraffin, and sectioned at a thickness of 10 μ. Radial and transverse sections were obtained from each segment. These were stained with safranin-aniline blue except in several instances where it was desirable to use specific combinations such as tannic acid–ferric chloride–resorcin blue to study phloic derivatives, or phoroglucinol–HCl in testing for the deposition of lignin.

Observations and Results

Cambial Explants without Applied Pressure

Histological observations reveal that the pattern of cell proliferation in cambial cultures greatly differs from similar tissue segments left attached to the parent tree. Proliferation is not confined to the young

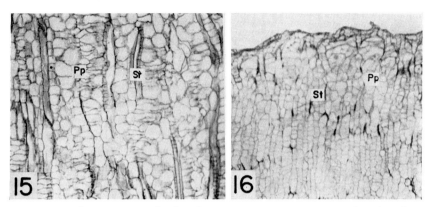

Figs. 15 and 16. Longitudinal and transverse sections, respectively, of explants after 7 days in culture without applied pressure. × 60. Pp, proliferated phloem parenchyma and companion cells; St, crushed and obliterated sieve tube members.

xylary derivatives occupying the outer surface, but as a rule all parenchyma cells within the initial explant, with the exception of mature sieve tube members, contribute to the formation of callus. By the end of 7 days most of the companion and phloem parenchyma cells in the mature phloem have greatly increased in size radially and many have undergone extensive cell division causing complete disruption of the organized phloem (Fig. 15). Accompanying this activity the cambial initials also proliferate so that their identity as an organized meristem is completely lost. Continued cell division and cellular enlargement result in the development of an extensive unorganized callus composed almost wholly of radially enlarged, undifferentiated parenchyma cells (Fig. 16). Small isolated nests of pitted, but weakly lignified, xylem elements are usually present deep within the callus near the older proliferated phloem tissues, although none of these differentiated elements was observed in the outer portion of the callus, or in subsequent transfers maintained for 90 days on the same nutrient medium.

Perhaps the most interesting contrast between the *in vivo* and *in vitro* cultures of the same material lies in the complete loss of the cambium in the latter and the apparent inability of the excised tissues to regenerate new cambia following proliferation.

Cambial Explants Maintained under Applied Pressure

The primary objective of these experiments was to determine to what extent physical forces per se could alter the pattern of development of cambial explants *in vitro*. In all cases reported thus far, the secondary cambial tissues of woody plants, when separated from their natural environment and planted on a nutrient medium, proliferate to form a callus-like tissue as previously described. That is, no one has yet obtained organized differentiation of normal xylem and phloem tissues from excised cambial cells grown *in vitro*.

As previously mentioned, when the cambium is separated from the bole of woody plants the separation usually takes place within the zone of newly formed xylem derivatives leaving the cambial cells relatively undisturbed on the phloem segment removed. This separation is always irregular, leaving a freely undulating tangential surface along the inner face of the cambial zone (cf. Fig. 3). Therefore, when cambial explants are transferred to a nutrient medium and placed under external pressure, some of the cells in recessed areas along the surface initially fail to make contact with the rubber membrane supporting the mercury column, and these cells undergo proliferation. Usually the ray derivatives proliferate most rapidly, although many of the exposed xylem mother cells also septate and contribute to callus formation during the initial 3–5 day period in culture. During this time the irregular surface of the cambial zone becomes filled with 2–5 layers of proliferated cells and hereafter the surface cells of the explant come under rather uniform mutual pressures (Figs. 17 and 18). Because external pressure is immediately applied to the cambial explants, the cambial initials remain intact in most cultures, i.e., they do not undergo proliferation as they do in cultures without applied pressure.

Most explants, under either level of pressure, produce normal elongate vessel segments forming continuous well-differentiated vessels after 7–14 days in culture. By this time, however, only 1–3 tiers of vessel segments have differentiated radially, and it is of special interest that the most advanced differentiated vessel segments lie adjacent or near to the fusiform initials (Fig. 19). This indicates that, upon transfer to synthetic media, normal patterns of cell division in the cambial zone are interrupted, which results in a reduction of activity in the xylem mother cell zone and the early maturation of vessel elements. It is also of interest that the xylem mother cells farthest removed from the cambial initials at the time of excision fail to continue their normal pathway of differentiation, but usually mature as shortened pitted elements following maturation of the more recently derived vessel segments near the cambial initials. This pattern of differentiation obviously results from the disturbance of spatial relationships among cells of the cambial zone, and it points to the necessity of mutual pressures in bringing about normal xylem differentiation.

Cultures maintained under pressure for 30 days produced, on the average, only 5–6 radial tiers of vessel elements making up rather small

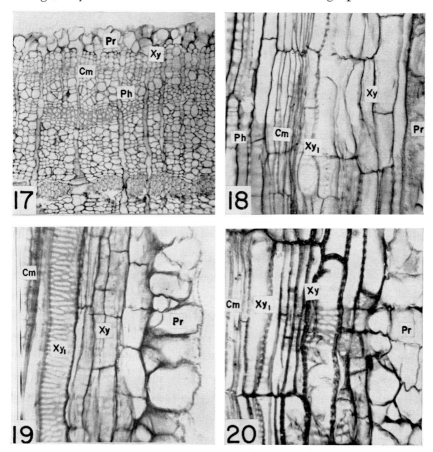

FIGS. 17 and 18. Transverse and longitudinal sections of *Populus* explants maintained under 0.05 atm pressure for 14 days. $\times$ 60 and 200 respectively. Pr, proliferated ray cells; Xy, xylem mother cells; Xy_1, differentiated vessel segments; Cm, cambial initials; Ph, functional sieve tube members.

FIG. 19. Longisection of 7-day-old explant under 0.05 atm pressure. $\times$ 250. Pr, proliferated ray cells; Xy, septate xylem mother cells; Xy_1, newly differentiated vessel segment.

FIG. 20. Longisection of 30-day-old explant under 0.1 atm pressure. $\times$ 250. Pr, proliferated ray cells; Xy, mature derivatives of original xylem mother cell zone; Xy_1, vessel segments produced in culture; Cm, cambial initials.

groups of isolated vessels in the vertical system, i.e., during the 30-day period of culture cambial activity and differentiation of xylem derivatives were not sufficient to obtain laterally continuous xylem throughout the explants (Fig. 20). This again reflects a reduction in cell division among the cambial initials and xylem mother cells in culture as compared to the

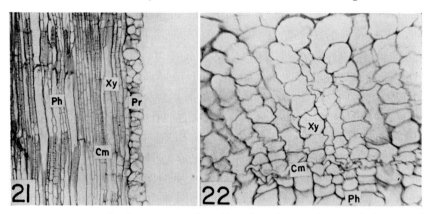

FIG. 21.   Longitudinal section of 7-day-old explant showing functional phloem and differentiation of xylem elements. × 60. Pr, proliferated ray cells; Xy, differentiating xylem elements; Cm, cambial initials; Ph, functional phloem.

FIG. 22.   Transverse section of explant after 21 days in culture under 0.1 atm applied pressure. × 200. Xy, xylem mother cells and differentiating vessel segments; Cm, crushed cambial initials; Ph, phloem.

in vivo condition. By varying the nutrition of explants in additional cultures it is likely that more extensive xylem can be produced. Secondary wall formation appeared normal in the differentiated xylem elements, but the walls were weakly lignified as indicated by the phoroglucinol–HCl reaction.

Insofar as could be determined, the current-year sieve tube members in the phloem remained functional. Definitive callose was only observed on the older nonfunctional sieve elements (Fig. 21). It was difficult to determine precisely the extent of new sieve tube formation during the short periods of culture owing to the presence of differentiating phloic elements when the cultures were established, and the failure to make more frequent collections for histological observations. A more detailed analysis of differentiation in the phloem than was made in the present study is needed.

Although there were no observable qualitative differences in differentiation between the two levels of pressure, the tissues maintained under 0.05 atm usually produced a few more vessel segments than those kept at the higher 0.1 atm level. It is also of interest to note that in some segments under both levels of pressure, the cambial cells appeared to be somewhat distorted owing to folding and bending of the radial walls (Fig. 22).

In additional experiments, cambial explants were allowed to proliferate for a 7-day period; then 0.1 atm pressure was applied to the callus parenchyma for an additional 30-day period. Essentially the same results were obtained in culture as were previously observed on surgically treated trees, i.e., the parenchyma cells of the callus began depositing secondary wall material, pitted throughout, although the walls were weakly lignified at the time of sampling.

Summary

The importance of physical forces and the role they play in the orderly processes of differentiation in living organisms has long been recognized. The present work only serves to demonstrate that various approaches are required for studying the many intriguing facets of growth and development. A statement of D'Arcy Thompson in his notable work on "Growth and Form"[2] seems particularly apt: "Cell and tissue, shell and bone, leaf and flower, are so many portions of matter, and it is in obedience to the laws of physics that their particles have been moved, moulded, and conformed. In general no organic forms exist save such as are in conformity with physical and mathematical laws."

The distinct differences observed between the pattern of proliferation and subsequent differentiation of bark strips left attached to the parent tree and similar strips cultured *in vitro* can undoubtedly be explained by the high nutritional level of the culture medium. Under these artificial conditions all parenchyma cells of the explant proliferate, causing loss of the cambial initials and obliteration of the phloem, resulting in the formation of a typical parenchymatous callus. The role of applied pressure in inhibiting this initial proliferation is clearly demonstrated, and justifies the conclusion that mutual cell forces are essential in obtaining normal differentiation of xylem and phloem. One of the most interesting aspects of these studies is the initially low pressures (0.05 atm) required to bring about distinct differences in patterns of cell division and maturation. Additional experiments are required to determine more precisely the lower limits of response to applied pressure.

Another interesting observation concerns the specific influence of pressure upon secondary wall formation. As long as proliferating cells are undergoing cytokinesis and extending primary cell walls, secondary wall formation does not ensue, and the cells of the callus remain po-

[2] *On Growth and Form,* 2nd ed. Cambridge University Press. 1942.

tentially meristematic. If, however, these cells are brought under slight external pressures, continued cell division and cellular enlargement are inhibited, at which time the protoplasts begin deposition of secondary wall material. This pattern of differentiation is generally recognized as it applies to cells which normally produce secondary walls, but little emphasis has been given to the possible role of physical forces in various stages of differentiation.

It seems highly significant that pressure alone can inhibit cell proliferation, prevent the regeneration of cambia in callus tissue, and bring about secondary wall thickening in callus parenchyma. These observations clearly suggest that in the search for endogenous mechanisms controlling differentiation at any level, one should not lose sight of the fact that hereditary control of organized development evolved in a physical as well as chemical environment. Thus, the demonstrable role of auxin in bringing about the differentiation of highly specialized tracheary elements in otherwise undifferentiated callus is only one step in a long chian of events leading to organized tissue and organ formation.

With improved and more refined experimental techniques, we should expect to learn much more about the complex interactions between physical and biochemical pathways in biological systems. Presently we need to learn more about the influence of physical forces on the orientation of cell divisions and cell plate formation in undifferentiated callus cultures and organized meristems. It may be, for example, that the widespread phenomenon of polarity, so essential to organized growth and development, is mediated through physical mechanisms during the early stages of cellular and tissue differentiation. There is little reason to doubt that various aspects of biophysics will play an ever-increasing role in problems concerned with histo-and morphogenesis.

DISCUSSION

WILSON: It seems quite possible that all the vessels which differentiated could have come from the 12 or 13 xylem mother cells which were present in the pieces taken out of the tree. That would mean that there were no divisions, no cell production, just differentiation. It would be nice if you could see periclinal divisions in the material under pressure.

BROWN: I am quite sure that new divisions have occurred, but I cannot say that more than two or three have occurred *in vitro*. Surely some of the vessel segments have differentiated from existing xylem mother cells. However, this pattern does not exist if there is no pressure. I had hoped to find a continuous band of xylem 2 mm thick, but this did not happen.

TOMLINSON: Is there any difference in behavior if you reverse the polarity of those strips?

BROWN: I have not done that *in vitro* in this particular material. If on the intact tree an 8-cm-long bark strip is released pointing upwards, callus formation does occur, but it very seldom gets up to the end of the strip. The pattern of differentiation of new cambium through the callus is not too different from what it was when the strips were pointed downward. There is much greater callus formation if the strip points downward because the nutrients and hormones move down the stem.

THIMANN: Would you say that the classical cambial cultures of R. J. Gautheret (1935) were really ray cultures?

BROWN: Not necessarily. Under *in vitro* conditions almost any parenchyma cell can, and usually does proliferate. The pattern is different on bark strips attached to the parent tree. In this case the ray cells do contribute most to the formation of callus.

ZIMMERMANN: Theodor Hartig (1845) made this observation more than a hundred years ago. He covered the exposed part with a piece of glass and found microscopically that regeneration of wood and bark originated in the rays.

BROWN: I had assumed that the only reason my experiments had not been done before was that we have only had polyethylene film for a few years.

ZIEGLER: You showed isolated phloem cells with callose; are they sieve tube members?

BROWN: What you actually saw was callus cells with definitive callose. I called them "phloem-like" cells. They were the first to differentiate from parenchyma cells. Later when the cambium became functional new sieve tube members were produced and apparently became functional.

ESAU: Could you relate this observation to the grafting experiment carried out by A. S. Crafts (1934)? Before cambium was formed, some phloem differentiated directly from callus cells. Your observation seems to be identical. The cells that differentiate from parenchyma are very likely sieve elements which precede cambial activity. You should examine them to see whether they are enucleate and whether they have connecting strands through the callosed walls. The tissue shown by you resembles certain virus-induced proliferations. The sieve elements in such proliferations are misshapen and may not show all the characteristics of sieve elements; but they certainly were on the way to become such elements.

ZIEGLER: At one place it looked as though there was a companion cell. It would be interesting if you could find a sieve cell without a nucleus and without a companion cell.

BROWN: I did not check this specifically, but in normal phloem of *Populus* the nucleoli remain for a long time; they are much larger than those of other cells. I cannot say that they are there as long as the phloem is functional, but they might have some role in RNA or DNA synthesis, or in the communication between companion cells and sieve elements.

ESAU: In normal development some sieve elements may have no companion cells, for example those of the protophloem of grasses. They are enucleate. These cells probably do not function very long, so whatever a nucleate cell is supposed to do is probably done by adjacent parenchyma cells. With regard to persistent nucleoli, they are extruded from the nuclei. As soon as they leave the nucleus they enlarge and usually develop a peculiar surface pattern. They resemble pollen grains. They remain in the sieve elements until the latter is crushed.

WILSON: If these are translocating sieve elements it would be a nice place to plug in an aphid, because one can feed the callus anything through the medium.

BROWN: Yes, and I would also like to observe living material in phase contrast.

WILCOX: Ordinarily the cambium does as you indicate. It septates and disappears. In cuttings the cambial callus or wedge that develops at the lower end may be made from considerable proliferation of callus between the wood and bark which forces the bark out in a wedge-shaped area. The cambium may then project out over the surface and contribute to the body of loose, friable callus which comes largely from the rays (E. Küster, 1916).

BROWN: Callus formation resulting from wounding or grafting of woody plants may arise in several ways depending upon what tissues are exposed, and even more important, what plane or face of the tissue is exposed. For example, ray cells exposed on the tangential surface of newly formed xylem readily proliferate if the wood surface is kept moist, whereas ray cells exposed on transverse sections of stems or pruned branches do not proliferate except in a narrow zone on either side of the active cambium. In stem cuttings, the entire cambial zone may proliferate at the basal end so that the cambium itself is lost, but in bark strips left attached to the tree, only the ray cells and some of the xylem mother cells proliferate leaving the cambium intact. At least this is the pattern I have observed in *Populus* and white pine (*P. strobus*). The regeneration of new cambia in callus parenchyma also assumes various patterns depending upon the orientation of the callus with respect to the existing original cambium and the direction of the stimulus which it exerts in bringing about differentiation in the callus parenchyma.

ZIMMERMANN: In those bark strips that were not pushed back to the tree was the new cambium on the inside of the bark strip continuous with the cambium above?

BROWN: Yes, the original cambium is continuous throughout.

TOMLINSON: Would it be possible to isolate bark strips the way you have done but maintain contact at each end? Split them through the cambium or close to the cambium and separate bark from wood.

BROWN: Yes, the tree might have to be bent a little. One could make two longitudinal slits and leave the strip attached at both ends; then the strip could be held away from the tree. Dr. Sax and I took out a strip of bark about 18 inches long and another one right beside it, one strip facing down and the other facing up. Then we twisted them together so that the cambia of the two strips faced each other. There was absolutely no proliferation. Just a distinct line between where the ray cells and the new xylem formed on either side, but they did not match up (Unpublished work at Weston and Arnold Arboretum, 1956).

REFERENCES

Ball, E. (1950). *Growth* 14, 295-325.

Brown, C. L., and Sax, K. (1962). *Am. J. Botany* 49, 683-691.

Crafts, A. S. (1934). *Botan. Gaz.* 95, 592-608.

Das, N. K., Patau, K., and Skoog, F. (1956). *Physiol. Plantarum* 9, 640-651.

Gautheret, R. J. (1935). *Compt. Rend. Soc. Biol.* 127, 259-261, 609-612.

Gautheret, R. J. (1953). *Rev. Gen. Botan.* 60, 129-173.

Gautheret, R. J. (1957). *J. Natl. Cancer Inst.* 19, 555-573.

Gautheret, R. J. (1959). "La Culture des Tissus Végétaux," 847 pp. Paris.

Geissbühler, H., and Skoog, F. (1957). *Tappi* 40, 257-262.

Hartig, Th. (1945). *Allgem. Forst- Jagdztg.* 11, 165-169.

Jacquiot, C. (1955a). *Compt. Rend.* 240, 557-558.

Jacquiot, C. (1955b). *Compt. Rend.* 241, 1064-1066.

Küster, E. (1916). "Pathologische Pflanzenanatomie," pp. 66-67. Fischer, Jena.

Skoog, F., and Miller, C. O. (1957). *Symp. Soc. Exptl. Biol.* 11, 118-131.

Steward, F. C., Mapes, M. O., and Mears, K. (1958). *Am. J. Botany* 45, 705-708.

Wetmore, R., and Sorokin, S. (1955). *J. Arnold Arboretum (Harvard Univ.)* 36, 306-317.

Wilson, J., and Wilson, P. M. (1961). *New Phytologist* 60, 63-73.

The Reaction Anatomy of Arborescent Angiosperms

A. B. Wardrop

Division of Forest Products, Commonwealth Scientific and Industrial Research Organization, Melbourne, Australia

I. Introduction

1. The Plant-Environment Relationship—Tree Form

The existence of a continuous interaction between a plant and its environment is axiomatic in studies of plant growth. This interaction may simply involve adjustment to altered conditions resulting from the growth of adjacent plants or it may be severe, as in instances of sudden climatic changes or soil subsidence. The mere existence of variable environmental conditions, however, involves a continuous response to them by the plant which is usually manifest, in trees, as a change in the direction or extent of growth of the stem or the branches.

In addition to these externally conditioned changes in the growth of the tree, changes also take place in the disposition of the branches to the stem as a result of the growth of the tree itself. Thus the increasing angle of divergence of the branches from the top of a tree toward its base implies that this angle changes during development. These changes, which are associated with the maintenance of tree form, must be attributed to intrinsic factors within the plant itself.

The capacity of the plant to adjust its orientation in space may be brought about by the differential growth, bending, or torsion of its members. These movements of the stem and its branches have been termed by Jost (1907) "movements of orientation."

2. Orientation Movements and the Morphology of Stems and Branches

In herbaceous plants orientation movements may be brought about by differential longitudinal growth on opposite sides of the organ showing response. In woody plants, however, and especially in the case of large trees, the process by which such movements are effected cannot be brought about by this means since longitudinal extension growth ceases after the formation of the secondary tissue systems begins. It has therefore been concluded that movements of orientation in stems with secondary growth must involve a process of bending. This process is illustrated (Fig. 1) in a young plant of *Tristania conferta* which was placed in a horizontal position and its recovery followed at intervals. The initial response can be seen to have taken place in the apex and was followed by a progressive bending of the stem at points at increasing distances from the apex and at which longitudinal growth was no longer possible.

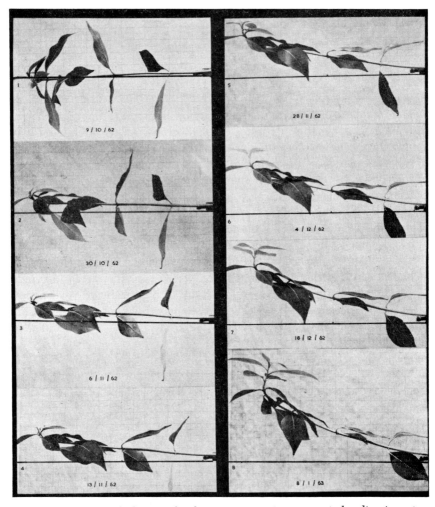

Fig. 1. A series of photographs showing progressive geotropic bending in a stem of *Tristania conferata*. When examined at stage 8 reaction wood was present along the entire upper side of the stem below the fourth pair of leaves from the apex.

Many examples of a similar process involving the bending of relatively large stems have been described in the literature. In one instance studied by Engler, the geotropic bending of a stem of *Picea*, measuring 23 cm thick, which resulted from severe soil subsidence was observed over a distance of 16.2 meters (Büsgen and Münch, 1929). Under experimental

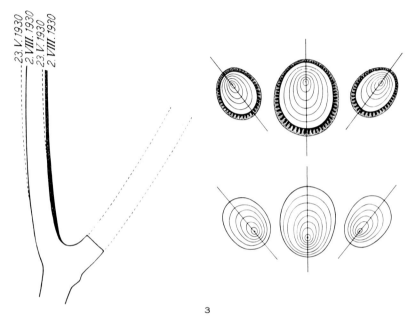

2   3

FIG. 2.   Movement of orientation in a forked branch of *Fraxinus excelsior* following removal of the adjacent branch. (Hartmann, 1949.)

FIG. 3.   A diagrammatic representation of the eccentricity of radial growth which is frequently associated with reaction wood formation in a branch and two laterals of *Taxus* (above) and *Linden* (below). (Rawitscher, 1932.)

conditions Jacobs (1939) has observed such bending in stems of *Pinus* and *Eucalyptus* between 2.5 cm and 10 cm thick at breast height.

Another example of orientation movements in woody plants is illustrated in Fig. 2. This shows the progressive movement of one member of a forked branch following removal of the adjacent branch (Hartmann, 1949).

The process of bending of stems and branches involved in movements of the above kind is frequently, but not always, correlated with a differential radial growth which results in an eccentric cross-sectional form of the stem or branch concerned. In general this eccentricity is toward the upper side of leaning stems or branches in angiosperms and toward the lower side in gymnosperms (Grossenbacher, 1915; Priestley and Tong,

1927; Rawitscher, 1932; Wergin, 1961) (Fig. 3). Although the tendency to eccentric development of a stem or branch shown in Fig. 3 is usual in arborescent plants, exceptions to it have been noted by a number of workers (Nečesaný, 1955b; Onaka, 1949; Priestley and Tong, 1927). Onaka (1949), in a wide survey recognized three types of response in the stem of angiosperms, viz., those showing eccentricity toward the upper side or to the lower side or those showing no eccentricity of growth. However, those plants showing no eccentricity in their branches or in leaning stems were mainly shrubs and vines and will not be considered further in this discussion, and those showing eccentric development to- ward the lower side (as in gymnosperms) consisted of a few genera, notably *Buxus, Gardenia* (Onaka, 1949), *Buxus, Actinodaphne, Viscum*, and *Rhododendron* (Kny, 1882). Kny's observations on the latter two genera were disputed by Onaka (1949).

From these observations the generalization that eccentric growth is toward the upper side of leaning stems or branches of most angiosperms with a well-developed arborescent habit appears justified. It may be noted, however, that when this eccentricity is apparent in only a few growth rings it may not be reflected in the form of the member as a whole. Furthermore it has been observed (Jaccard, 1938; Wardrop, 1956) that eccentricity of a given growth ring may vary at points along a single branch or stem (see below).

According to Jaccard (1938), when a stem or branch exhibited greater radial increment on one side there was a decreased radial increment on the opposite side, i.e. there was a compensation of radial growth, so that the total cross-sectional area of the xylem formed was no greater than when the increment was concentric.

The xylem and phloem which are formed on the upper side of a lean- ing stem or branch often differ in their macroscopic appearance and anatomy from that of the tissues opposite or adjacent to them. Since these morphological and anatomical changes appear to be associated either causatively or in consequence of the reaction of the stem or branch to changed internal and external conditions, these organs may be said to exhibit a "reaction anatomy," and more specifically the terms "reaction xylem" (tension wood) and "reaction phloem" may be used to describe the xylem and phloem developed under these conditions.

Thus in leaning stems undergoing orientation movements two features, their eccentric radial growth and their development of a characteristic reaction anatomy, can be recognized. However, it must be emphasized that, while both of these features can be seen in most instances, they are not necessarily correlated. Thus White (1962) has described a branch of

Sassafras in which characteristic reaction wood was present on the upper side but which showed eccentric growth toward the lower side.

In the following discussion it is proposed to describe the anatomy and fine structure of reaction wood and reaction phloem of arborescent angiosperms and to review evidence of the relation of the formation of these tissues to movements of orientation and to the mechanism by which such movement may be effected.

II. The Anatomy of Reaction Wood

The extent to which the anatomy of the reaction wood formed in stems and branches is modified is extremely variable. A survey of its occurrence in different families was made by Nečesaný (1955b), who con-

FIG. 4. *Eucalyptus gigantea.* A transverse section showing compact reaction wood (tension wood) extending over a growth ring.

FIG. 5. *Eucalyptus gigantea.* A transverse section showing normal wood in the upper growth ring, some reaction wood and normal wood in the middle growth ring, and intense compact reaction wood formation in the lower growth ring. Note the extreme reduction in the size and number of the vessels in the lower ring.

FIG. 6. *Emmenosperma alphitionioides.* A transverse section showing somewhat diffuse formation of reaction wood fibers. (Wardrop and Dadswell, 1955.)

cluded that its formation is more common in those families in which the wood is less specialized. Some species, such as *Fraxinus* (Clarke, 1937) and *Tilia* (Jaccard, 1917; Onaka, 1949) are reported to show no great modification in their anatomy although their degree of lignification is reduced (Priestley and Tong, 1927), whereas in species such as *Fagus* and *Eucalyptus* the anatomical modification is very great (Fig. 4) and is also accompanied by a reduction in the level of lignification. In view of this variation both within a species and in different species, the procedure here followed is to describe the anatomical features of reaction wood showing extreme modification from the normal condition, but to bear in mind the possible existence of intermediate degrees of anatomical modification.

Reaction wood is characterized by the presence of fewer and smaller vessels than normal wood and a corresponding increase in the proportion of fibers which are conspicuously thick walled (Fig. 4). Part or all of the cell wall is unlignified or nearly so. All the fibers in dense bands of tissue may show these characteristics (Fig. 5), or in some instances such fibers may occur diffusely between apparently normal fibers (Fig. 6). Both the ray and vertical parenchyma are relatively unmodified. In *Sassafras*, however, White (1962) noted the absence of oil cells from the rays of reaction wood.

In evergreen species such as *Eucalyptus*, reaction xylem may occur in both the earlywood and latewood and may extend over more than one growth ring, although the detailed structure of the fibers may show some difference between earlywood and latewood (Wardrop and Dadswell 1955). In deciduous trees, however, such as aspen, birch, and alder (Ollinmaa, 1959) and beech (Sachsse, 1961), the reaction wood is most developed in the earlywood and does not extend to the last-formed cells of the latewood.

The more detailed features of the tissue elements of reaction wood are discussed in further detail below.

1. THE VESSELS

Because the vessels of reaction wood are usually smaller and less numerous, the percentage volume of the wood-occupied vessels is less than in normal wood. In *Fagus sylvatica*, Chow (1946) found that the vessels occupied 21.8% of the volume of the reaction wood compared with 32.9% for normal wood. In a survey of some 31 species, Onaka (1949) measured the vessel diameter in tangential and radial directions and found the vessel diameter less in the reaction wood of all but four species. The number of vessels per square millimeter was less in the reaction xylem than in the normal xylem in 29 of the 31 species studied. These observations were confirmed by the detailed analyses of Ollinmaa (1959). The vessel walls are usually well lignified, but in instances of extreme reaction xylem formation, their level of lignification may be reduced.

2. THE PARENCHYMA

The parenchyma cells of reaction wood do not show any great modification of their cell-wall structure. Because of the fewer vessels present, the proportion of vasicentric parenchyma is reduced in those species in which this tissue occurs. In aspen and alder, Ollinmaa (1959) observed that both the number of medullary rays and the volume of the xylem occupied by the rays was less in the reaction xylem than in normal xylem. However, these changes may simply reflect the change in cross-sectional form of the stem owing to eccentric growth, since, as pointed out by Sachs (1882), the rays tend to follow a path normal to the stem surface and as a consequence of the eccentric growth would be expected to curve away from each other. It is of interest, however, that new rays are apparently not initiated as the original ones become progressively separated (Bünning, 1952).

3. The Fibers

(a) *The Dimensions and Form of Fibers.* Measurement of the average length of fibers from reaction wood of a large number of species by Chow (1946), Onaka (1949), and Nečesaný (1955a) showed them to be longer, than those taken from wood on the opposite side of the stems. This was confirmed by the more detailed measurements of fiber length distribution from similar tissues by Ollinmaa (1959). However, in *Populus*, Giovanni (1953) reported the reaction wood fibers to be shorter than in normal wood and Dadswell and Wardrop (1956) found the reaction wood fibers to be longer, shorter, or equal in length to the normal fibers. Sachsse (1961) in *Fagus*, and Scurfield and Wardrop (1962) working on experimentally induced reaction wood, found the fiber length to be similar to that in normal xylem.

In part, these conflicting observations may result from the position in the stem from which the samples were taken, i.e. whether the fibers from reaction wood were compared with the wood opposite to it (Onaka, 1949) from a point higher or lower in the stem, but of the same growth ring (Dadswell and Wardrop, 1956), or from wood laterally adjacent to it (Ollinmaa, 1959). Again, the position in the growth ring would also be expected to be of significance (Bisset and Dadswell, 1950).

A further factor which may account for the differing results of fiber length measurements is rate of radial growth of the stem or branch in which the reaction wood was formed. Thus it was shown by Amos *et al.* (1950) that in normal wood formation the fiber length is inversely related to the rate of radial growth. Since the formation of reaction wood is usually associated with a differential radial growth of the stem or branch, the fiber length could be expected to be greater or less than that of the normal xylem, depending on whether the eccentricity of radial growth resulted from an increased duration of division or rate of division in the cambium. In some instances, at least, it is known that the duration of cambial activity is greater on the side of stems forming reaction wood. (see below).

The cross-sectional form of fibers in reaction wood does not differ markedly from those of the wood opposite to it. In some species, notably *Populus alba*, the reaction wood fibers are somewhat narrower radially and have a more rectangular form in cross section as compared with the more polygonal shape of the fibers in the wood opposite it. Onaka (1949) has noted a number of additional species in which this is so, but does not consider it to be a general feature of the tissue.

It is of interest that the tips of reaction wood fibers show fewer bifurcations and other distortions than do the fibers opposite to it. This has been shown for experimentally induced reaction wood by Burns (1942) and also for tissue occurring under natural condition by Giovanni (1953). In addition Giovanni has shown that the longitudinal extent of overlapping of fibers is less in the reaction wood. These features will be considered further below.

(b) *The Layered Structure of the Fiber Wall.* In the cell wall of mature normal fibers both the primary wall and secondary wall can be recognized. Typically, the secondary wall consists of three layers (S_1, S_2 and S_3) which differ in both composition and physical texture (see the paper by Wardrop earlier in this volume).

The fibers of reaction wood show some modification of this typical pattern of cell-wall structure. Basically this consists of the replacement of either the layer S_2 or the layer S_3 by an unlignified layer which in section has a translucent swollen and gelatinous appearance; or such a layer may be formed in addition to the normal three layers of the secondary wall (Wardrop and Dadswell, 1955). Although there is no reason to regard this additional or replacing layer as other than a special layer of the secondary wall its appearance has led to its being termed the "gelatinous layer." When this layer replaces the normal layer S_2 it may be designated $S_2(G)$, so that if the layering of a normal fiber is represented as $P + S_1 + S_2 + S_3$ (Fig. 7a) the layering of the fibers of reaction wood may be represented as $P + S_1 + S_2(G)$ (Figs. 7b and 8), $P + S_1 + S_2 + S_3(G)$ (Figs. 7c and 8), or $P + S_1 + S_2 + S_3 + S_4(G)$ (Figs 7d and 9). The structure $P + S_1(G)$ has not been recorded. Examples of these different types of organization are shown in Figs. 8–12 and in Figs. 19 and 20.

The presence of "gelatinous fibers" in wood was recognized by many early workers, but it was Metzger (1908) who first recognized these as characteristic of reaction wood, and because of their supposed function of resisting stress in the xylem he termed these "tension fibers."

The extent of development of the layer G is variable both in its extent and form, both within and between species. In some genera, however, such as *Acacia*, the layer is characteristically convoluted. This is shown in Figs. 10a and 10b in which it is shown in both convoluted and non-convoluted condition. In instances of severe reaction wood formation, the lumen may be almost filled (Figs. 8 and 11).

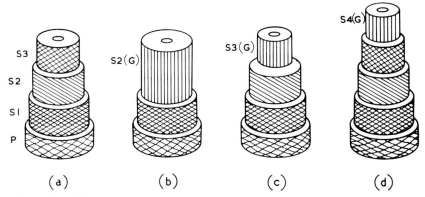

Fig. 7. A diagrammatic representation of variation in cell-wall organization of wood fibers associated with the formation of reaction wood. (a) A normal wood fiber of structure $P + S_1 + S_2 + S_3$; (b) a reaction wood fiber of structure $P + S_1 + S_2(G)$; (c) a reaction wood fiber of structure $P + S_1 + S_2 + S_3(G)$; (d) a reaction wood fiber of structure $P + S_1 + S_2 + S_3 + S_4(G)$.

P = primary wall, S_1 = outer layer of the secondary wall, S_2 = middle layer of the secondary wall, S_3 = inner layer of the secondary wall, SG = gelatinous layer replacing or formed in addition to the normal three secondary wall layers.

The layer G is usually unlignified or lignified to a very limited degree. This can be seen from staining reactions such as safranin–light green (Fig. 4), phloroglucinol–hydrochloric acid, and the Coppick and Fowler stain. The reduced lignification is also apparent in the low absorption of the layer in ultraviolet photomicrographs, such as those shown in Figs. 8 and 11. This was demonstrated semiquantitatively in the ultraviolet microspectrophotometric studies of Lange (1954). In ultraviolet photomicrographs the layer G often appears quite homogeneous, but it may show discontinuities in the form of a concentric zone or zones of absorption (Fig. 8). These are especially apparent when the layer is convoluted (Fig. 12). Frequently there is some absorption adjacent to the lumen (Fig. 8). Fine radial striations are also apparent in some instances. In two species, viz., *Ocotea rubra* (Jutte, 1956) and *Quercus lyrata* (Wahlgren, 1959) reaction fibers were observed in which the layer S(G) showed discontinuities resembling those shown for *Fagus* in Fig. 12, but the inner part of the layer showed definite lignification. In the absence of corresponding studies in fine structure on these species it cannot be said

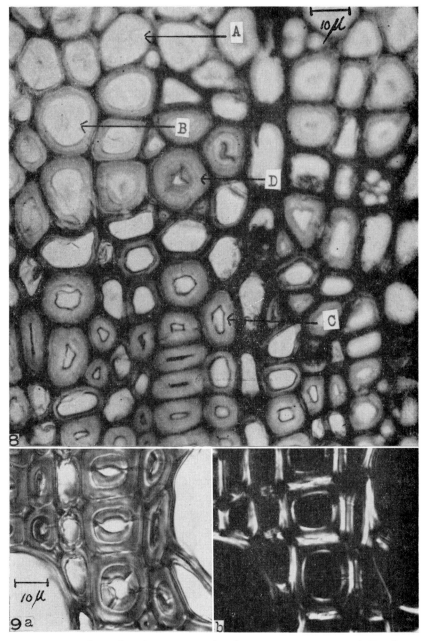

FIG. 8. An ultraviolet photomicrograph of a transverse section of *Eucalyptus elaeophora* showing reaction wood fibers of organization $P + S_1 + S_2(G)$ (cell A) and $P + S_1 + S_2 + S_3(G)$ (cell B), as well as normal fibers (cell C). In C note the

if this represented a condition of lignification of part of the layer G^1 or whether the lignified region is also paralleled by changes in physical organization.

The lignification of other layers of the secondary wall, the primary wall, and intercellular layer is also variable, but usually is less than in normal wood (Wardrop and Dadswell, 1948). Gross analyses and staining reactions indicate that the layer SG consists predominantly of cellulose (Jayme, 1951; Wardrop and Dadswell, 1948). It stains with iodine–sulfuric acid, and with dyes such as light green, and leaves little or no residue on dissolution with sulfuric acid. It is stained feebly by ruthenium red and by the pectin staining method of Albersheim *et al.* (1960). After hydrolysis the staining with ruthenium red is enhanced.

In reaction wood fibers and fiber tracheids in which the layer G is present, the pit chamber is reduced, and the canal is slitlike and is oriented almost parallel to the fiber axis. The number of pits is small.

(c) *The Submicroscopic Organization of Fibers of Reaction Wood.* As indicated in the preceding section, structural modification of the tissue elements of the reaction wood is confined to the fibers and fiber tracheids so that it is pertinent to discuss the cell-wall structure of these elements in some detail.

The texture of the cell-wall layers other than the layer G appears to be basically similar to that present in normal fibers. On its outer surface the primary wall (Fig. 13) shows the typical intertangled arrangement of microfibrils and does not show recognizable differences from that in normal fibers.

The layer S_1 of reaction fibers often appears thinner than in normal fibers, especially those in which layering is of the type $P + S_1 + S_2(G)$. The birefringence in transverse section of the S_1 layer is also lower than in normal fibers (Wardrop and Dadswell, 1948), but is not known whether this reflects a difference in microfibril orientation or in composition.

---

[1] Examination of specimens of Ocotea in the wood collection of this laboratory suggest this is so.

---

sharp absorption by the terminal lamella adjacent to the lumen, and the diffuse absorption adjacent to the lumen in the cell D and the absence of absorption in the cell A.

FIG. 9. A transverse section of a specimen from the Flacourtiaceae (New Guinea) showing reaction wood fibers with the organization $P + S_1 + S_2 + S_3 + S_4(G)$ (cf. Fig. 7.) (a) Normal illumination; (b) between crossed nicols. (Wardrop and Dadswell, 1955.)

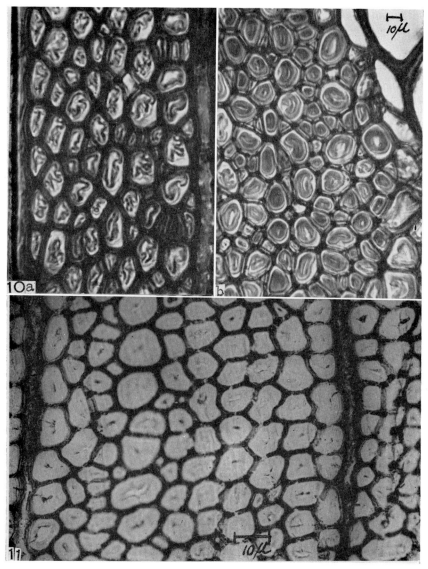

Fig. 10. *Acacia melanoxylon*. Transverse sections showing the S(G) layer. (a) In the convoluted form and (b) in the nonconvoluted form. (Wardrop and Dadswell, 1948.)

Fig. 11. *Eucalyptus gigantea*. An ultraviolet photomicrograph of reaction wood fibers in which the S(G) layer showed extreme development with uniform texture.

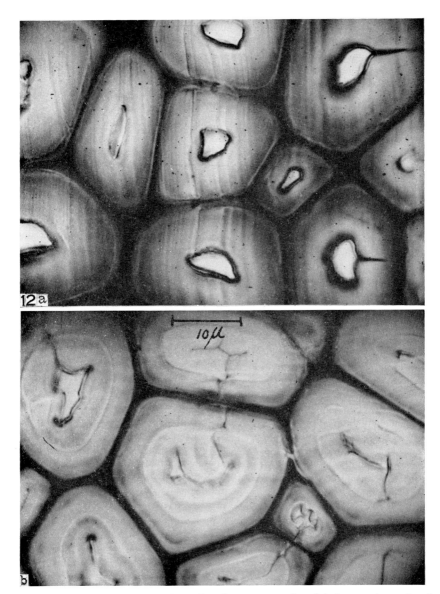

Fig. 12. *Fagus sylvatica.* Ultraviolet photomicrographs of (a) normal wood and (b) reaction wood. In (b) the S(G) layer of the reaction wood shows some heterogeneity of absorption. In some of the cells the tendency for the inner bands of the S(G) layer to be convoluted can be seen. (Wardrop and Dadswell, 1955.)

In the electron microscope the S_1 layer shows the presence of a number of lamellae of opposed helical orientation (Fig. 14). Presumably
variation in the thickness of this layer results from variation in the number of lamellae present. In reaction xylem fibers in which the layers S_2
and S_3 are present there is no indication that the organization of these
layers differs from that in normal fibers.

From the optical studies of Jaccard and Frey (1928) it was established
that the major extinction position of the fibers was approximately axial
and it was concluded that the molecular orientation in the layer $S(G)$
was apparently parallel to the fiber axis. This was confirmed by the X-ray
diffraction studies of Preston and Ranganathan (1947) and by Wardrop
and Dadswell (1948), as well as by Correns et al. (1956) and Messeri
(1953).

Electron microscopic studies have confirmed the axial orientation of
the microfibrils (Wardrop and Dadswell, 1955). This is illustrated in
Figs. 14–16. It may be noted that in tangential section the microfibrils
show close lateral association within the lamellae (Fig. 16), which are
visible in radial section (Fig. 16). This lateral association of the microfibrils within the lamellae may reflect a preferential orientation of the 101
plane parallel to the cell surface as is known to be the case with some
algae. It may be noted that Frey-Wyssling (1954) has suggested that the
101 plane is the plane of lamellation in his model of the molecular
structure of the microfibril.

In the wet replica of a reaction fiber of *Acacia podalyriaefolia* (Fig. 15)
two lamellae of the layer S_1 can be seen together with the layer $S_2(G)$.
In the latter two, deformations (slip planes) can be seen. These cell-wall
deformations, which are considered to arise from the operation of compression and shear force, were first described by von Hohnel for phloem
fibers but are also of frequent occurrence in the fibers of normal and reaction wood (Wardrop and Dadswell, 1947).

The physical texture of the SG layer has been investigated in various
ways. From measurement of the radial breadth of the 002 arcs of the
X-ray diffraction diagrams, the crystalline regions (micelles) within the
microfibrils were concluded to be somewhat wider than in normal wood
(Wardrop and Dadswell, 1955). The change in breadth of the 002 line
before and after hydrolysis was approximately the same for both normal
and reaction wood, and from this it was concluded that the magnitude of

---

Fig. 13. *Eucalyptus elaephora.* A carbon replica of the wet surface of a mature
fiber of reaction wood showing the primary wall.

Fig. 14. *Acacia podalyriaefolia.* A carbon replica of a wet section of reaction wood
showing the crossed helical structure of the layer S_1 and the axially oriented microfibrils in the layer $S_2(G)$.

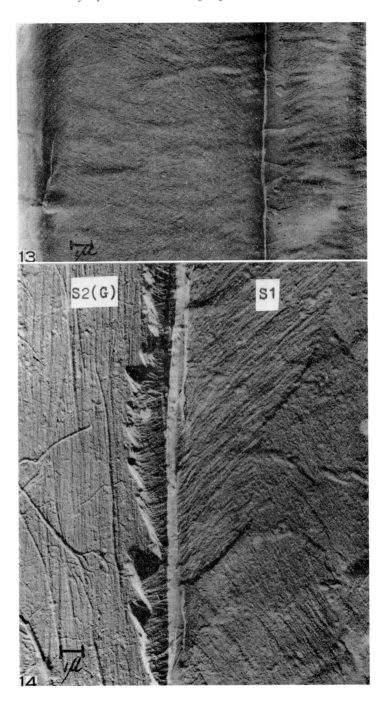

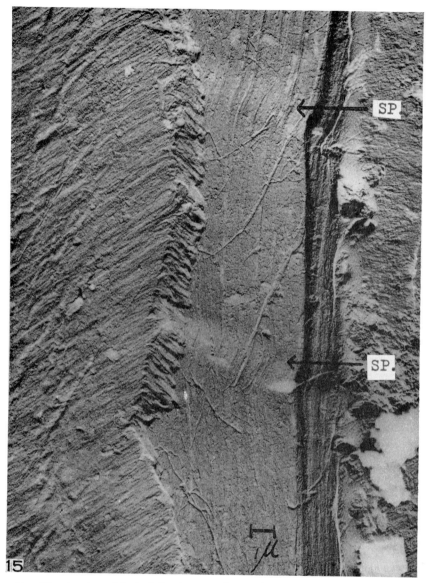

FIG. 15. *Acacia podalyriaefolia*. A wet carbon replica showing two lamellae of the layer S_1 of a fiber and slip planes in the S(G) layer of an adjacent fiber.

FIG. 16. *Liquidambar styraciflua*. A tangential longitudinal section of a reaction wood fiber showing the close tangential association of the microfibrils in the S(G) layer (after removal of the methacrylate embedding medium). (Scurfield and Wardrop, 1962.)

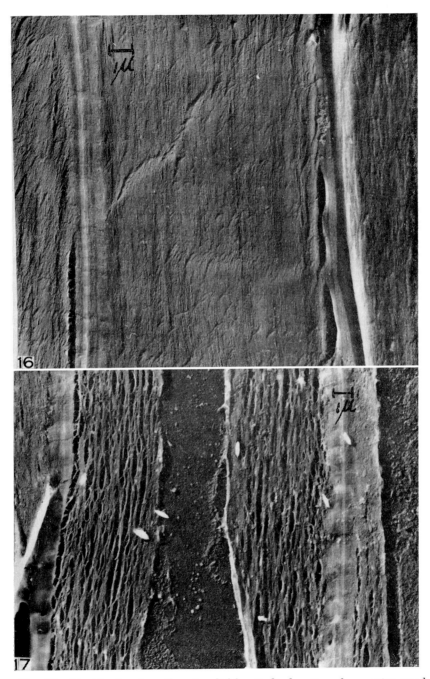

Fig. 17. *Liquidambar styraciflua*. A radial longitudinal section of a reaction wood fiber showing the lamella of the S(G) layer in the radial plane (after removal of the methacrylate embedding medium).

the paracrystalline phase was of the same order in both tissues. Measurements of line breadth in fresh reaction wood after replacement of water by nonpolar solvents indicated that the SG layer was highly crystalline, even before drying.

The X-ray diffraction diagram of reaction xylem is characterized by the large number of reflections recorded and the low dispersion of the 002, 101, 10$\bar{1}$, and 021 arcs. The 021 arc in particular is recorded very strongly (Fig. 18). These differences can be correlated directly with the degree of development of the SG layer. Thus Fig. 18 shows the X-ray diffraction diagram for normal wood (Fig. 18a) and three degrees of development of the layer SG (Figs. 18b–d). The increasing sharpness of the

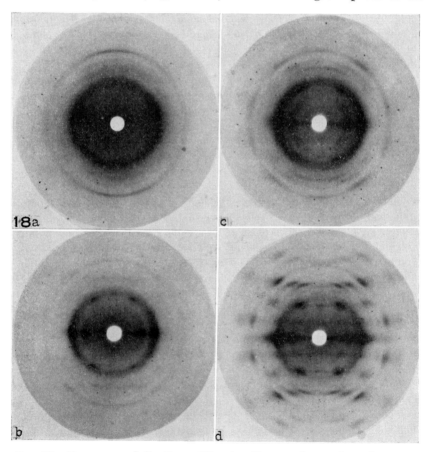

FIG. 18. *Ficus macrophylla.* X-ray diffraction diagram of normal wood (a), and of reaction wood (b–d) in which the S(G) layer was developed to an increasing degree (CuK radiation; Specimen to film distance, 4 cm). (Wardrop and Dadswell, 1955.)

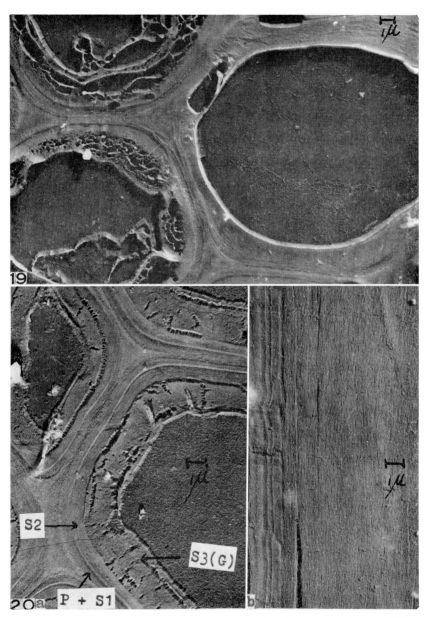

FIG. 19.   *Tristania conferta.* A transverse section showing two reaction wood fibers at left and a normal wood fiber at right. (Methacrylate embedding medium removed). (Scurfield and Wardrop, 1962.)

FIG. 20.   *Acacia podalyriaefolia.* (a) A transverse section of reaction wood fibers in which the S(G) layer appears markedly less disturbed than in Fig. 19; (b) a longitudinal section through the S(G) layer (epoxy embedding medium removed).

equatorial arcs is apparent, so that the diagram of fibers in which the layer S(G) is well developed corresponds with the fiber diagram of normal wood on which that of the axially oriented SG layer is super-imposed.

Jaccard and Frey (1928a) observed that in *Populus alba* the swelling of reaction wood was less than normal wood and that the uptake of water after drying was less than in normal wood, although the initial water content of the reaction wood was greater. In *Eucalyptus regnans*, how-ever, it has been observed that the water content per unit dry weight of reaction wood is less than in normal wood. The equilibrium moisture con-tent of reaction wood is less than normal wood. This is consistent with the measured swelling values of Jaccard and Frey (1928b), and with the higher degree of crystallinity of the SG layer.

It is also consistent with the above observations that on drying the SG layer undergoes extreme and largely irreversible shrinkage (Wardrop and Dadswell, 1955). This may be due in part to the lack of lignification of the layer since similar effects are observed in unlignified hair cells such as cotton. When examined in the electron microscope after metha-crylate embedding the layer appears very porous and shows large spaces between the microfibril aggregates (Fig. 19). This appearance is, how-ever, an artefact (Côté and Day, 1962; Scurfield and Wardrop, 1962). This is demonstrated by the different appearance of the layer in sections cut after embedding in epoxy resins (Araldite, Fig. 20). Thus, in view of the high shrinkage of the layer, the microfibrils must be relatively widely separated from each other in the fresh condition. Observations such as that in Fig. 20, indicate that they are uniformly distributed and this does not necessarily mean that the layer is porous in the sense of possessing large capillary spaces (Sachsse, 1962). The implications of these observations in relation to the observed greater semipermeability of reaction wood (Jaccard and Frey, 1928b) must await further investiga-tion.

III. The Anatomy of Reaction Phloem

That there are changes in the phloem paralleling those taking place during the formation of reaction xylem was first recognized by Metzger (1908). Subsequently Onaka (1949) and Dadswell and Wardrop (1955) observed that the development of reaction xylem was paralleled by a similar eccentric development of reaction phloem on the same side of the stem and that the phloem fibers possess greatly thickened unligni-fied cell walls (Fig. 21a–c), the organization of which differed from that of normal fibers by the extensive development of the layer S_2 (Dadswell and Wardrop, 1956) (Fig. 22).

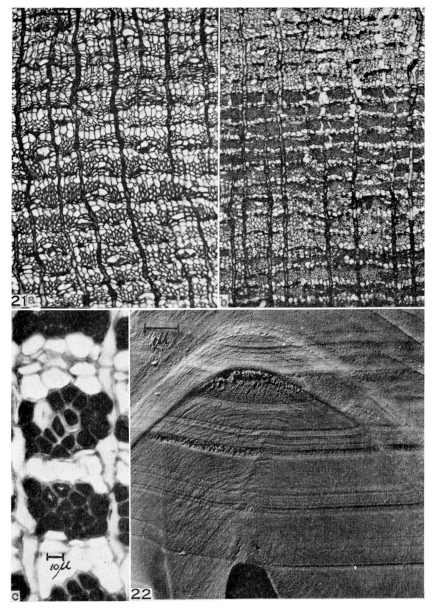

FIG. 21. *Eucalyptus elaeophora.* (a) A transverse section of normal phloem. (b) A transverse section showing two zones of reaction phloem. (c) Reaction phloem fiber stained with chlor-zinc iodide. Note the great development of the layer S_2 (G).

FIG. 22. *Tristania conferta.* An electron micrograph of a transverse section of a reaction phloem fiber showing great development of the layer S_2(G) (cf. Fig. 21c). (Scurfield and Wardrop, 1962.)

The anatomy of reaction phloem in experimental material was studied in greater detail by Scurfield and Wardrop (1962). These studies showed that there was no change in the basic anatomical pattern of the phloem but that there were simply more cells of each type making up the phloem. Thus in *Eucalyptus* the sequence

sieve tubes and companion cells–parenchyma–tannin-containing parenchyma–fibers

was repeated more often on the side of the stem containing reaction xylem. Electron microscopic examination of the reaction phloem fibers confirmed the earlier optical studies (Fig. 22).

IV. The Differentiation of Reaction Wood

1. Cambial Activity and Reaction Wood Formation

Since the development of reaction wood is usually associated with eccentric radial growth of the branch and stem in which it occurs it implied that the development of this tissue is associated with an increase in the duration or rate of cambial activity. Evidence of an increased duration of cambial activity can be obtained from both field and experimental studies. Thus in examination of leaning stems in the field it is frequently observed (Wardrop, 1956) that the bark "slips" on the upper side of the leaning stem before this is apparent on the lower side. Similar phenomena have been observed in branches (Priestley and Tong, 1927). Evidence of the basipetal progress of this activity has also been obtained. That the "slipping" of the cambium reflects the inception of cambial activity has been shown by microscopic examination (Priestley *et al.*, 1933).

That correlative phenomena are involved in the formation of the tissue was shown by the investigations of Priestley and Tong (1927), Onaka (1949, 1950), and Wardrop (1956). Thus it was observed by Onaka (1949) that eccentric growth did not occur in bent stems from which the apex was removed or if a circular incision was made around the stem, and furthermore no recovery of the stem was observed. Wardrop (1956) observed that if a stem was bent for some time and then the apices of the stem and branches were removed, recovery of the stem continued. However, if the apices were removed prior to bending no recovery took place and no reaction wood was formed, until axillary buds became established.

These observations indicate that the site of the stimuli governing geotropic response lies in the apex but once this process has been initiated it can continue at least for a time without the participation of the apex. If some hormone mechanism is assumed after removal of the apex then it is reasonable to suppose that the source of such a hormone may be in the leaves as suggested in the experiments of Onaka (1950) and of Jacobs (1956).

The distribution of auxin in stems and branches undergoing reaction xylem formation under natural conditions does not appear to have been investigated, but Nečesaný (1958) has studied this in artifically bent stems. Ether extracts were made from the differentiating zone from the upper lower sides of a bent stem of *Populus alba* following the method of Luckwill (1952), and the effect of chromatographically separated components of the extracts on the extension or inhibition of coleoptiles of *Triticum aestivum* was measured. It was observed that substances stimulating elongation of the coleoptile sections were present mainly on the lower side (Fig. 23). IAA appeared to be the most important of the stimulating substances. It will be appreciated that the influence of the

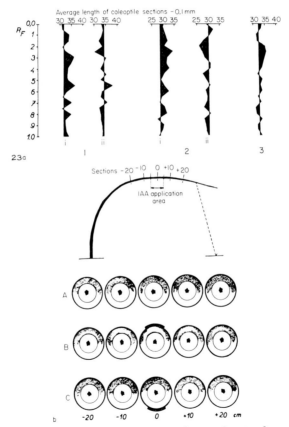

FIG. 23. (a) Chromatographic separation of growth stimulators (right) and growth inhibitors (left of the vertical axis) from the cambium of (1) *Populus alba*, (2) *Pinus sylvestris* (i, lower side, and ii, upper side), (3) chromatograph of IAA solution (100 µg/ml). (Nečesaný, 1958.) (b) The effect of the application of IAA paste to bent stems of *Populus monilifera* (reaction wood, dotted; IAA paste, heavy lines).

substances which enhance or inhibit the elongation of coleoptile sections on the cells of the tissues in which they occur cannot be easily assessed, since their effects on different test tissues may differ. This has been observed in the case of an inhibiting substance extracted from woody shoots by Barlow *et al.* (1959).

Evidence was obtained by Nečesaný (1956, 1958) that the substances extracted may be related to both cell division and cell elongation. Thus he observed that the thickness of callus developed in cuttings from horizontally grown branches was less on the side containing reaction wood. Furthermore roots developed on the side opposite the reaction wood. Nečesaný considered that the greater development of callus on the side opposite the reaction wood could be attributed to a higher concentration of IAA in that region.

Although reaction wood of gymnosperms can be induced by the application of IAA (Wershing and Bailey, 1942), in experiments performed so far on the application of IAA and other substances it has not been possible to induce reaction xylem formation in angiosperms by this means (Onaka, 1949; Wardrop, 1956). However, Nečesaný (1958) observed that when IAA was added to the upper side of stems in which reaction wood was undergoing formation the further formation of this tissue was reduced, at least for a time (Fig. 23a). The application of IAA to the lower side of such stems was without effect on reaction wood formation. It was observed further that the fiber length was least on the side of IAA application, so that if it is accepted on the basis of Nečesaný's observations that the formation of reaction wood results from a differential distribution of IAA and other growth-regulating substances in the stem, it would be expected that the fiber length would be greater in the reaction wood than in the xylem opposite it. This would be in agreement with the observations of Nečesaný (1955a), Ollinmaa (1959), and Onaka (1949) reported above.

Insofar as eccentricity of radial growth is associated with the formation of reaction wood, it is apparent that the development of this tissue is determined in the first phase of differentiation, that is, at the phase of cell division in the cambium. This is also apparent in the rapid differentiation of vessels which are reduced both in size and number compared with those of normal wood and in the fact that the differentiation of the phloem is also modified (see below). The experiments of Casperson (1960) also support this conclusion.

It has been observed that, unless the degree of lignification of the cell-wall layers other than the layer SG is modified, there is little to distinguish reaction wood fibers until differentiation of this layer begins. In investigations to this stage there is no indication of the reason for the formation, especially in stems, of the compact (Fig. 5) or the diffuse type of reaction wood (Fig. 6).

2. THE DEVELOPMENT OF THE S(G) LAYER

The S(G) layer is first apparent as an unlignified, sometimes convoluted, layer lying adjacent to the layers S_1, S_2 or rarely the layer S_3 of the secondary wall (Fig. 24) (Scurfield and Wardrop, 1962). The differentiation of fibers containing this layer is prolonged. This is apparent in the persistence of the protoplast in reaction wood fibers compared with those on the opposite side of the stem. In fibers in which the S(G) layer is not convoluted, it shows a progressive thickening until the lumen of the cell may be almost completely filled. In fibers in which the layer shows convolution (Fig. 24), it is observed to thicken in the convoluted form and then to straighten on to the existing cell wall and this is then followed by the development of a further convoluted part of the layer which subsequently is also straightened and deposited on the existing part of the S(G) layer (Fig. 24). In some species, however, such as *Acacia*, the S(G) layer retains its convoluted form even in mature cells (Fig. 10).

It was shown by Scurfield and Wardrop (1962) that before the straightening of the convoluted layer was complete it often showed slight birefringence which was absent in mature cells and could be reduced or eliminated by dehydration in alcohol. Furthermore, in the differentiating fibers it was observed that the inner part of the S(G) layer stained more intensely with basic dyes, such as light green (this was also the case with the fibers of reaction phloem), and with Congo red. In mature fibers the intensity of staining with Congo red was greatly reduced.

The latter observation may be explained in terms of a change in texture of the layer. Thus from the studies of Wälchli (1947) it is known that Congo red exists in the form of micelles, the size of which is determined in part by the solvent, so that the intensity of staining will be at least partly determined by the magnitude of the intermicrofibrillar regions. If it is assumed that the microfibrils increase in their degree of crystallinity during maturation of the cell wall, for example by crystallization of the surrounding paracrystalline phase; and that this results in an increase in the density of packing of the microfibrils, then the decreased intensity of staining in the older regions of the layer could be explained. Such a change may involve synaeresis of a paracrystalline phase and might be expected to take place in its most extreme form in the cells showing initial convolution of the S(G) layer. Since this process would involve crystallization, this change would be expected to be irreversible except under conditions which invoke disruption of the hydrogen bonds between adja-

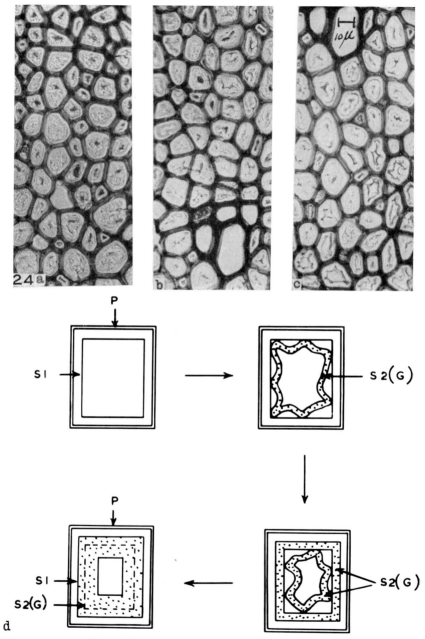

FIG. 24. *Grevillea robusta*. Ultraviolet photomicrographs of transverse sections showing three steps (a–c) in the development of the layer $S_2(G)$ in this species. The decreasing degree of convolution of this layer is apparent (Scurfield and Wardrop, 1962). A diagrammatic representation of the development of the layer $S_2(G)$ is shown in (d).

cent molecules. In this context it is of interest to note that Onaka (1949) has observed that the unconvoluted S(G) layers of mature cells become convoluted when swollen in reagents such as nitric acid.

If the above hypothesis of the changed staining with Congo red is correct, it might also be anticipated that the crystallization taking place would lead to an enhanced degree of perfection of molecular orientation and would result in the decreased birefringence of the S(G) layer in transverse section. It would also be anticipated that such a change would lead to the secretion of the freed water into the cell vacuole.

3. Lignification of Reaction Wood

The pattern of lignification during reaction wood formation is basically similar to that observed in normal wood. Thus, after the surface growth of the differentiating fibers is complete, the deposition of lignin can be seen near the corners of the adjacent fibers in either the cell wall or middle lamella (Wardrop, 1957). Lignification may then extend to the layer S_1, S_2 and any other of the secondary wall layers present in the particular cell. With the deposition of the S(G) layer, however, little or no lignification of this layer takes place, so that in the fully differentiated cells it shows almost no ultraviolet absorption (Fig. 11). The absorbing terminal lamella may be observed lining the lumen in carefully prepared sections (Figs. 8, 12).

Measurement of the absorption in lignified regions of normal and reaction wood cells shows that usually the amount of lignin in the whole cell wall is less in the reaction wood fibers. This has been confirmed by chemical analyses of corresponding tissues (Jayne, 1951; Wardrop and Dadswell, 1948). This overall reduction in lignification of reaction wood has been suggested by Dadswell and Wardrop (1956) to be a more fundamental change in the differentiation of the tissue than the associated modifications in anatomy which occur, since it may be seen even in species in which the layer S(G) does not develop.

It may be noted that Bland (1958a) has found no significant differences between the lignin of reaction and normal wood of angiosperms, but the lignin of the wood opposite the reaction wood differed in its methoxyl content and in the ratio of syringyl to guaiacyl nuclei. Evidence was also obtained by Bland (1958b) that the mechanical association of lignin with the other wall contituents was different in reaction wood from that in the wood opposite to it.

The above observations relate especially to those cases in which the S(G) layer appeared to be of uniform texture. However, as already pointed out this layer in some species contains ultraviolet absorbing bands within it (Fig. 12). Such bands do not give conclusive staining reactions for lignin, although this could be due to the small amount of absorbing substances present. The observations of Scurfield and Wardrop (1962) showed that they stain with permanganate but are not associated with changes in microfibril orientation (Fig. 25). Examination of fixed material in which the convoluted S(G) layer was in the process of flattening against the existing wall showed the presence of permanganate-staining material but this could not be shown to be of cytoplasmic origin.

In some mature cells ultraviolet absorption adjacent the lumen was apparent (Figs. 8, 26). Recent observations (Scurfield and Wardrop, 1963) are not conclusive as to whether it is due entirely to lignin or results from the diffusion of ultraviolet-absorbing substances into the wall as a consequence of a progressive breakdown of the plasmalemma. Staining reactions such as the phloroglucinol-HCl stain and the Coppick and Fowler stain do not give conclusive results on this point.

Evidence that the plasmalemma tends to break down releasing diffusible cytoplasmic constituents into the wall is likewise inconclusive, but it may be noted that in ultraviolet photomicrographs of formalin-fixed material the "terminal lamella" appears less well defined in the fibers of reaction wood compared with those of normal wood.

Thus in the normal cells, C, of the section shown in Fig. 8 the terminal lamella can be seen as a sharp absorbing line adjacent the lumen. In the reaction wood cells, D, showing absorption in the S(G) layer the terminal lamella appears less well defined and the wall shows a zone of absorption surrounding it. This is also apparent in Fig. 26. In the cells showing no absorption in the S(G) layer, Cell B of Fig. 8, the boundary of the S_2 and $S_3(G)$ layers is marked by a sharp line of absorption resembling the terminal lamella in the normal cells. In electron micrographs analogous effects have been observed. Although these results suggest that the absorption in the S(G) layer adjacent to the lumen may result from the diffusion of cytoplasmic components into the wall the elucidation of this point must await cytological examination.

A further feature of the S(G) layer is that it often shows an intense peroxidase activity which may persist after the formation of reaction wood has ceased. This was first observed by Wardrop and Scaife (1956) and more recently has been studied further in this laboratory by Scurfield and Wardrop (1963). In the differentiating wood the peroxidase activity is high in the cambium and then, as normal wood, decreases in cells of increasing maturity. At first the S(G) layers give little or no staining when the benzidene-peroxidase reaction is used. However, as the layer develops it shows an increased intensity of staining which is greater in the mature cells. It thus appears that the pattern of peroxidase distribution in the differentiating reaction xylem is similar to that in normal xylem, but with the development of the S(G) layer renewed peroxidase activity begins. Although the reason for the enhanced peroxidase activity of the S(G) layer in the concluding stages of its develop-

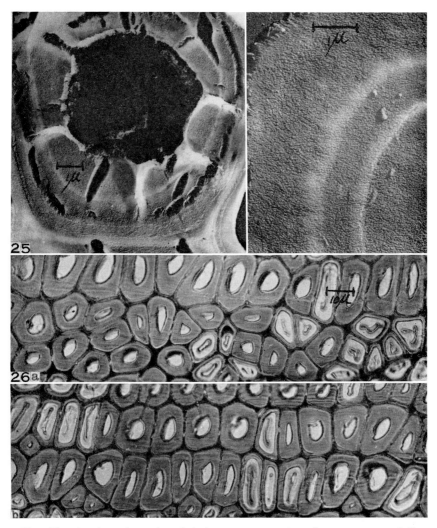

Fig. 25. *Acacia melanoxylon.* (a) A transverse section of a reaction wood fiber stained with potassium permanganate and showing the heterogeneous structure of the layer $S_2(G)$. This is shown at greater magnification in (b). In (a) it can be seen that the region of intense staining does not correspond to a difference in microfibril orientation. (Scurfield and Wardrop, 1962.)

Fig. 26. (a and b). Transverse section of two areas of diffuse reaction wood photographed in ultraviolet light, showing zones of diffuse ultraviolet absorption adjacent to the lumina.

ment is unknown it is an interesting speculation that this may be associated with the increased ultraviolet absorption of the wall and may indicate the diffusion of peroxidase from the cytoplasm along with other cytoplasmic components. In other studies (Wardrop and Davies, 1959) it was shown that, with the use of the model system of eugenol-peroxide-peroxidase of Siegel (1953), normal differentiating xylem showed increased ultraviolet absorption in the partly differentiated xylem and cambium zone, after reaction with eugenol and peroxide. In our investigations so far it has not been possible to effect lignification of the S(G) layer in this artificial system in the same way. It was noted that the benzidene reaction was not obtained in the reaction wood after heating sections to 100°C in water. However, it was still obtained, although in reduced intensity, in the cambium zone, so that some difference between the substances giving the benzidene reaction in the reaction wood and in the cambium is possible. With triphenyltetrazolium chloride a positive reaction was observed in the cambium, but not in the S(G) layer of the reaction wood fibers.

Although the reason for the absence or reduction of lignification of the SG layer and its failure to lignify in artificial systems has not been found, there are a number of possible causes which may be considered. Among these is the possibility that the substance giving the positive benzidene reaction in the SG layer was not peroxidase, or that the carbohydrate substrate of the SG layer was unsuitable for the reaction to proceed, as has been established in some artificial systems by Siegel (1956). Again, in the natural system there is the possibility that substances inhibiting lignification, such as ascorbic acid or the reduced form of glutathione detected by Higuchi (1955), were present, or that there was a deficiency of lignin precursors.

In natural systems the possibility that the lignification of the reaction wood is inhibited by a deficiency of lignin precursor has been investigated by Correns (1961) and by Wergin (1961). Correns suggested that the inhibition of lignification was due to a lack of precursor at the most critical point in lignin synthesis from carbohydrate, viz., the formation of the aromatic nucleus in the shikimic acid pathway. He therefore treated chestnut plants which were actively forming reaction wood by raising the bark and placing small quantities of quinic acid in contact with the differentiating xylem. It was observed that for a time the formation of reaction wood was inhibited and normal lignified fibers were formed. With substances nearer lignin on the path of synthesis no inhibition of the reaction wood formation was observed, so that Correns concluded that the entire synthetic mechanism of lignification beyond and including the formation of the aromatic nucleus was absent.

The effect of quinic acid has been investigated further by Wergin (1961), who injected quinic acid, phosphate buffer, and, distilled water through the leaves of chestnut plants which were bent to induce reaction wood formation. It was observed that there was an inhibition of reaction wood formation with each of the solutions so that normal xylem was formed near the point of injection, but no inhibition was observed lower in the stem. These results thus conflict with those of Correns, and Wergin concluded that the inhibition of lignification in reaction wood did not result from a deficiency of precursor.

Although as pointed out above the level of lignification in reaction wood formed under natural conditions is low, Priestley and Tong (1927) have reported an experiment in which lignification of this tissue was induced. A number of 3-year-old plants of *Acer* were allowed to grow with the stem horizontal for a period of 6 weeks. The plants were then rotated through 180° so that the side previously uppermost faced downwards. On examination four weeks later the broad band of wood formed during the first treatment was throughly lignified. Later Wardrop (1957) performed a similar type of experiment in which vertically growing stems were deflected first in one direction for an extended period and then in the opposite direction. Using staining reactions, however, he obtained no evidence of lignification of the reaction wood formed during the first treatment. More recently Scurfield and Wardrop (1963) have carried out essentially similar experiments to those of Priestley and Tong and from the change in ultraviolet absorption of the S(G) layer it was apparent that some lignification occurred.

These observations obviously support the contention of Freudenberg that there is a centripetal diffusion of a lignin precursor into the differentiating xylem. Priestley and Tong (1927) concluded on the basis of their experiments that, while gravity influences the activity of the cambium associated with the formation of reaction wood, the process of lignification is affected independently, and proceeds most rapidly on the lower side of the inclined stems and branches. In this context the chemical differences between the lignin of the reaction wood and the wood opposite to it described by Bland (1958a, b) are of particular interest.

From the above discussion the need for further investigation of the process of lignification in reaction xylem is apparent, especially in relation to the causes of decreased lignification, the role of IAA, and the relation of this process to the increased synthesis of polysaccharides involved in the development of the S(G) layer.

V. Investigations Relating to the Causes of Reaction Wood Formation and Its Function

As pointed out above, reaction wood usually occurs on the upper side of leaning stems and branches (Fig. 3). However, surveys of plants growing under a variety of natural conditions show that in stems the reaction wood may vary greatly in its tangential distribution in successive growth rings, and similarly the degree of eccentricity of growth rings is very variable (Jaccard, 1938). In branches the reaction wood may be found on the lower side of branches growing under natural conditions. Even in apparently straight trees reaction wood is usually found at some point in the stem as well as the branches. This is illustrated for a 2-year-old stem of *Eucalyptus goniocalyx* shown in Fig. 27. This tree, which had grown in the open, leaned about 10° in the southwest in the main part of the stem although the apex was vertical. The changing tangential distribution of the reaction wood in the stem is illustrated in Fig. 27b and in general tended to be concentrated in the northeast sector of the growth ring, i.e., on the side opposite the direction in which the tree was leaning. In the branches, reaction wood distribution was variable and, although usually present on the upper side, it was observed on both their upper and lower sides in many instances. It will be apparent that an understanding of the distribution of reaction wood in stems and branches under natural and experimental conditions will depend on a knowledge of the environmental and intrinsic factors which cause its formation, as well as a knowledge of the way in which its formation is involved in movements of orientation. Both of these questions are considered in the following sections of this discussion.

1. Evidence Relating to Possible Factors Causing Reaction Wood Formation

(a) *Reaction Wood Formation as a Stress Response.* From the observed distribution of reaction wood, it was proposed by Metzger (1908) that reaction wood formation resulted from tension stresses on the upper side of branches and leaning stems, and this led him to describe the wood so formed as *Zugholz.* The corresponding term "tension wood" has been widely used to describe this tissue. The view that reaction wood was a response to stress was supported by the observation that this tissue was induced in 7–14 days when branches were weighted or stems were bent out of their normal vertical position.

Much early work on the effects of tensile stersses on plant anatomy and growth is relevant to the idea that these forces induce reaction wood formation. Thus Vöchting (1908) observed that the development of mechanical tissue was enhanced in the petioles of squash fruits which were allowed to hang on the vine as compared with that of the petioles of fruits resting on the ground. Burch (1912) and Haberlandt (1914) observed that the development of mechanical tissue was greater in tendrils experimentally loaded during growth. It was further observed by Rasdorsky (1925) that stems of *Helianthus* which were grown supported

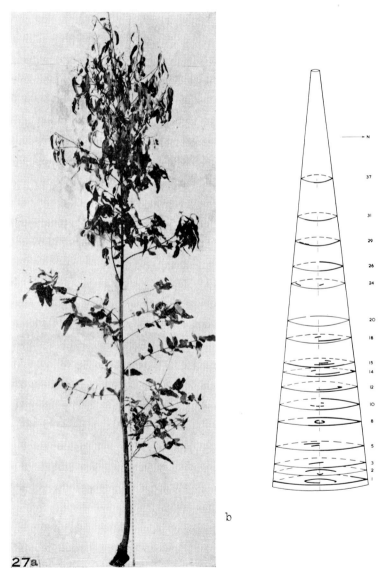

FIG. 27. *Eucalyptus goniocalyx.* (a) a young tree which was growing in open country and leaning ca. 10° to the southwest. The distribution of reaction wood in the stem is shown in (b).

so that there was no pressure of the stem at the base did not develop sufficient mechanical tissue to maintain the stem in an erect position when the supports were removed. The effect of tensile stresses was investigated by Bucher (1906), who found that when a growing shoot was kept horizontal the cells on the upper side were smaller and thicker than those on the lower side. Vöchting (1908) also observed that, when a plant was placed in a horizontal position and weights were hung on its end, there was a considerable increase in the cross section of the stem. The early experiments of Knight (1811) are also relevant to the possible influence of mechanical stimuli on xylem development. Jacobs (1939) observed that, in stayed trees, the portion of the stem allowed to sway in the wind grew more rapidly than the region of the stem in which movement was prevented. More recently Setterfield (1959) has observed that, in young bean plants which were grown horizontally in glass tubes, the cortical cells on the upper side possess thicker cell walls in which the cellulose microfibrils are axially oriented, whereas the cortical cells on the lower side have thinner cell walls, and in these the microfibrils are oriented almost transversely.

Evidence such as the above suggests that conditions of tension existing in leaning stems or in branches and resulting from their weight could be a factor inducing the abnormal characteristics of the wood now recognized as reaction wood. However, it will be apparent that the weight of the stem and branches is really an indirect manifestation of the influence of gravity and the possibility of a direct gravitational influence was therefore investigated.

(b) *Reaction Xylem Formation as a Gravitational Response.* Experiments suggesting that gravity may influence the formation of reaction xylem in gymnosperms were carried out by Ewart and Mason-Jones (1906), in angiosperms by Jaccard (1919, 1938) and Onaka (1949), and more recently by Hartmann (1949). It was observed that when plants are grown at increasing angles from the vertical, the reaction wood forms consistently on the upper side of the inclined stems and increases up to an angle of inclination of 90° and then decreases again, no reaction wood being formed when the stem is pointing vertically downwards. In a field study it was observed by Berlyn (1961) that the amount of reaction wood formed in stems of *Populus deltiodes* was positively correlated with the degree of lean of the trees.

A second type of observation was that made by Jaccard (1938) and by Burns (1942) in which stems and branches were bent into vertical and horizontal loops. In these experiments it was observed that the reaction wood formed on the upper side of the vertical loops (Fig. 28a) irrespective of whether it was placed initially in tension or compression.

In a detailed study of such loops in white ash it was observed (Burns, 1942) that the stem was eccentric toward the upper side at both the top and the bottom of the loops. Furthermore, the fibers on the upper side, at both the top and bottom of the loops, were longer and had thicker

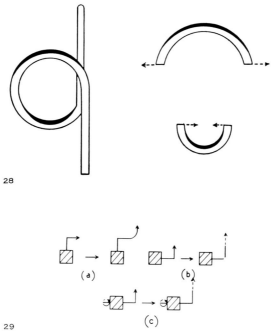

28

29

FIG. 28. A diagrammatic representation of the distribution of reaction wood in loops made in angiosperm stems. The reaction wood was formed on the upper side of the loops irrespective of whether the stem was placed initially in tension or compression. At the right the movement of the upper and lower segments of the loop observed when cut horizontally is shown. (Aften Jaccard, 1938).

FIG. 29. A diagrammatic representation illustrating various experiments on reaction wood formation in *Tristania conferta*. (a) Stem bent horizontally and allowed to recover; reaction wood was present along the entire upper side of the horizontal regions and at both bends. (b) Stem bent so that the apex remained vertical; reaction wood was present along the upper side of the horizontal region to the bend. (c) As (b) but the plant was placed on a horizontal klinostat; no reaction wood was formed.

walls, and were less distorted at their tips than those on the lower side. In horizontal loops, it was observed by Jaccard (1938) that the eccentricity was toward the upper side and that reaction wood also was present in that position. These observations were interpreted to mean that gravity is a predominant stimulus governing the formation of reaction wood. Further evidence of the possible influence of gravity on reaction wood formation was obtained by Jaccard (1939, 1940), who studied the anatomical changes in stems subjected to centrifugal force which could, under the conditions of the experiment, be made to wholly or partially counteract the force of gravity. The plants were placed on the perimeter of a horizontally rotating disk. It was observed that the growth proceeded so that curvature toward the center of the disk took place and that the tissue formed on the inner surface of the stems resembled reaction wood. Thus a similar response was observed in the wood when the gravitational force was replaced by a continuous centrifugal force.

Apart from the early experiments on gymnosperms by White (1908) little use of klinostats appears to have been made in studies of reaction wood formation. However, in recent studies in this laboratory the experiment illustrated in Fig. 29 was carried out. Plants were bent so that the tip was placed in a position at right angles to the axis but was left free to recover. When such a plant was left in an upright position the tip showed positive geotropic response and reaction wood was formed on the upper side of the horizontal part of the stem and at both points of bending.

When a plant treated in this way was placed horizontally with its tips bent into a vertical position (Fig. 30b) reaction wood was formed on the upper side of the horizontal part of the stem. Again when a plant treated as in Fig. 30a was placed on a horizontal klinostat (1 revolution per 25 minutes) (Fig. 30c) no change in orientation of the apex occurred and no reaction xylem was formed. In these experiments stress was applied at the bend in the stem, but unless a continuous gravitational stimulus was operative no reaction wood was formed.

This series of experiments (Fig. 30a–c) is consistent with the view that gravity is a dominant factor governing the formation of reaction wood.

(c) *Reaction Wood Formation as an Intrinsic Growth Response.* Although the experiments in the preceding section indicate that gravity is a major factor conditioning the formation of reaction wood, some observations on the distribution of reaction wood in branches cannot be explained readily in terms of a gravitational stimulus.

Of special interest is the observation made first by Jaccard (1919) and Hartmann (1949) and since confirmed by Wardrop (1956) and by Dyer (1955). Thus, if a branch was displaced obliquely downwards (Fig. 30) reaction wood was formed on the upper side. If, however, the branch was displaced upwards (Fig. 30), reaction wood was formed on the lower side.

In both of these experiments the orientation of the branch was altered in relation to the gravitational field, but unlike the results of stems bent into loops (Fig. 28) the position of the reaction wood was not constant, so that if stress is not a determining factor it must be assumed that some intrinsic factor governing the orientation of the branch to the stem must be involved.

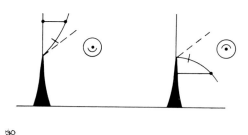

30

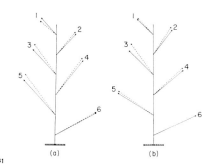

31

(a) (b)

Fig. 30. Different reaction wood distribution when branches are bent (a) upwards and (b) downwards.

Fig. 31. A diagrammatic representation of the orientation movements of branches in young trees of *Liquidambar styraciflua* in which the apical shoot had been removed. (a) Grown vertically; (b) grown on a horizontal klinostat, but the branch position was determined while the plant was standing vertically. The broken lines indicate the initial and the full line the final position of the branches after 4 months' growth.

The nature of such an intrinsic factor has been considered by Hartmann (1949). From the above type of observation Hartmann postulated that for each branch there exists an "intrinsic growth direction" and that the formation of the reaction wood was induced when the orientation of the branch in relation to the stem was changed from this direction. A similar concept has been discussed by other investigators.

Thus Jost (1907) proposed that there exists for the different organs of the plant "a condition of rest," which, if altered by its own growth or by environmental changes, results in a response by the plant in such a way as to restore this condition. A similar idea is contained in the use by Büsgen and Münch (1929) of the term "reaction norm" of a tree, or of its branches in relation to its stem, and Jaccard's recognition (1938) of a "proper spatial setting" of a branch or stem.

If in the growth of the tree it is accepted that there exists an "intrinsic growth direction" of the branches in relation to the stem it follows that, when the orientation of a branch is disturbed from this direction, it is also changed in relation to the gravitational field. Since the experiments described above indicate that reaction wood formation may be induced by both of these factors, the extent of formation of the tissue would be expected to be the resultant of their interaction.

The concept on an "intrinsic growth direction" would involve the assumption that this direction would change during the development of the plant. Furthermore, the removal of the apex, which involves a change in the form of the tree, would involve an alteration in the "intrinsic growth direction" of the branches. The question arises, however, of to what extent the "intrinsic growth direction" is an expression of the organization of the plant and to what extent it is itself determined by the gravitational field.

In view of these questions some preliminary observations have been made on the relation of reaction wood formation to orientation movements in branches of *Liquidambar styraciflua*. Over a period of 3 months it was observed in actively growing 2-year-old plants that the uppermost branch showed a slight movement toward the axis, but all the lower branches moved away from the axis.

To explore these changes further, four 2-year-old plants were treated to remove the apical shoot (ca. 15 cm in length) approximately 4 cm above the first lateral branch. One pair of the plants was allowed to grow with the stem in its normal vertical position. The second pair was placed on a horizontal klinostat. During the succeeding 4 months the angle of orientation of the branches to the stem was determined and the final positions are indicated in Fig. 31. In the vertical plants the topmost branch, 1, showed strong reorientation toward a vertical position and the formation of reaction wood on its upper side continued through the period of the experiment (Fig. 32). In branches 2–6 slight downward orientation occurred and there was slight reaction wood formation on the lower side early in the experiments, but normal wood was being formed at the conclusion of the experiment. In the plants on the klinostats the topmost branch, 1, showed a slight downward movement when the plant was placed vertically, but no reaction wood could be detected. In branches 2–6 the behavior of the branches was similar to that in the vertical plants with respect to both their direction of orientation movement and the presence of a small amount of reaction wood on the lower side.

In assessing the above observations it will be clear that in the klino-stat-treated plants the effect of the gravitational field was not made as uniform as when a stem is rotated about its own axis, but the direction of the gravitational field was changed compared with the vertical plants.

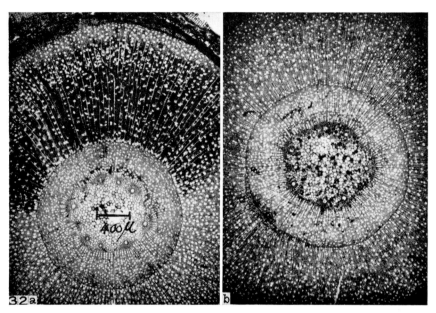

FIG. 32. (a) A transverse section of the topmost branch of a plant treated as in Fig. 31a showing strong reaction wood formation. (b) A similar section cut from a branch of a plant treated as in Fig. 32b and containing no reaction wood.

It is clear that in the decapitated plants all but the uppermost branch behaved as in the vertical intact plants, and the change in the gravitational stimulus in relation to the stem over the duration of the observations was affected only in the degree of negative geotropism of the upper-most branch. The formation of the reaction wood in the decapitated plants was greatest in the uppermost branch of the vertical plants. In all branches the distribution of reaction wood appeared to be conditioned by the sign of the geotropic movement which occurred.

If the assumption of apical dominance by the topmost branch is to be regarded as an intrinsic response by the plant directed toward the maintenance of the form of the tree, the above observations suggest that this effect is conditioned strongly by the gravitational field and does not reflect an intrinsic pattern of growth by the plant which is independent of gravity. On the other hand, the distribution of the reaction wood was in general related to the direction of movement of the branches in the vertical plants, and was not consistent in relation to the gravitational field. In other words, the above observations suggest that the degree of reaction wood formation and its distribution in the branch are related to the sign of the geotropic movement in the part of the branch in which it occurs. This movement does not appear necessarily related to the orientation of the apex.

2. The Relation of Reaction Wood Formation to Movements of Orientation

In the preceding discussion it has been shown that in many species there is a correlation between the development of a more or less characteristic reaction anatomy and movements of orientation.

Examples of this are seen when stems are displaced from the vertical position under both natural and experimental conditions (Fig. 1). Such movement with associated reaction wood formation can also be seen in observations such as that of Hartmann (Fig. 2) and in the response of branches when the apex is removed (Fig. 31). However, it should be pointed out that there exist in different species alternative forms of behavior in response to a particular environmental change. Thus, although many stems show a slow apparently geotropic bending, when the axis is displaced from the vertical in other species this bending may not occur and a new growing apex is established by the growth of axillary or epicormic buds (Wareing and Nasr, 1961). In such species reaction wood is not formed (Onaka, 1949). This behavior is common in shrubs but it may be induced in species normally showing gradual recovery of the axis, such as *Eucalyptus*, by bending the apex downwards beyond the horizontal position. A great growth of epicormic shoots then takes place; one of these assumes dominance and the original axis shows no recovery. However, in stems and branches showing regular development of reaction wood, the question arises whether the formation of the tissue causes the orientation movements of the axis or branch or whether it is formed as a result of the orientation movement which has taken place. This involves consideration of whether the development of the reaction wood forms part of or reflects a growth mechanism of the plant or whether its formation is morphogenetically determined in the cambium as a response by the plant to meet a need in its further development. This latter view implies a quality of directiveness toward an end in the formation of this tissue such as has been recognized in the development of many organisms and discussed extensively by Russell (1945). In studies of reaction wood formation both of these views have been advanced and some consideration may be given to the evidence on which they are based.

(*a*) *The Development of Reaction Wood as a Cause of Movements of Orientation.* Several lines of investigation suggest that the develop-

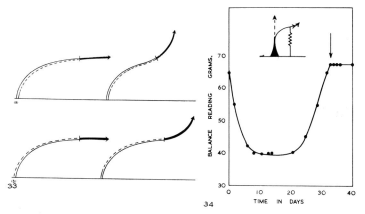

Fig. 33. The effect of destroying the cambium on geotropic bending of horizontally growing stems. (a) Cambium removed from the lower side. (b) Cambium removed from the upper side of the stem.

Fig. 34. A graph showing the change in load on a spring balance during geotropic recovery of a young tree of *Liquidambar styraciflua* treated as shown in the diagram. Note the initial stress relaxation in the stem followed by a period of rapid recovery which was accompanied by reaction wood formation. At the point marked by the arrow the buds were removed and the tree was defoliated, and the stem was artificially loaded to compensate for the loss in weight of the leaves.

ment of the reaction wood in the stem or branch can result in movements of orientation. Thus, as pointed out above, there appears to be a general association of the development of reaction anatomy with such movements.

Although the distribution of reaction wood has been studied under a wide variety of conditions in which movement may be assumed, there are relatively few instances in which its formation has been correlated with measurements demonstrating such movements (Figs. 2 and 31). For stems displaced from the vertical the correlation was shown in the experiments of Jacobs (1939) and of Wardrop (1956) and in the young plant shown in Fig 1. In further experiments it was also observed by Wardrop (1956) that, if stems were bent into a horizontal position and the cambium was removed from the upper side of the stem (Fig. 33), no recovery took place in the wounded area, i.e., the region in which reaction wood would be expected to develop. If, however, the cambium was damaged on the lower side of the bent stem, recovery was not inhibited. This observation suggests that for recovery to take place it is necessary only that the cambium be active on the stimulated upper side of the stem which is responsible for reaction wood formation.

Observations such as the above point to a correlation of reaction wood formation with movements of orientation. If the formation of reaction wood is to be regarded as the cause of such movements then a mechanism by which such movements are effected must be sought.

In the investigations of Jaccard (1938), and later those of Münch (1938) and of Jacobs (1939), it was demonstrated that the formation of reaction wood was associated with the development of considerable growth stresses. Thus it was observed in normal vertically growing stems that, if a segment of the stem was removed from the tree and sectioned longitudinally, the outermost sections contracted in length while those passing through or near the center of the stem elongated so that the center of the stem was in a state of compression relative to the outside of the stem. When stems containing reaction wood were examined in this way, it was found that the contraction of the reaction wood was very much greater than that of the tissues adjacent or opposite to it. From this it may be concluded that, within the stem, this tissue was present in a state of high longitudinal tension. The existence of such stresses is also demonstrated by the observation that when sections removed in the manner described above are heated in water further contraction occurs which is greater in the reaction wood than in normal wood.

An additional demonstration of the development of growth stresses associated with reaction formation was made by Jaccard (1938). He observed that, when stems or branches were bent in the form of loops and allowed to grow for an extended period (Fig. 28), if these loops were cut the upper segment extended, while the lower segment contracted, presumably as a result of the reaction wood formation. The existence of such stresses was suggested by Münch to be the cause of movements of orientation in woody stems, and he considered that the longitudinal contraction of the reaction wood caused a mechanical bending of the stem. Münch (1938b) compared the contraction in woody stems with other known contractile systems in plants such as the contractile roots of some species. The extent, however, to which such a comparison is valid remains to be demonstrated.

From the microscopic structure of reaction wood fibers and in view of the swollen appearance of the S(G) layer, it was proposed by Münch that this layer exerted a pressure on the outer region of the secondary cell wall which, because of its helical organization, was caused to contract in a longitudinal direction, thus giving rise to the growth stresses.

Some observations which may give support to this hypothesis are contained in the work of Scurfield and Wardrop (1962), in which it was observed (Fig. 24) that during differentiation of the reaction wood the S(G) layer, which initially showed some convolution, gradually straightened out onto the already formed cell wall. It will be recalled that this was explained by the assumption that the S(G) layer was deposited in the partially crystalline condition, that crystallization of the cellulose took place during aging of the cell wall, and that this was reflected in the changed staining with Congo red and the decreased birefringence of the S(G) layer. Such crystallization of the cellulose would result in water being secreted in the cell vacuole and this would enhance further flattening of the convoluted layer against the cell wall. Such a change, while appearing broadly consistent with Münch's hypothesis, however, does not explain the fact that in some species, e.g., *Acacia*, the S(G) layer retains this convoluted form even when the cells are mature (Fig. 10).

Although the means by which the stress is generated in reaction wood is not clear, the existence of such stresses could provide a possible means by which movement of stems and branches could be effected. However, it will be appreciated that growth stresses demonstrated in mature tissues are present even when the cells are dead, so that if the bending of the stem resulted from the operation of such forces then this process would be expected to be a cumulative one depending on the amount of reaction wood formed and would be expected to continue at least for a time when the cambium was inactive. To test such a view a number of stems were bent downwards and held in a horizontal position by a spring balance (Fig. 34) in the manner previously described by Wardrop (1956). The subsequent movements of the stem could be followed by the reading on the balance. The curve obtained for one such tree is shown in Fig. 34. The initial decrease in the values of the balance reading resulted from relaxation of stress in the stem following the initial bending. With the progressive development of reaction wood, recovery began. After 30 days, when the stem was showing rapid recovery, all leaves and buds were removed, or it was injected with poisons and the leaves were removed. The loss in weight due to this treatment was offset by attaching weights to the stem to give the balance reading recorded before defoliation. After this treatment no further recovery was observed so it was concluded that the active participation of the differentiating reaction wood was necessary for recovery to occur. This experiment does not preclude the possibility that active stresses causing recovery are generated during differentiation of reaction wood, but suggests that the accumulated stresses demonstrated in mature tissues are not a major factor influencing movements of orientation.

(*b*) *Development of Reaction Wood as a Result of Movements of Orientation*. In some investigations the view has been taken that, although the development of reaction anatomy is associated with orientation movements, the development of these tissues resulted from such movements rather than causing them. Thus, Frey-Wyssling (1952) proposed that the stem or branch of a tree should be regarded as a viscoelastic body capable of deformation under stress over prolonged periods of time, i.e., the members of the plant undergo creep. Frey-Wyssling pointed out that, this being so, the forces necessary to deform the branch or stem would be very much less than the forces expected on the basis of the strength properties of the wood. He suggested that forces arising in the cambium and acting over a prolonged period would be sufficient to bring about such mechanical bending of the stem, and proposed that the development of reaction wood was to be regarded as a response by the tree serving to maintain the new orientation of the stem. It was also pointed out that the organization of reaction wood fibers appeared to be an adaption of normal fiber structure which would resist such tensile stresses. This view did not, however, appear feasible in view of the experiments shown in Fig. 33, in which recovery of bent stems from which the cambium had been removed on the lower side was shown to take place. Such recovery could only result from an active contraction of the tissues on the upper side of the stem. More recently, however, the work of Casperson (1960) on seedlings of *Aesculus* has suggested that the formation of reaction wood may not govern the growth responses by the plant. In this work it was shown that, in the epicotyls of seedlings which had been bent horizontally, the S(G) layer could be detected from 6 to 10 days after bending, although response by the plant was apparent after 1 day. It was observed that the cells containing the S(G) layer were 10–25 cells removed from the cambium and measurements showed that there was a daily increase of 2–3 cells per day, so Casperson concluded that the stimulus governing the formation of the S(G) layer acted in the cambium and not on the differentiating xylem. This conclusion is consistent with other evidence described above. In a further series of experiments *Aesculus* seedlings were placed in a horizontal position on the first day after germination and on each subsequent day the pots containing them were rotated through 180°. A curvature reaction was observed, but the reaction taking place on one day did not correct that which had taken place previously so that the stem assumed a sinuous form. The plants were then placed in an upright position and allowed to grow for a further period. On the first day after being placed upright no reaction wood was detected. After 4 weeks, however, reaction wood cells were present in every zone of curvature and were present on the side of the stem which had been uppermost while the plants were horizontal. It was thus concluded that the stimulus governing the formation of the S(G) layer affected the cambium within 24 hours, and that this change lead to the formation of the S(G) layer after more than 10 days. In view of these observations Casperson found it questionable that the development of reaction wood was responsible for orientation movements of the plants.

In a third series of experiments Casperson increased the time between rotating the pots from 1 day to 1 week and observed that the curvature produced during the first week was not offset by growth during the subsequent week, although reaction wood was formed on both sides of the stem. Casperson concluded that the reaction wood with the S(G) layer in the fibers was formed as a result of the tensile stresses operating within the stem, and was not the cause of the orientation movements observed.

Although these observations of Casperson indicate that the formation of reaction wood is determined in the cambium in a period of less than 24 hours, the treatment of the plants was such that the reaction wood ultimately formed was symmetrically disposed on the two sides of the stem, and, since the curvatures associated with reaction wood formation are usually slow, the failure of the treated stems to show visible straightening during the period of the experiment can be understood.

(*c*) *General*. From the above it can be seen that reaction wood is generally associated with demonstrated movements of orientation in stems and branches. That its formation on one side of a stem when the cambium was destroyed on the opposite side resulted in curvature of a stem suggests that it is associated with the active contraction of the tissue during its differentiation. The observation that debudding and defoliation prevent orientation movements indicates that static growth stresses are not involved in orientation movements. These observations are consistent with the view that the formation of reaction wood forms part of a mechanism by which orientation movements are effected.

The fact that the structure of reaction wood fibers appears to represent an adaptation to resist conditions of tensile stress and so is to be regarded as a result of orientation movements does not appear valid, since such tensile stresses exist within all stems, and are not confined to those undergoing orientation movements.

VI. Summary and Conclusions

A survey of the literature and of recent experimental work shows that, in general, leaning stems and branches of angiosperms are characterized by an eccentricity of radial growth in both the xylem and phloem. This eccentricity is usually, but not necessarily, associated with changes in anatomy of the xylem and phloem which may be designated a reaction anatomy.

Reaction wood (tension wood) shows extreme variability in its characteristics. It may appear to be essentially similar to normal wood except for a reduced level of lignification especially in the fibers. At the other extreme it may show a great reduction in the number and size of the vessels, and the fiber walls may show an alteration of the typical layered structure by the development of the so-called gelatinous layer, which may replace either the middle or inner layer of the secondary wall or may be present as an additional layer of the secondary wall. The gelatinous layer consists of axially oriented cellulose microfibrils and is unlignified or only slightly lignified. The reaction wood fibers differ in their dimensions, and show less bifurcation at their tips than normal wood fibers. The ray and vertical parenchyma systems are unchanged.

The reaction phloem shows the same pattern of tissue arrangement as normal phloem, but the phloem fibers have greatly thickened walls which usually result from the elaboration of one of the normal layers of the cell wall. There is usually a reduction in the level of lignification of the fibers.

The differentiation of reaction wood frequently involves the early inception of cambial activity (associated with eccentric radial growth). The surface growth of the differentiating fibers and the development of the secondary wall appear to follow the pattern of normal fibers until the "gelatinous" layer is formed. This layer is frequently formed as a band of cellulose partially detached from the existing wall, appearing convoluted in cross section, and gradually straightens onto it. This process may be repeated a number of times. In some species the process of straightening of the convoluted gelatinous layer does not take place. Although lignification of the gelatinous layer does not take place to any great extent under natural conditions it can be increased under experimental conditions. The gelatinous layer may show some ultraviolet absorption as concentric rings or in a zone adjacent the lumen. It has not been established with certainty whether this absorption is due to lignin or to substances diffusing from the cytoplasm. Early in its differentiation the gelatinous layer of the fibers shows no peroxidase activity but this increases when the formation of the layer is complete.

A survey of the various factors which have been suggested as causing reaction wood formation indicates that gravity is a major influence governing its formation and distribution. It would appear that the gravitational stimulus acts directly on the cambium although correlative phenomena associated with the normal differentiation of xylem are also involved.

The formation of reaction wood appears to be associated with movements of orientation in the branches and stems in which it occurs, the side of the member on which the tissue is formed tending to become concave. Experimental evidence suggests that the process of bending involved in the orientation movements does not result from the operation of static growth stresses within the stems and branches, but is the result of forces developed during the active differentiation of the reaction wood.

ACKNOWLEDGMENTS

The author is indebted to his colleagues Dr. H. E. Dadswell, Mr. G. W. Davies, and Dr. G. Scurfield for helpful discussion during the preparation of this paper, and to Mr. F. J. Daniels for technical assistance.

DISCUSSION

COLVIN: This case of syneresis, or apparent syneresis, of the reaction wood, recalls the very interesting observation of Rånby (1961) that in never-dried bacterial cellulose the accessibility of the microfibril to deuterium oxide, or whatever else is used, is about 50%. In dried cellulose the accessibility is down to about 30%. In other words the crystallinity increases upon drying. I believe this is an analogue to what you are getting after the syneresis is complete. This obviously means that the mechanism of deposition of the cellulose microfibrils in the reaction wood is markedly different from that of ordinary cellulose. How could this come about? Why do the cellulose microfibrils of the reaction wood portion synerese? This apparently does not occur with ordinary wood.

WARDROP: You could imagine an analogous process going on in the formation of normal secondary wall in individual lamellae. You might not detect this very easily. It is peculiar that this thick, microscopically visible band of cellulose is formed.

PRESTON: Can one assume that the contraction of the cell is due to some dehydration?

WARDROP: If so, it would be very slight. Lundegardh in Sweden spun wood in the centrifuge to determine the free water. We have done experiments like that with tension wood and tried to estimate free water and the water in the wall. There is about 10% less than in normal wood.

PRESTON: If dehydration is involved, or if newly developed tracheids and fibers for any other reason decrease in diameter, then the greater longitudinal contraction of tension wood might be explained. Let us consider first a simple model in which the microfibrils of the wall are wound helically round the cell in one helix only: It was shown long ago (Preston, 1942) that if l_1 is the length of a wet cell and θ_1 the angle of the spiral winding to cell length, if l_2 and θ_2 are the corresponding values for the drier cell, and if x is the relative contraction of the girth of the cell and y the relative contraction in length of the spiral winding, then

$$\left(\frac{l_2}{l_1}\right)^2 = \frac{(1+x)^2/(1+y)^2 - \sin^2\theta_1}{(1+x)^2(1-\sin^2\theta_1)}$$

The cell will lengthen or shorten on drying according to the value of θ_1 if x and y are constants. This is because, as the cell shrinks, the factor y tends to make the cell shorter while lateral shrinkage tends to make it longer, and the balance depends on the value of θ_1. The equation was shown applicable within limits for both conifer tracheids and angiosperm fibers. For values of θ less than 40° the cell decreases in length as it shrinks laterally and for values greater than 40° it elongates (as does, for instance, rope). With tension wood, therefore, the wood elements would contract strongly on dehydration whereas in normal wood there would be less contraction, no change in length, or elongation depending on the value of θ there. The contraction y in the length of the spiral winding depends upon some angular dispersion of the microfibrils about their common direction; it amounts to about 2% in ramie fibers and was estimated to be about 4% in tracheids and wood fibers (Preston, 1942).

The multilamellar nature of the walls of these cells makes the phenomenon more complicated than this simple treatment suggests, but the changes in length would still be of the same kind and in approximately the same degree.

WARDROP: I think the magnitude of the change in water content would have to be greater.

PRESTON: When the layer is laid down it is convoluted; when it moves on to the wall it must increase in diameter. This is the equivalent of drying out.

WARDROP: Yes, water must go into the lumen.

FREY-WYSSLING: You said that you did not agree with the view that there was first a growth reaction and then consolidation of this state. It is known that herbaceous plants can bend by growth reactions. I do not see why woody plants should do it in another way. Casperson (1960, 1961) has shown that these two reactions can be separated in very young stems. There must be an extension of the under side of the stem by growing cells. A secondary wall is deposited when elongation is finished. I cannot see how stress or pressure can be changed by apposition of secondary wall material. This must be done by the living protoplast in the growing cell.

WARDROP: If, in the experiments by Jaccard (1938), the loop is cut, the upper part expands, so that the tension wood is apparently associated with a contraction. In our own experiments upward bending of the stem occurred even after removal of the cambium from the lower side. This bending can only be explained by contraction of the upper side. Dr. Zimmermann told me about a case he has of aerial roots of *Ficus* which form tissue very like tension wood. They grow down into the ground into containers and they pull the pots up off the ground. This, again, is unquestionably contraction. All this supports the view that the formation of tension wood causes contraction. I cannot see how contraction can occur in a turgid cell and therefore I have tended to look for the responsible forces in the secondary wall.

THIMANN: During Dr. Wardrop's paper I found myself trying to construct a theory of all these phenomena, especially the causation of tension wood, at the hormonal level. I would like to suggest to you a general theory of compression wood, tension wood, and epinasty, in terms of auxin, which may provide at least a skeleton on which observations can be hung. We know more about compression wood than about tension wood. From the early work of Wershing and Bailey (1942) and others we know that it is imitable by high (but perhaps not unphysiologically high) concentrations of auxin. *Rotholz* obtained in this way is, according to Dr. Bailey, indistinguishable from normal pine *Rotholz*. I think it is not going very far to say that compression wood is the result of excess auxin. It is imitable by high auxin and it is formed under conditions where you would expect high auxin, on the lower side. Let us suppose that angiosperms and gymnosperms are not different in principle and that auxin also goes to the lower side of horizontally placed angiosperms. In sunflower and lupine seedlings placed horizontally, indeed, we know that auxin does move to the lower side. Hence, in angiosperms we are forced to the deduction that tension wood develops owing to a reduction in the amount of auxin in the tissue. You will agree, and Jaccard's experiments show, that it is not directly a result of tension. It is simply formed on the upper side of the tissue which is placed horizontally. Therefore, that puts it directly in line with compression wood. It is wood that is formed on the upper side and the upper side has less auxin than normal. Dr. Wardrop indicated that in this "tension wood" there is, at least in the innermost parts of the cell, an apparently great excess of peroxidase. I call your attention to the peculiar, and I think extremely important, reactions of peroxidase in controlling growth. It was shown some years ago by Peter Ray in my laboratory, and also by one or two others, that IAA is converted to a complex product which is an oxindole derivative (probably 3-methyleneoxindole, but its exact nature is not clear because it polymerizes very fast) in the presence of an enzyme which we used to call indoleacetic oxidase but which we now know is in fact peroxidase. Thus, in the presence of active peroxidase IAA would be destroyed and its level therefore decreased (Ray and Thimann, 1956; Ray, 1960). This apparently happens in tension wood, so this may contribute to a decreased level of IAA. I have mentioned this system because I believe it has much more to it than meets the eye, because peroxidase is strongly inhibited by diphenols and polyphenols, especially di-*ortho*-phenols. The inhibition has a peculiar *mutual* quality in that the di- and polyphenols are also oxidized by peroxidase to polymeric products, and this reaction is inhibited by IAA. Ray was able to show that IAA inhibits peroxidase almost as powerfully as does cyanide; horseradish peroxidase was inhibited 50% by 10^{-4} M cyanide or 2×10^{-4} M IAA. So here is a system in which the IAA controls the formation of polyphenolic polymers. The polyphenols in turn control the destruction of IAA. In compression wood we have apparently an excess of lignin; it looks red, and presumably the reaction is going to lignin. In tension wood it would be going to paler-colored peroxidation products. I do not pretend to work this out in detail.

What we essentially have in epinasty is that a branch grows at a constant angle. Dr. Wardrop showed very interesting experiments of this sort in which the branch was bent up or down. Now the branch grows at a constant angle because in the lateral branch there is a balance between two forces acting on the auxin. On the one hand IAA coming from the leaves and terminal bud of the branch is diverted to the lower side, tending to cause a geotropic curvature and make the branch become vertical, but it does not do so because there is a second force operating, which tends to drive auxin from the bud to the upper side. What this force is, we do not know. We do know that it is there. If plants are grown in a clinostat, then the epinastic angle completely changes and, if, for instance, the plant is defoliated and auxin applied to the petiole tip, symmetrically supplied auxin now causes asymmetrical growth; it causes downward curvature so that one side grows more than the other side. We thus know that there is in the tissue an asymmetric force tending to drive the IAA to the upper side (Lyon, 1963). In many plants this is dependent on the apical bud, and if the apical bud is removed the epinasty of one or more branches changes (e.g., Münch, 1938b). There are some famous exceptions like *Araucaria* and spruce in which even isolated lateral shoots, rooted and removed from all apical dominance, continue to grow horizontally. These are plants in which this force is somehow permanent and there are others in which it is somehow dependent on an influence from the tip. So we do not need to know what it is, but we know that it is there. In these experiments, if the branch is pulled up, tension wood develops on the lower side, whereas if we pull it down, tension wood develops on the upper side. If the epinastic angle of this branch depends on a balance between endogenous and gravitational forces, then the more nearly we place it vertically, the more we reduce the gravitational force so that the endogenous force overbalances and we get more IAA going to the upper side; as a result the tension wood, which we have just deduced is the result of a *deficiency* of IAA, appears on the under side. This is exactly as would be predicted. The reverse is true if we pull the branch toward the horizontal: more IAA goes to the lower side and the tension wood is formed on the upper side. One can thus begin to see a general theory which would unify all these phenomena.

WAREING: On the other hand, reaction wood can be formed even in a leader which does not have any innate epinasty, which would seem to be a difficulty. In our experiments we took vertically growing shoots and placed them horizontally, and we still found more cambial activity on the upper side. If, as it seems to happen, these phenomena occur with leading shoots, which presumably do not have the "endogenous" mechanism, it seems to constitute a difficulty.

THIMANN: I do not think that your objection holds. You may be just imitating with gravity what the normal tension wood does by the endogenous phenomenon.

CÔTÉ: Does not Onaka (1949) state that there are some species in which no G layer is formed in tension wood? How would you explain this on the basis of what we have discussed before?

WARDROP: I have discussed this in the paper. *Fraxinus*, for instance, does not form a G layer according to some investigators, yet Burns (1942) has shown it to be present in specimens studied by him. There is always a great reduction in lignification even when the G layer cannot be recognized.

CÔTÉ: Would you say then that in basswood it would be possible to have very little eccentricity, no G layer, and still have tension wood present?

WARDROP: Jaccard (1938), working on *Tilia*, found not much modification in the xylem, but very great modification in the phloem. I do not think, even though we tend to put all the emphasis on the xylem, that we can ignore the phloem. In relation to Dr. Thimann's remarks, when Nečesaný planted cuttings containing tension wood, the roots were formed on the side opposite the tension wood. This added to his contention that the IAA is in greatest concentration on the lower side.

ALVIM: The flower stalk of *Agave americana* normally should grow straight, but at an altitude of 3000 meters above sea level it grows as a repeating S curve. This is a common thing in the Peruvian Andes. The first bending is always toward the sunrise. Then it starts the S curve. Possibly at high elevations low temperature interferes with normal hormone synthesis.

REFERENCES

Albersheim, P., Mühlethaler, K., and Frey-Wyssling, A. (1960). *J. Biochem. Biophys. Cytol.* **8**, 501.

Amos, G. L., Bisset, I. J. W., and Dadswell, H. E. (1950). *Australian J. Sci. Res.* **B3**, 393.

Barlow, H. W. B., Hancock, C. R., and Lacy, H. J. (1959). *Proc. Intern. Conf. Plant Growth Regulators, Ames, Iowa, 1959*, p. 140.

Berlyn, G. P. (1961). *Iowa State J. Sci.* **35**, 367.

Bisset, I. J. W., and Dadswell, H. E. (1950). *Australian Forestry* **14**, 1.

Bland, D. E. (1958a). *Holzforschung* **12**, 36.

Bland, D. E. (1958b). *Holzforschung* **12**, 102.

Bucher, H. (1906). *Jahrb. wiss. Botan.* **43**, 271.

Bünning, E. (1952). *In* "Survey of Biological Progress" (G. S. Avery, Jr., ed.), p. 105. Academic Press, New York.

Burch, W. D. (1912). *Botan. Gaz.* **53**, 453.

Burns, G. P. (1942). *Vermont Agr. Expt. Sta. Bull.* **492**.

Büsgen, M., and Münch, E. (1929). "The Structure and Life of Forest Trees." Chapman and Hall, London.

Casperson, G. (1960). *Ber. Deut. Botan. Ges.* **73**, 349.

Casperson, G. (1961). *Naturwissenschaften* **48**, 701.

Chow, K. Y. (1946). *Forestry* **20**, 62.

Clarke, S. H. (1937). *Forestry* **11**, 85.

Correns, E. (1961). *Paperi ja Puu* **43**, 47.

Correns, E., Wergin, W., and Ruscher, C. (1956). *Faserforsch. Textiltech.* **7**, 565.

Côté, W. A., and Day, A. C. (1962). *Forest Prod. J.* **12**, 337.

Dadswell, H. E., and Wardrop, A. B. (1955). *Holzforschung* **9**, 97.

Dadswell, H. E., and Wardrop, A. B. (1956). *8th Intern. Botan. Congr., Paris*, (1954) Sect. No. 13, 85.

Dyer, D. (1955). *J. Oxford Univ. For. Soc.* Ser. 4, **4**, 19.

Ewart, A. C. J., and Mason-Jones, A. G. (1906). *Ann. Botany (London)* **20**, 201.

Frey-Wyssling, A. (1952). *Ber. Schweiz. Botan. Ges.* **62**, 583.

Frey-Wyssling, A. (1954). *Science* **119**, 80.

Giovanni, M. V. di (1953). *Nuova Giorn. Botan. Ital.* [N.S.] **60**, 239.

Grossenbacher, J. G. (1915). *Trans. Wisconsin Acad. Sci.* **18**, 1.

Haberlandt, G. (1914). "Physiological Plant Anatomy." Macmillan, London.

Hartmann, F. (1949). "Das statische Wuchsgesetz bei Nadel- und Laubbäumen. Neue Erkenntnis über Ursache, Gesetzmässigkeit und Sinn des Reaktionsholzes." Springer, Vienna.

Higuchi, T. (1955). *J. Japan. Forestry Soc.* **37**, 502.

Jaccard, P. (1917). *Rev. Gen. Botan.* **29**, 225.

Jaccard, P. (1919). "Nouvelles recherches sur l'accroissement en épaisseur des arbres." Mémoire primé et publié par la Fondation Schnyder von Wartensee à Zurich, Switzerland.

Jaccard, P. (1938). *Ber. Schweiz. Botan. Ges.* **48**, 491.

Jaccard, P. (1939). *Ber. Schweiz. Botan. Ges.* **49**, 135.

Jaccard, P. (1940). *Ber. Schweiz. Botan. Ges.* **50**, 279.

Jaccard, P., and Frey, A. (1928a). *Jahrb. Wiss. Botan.* **68**, 844.

Jaccard, P., and Frey, A. (1928b). *Jahrb. Wiss. Botan.* **69**, 549.

Jacobs, M. R. (1939). *Commonwealth Forestry and Timber Bur. Bull.* **24**, Canberra.

Jacobs, M. R. (1954). *Commonwealth Forestry and Timber Bur. Bull.* **28**, Canberra.

Jacobs, W. P. (1956). *Am. Naturalist* **10**, 163.

Jayme, G. (1951). *Holz Roh- u. Werkstoff* **9**, 173.

Jost, L. (1907). "Lectures on Plant Physiology." Clarendon Press, Oxford.

Jutte, S. M. (1956). *Holzforschung* **10**, 31.

Knight, T. A. (1811). *Phil. Trans. Roy. Soc., London* p. 209.

Kny, L. (1882). "Ueber das Dickenwachstum des Holzkörpers." Berlin.

Lange, P. (1954). *Svensk Papperstid.* **57**, 235.

Luckwill, L. C. (1952). *Nature* **169**, 375.

Lyon, C. T. (1963). *Plant Physiol.* **38**, 145-152.

Messeri, A. (1953). *Atti Accad. Nazl. Lincei. Rend., Classe sci. fis. mat. e nat.* **14**, 315.

Metzger, K. (1908). *Naturw. Z. Forst- u. Landwirtsch.* **6**, 249.

Münch, E. (1938a). *Flora (Jena)* **32**, 357.

Münch, E. (1938b). *Jahrb. Wiss. Botan.* **86**, 581-673.

Nečesaný, V. (1955a). *Prírodoved. Sb. Ostrav. Kraje* **16**, 184.

Nečesaný, V. (1955b). *Sb. Vysoke Skoly Zemedel. Lesnicke Brne Rada C* **3**, 131.

Nečesaný, V. (1956). *Drev. Výskum* **1**, 17.

Nečesaný, V. (1958). *Phyton (Buenos Aires)* **11**, 117.

Ollinmaa, P. J. (1959). *Acta Forest. Fennica* **72**, 5.

Onaka, F. (1949). *Mokuzai Kenkyu* **1**.

Onaka, F. (1950). *Univ. Kyoto Bull.* **18**.

Preston, R. D. (1942). *Forestry* **16**, 32.

Preston, R. D., and Ranganathan, S. (1947). *Forestry* **21**, 92.

Priestley, J. H., and Tong, D. (1927). *Proc. Leeds Phil. Lit. Soc.* **1** (Pt. 5), 199.

Priestley, J. H., Scott, L. I., and Malins, M. (1933). *Proc. Leeds Phil. Lit. Soc.* **2**, 365.

Rånby, B. G. (1961). *J. Polymer Sci.* **51**, 9.

Rasdorsky, W. (1925). *Ber. Deut. Botan. Ges.* **43**, 332.

Rawitscher, F. (1932). "Der Geotropismus der Pflanzen." Fischer, Jena.

Ray, P. M. (1960). *Arch. Biochem. Biophys.* **87**, 19-30.

Ray, P. M., and Thimann, K. V. (1956). *Arch. Biochem. Biophys.* **64**, 175-192.

Russell, E. S. (1945). "The Directiveness of Organic Activities." Cambridge Univ. Press, London and New York.

Sachs, J. (1882). "Textbook of Botany." Clarendon Press, Oxford.

Sachsse, H. (1961). *Holz Roh- u. Werkstoff* **19**, 253.

Sachsse, H. (1962). *Holz Roh- u. Werkstoff* **20**, 33.

Scurfield, G., and Wardrop, A. B. (1962). *Australian J. Botany* **16**, 93.

Scurfield, G., and Wardrop, A. B. (1963). *Australian J. Botany* (in press).

Setterfield, G. (1959). *Abstr. 9th Intern. Bot. Congr., Montreal* **2**, 355.

Siegel, S. M. (1953). *Physiol. Plantarum* **6**, 134.

Siegel, S. M. (1956). *J. Am. Chem. Soc.* **78**, 1753.

Vöchting, H. (1908). "Untersuchungen zur experimentellen Anatomie und Pathologie des Pflanzenkörpers." H. Laupp, Tübingen.

Wahlgren, H. E. (1959). Report No. 2089. U.S. Dept. Agr., Forest Prods. Lab., Madison, Wisconsin.

Wälchli, O. (1947). *Holzforschung* **1**, 20.

Wardrop, A. B. (1956). *Australian J. Botany* **4**, 152.

Wardrop, A. B. (1957). *Tappi* **40**, 225.

Wardrop, A. B., and Dadswell, H. E. (1947). *Australia, Commonwealth Sci. Ind. Res. Org., Bull.* **221**.

Wardrop, A. B., and Dadswell, H. E. (1948). *Australian J. Sci. Res.* **B1**, 3.

Wardrop, A. B., and Dadswell, H. E. (1955). *Australian J. Botany* **3**, 177.

Wardrop, A. B., and Davies, G. W. (1959). *Holzforschung* **13**, 65.

Wardrop, A. B., and Scaife, E. (1956). *Nature* **178**, 867.

Wareing, P. F., and Nasr, T. A. A. (1961). *Ann. Botany (London)* **25**, 321.

Wergin, W. (1961). *Faserforsch. u. Textiltech.* **13**, 51.

Wershing, H. T., and Bailey, I. W. (1942). *J. Forestry* **40**, 411.

White, D. J. B. (1962). *J. Inst. Wood Sci.* **10**, 74.

White, J. (1908). *Proc. Roy. Soc. Victoria* **20**, 107.

Cytology of
Aging Ray Cells[1]

A. Frey-Wyssling

Swiss Federal Institute of Technology, Zurich, Switzerland

The cell organelles of ray cells are studied starting from the cambium over as many as 50 to 60 year rings. In sapwood the active nucleus is of elliptical shape; deeper in the wood, it rounds off, loses its stainability, decays, and finally disappears completely. In timbers with heartwood its disappearance occurs in the so-called transition zone. The same is true for starch granules. Only when they have disappeared do phenols show up and transform the tissue into heartwood by staining its cell walls into deeper shades. Fat does persist in the transition zone. But there is an indication of partial saponification so that fatty acids accumulate in the ray cells of the heartwood.

Mitochondria, which readily reduce Janus green B in the sapwood, lose this capacity in the transition zone and degenerate. This fact is correlated with a diminished respiration activity of the living wood parenchyma.

It is concluded that, at a certain distance from the cambium, aerobiosis of the sapwood gradually turns over to anaerobiosis from lack of oxygen. This conclusion seems to be contradicted by the heartwood pigments which are oxidation products of the mentioned phenols. But that process evidently needs only a minimum oxidative potential which would be too small for respiration reactions.

---

[1] Only a short abstract of the paper given at the Cabot Foundation Symposium is included here. Most of the information in the presented paper had been published by A. Frey-Wyssling and H. H. Bosshard in 1959 (*Holzforsch.* **13**, 129). Additional, newer information on the subject may be found in Fahn, A., and Arnon, N. (1963), *New Phytol.* **62**, 1.

Xylem in Roots of Pinus resinosa Ait. in Relation to Heterorhizy and Growth Activity

HUGH WILCOX

State University College of Forestry, Syracuse, New York

Introduction

The observations reported in this paper are the outgrowth of a study of the seasonal development of mycorrhizae of *Pinus resinosa* Ait. in nursery seedlings and in young plantation trees. The root systems of pines occupy a classic position in the pioneering investigations of mycotrophy and are considered by many botanists and foresters as the representatives *par excellence* of a heterorhizic root system composed of contrasting long- and short-root branches (Figs. 1 and 3). The term "heterorhizy" was applied to woody plants by von Alten (1909) and Noelle (1910) to signify the phenomenon whereby the same plant can form various root types. The long- and short-root characteristic is only one manifestation of heterorhizy.

Von Alten (1909) and Noelle (1910) presumed that the qualitative and quantitative differences in root types were an expression of specialization in root function. The anatomy and morphology of short roots and long roots in *Pinus* have been reported in considerable detail by Melin (1923), Aldrich-Blake (1930), Hatch and Doak (1933), and Hatch (1937). These well-known researches have led to a general acceptance of the concept of heterorhizy in *Pinus* and have strengthened the belief that roots exhibit structural and developmental differences correlated with physiological specializations. However, the exact nature of the physiological roles of the different types of roots and the significance of the morphological variability under various ecological conditions have not been solved despite the voluminous literature on the subject.

The belief has been stated that the tracheary elements of roots are most likely to reflect closely the influences of the soil environment and the needs imposed by water absorption. The writer was familiar with some of the successes of botanists and wood technologists in relating cell size variations and concomitant fluctuations in form and structure of the cells of the secondary xylem to morphological and physiological problems and expected that similar data were available for variations in primary xylem. However, the extensive literature on root anatomy relates largely to systematics and phylogeny and does not lead necessarily to a satisfying picture of the manner in which the dimensions and configuration of primary xylem are affected by the numerous factors or complexes of factors in the internal and external environments.

The fact that the differentiation of primary xylem occurs under the more immediate aegis of the apical meristem than does secondary xylem imparts especial importance to the former as a fundamental problem in plant morphogenesis. It is the purpose of the author to describe some of the fluctuations in growth activity and root anatomy encountered in the study of red pine and to point out some of the problems raised.

Root Morphology

The terminal root portions of a seedling or a mature red pine tree vary widely in diameter and morphology. This variation makes it necessary to employ some scheme of classification in describing roots in experimental investigations. Figure 2 shows the classification used in the present study. It is based on the scheme devised by Noelle (1910) and elucidated by Aldrich-Blake (1930). The classes of roots termed "pioneer" and "mother" root were described by these authors, but the classification "subordinate mother" root was devised in the present study.

The classification shown in Fig. 2 applies only to the so-called long roots, which are the relatively permanent branches that are of importance in developing the framework of the root system. Each of the classes of long roots possesses variable numbers of very short root branches, appropriately called short roots. These structures are more or less ephemeral, and the majority of them are lost during the first or second season after

---

Figs. 1–5. Morphological features of terminal root portions from the root system of *Pinus resinosa*. Fig. 1. Distal root portion from a first-order lateral of 3-year-old seedling. × 1. Fig. 2. Terminal portions from various classes of long roots from a 30-year-old plantation. Classification based on root diameter and degree of branching. Explanation in text. × ½. Fig. 3. Higher-magnification view of distal portion of a subordinate mother root with characteristic mycorrhizal short roots. × 5. Fig. 4. Subordinate mother root showing appearance resulting from repeated cycles of growth activity. × 2½. Fig. 5. Short-root apex showing remnants of metacutization layers from recurrent periods of dormancy alternating with brief periods of growth. × 75.

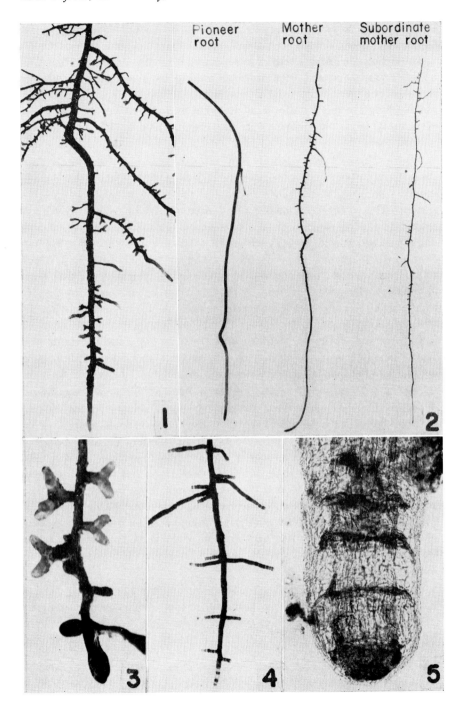

Pioneer root   Mother root   Subordinate mother root

their formation. The short roots are commonly converted into mycorrhizae.[1]

Table I shows dimensional data representative of pioneer, mother, subordinate mother and short roots from mature trees and also of different
orders of root branching from 2-year-old seedlings. The roots of a 2-year-
old seedling are more uniform in diameter and do not yet possess diameters as large as the pioneers in the classification scheme devised for
mature trees.

Figure 2 and Table I show that the pioneer roots are the largest-
diameter members of the root system. Noelle (1910) aptly termed them
pioneers because they are instrumental in the rapid extension of the root
system. The average diameter of approximately 1.6 mm corresponds
closely to the pioneer roots of *Pinus laricio* Pior. var. *corsicana* Loud.
These were reported by Aldrich-Blake (1930) to vary in diameter between 1.0 and 2.2 mm. The red pine pioneers are sparsely branched, which
also agrees with the observations of Noelle and Aldrich-Blake. The roots
of Corsican pine were reported by the latter author to bear many daughter root initials, which, with few exceptions, were suppressed immediately
after breaking through the cortex of the parent root. Pioneer roots of
Pinus resinosa are never plentiful and are most frequently encountered
during late spring and again during late summer and early autumn, during the two periods of peak root-growth activity.

The measurements of mother roots show that these are smaller in
diameter than pioneers. They are also generally shorter in length and
are more plentifully branched. In fact, the term "mother" refers to the
latter characteristic. The mother roots from plantations correspond in
diameter to the first-order laterals of the 2-year-old seedlings measured in
this study. Aldrich-Blake reported that the mother roots of Corsican pine
varied in diameter between 0.38 and 0.76 mm, thus indicating smaller
mother roots than those considered to be mother roots in this study. The
field collections of red pine always contained mother roots; these were
actively growing mostly during the same periods as the pioneer roots.
Mother and pioneer roots were inactive from mid-December to mid-
April.

The long roots designated as subordinate mother roots in Fig. 2 and
Table I are conspicuously finer than mother roots and possess a diameter
which is an order of magnitude smaller. These roots were comparable in
diameter to the second-order laterals of the 2-year-old pine seedlings.

---

[1] Classifications of infected and noninfected short roots are presented in detail by
Melin (1923) and Dominik (1959), but for purposes of the present investigation
short roots are not subdivided.

TABLE I

DIAMETER MEASUREMENTS OF RED PINE ROOTS[a]

Class of roots	A			B			C	
	No. of roots	Diam in mm Avg.	Range	No. of roots	Diam (mm) Avg.	Range	Diam (mm) Avg.	Range
Pioneer	10	1.66	(1.32–1.81)	6	1.60	(1.40–1.86)	—	
Mother	26	0.85	(0.74–1.21)	11	0.95	(0.78–1.15)	—	
Subordinate mother	37	0.54	(0.36–0.71)	32	0.54	(0.34–0.75)		
Short roots	207	0.42	(0.23–0.50)	74	0.36	(0.26–0.46)	0.34	(0.26–0.41)
Primary	—	—		—	—		1.03	
First-order lateral	—	—		—	—		0.99	
Second-order lateral	—	—		—	—		0.55	

[a] Key: A, Plantation near Phoenix, New York, August 6, 1958. B, Highland Forest, New York, September 23, 1958. C, two-year-old seedlings from College of Forestry Nursery.

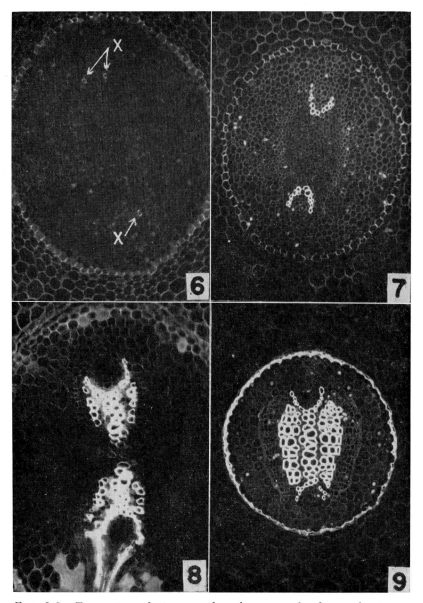

FIGS. 6–9. Transections of pioneer and mother roots of red pine showing successive stages in the development of xylem elements. All × 80. FIG. 6. Diarch pioneer root with a single matured protoxylem element at one xylem pole and two elements at the other. Casparian strips are visible in the endodermis. Section at a distance of 69 mm from the apical initials in an actively growing root with 1½ cm of white apex. Root diameter 1.73 mm. First-matured protoxylem elements are marked with "X." FIG. 7. Pioneer root showing completion of the horseshoe-shaped

Although these roots possessed a diameter almost the same as that of the true short root, they were obviously long roots in character. They were more closely branched than the mother roots and frequently possessed larger numbers of mycorrhizae. Their root apices possessed a pointed root cap in contrast to the rounded apex of the short root. These fine roots were plentiful in all collections and a separate designation was given to them because of their distinctive appearance.

The above classification of long roots into pioneer, mother, and subordinate mother and the recognition of short roots are necessary for the meaningful study of primary xylem in red pine. The importance of these distinctions will become evident in what follows.

Development of Primary Xylem in Long Roots

The first mature primary xylem tracheids in long roots of red pine are found at distances from the apical meristem which vary with the growth rate and the diameter of the root. As would be expected from the studies reported by Wilcox (1962a), the distances are greater in the larger-diameter roots and in the roots of more rapid growth rate. In dormant roots of all classes, mature primary elements are found very close to the apical initials.

All of the roots investigated were found to be diarch in structure throughout their lengths. This corresponds to the situation reported by Noelle (1910) and Liese (1926) for *Pinus sylvestris* and claimed as a distinctive feature of this pine in contrast to other *Pinus* species.[2] Studies were not made of the seedling radicle of the 1-year-old red pine seedling to ascertain the number of xylem positions at this early stage of development, but it can be safely said that the diarch condition at least prevails throughout the greater portion of the life of red pine.

Viewed in transverse section the two primary xylem poles develop in the form of two horseshoes, each surrounding a primary resin canal. The bases of the horseshoes face each other and the open ends face radially outward. The first primary xylem elements to mature are found at the

---

[2] Other coniferous genera reported by Noelle (1910) to be almost always diarch are *Picea, Tsuga, Pseudotsuga, Cedrus,* and *Araucaria.*

---

body of primary xylem tracheids. Suberization visible on inner tangential walls of some of the endodermal cells. Root diameter 1.71 mm. FIG. 8. Freehand section of pioneer root showing centripetal development of central body of primary xylem extending inward from horseshoes. First-mature secondary tracheids flanking the extending arms of metaxylem. Note lateral root attachment. Root diameter 2.17 mm. FIG. 9. Mother root showing completed primary xylem body and one annual increment of secondary xylem. Metaxylem elements are separated from secondary tracheids by a uniseriate layer of parenchymatous cells. Endodermis completely suberized and partially collapsed. Root diameter 1.23 mm.

points of the horseshoes. As shown in Fig. 6 they mature at about the same time as the Casparian strips in the endodermis. The primary tracheids mature centripetally along both sides of both horseshoes until each is completely delimited as shown in Fig. 7. This sequence of development differs from that described by Noelle (1910) and Liese (1926) for *Pinus sylvestris* where the first xylem to mature is at the bases of the horseshoes.

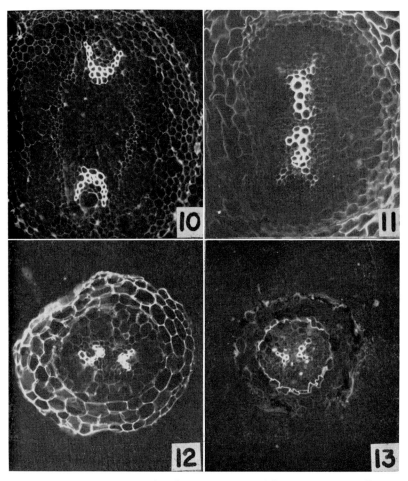

Figs. 10–13. Transections of red pine roots of different diameters illustrating variations in the configuration of the vascular strands and in the size of stele. Freehand sections of fresh material. All × 120. Fig. 10. Pioneer root at a distance of 6 cm from the root apex. Root diameter 1.70 mm. Fig. 11. Mother root at a distance of 8 cm from the root apex. Root diameter 1.15 mm. Fig. 12. Subordinate mother root at a distance of 2 mm from the root apex. Root diameter 0.44 mm. Fig. 13. Nonmycorrhizal short root. Section at the base of a 5-mm root.

After completion of the horseshoes the continued development of primary xylem tracheids occurs centripetally from the base of each horseshoe. Maturation of primary xylem continues until a juncture is formed in the center of the root. The completed xylem bridge between the two horseshoes consists of 1 to 3 rows of tracheids which may or may not appear in regular files along the diameter between the horseshoes (Fig. 9).

In large-diameter roots, a cambium develops in flanking positions on the sides of the horseshoes and secondary tracheids mature concomitant with the centripetal maturation of primary xylem (Fig. 8). The complete primary body is separated from the secondary body of tracheids in the center of the root by a uniseriate row of parenchymatous cells on either side. The vascular cambium is not formed over the primary xylem poles until the root is more than 2 years old. The horseshoes form a distinctive pattern until after that time, and are even discernible in roots several years in age.

The sequence of development described above applies to all classes of long roots in red pine. The obvious differences in roots of different diameters are in the distances between the horseshoes and in the number of tracheids in the central xylem plate. Some of these differences are shown in Figs. 10–13.

Morphological Characteristics of Primary Tracheids

The first-matured tracheids have relatively thin helical thickenings with numerous connections (Figs. 14, 18–20). The distance between the thickenings tends to vary with the diameter of the tracheids; the thickenings are thinner and further apart in the larger tracheids. Frequently the helical cells fail to form a continuous longitudinal file and either or both ends of a tracheid may abut against a parenchyma cell in the same longitudinal file (Fig. 20).

Rapid transitions occur in the type of pitting between the tracheids of successively maturing elements along the horseshoes. The helically thickened tracheids frequently occupy a single longitudinal file at the tips of the horseshoes. The next radially contiguous file of tracheids may appear reticulate in surface view with no discernible helical pattern. The third contiguous file of the ontogenetic sequence may be pitted, either with irregularly disposed pits or with widely spaced pits in good longitudinal alignment. The first-matured helical elements at the beginning of the ontogenetic sequence do not appear to possess the bordered pits disposed amongst the helices as reported in shoots of pine species (Bailey, 1925; Bierhorst, 1960).

In addition to the differences in wall sculptoring along the ontogenetic sequence from protoxylem to metaxylem, there are also differences in

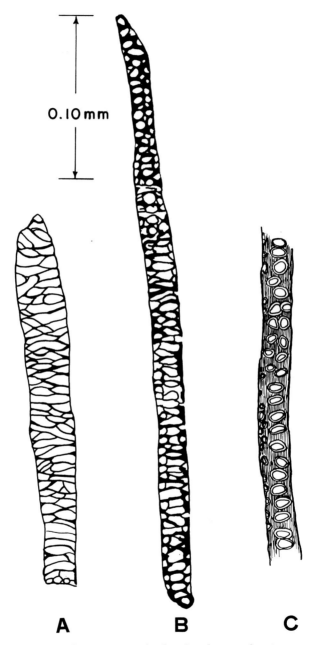

0.10mm

A   B   C

FIG. 14. Drawings of primary tracheids of red pine showing secondary wall development in the successive elements in an ontogenetic sequence. A, First-matured helical protoxylem element from the tip of the horseshoe. B, Reticulate element adjacent to the helical element in A. C, Early pitted element with randomly scattered bordered pits. Explanation in text.

lengths of the tracheids. The helical protoxylem elements are conspicuously shorter than the other elements in the sequence.

Before leaving discussion of the morphological features of the primary xylem, special attention should be paid to the extreme size variations exhibited by the first-formed primary tracheids. These helical elements exhibit rather predictable size variations in the different diameter roots. They vary directly with the size of the root, tending to be longer and radially wider in elongating pioneer roots than in mother roots or subordinate mother roots (Table II). The radial diameter of tracheids generally

TABLE II

DIMENSIONS OF FIRST-MATURED, HELICAL PROTOXYLEM TRACHEIDS IN GROWING RED PINE ROOTS

Class of root	Length (microns)	Radial width (microns)
Pioneer	370	21
Mother	420	18
Subordinate mother	240	17
Short-root	185	16

exceeds the tangential diameter because the cells are elongated parallel to the sides of the horseshoe.

In addition to the predictable size variations in growing roots of different diameter classes, the first-formed primary xylem elements show conspicuous vertical shortening as roots become dormant (Figs. 16 and 17; Table III). The change in length along a longitudinal file tends to occur

TABLE III

LENGTH OF FIRST-MATURED, HELICAL PROTOXYLEM TRACHEIDS IN DORMANT ROOTS[a]

Class of root	Length (microns)	Radial width (microns)
Pioneer	89	20
Mother	94	14
Subordinate mother	160	14
Short-root	91	20

[a] Short elements also occur in the protoxylem at the points of lateral root attachment. These are avoided in the measurements.

abruptly with the shortest mature helical elements occurring opposite the metacutization layers. It is evident that the process of xylem maturation proceeds for an appreciable time following the cessation of elongation. As a matter of fact, it appears that the maturation of these first-matured helical tracheids always occurs basipetal to the zone of active root elongation since no distorted helical elements were ever found. For this reason, the criterion of maturation during elongation cannot be used

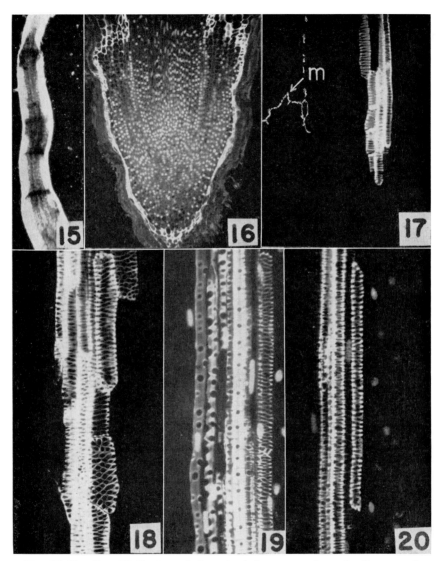

F<small>IG</small>. 15–20. F<small>IG</small>. 15. Portion of cleared whole mount of a subordinate mother root of red pine showing progressive enlargement of root diameter following periods of dormancy. × 15. F<small>IG</small>. 16. Dormant root apex showing configuration of dormancy layers in relation to apical meristem. Root diameter 1.30 mm. × 55. F<small>IG</small>. 17. Short protoxylem tracheids maturing in the vicinity of the metacutization layer following the cessation of elongation. Metacutization layer (m) and Casparian strips are accentuated with white ink. × 20. F<small>IG</small>. 18. Short protoxylem tracheids in vicinity of dormancy layers in a dormant root apex. The lengths of the tracheids increase rapidly in the longitudinal file basipetal to the metacutization layer. The lower end of the broad, short element in the lower portion of the photograph is 280 microns as a basis for designating these elements as protoxylem tracheids. Nevertheless, these tracheids are here considered as protoxylem and are so designated on the basis of their position. They are situated at the initial sites from which centripetal maturation proceeds during development of the primary xylem. The later-formed primary tracheids are considered metaxylem elements. No sharp distinction can be made between protoxylem and metaxylem tracheids.

In addition to the length variations of the protoxylem elements described above, some recognition should be made of the distinctive differences in shape as viewed in cross section between these elements and those formed later. A superficial view of the horseshoe-shaped body of early primary xylem gives the impression that the tracheids at the tips of the horseshoes are appreciably smaller in diameter than those occurring along the inner curve of the U (Fig. 10). Measurements show that, although the outer elements are flattened against the border of the resin canal, their radial diameters, i.e., along the axis of the horseshoe, are generally equal to the diameters of the isodiametric tracheids in the center of the U. The diameters of the tracheids situated in the xylem plate are markedly larger than those anywhere in the horseshoe. Also there is a gradual increase in size toward the center, with the large central primary tracheids equal in diameter to the secondary tracheids in the first increment of secondary xylem.

Changes in Diameter of the Primary Xylem Body

The ease with which the horseshoes of early primary xylem can be delimited in the root, even after several years of secondary growth, makes it possible to measure the distances between them throughout the length of older roots. Such measurements of entire first-order and second-order laterals of red pine seedlings at the end of the third growing season showed a progressive increase in diameter of the primary xylem body with age (Table IV). It is not known how long this increase continues; but, presumably, the size of pioneers collected from the plantations indicates the upper limit.

Since the new growth of a root emerging from dormancy frequently appears larger in diameter than the root proximal to the point of stoppage, it is logical to assume that part of the difference is due to an increase in

from the level of junction between the metacutization layer and the endodermis. × 210. Fig. 19. Longisection showing the transitions in wall structure and pitting of successively maturing tracheary elements along one side of the horseshoe of a vascular strand. The single longitudinal file of helically thickened tracheids is at the beginning of the ontogenetic sequence. × 210. Fig. 20. Ontogenetic sequence on the other side of the horseshoe shown in Fig. 19. × 210.

TABLE IV

DISTANCES BETWEEN HORSESHOES AT VARIOUS DISTANCES FROM THE MERISTEM
IN CERTAIN ROOTS OF A 3-YEAR-OLD SEEDLING

Distance from meristem (cm)	Distance between horseshoes[a] (microns)	Distance from meristem (cm)	Distance between horseshoes[c] (microns)
2½	360	1	167
5	428	2	195
7	414	3	195
9	380	4	222
11	387	5	208
13	387	6	208
15	248	7	208
17	221	8	208
19	262	10	208
21	269	12	236
23	269	14	138
25	269	16	182
27	269	20	97
29	249	22	104
31	207	24	110
33	207		
35	179		
37	152		
39	138		
41	124		
43	124		
45	110		
47	69		
49	83[b]		

[a] In a first-order lateral designated as root ACA, sampled on October 30, 1957.
[b] Base of root.
[c] In a second-order lateral designated as SO. #5 from the basal portion of root ACA.

diameter of the body of primary xylem.[3] Measurements of the distance between the two horseshoes of a first-order lateral of a seedling at the beginning of the third growing season after 5 cm of new growth showed the distance to be 0.438 mm at a level 4 mm distal to the point of stoppage and 0.292 mm at a level 6 mm proximal to the stoppage. The points of growth stoppage could not be determined in older root portions but the observation that the distances between horseshoes do not increase gradually but in a number of abrupt steps (Table IV) would support the assumption that the changes are associated with increments of growth. Further support is afforded by the field samples. Figure 15 shows a par-

---

[3] Allowance must also be made for the frequently noted decrease in diameter of the older cortical tissue with aging.

tially cleared whole mount of a root which has undergone repeated cycles of growth as shown by the dark-appearing remnants of the metacutization layers. It will be noted that there is a progressive increase in both total and stelar diameter which appears to be related to successive increments of growth. In this case, the stoppages are close together and it is likely that these represent intraseasonal cycles of growth. Further evidence of intraseasonal growth cycles is shown by the appearance of the roots in Figs. 4 and 5, where it will be noted that root apices are beaded in appearance from the cyclic growth activity. This beaded appearance is evident in both the long- and short-root branches and has been reported often as a feature of mycorrhizae. The fact that it is common in plantations, particularly in roots from near the soil surface, would tend to indicate that the intraseasonal cycles are associated with repeated periods of moisture stress occurring during the growing season. The ability of roots which have broken their winter dormancy to undergo repeated periods of growth and stoppage with induced drought has been demonstrated in red pine seedlings grown in observation boxes (Merritt, 1959).

Primary Xylem in Short Roots

Since subordinate mother roots and short roots are approximately the same diameter, it is of interest to compare them anatomically. Both root types are diarch with the horseshoes reduced in size and separated by very few tracheids. The first-matured helical elements are similar in morphology and in both cases are narrow in comparison to the larger long roots. In both classes of small roots, the transition to pitted elements is very abrupt in the ontogenetic sequence, and longisections through the two horseshoes frequently show a single verticle file of helical elements on either side of a few vertical files of pitted elements. The diameters of the tracheids in the horseshoe are approximately equal to those in the center of the root; and, due to the compact arrangement, the diarch structure is difficult to distinguish in the mature primary body. In the smallest of the short roots, it is difficult to distinguish the primary resin canals and it is possible that one or both may be absent. This compacted arrangement probably accounts for the frequent reference to monarch short roots in *Pinus* (Noelle, 1910; Aldrich-Blake, 1930; Hatch, 1937). A developmental study of such short roots always reveals two xylem poles.

The difference between mycorrhizal short roots and subordinate mother roots does not appear to be a result of invasion or noninvasion by mycorrhizal fungi; the same fungus appears to occur in both roots. Even though these two classes of root intergrade in diameter, it would appear that the slightly larger meristem of the subordinate mother root is conducive to increased elongation. Perhaps a certain rate of elongation or a minimal growth increment is required in order for a root to augment the size of its primary body and become, or remain, long root in character. In addition, a certain minimal size of stele with residual promeristem is required for the development of a vascular cambium and the development of a secondary body. Otherwise, any subsequent increase in size of apical meristem or primary body would be futile because of the inadequate body of primary xylem at the base of the root. A root does not gain much added strength at its point of attachment to the mother root by attachment of the cortical tissues of the two roots, but is supported almost solely by the attachment of the primary vascular tissues. If the primary body is extremely reduced and no secondary attachment is formed, the root becomes easily dislodged from its attachment to the mother root. Sufficient stresses develop in the soil to insure a constant attrition of smaller roots. The slightly better retention of a mycorrhizal short root may be due to the slightly greater support afforded to it by the distended cortex and the binding action of mycelia to strengthening structures in the substrate.

Relation of Anatomy to Problems in Morphogenesis

It is interesting to note that the diarch condition is constant throughout the root system of red pine. This constancy prevails despite the differences in diameter between roots and the changes in diameter within roots. According to Noelle (1910) all Araucariaceae and many of the Abietaceae are diarch throughout; all Taxodiaceae and Cupressaceae are polyarch. He considered the long roots of *Pinus* to be polyarch except for *Pinus sylvestris*, which he considered uniquely diarch. It is evident from the results reported above that *Pinus resinosa* corresponds to *Pinus sylvestris* in the constancy of the diarch condition; and, therefore, Noelle's (1910) generalization on the numbers of vascular strands in *Pinus* is open to question.

In contrast to the examples noted above and those mentioned earlier, some root systems show variation in the number of xylem strands between root classes and fluctuation in number of strands within individual roots. These differences approximately parallel the differences in root diameter (Noelle, 1910; Wilcox, 1962b). These differences are too self-evident to merit discussion.

A causal relationship is frequently accepted between root diameter and the number of vascular strands (Wardlaw, 1928; Bower, 1930; Aldrich-Blake, 1930). Torrey (1955) studied pea roots which showed various transitions in number of vascular strands and found no correlation between vascular complexity and either total root diameter or the diameter of the mature vascular cyclinder. However, he reported that the roots appeared to show a relationship between the diameter of the procambium at the level of pattern inception and the complexity of vascular pattern. In red pine, it appears that the diarch condition bears no relation whatsoever to the size of the meristem. If the meristem is responsible for the determining influence on vascular pattern, it is evident that, whether the body of meristematic cells and their derivatives is small or large, it determines the identical pattern. It would appear that size and geometrical relationships can be ignored in analyzing the physiological basis of pattern formation in red pine.

A more fruitful approach to morphogenesis than the study between root size and vascular pattern is the relation between root size and growth activity. The data on size changes of the primary xylem body suggest a close correlation with growth. The pattern of root behavior of emerging long roots seems to be as follows: (1) The primary body decreases slightly in size after emergence from the mother root, indicating an arrest of growth or a delay in acquiring the subsequent growth rate; (2) a gradual increase in diameter during the growing season; (3) a sharp drop in diameter upon approaching dormancy; (4) a sudden increase in diameter upon emerging from dormancy; (5) another gradual increase in diameter throughout the new growing season. A repetition of the rhythmic increases and decreases occurs during cycles of growth, with the upper limit on size of primary body determined by some internal mechanism.

Another problem presented by the results of this study is related to the variations encountered in wall pattern and length of tracheary elements within the ontogenetic sequence of primary xylem maturation. The retention of helically thickened elements is an interesting phenomenon in a root where maturation of xylem elements never occurs until after the cessation of elongation. Also, it would be of interest to investigate division patterns in the tracheary elements to discover the explanation for the shorter lengths of the protoxylem elements.

At this point, it might be desirable to examine the validity of the concept of heterorhizy as explained in the introduction. Do the observations on variations in root morphology, and particularly of tracheary elements, support a theory of root specialization for special functions? No one would deny some of the truths responsible for this theory. On strictly morphological grounds, it can be recognized that short roots are generally a conspicuous feature of the red pine root system and their existence is obvious. Also on a functional basis, it cannot be denied that long roots are more effective in extending the root system to new territory. The difficulty arises in applying the term heterorhizy *sensu strictu* to imply that the two types of roots were developed to serve separate functions which each can serve better than the other. Although the pioneer root serves the purpose of extending the root system, and the mother root enriches the root system by its intensive branching, it is evident that these roots also serve to absorb water and nutrients. Furthermore, it is difficult to see why the short root should be markedly more efficient in comparison with the other root types in absorbing water. The structure and configuration of the xylem and its proximity to the surface of the root are very similar in the short root and in the subordinate mother root; it would appear that if the particular properties of these are really reliable criteria of efficiency, the latter would have the same efficiency plus the added advantage of a greater growth potential. On this basis, it appears that it is unfortunate for red pine that the short roots do not grow out.

The development studies would tend to indicate that there is no intrinsic difference in tracheary morphology which would correlate with differences in efficiency of function. It is not clear how the variation of pattern of xylem arrangement or size in the primary body would correlate with efficiency of function. Such information as exists on conducting areas would indicate that cross-sectional areas of an absorbing root possess a considerable safety factor so that it can handle the requirements for water passing through that particular position. The claims (Noelle, 1910) for a larger relative volume of conducting tissue or for greater relative efficiency of the constituent tracheids in a short root are hard to substantiate. It seems more than likely that any such supposed advantages are exceeded by the disadvantages of mechanical weaknesses in attachment of these roots and their high mortality.

Leaving the question of absorbing efficiency aside, it has to be acknowledged that a large proportion of the material absorbed by the pine root system must enter through short roots, merely because they constitute a major percentage of the ultimate root branches. This dependence on short roots together with the observed mortality of these roots leads to the obvious conclusion that the thrift of red pine depends on the continued renewal of these structures. Indeed, the benefit ascribed to the presence of mycorrhizae has sometimes been attributed to the stimulation of dichotomy of short roots and consequent increases in absorbing surface (Hatch and Doak, 1933). However, it should be pointed out that concomitant to the need for a constant supply of well-attached absorbing short roots would be the need for increasing numbers of vigorously growing subordinate mother roots. The meristems of these should be of sufficient thrift to insure the increase in size of their primary body to provide increasing numbers of mother roots. A possible alternative to this maintenance of healthy meristems is seen in the deterioration of meristems, the loss of short roots, and the decline in vigor of root systems frequently seen on "red pine decline" areas in central New York. Certainly, size and vigor of the constituent meristems are all-important to the thrift and vigor of a root system. The characteristics of the primary xylem body throughout the root system are a reflection of this status.

DISCUSSION

Esau: Protoxylem and metaxylem are merely terms to indicate the earlier and the later stages of the differentiation of primary xylem. We should not attach to the definitions reference to specific characteristics of cell wall structure or to whether or not cell elongation occurs, because then we could not apply these terms consistently. I would like to use the terms as they were first introduced, merely to indicate the beginning of differentiation. The first xylem elements and the first phloem elements would be protoxylem and protophloem. Usually they indicate the pattern of differentiation as, in your pictures, the beginning of exarch differentiation from double poles. I do not think that we should be too concerned about whether or not elongation occurs. It so happens that in the shoot protoxylem differentiates before the elongation is completed and therefore the elements are very much stretched. In roots, the major elongation occurs where the protophloem differentiates. By the time protoxylem differentiates, elongation is finished.

Wilcox: In this case I can use protoxylem in a positional sense?

Esau: Yes, it should be used in a positional sense but with reference to the whole vascular system. For example, I would not look for protoxylem in each individual bundle in a stem or a leaf. In a stem there would be protoxylem only in the major leaf traces in the closest position to the internode where the pertinent leaves are attached. Many bundles have no protoxylem. Some do not have any metaxylem, only secondary xylem. The xylem is built up by the vascular cambium.

Wilcox: My problem here is that I hardly think the whole horseshoe could be called protoxylem; therefore, I just say the protoxylem positions and speak of the horseshoe as primary xylem.

Esau: Where to draw the limit between protoxylem and metaxylem is, of course, completely theoretical.

Zimmermann: But are the structural features of protoxylem elements not very striking? There is an unlignified, flexible primary wall and a lignified secondary wall in the form of a helix or rings. It can function during stretching although it is dead. Whether they are stretched or not does not matter, but they *can* stretch.

Esau: The usual situation is that the first xylem elements have very small amounts of secondary wall, which, of course, is laid over a plastic, extensible, primary wall. This type of development appears to be a response to the environment in which the cells differentiate. For example, irradiated roots do not elongate and the very first xylem elements in the protoxylem position develop a pitted wall, just like the wall of a secondary element (Smith and Kersten, 1942). If you call protoxylem only those elements that have rings or spirals you limit the term to certain plant parts, mainly those that elongate during xylem differentiation and would have to say that you could experimentally prevent the development of protoxylem. To me protoxylem is most useful as a positional term.

Wilson: There seems to be a difference in function between the pioneer roots and the mother roots in that the mother roots produce many laterals. This means that the mother roots can occupy space faster.

Wilcox: A root system possessing numerous pioneer roots soon extends to much greater distances than one without pioneers. This produces a mode of root branching which Büsgen (1901) called "extensive." A root system with numerous mother and subordinate mother roots results in a greater ramification within a smaller soil volume. Büsgen called this mode of branching "intensive." He characterized the root systems of several European tree species as intensive or extensive on the basis of this distinction.

WILSON: What about seedlings that will not grow, I think in Australia, until mycorrhizal fungi are put in the soil?

WILCOX: It has been demonstrated many times that there are adverse sites in which seedlings benefit phenomenally from infection with fungi. However, I have grown seedlings repeatedly under conditions of good nutrition without mycorrhizal infections. I feel that mycorrhizae are beneficial only under adverse conditions and are superfluous under good conditions. This is a matter of opinion; I do not have any experimental evidence.

RICHARDSON: Is there any incontrovertible evidence that any species *requires* mycorrhizae?

WILCOX: I do not think so. There is good evidence that on places that had never had trees before, or where trees definitely had difficulty, they benefited from mycorrhizae. For instance, E. Hacskaylo (1961) showed this for the pine in Puerto Rico.

REFERENCES

Aldrich-Blake, R. N. (1930). *Oxford Forestry Mem.* 12, 1-64.

Bailey, I.W. (1925). *Ann. Botany (London)* 34, 578-598.

Bierhorst, D. W. (1960). *Phytomorphology* 10, 249-305.

Bower, F. O. (1930). "Size and Form in Plants." Macmillan, London.

Büsgen, M. (1901). *Allgem. Forst u. Jagdztg.* 77, 273-278, 305-309.

Dominik, T. (1959). *Mycopathol. Mycol. Appl.* 11, 359-367.

Hacskaylo, E. (1961). *In* "Recent Advances in Botany," Vol. II, pp. 1744-1748. Univ. of Toronto Press, Toronto, Canada.

Hatch, A. B. (1937). *Black Rock Forest Bull.* 6, 1-168.

Hatch, A. B., and Doak, K. D. (1933). *Arnold Arboretum (Harvard Univ.)* 14, 85-99.

Liese, J. (1926). *Z. Forst- u. Jagdw.* 58, 129-181.

Melin, E. (1923). *Falk, Mykol. Untersuch.* 2, 73-201.

Merritt, C. (1959). "Studies in the Root Growth of Red Pine (*Pinus resinosa* Ait.)." Ph.D. Thesis, Univ. of Michigan, Ann Arbor, Michigan.

Noelle, W. (1910). *Botan.* 68, 169-266.

Smith, G. F., and Kersten, H. (1942). *Torrey Botan. Club Bull.* 69, 221-234.

Torrey, J. G. (1955). *Am. J. Botany* 42, 183-198.

von Alten, H. (1909). *Botan. Z.* 67, 175-199.

Wardlaw, C. W. (1928). *Phil. Trans. Roy. Soc. Edinburgh* 56, 19-55.

Wilcox, H. (1962a). *Am. J. Botany* 49, 221-236.

Wilcox, H. (1962b). *Am. J. Botany* 49, 237-245.

Tree Growth Periodicity in Tropical Climates

Paulo de T. Alvim[1]

Inter-American Institute of Agricultural Sciences of the Organization of American States (Andean Zone), Lima, Peru

The seasonal periodicity of the vegetation in temperate regions can easily be traced to variation in climatic factors, such as daylength and temperature. Among species growing in tropical regions seasonal periodicity in growth and flowering is also a very common phenomenon. However, because tropical climates are often regarded as nonseasonal, there is much uncertainty as to the factors controlling growth periodicity under tropical conditions. The literature on the subject is rather extensive, but the great majority of the studies were carried out at a time when plant-climate relationships were very poorly understood, particularly with reference to the important roles of photoperiodism and thermoperiodism. In tropical areas subjected to seasonal drought clear correlation between growth periodicity and rainfall has often been established, but in regions with fairly uniform rainfall distribution the situation seems rather confusing.

Quite often periodical phenomena in tropical plants have been attributed to "internal rhythm" or "inherent rhythm," meaning that changes take place in the plant independent of external factors. No doubt internal rhythm is easily recognizable when growth periodicity is predominantly controlled by stages of development or age of the plant. In the banana plant, for instance, each pseudostem has its own growth cycle, producing the inflorescence after a certain number of leaves are formed, after which it stops growing. A banana plantation in a tropical area with uniform rainfall or under irrigation has plants in all stages of development at any period of the year and as a rule shows no seasonal variation in crop production. In papaya (*Carica papaya*) once a certain number of fruits have been formed, flowering and vegetative growth are markedly reduced, to be resumed after the crop is harvested. As in the banana, the correlation between fruiting and vegetative growth frequently overshadows the influence of external factors, so that fruit production of

---

[1] Present address: Centro de Pesquisas do Cacau, Itabuna, Bahia, Brazil.

the plantation as a whole becomes nonseasonal. However, many references to internal rhythms found in the older literature are far from convincing and must wait for careful research on microclimate before they are accepted.

This paper is an attempt to study the periodical changes of rest and activities of tropical trees in the light of recent physiological concepts concerning the relationships of plants with their environment. It should be regarded primarily as a review of possible factors associated with the seasonal behavior of trees in the tropics.

Growth Behavior of Tropical Trees

Obviously periodical phenomena are more strikingly noticed in areas with well-defined seasonal variation in rainfall, temperature, or daylength. The amplitude of seasonal changes in three different tropical areas is

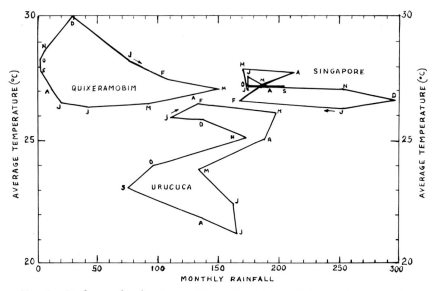

Fig. 1. Hythergraphs showing variation of rainfall and temperature in a thorn-deciduous forest climate (Quixeramobim, 4° 30′S, Brazil), a rain forest climate with seasonal differences in temperature (Uruçuca, 14° 30′S, Brazil), and a nonseasonal climate (Singapore, 1° 18′N).

shown by the hythergraphs in Fig. 1, in which monthly mean temperatures are plotted against monthly mean totals of rainfall. At Quixeramobim (4° 30′ S) in the thorn-deciduous forest region of Brazil, growth periodicity is markedly controlled by rainfall; at Uruçuca (14° 30′ S), Brazil, temperature differences and/or length of day are the predominant factors; at Singapore (1° 18′ N) the climate is practically nonseasonal and growth periodicity, although present, is less pronounced than in the other two areas mentioned and limited to a smaller number of species.

As suggested by Koriba (1958) differences in growth periodicity among tropical trees are better understood if we consider first the behavior of the growing point of the plants. When the growing point is permanently active, producing leaves successively throughout the year, the tree is "evergrowing." When the growing point ceases to grow or slows down after forming a certain number of leaves, or tends to form an inflorescence, the growth of the plant becomes intermittent. Some morphological characteristic can often be used to differentiate evergrowing from intermittently growing species. The leaves of the former are usually uniform in size and color, except for a few young ones, and the internodes are nearly equidistant, with a gradual change in bark color from tip to base. In trees with intermittent growth the leaf size and length of internodes are not uniform; scars of scale leaves that protected the young shoot initially are often noticed at the base of the shoot of each season, and there is usually a sudden transition in bark color, wearing off of epidermis, appearance of cork layer, frequency of lenticels, etc. (Koriba, 1958). Many tropical trees with intermittent growth are also deciduous, remaining leafless during part of the year. Koriba reports that among all the trees of Malaya the evergrowing trees, even with the addition of Palmaceae, Coniferae, and the tree ferns, amount to less than 20% probably 15%. The deciduous trees total about 5% and the evergreen trees with intermittent growth 75%.

Most studies on growth periodicity in the tropics have been carried out with deciduous species and, to a lesser extent, with intermittently growing evergreens. There is little doubt, however, that even among the so-called evergrowing trees the rate of growth is not uniform but exhibits some seasonal variation associated with external factors. Coffee, for instance, a typical evergrowing plant, when grown at Chinchiná (4° 5′ N), Colombia, under fairly uniform temperature and absence of dry season, usually shows two peaks of intensive growth alternated with two periods of reduced activity. Higher growth activity usually occurs around March and September and does not seem correlated with changes in temperature or rainfall (Huerta, 1962). Differences in solar radiation are apparently associated with growth behavior. The point to emphasize here is that, depending on climate, periodical changes in growth are often observed in evergrowing trees although they are not as conspicuous as in the case of deciduous or intermittently growing trees.

Periodicity in the tropics is noticed not only in leaf production and leaf fall but also in cambial activity, flowering, and fruiting. These various physiological processes are often related to each other but their relationships with environmental factors can be better analyzed if we consider them under separate topics.

Leaf Production

Periodicity in leaf production is more evident in intermittently growing trees, particularly in species such as cacao (*Theobroma cacao*) and mango (*Mangifera indica*), whose leaves have a reddish color when they are young.

Many studies have been performed with cacao to establish possible causal relationships between leaf periodicity and environmental factors. McDonald (1932-1933), in Trinidad, reported that leaf production or "flushing" of cacao was apparently correlated with soil moisture or atmospheric humidity, and would be induced in some cases by the occurrence of a dry period after the rainy season and in other cases by the reverse, i.e., the beginning of rains after a relatively dry period. This hypothesis was not confirmed by Humphries (1944), who advanced the theory that leaf flushes were primarily controlled by the "maximum air temperature in the shade." Whenever this temperature reached a value above 83° F (28.3° C), the dormant buds were induced to grow, producing a new flush of leaves. Greenwood and Posnette (1950), in Ghana, also did not find any correlation between soil moisture or air humidity and flushing of cacao, and concluded that Humphries' hypothesis was apparently satisfactory to explain the phenomenon.

Alvim (1956b), working in the tropical lowlands of Costa Rica, took biweekly data on growth condition of 400 branches of 80 cacao trees (5 branches per tree) for a period of 26 consecutive months. Tables were prepared showing variations in the percentage of buds in various growth conditions, and correlation coefficients were calculated between climatic factors (rainfall, daily hours of insolation, mean daily maximum temperature, mean daily minimum temperature, mean daily average temperature, and mean diurnal temperature range) and the percentage of dormant shoots and flushing shoots (Fig. 2). This study showed that each flushing cycle, from bud bursting to the hardening of leaves, takes about 8 weeks. The period of leaf expansion, when flushing becomes more conspicuous because of the reddish color of the leaves, occurs in the fourth week after bud bursting starts. In this study the factor most closely correlated with bud bursting or flushing initiation was found to be the mean diurnal temperature range. Maximum temperature and number of hours of insolation were also positively correlated with bud bursting, but heat in itself did not seem to be the factor inducing flushing, as suggested by Humphries; otherwise one would expect to have more intensive flushing during the warmer months (May to September) and not during the beginning of spring (March) and beginning of fall (September-October) as seen in Fig. 2. Alvim suggested that flushing was apparently induced by a thermoperiodic mechanism, i.e., a mechanism requiring a relatively high temperature during the day alternating with a relatively low temperature at night. In Costa Rica this diurnal temperature range associated with flushing seemed to be greater than about 9°C.

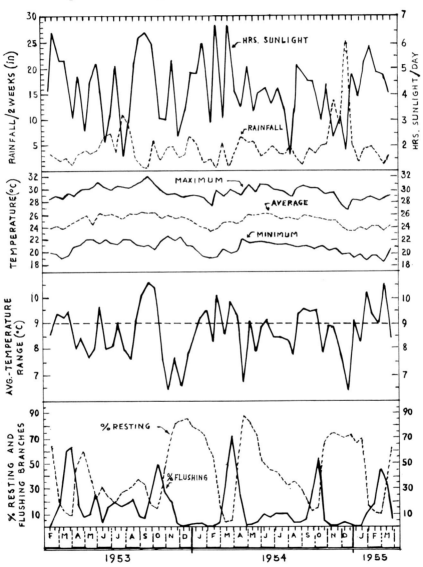

FIG. 2. Seasonal variation of leaf production of cacao and changes in climatic factors in the lowlands of Costa Rica (10°N).

A recent study by Piringer and Downs (1960) demonstrated that cacao is very sensitive to photoperiodism, growing more and producing more leaves under 12- and 16-hour than under 8-hour days. Several other tropical species react to photoperiodism in the same way as temperate plants insofar as vegetative growth is concerned, i.e., longer days favor growth and shorter days reduce it (Downs, 1962; Njoku, 1958; Piringer and Downs, 1955; Piringer et al., 1958). It is possible that, under tropical conditions during periods of reduced illumination, daylength is sufficiently shorter to reduce growth or induce dormancy in intermittently growing species. Furthermore, because there is generally a higher diurnal temperature range in the tropics during those periods of higher illumination (fewer clouds, and therefore cooler nights and warmer days), it is also possible that flushing is primarily controlled by solar radiation, the correlation with temperature range being only casual.

It is worthwhile to mention at this point that in the equatorial area of uniform climate of Singapore several intermittently growing species have been listed (Koriba, 1958) as having two main peaks of flushing during the year, one in February-March and the other in August-September (e.g., *Kurrimia paniculata, Castanopsis* spp., *Quercus* spp., *Callophyllum inophyllum, Garcinia mangostana, Parinarium corymbosum, Nephellium lappaceum, Gordonia* spp.). As mentioned before, March and September are also the two main periods of growth for coffee in Colombia. The frequency with which higher growth activity in tropical areas occurs at these two periods seems to indicate a probable relationship with higher solar radiation, as these are the periods when the sun crosses the equator (equinoxes). In other words, higher illumination during the equinoxes would act as long days, i.e., promote growth, whereas lower radiation in other periods would reduce growth.

As latitude increases north or south of the equator, the response of tropical plants to daylength becomes more evident. Thus in Sao Paulo (25° S), Brazil, according to Simão (1960), mango flushes very intensively in August, followed by 6 or 7 minor flushings from September to March, but shows no flushing from April to July, when days are shorter. Cacao in Bahia (15° S), Brazil, flushes 4 or 5 times from September to April (peaks in September and February-March), and not at all from May to August. The same absence of flushing during shorter days is observed in Costa Rica (10° N) from November to January.

Leaf Fall

The periodicity of leaf fall is related to the periodicity of leaf production. In evergrowing plants the fall of old leaves usually does not have a seasonal periodicity but seems to be only a function of leaf age. In intermittently growing evergreens leaf shedding generally follows the rhythm of leaf production and often occurs simultaneously with the growth of new leaves or only a few days before; in some species it occurs shortly after the new leaves become fully expanded (Richards, 1957). In typical deciduous trees the old leaves fall some time before the expansion of the new leaves so that the plant is bare for a period of weeks or months.

As pointed out by Richards (1957), the variation in growth behavior among rain forest trees is so great that a distinction between evergreen and deciduous species is sometimes difficult to establish. Most authors regard as evergreens those in which the tree bears a substantial number of leaves at all times, whereas deciduous species become bare, or almost so, if only for a few days. However, Volkens (1912) adopted a different definition; he regarded as evergreen only species in which leaves of at least two flushes are simultaneously present throughout the year. According to this definition trees which lose their old leaves at one time, but acquire a new set without an intervening bare period, may be classified as deciduous. Richards (1957) recognizes that this usage may be advantageous from a physiological point of view, but is less useful for most other purposes.

The relative importance of the external and internal factors in controlling leaf fall in tropical climates has been much discussed. That in intermittently growing evergreen trees leaf fall generally follows the rhythm of leaf production seems to suggest a competition for food and/or plant hormones between young and old leaves. In such cases an internal mechanism connected with leaf abscission is probably present, although its primary cause derives from factors inducing leaf production. Similarly, when leaf shedding occurs simultaneously with flowering, as in *Erythrina* spp., *Bertholetia excelsa, Jecaranda mimoseifolia, Tabebuia barbata, Chorisia speciosa,* and *Lecythis usitata,* internal competition may be involved. However, there are many tropical trees which flower 2 to 4 months after the new leaves are formed, as in *Bridelia retusa, Lagerstroemia flos-reginae, Cassia fistula,* and *Meliostoma arnottiana* (Wright, 1905). Furthermore, seasonal leaf shedding sometimes starts much before the plant reaches a flowering stage (Walter, 1962). Beard (1946) reports that among the deciduous trees of Trinidad about half the species flower when in leaf and fruit when bare; about a quarter flower when bare and fruit in the same or the following dry season, and another quarter flower in the dry season when bare, and fruit in the following wet season.

At least two external factors must be recognized as closely associated with leaf fall in the tropics: water stress and daylength. The influence of water stress is clearly seen in climates subjected to seasonal drought, as in

Rangoon (Burma), Sokoto (Nigeria), Pasoeroean (Java), and northeastern Brazil, where deciduous forests are found. In the extensive area of northeastern Brazil which is covered by the thorn-deciduous forest known locally as "caatinga" practically all trees lose their foliage during the dry season and produce new leaves shortly after the onset of rains. In deciduous trees leaf shedding almost invariably occurs during the dry period. The proportion of deciduous trees reduces as the climate becomes wetter. This influence of moisture deficiency has been noticed even in areas with fairly uniform rainfall distribution, as in Singapore, where several species lose their leaves after relatively short dry spells, sometimes twice or even three times during the year (Koriba, 1958). This, however, is by no means a general rule for Singapore, as many species shed their leaves independently of dry spells (Koriba, 1958). In the periodically dry region of western Java teak (*Tectona grandis*) loses its leaves during the dry season, but when cultivated in the wetter area of eastern Java it behaves like an evergreen (Walter, 1962).

The influence of daylength becomes apparent when we compare the leaf fall periodicity of the same species growing north and south of the equator. Several trees growing at Paradeniya (7° N), Ceylon (e.g., *Hevea brasiliensis*, *Bombax malabaricum*, *Manihot glaziovii*, and *Erythrina velutina*), drop their leaves between December and March, but at Buitenzorg (7° S), Java, those same species shed their leaves from June to August (Wright, 1905). *Hevea brasiliensis* and *Erythrina* spp. lose their leaves in January-March in Costa Rica (10° N) and in July-September in Peru (10° S) and Bahia (15° S), Brazil. In other words, at latitudes with seasonal differences in daylength, even as slight as in the above localities, leaf drop usually occurs when days are shorter. This strongly suggests the presence of a red/far-red mechanism similar to the one which regulates leaf fall in plants of temperate regions.

At Singapore where daylength is nearly uniform throughout the year, many trees exhibiting seasonal leaf fall at some distance from the equator become nonseasonal, i.e., shed their leaves at irregular intervals, either shorter or longer than 1 year (e.g., *Ficus variegata*, *Lagerstroemia flosreginae*, *Cassia fistula*, *Tamarindus indicus*, *Hevea brasiliensis*, *Cedrella glaziovii*, *Parishia maingayi*, *Heritiera macrophylla*) (Koriba, 1958). It would be interesting to determine whether leaf fall in equatorial areas such as Singapore would be related to reduced solar radiation.

Not all tropical plants lose their leaves during shorter days. For example, at Lima (12° S), *Jacaranda mimoseifolia*, a commonly cultivated ornamental tree, sheds its leaves in December-January, when days are longer. Inasmuch as flowering also occurs at this period, it is possible that long days are necessary for flowering of this species, leaf shedding resulting mainly from competition for food and/or hormones between flowers and leaves, as previously suggested.

Cambial Activity

Periodicity in cambial activity produces growth rings in the stems of perennial plants. In temperate zone species, according to Larson (1962), ring formation is related to auxin gradients. In spring the first flush of growth is rapid and the resulting high auxin synthesis stimulates production of a zone of earlywood cells throughout the cambial region of the tree. As the season advances terminal growth ceases, auxin synthesis declines, and latewood formation is initiated. As a rule the period of higher cambial activity coincides with the period of higher photosynthetic production (Kozlowski, 1962).

It is well known that the majority of rain forest trees do not show annual growth rings such as are found in temperate zone trees, but there is a relatively high proportion of species showing clear demarcation of radial growth activity. An analysis of the work of Maniere (1958) on the wood anatomy of trees from different regions of Brazil reveals that in 60 species from the rain forest regions of the Amazon Basin, 21 (35%) showed clear growth rings, 13 (22%) had poorly defined rings, and 26 (43%) showed no rings at all. In regions with seasonal climates of central and southern Brazil, out of 177 trees studies, 107 (60%) showed clear rings, 51 (25%) showed poorly defined rings, and 19 (11%) were ringless. Chowdhury (1961) estimates that 25% of rain forest trees in India show growth rings.

Age estimation in rain forest trees by means of growth rings is unreliable, not only because of poor definition of rings in most species but also

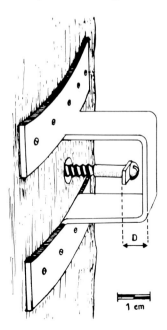

FIG. 3. Dendrometer used to measure cambium growth of cacao, modified from Byram and Doolittle (1950). Distance "D" was measured at biweekly intervals with a micro caliper.

1 cm

because, even when the growth zones are clearly defined, they may be formed only after the tree has reached a certain age (Richards, 1957). Furthermore, when multiple leaf flushes occur the growth pause that follows usually originates as a "false ring," as noted by Larson (1962).

The relationship between leaf fall and cambial activity was studied by Simon (1914) and Coster (1927-1928). During the bare period of deciduous species the cambium does not divide and activity is not resumed

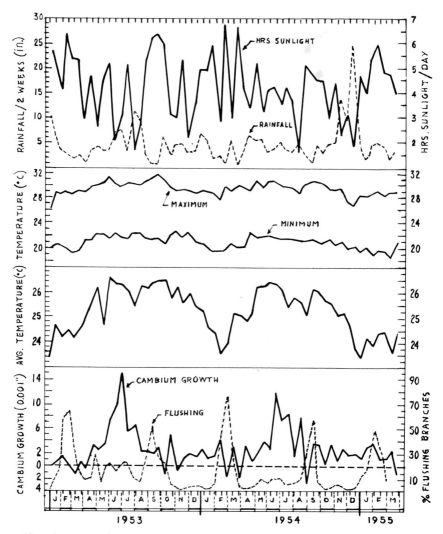

FIG. 4. Seasonal variation of cambium growth and flushing of cacao together with climatic factors in the lowlands of Costa Rica.

until the new leaves unfold. This cessation of cambial activity makes the rings quite visible. Coster (1927-1928) stated that clear rings in tropical regions are found only in deciduous trees, but Chowdhury (1961) found well-marked rings in some tropical evergreens, such as *Pterocarpus dalbergiodes, Colubrina* sp., and *Peronema* sp. .

The periodicity of cambial activity of cacao was studied by Alvim (1956a) in the tropical lowlands of Costa Rica. A slightly modified model (Fig. 3) of Byram and Doolittle's dendrometer (1950) was used to measure radial growth at biweekly intervals for a period of 26 months. The average growth of 12 trees is presented in Fig. 4, together with data on leaf flushing (from Fig. 2) and meterological data. Cambial activity was higher in June and July, when the radial increment reached a value of 0.254–0.381 mm for several 2-week periods. The average annual increase in trunk diameter was 3.81 mm. Cambial growth was markedly reduced, frequently reaching a negative value, at the time or soon after intensive flushing occurred. Radial growth was found to be positively correlated with average air temperature and negatively correlated with number of hours of bright sunlight. There was no significant correlation between cambial growth and rainfall. The negative correlation with number of hours of sunlight was regarded as a possible consequence of water stress, but since solar radiation was positively correlated with flushing, food or hormonal strain in the plant could also be responsible for reduced cambial activity during periods of higher illumination. Because diameter growth, in contrast to height growth, seems to depend primarily on current photosynthesis (Kozlowski, 1962), it is possible that higher cambial activity during June and July results from favorable conditions for photosynthesis associated with limited flushing at that time.

Flowering

Tropical plants may be grouped into four classes with regard to flowering periodicity: everflowering, nonseasonal flowering, gregarious flowering, and seasonal flowering. This is essentially the same classification as that suggested by Koriba (1958).

Everflowering species produce flowers throughout the year. They are also evergrowing, although not all evergrowing are everflowering. Examples of everflowering trees include *Hibiscus* spp., *Ficus* spp., and *Carica papaya*.

Nonseasonal flowering plants show much variation from plant to plant and even from branch to branch. Flowers are not continuous on the same plant. At Singapore the following species as well as others, behave as nonseasonal flowering: *Spathodea campanulata, Michelia champaca,*

Cassia fistula, Cassia splendens, Lagerstroemia flos-reginae (Koriba, 1958). Most of these species became seasonal-flowering when grown at some distance from the equator, as in Ceylon and Java (Wright, 1905).

Gregarious flowering is also indefinite on the calendar, but occurs simultaneously in all individuals of a species, sometimes over areas of square kilometers. The best investigated species showing gregarious flowering are *Coffea*, the pigeon orchid (*Dendrobium crumenatum*), and other epiphytic orchids of Malaya (Coster, 1926; Koriba, 1958; Walter, 1962). In such species flower buds appear continuously, but remain in a resting stage until anthesis is suddenly induced by some external stimulus. The resting period may last several weeks or months. The nature of the external stimulus causing anthesis has been much discussed. Nearly always, flowering occurs after a thunder shower following a dry spell. Usually the interval between shower and flowering varies from 8 to 11 days according to species and temperature. It has been suggested that the response to rain is not due to a direct effect of water or to any electrical phenomenon, but to the sudden fall of temperature or "cooling shock" (Koriba, 1958; Richards, 1957; Went, 1957). However, Alvim (1960) was able to demonstrate experimentally that the critical factor for gregarious flowering in coffee is not rain itself but the dry spell preceding it. In the desert coast of Peru coffee buds remained dormant for several months when the plants were irrigated at weekly intervals, but when irrigation was suspended for 3 to 5 weeks, simultaneous flowering invariably occurred about 10 days following the first irrigation. Alvim suggested that under tropical conditions water stress has an effect comparable to chilling, whose effectiveness in breaking dormancy of temperate zone plants is well known. Perhaps one could speak of "hydroperiodism" (dry period followed by wet period) as a major form of seasonal control of growth under rain forest climates.

Chilling and moisture stress seem to be equally effective in breaking dormancy of coffee flower buds. This suggestion is based on the observations of Franco (1962) on mature coffee growing outside in nutrient solutions at Campinas (25°S), Brazil. Obviously, water is never deficient for such plants, but flowering always occurs at the end of the winter (August-September) usually following the onset of rains and simultaneously with plants in nearby plantations. This would seem to be induced by low temperatures during the winter or by a sudden drop of temperature caused by rain. Inasmuch as chilling and moisture stress both decrease the free energy of water in the plant, it does not seem unjustifiable to expect some similarity in their physiological influences on bud dormancy.

Various species of *Bambusa, Strobilanthes, Hopea, Schornia*, etc. have the peculiarity of showing gregarious flowering at intervals of several years (Richards, 1957; Walter, 1962). Bamboos flower at intervals of 7–13 years in southern Brazil and die after their fruits have ripened. Much longer intervals (30–32 years) have been observed in other areas (Walter, 1962). As suggested by Walter (1962), moisture stress is probably associated with stimultaneous flowering of bamboos. This author observed flowering and death in many plants following a severe drought in 1951-52 in northern Australia, but plants in low-lying sites of the same region, where the soils remained relatively wet, did not flower or die. The Amazon trees *Spathelia excelsa* and *Tachigalia myrmecophila* also flower just once in their lifetime and die after ripening their fruits (Rodrigues, 1962).

Seasonal flowering is commonly found only in areas with periodical dry season or seasonal variation in daylength. According to Richards (1957), in most rain forest climates, including those in which the dry season is severe, flowering occurs chiefly in the dry weather (e.g., Ceylon, Nigeria, British Guiana, and Java). Schimper (1935) reports on the basis of data by Koorders and Valeton that for the whole island of Java 63% of the species flower in the dry season, about 8% in the wet season, and 29% at times unrelated to season. The frequency of flowering during dry periods gives further support to the suggestion of the influence of moisture stress on bud rest.

As latitude increases and seasonal differences in length of days and temperature become accentuated, many species considered everflowering or nonseasonal flowering when grown in equatorial regions become markedly seasonal. Cacao, for instance, flowers almost continuously throughout the year when grown in nonseasonal equatorial areas, but in Bahia (15° S) and Costa Rica (19° N) it produces practically no flower from May to August and November to January, respectively; i.e., when days are shorter and temperature lower. In equatorial areas coffee produces flower buds continuously and shows several crops of flowers throughout the year, but in São Paulo (25° S), Brazil, flower bud differentiation only occurs from May to July, when days are shorter, and flowering usually takes place at the beginning of the rainy season from September to November (Alvim, 1958). It has been shown experimentally that coffee is a typical short-day plant with regard to flower bud differentiation (Franco, 1962; Piringer and Downs, 1955).

Conclusions

It is evident from this review that most of our knowledge on the periodicity of growth in tropical climates derives from empirical field observation. Growth experiments under controlled conditions, now a routine type of research in most laboratories where growth chambers or "phytotrons" are available, have only been carried out to a very limited extent with tropical species. The value of such studies in elucidating causal relationships between growth behavior and environmental factors cannot be overemphasized.

In future studies under field conditions special attention should be given to factors which have so far received little attention in the tropics, such a total radiation, as measured by solarigraphs or pyroheliometers, and changes in radiation quality. The influence of thermoperiodism and moisture stress on growth initiation or breakage of bud dormancy should also receive further attention.

ACKNOWLEDGMENTS

The author wishes to thank the following persons who kindly furnished some information for this paper: J .Tosi, P. Cavalcanti, Bertha L. Morretes, G. Budowski, J. Murça Pires, and B. B. Calzavara.

DISCUSSION

THIMANN: If your suggestion about daylength was correct, it might be interesting to check the overcast at sunrise and sunset.

ALVIM: Unfortunately, the only data we have are based on a heliograph, a simple device recording the burning of paper; this does indicate cloudiness, but we did not try to correlate it with the time of day.

WILCOX: Koriba (1958) mentioned the appearance of intermittent trees on the Malay Peninsula. When trees got older some individual branches would be growing, while some others would be losing leaves, and still others would be making flushes. He adduced from this the autonomous behavior of meristems.

ALVIM: This is common. Mongo trees, for example, often flush on one side and are dormant on the other; *Erythrina* sometimes sheds leaves on one side while the other side retains leaves. I have never seen a case where there was not some difference in environment which could be associated with it. For instance, in a mango tree if one side is shaded, there are bound to be differences in the growth behavior of that side. Mango trees growing around São Paulo (25° S) produce more fruit on the northern side of the tree than on the southern side. This appears to be a result of higher illumination on the northern side (Simão, 1960). Differences in soil could also cause it. There are indications that minerals taken from one side are not uniformly distributed to the plant.

ZIMMERMANN: Internal cycles are well known in zoology. If mice are kept in a constant environment, they exhibit a diurnal cycle of activity. That this cycle is not induced by the environment is shown by the fact that individuals slowly deviate from the 24-hour period. One of them might shift 5 minutes every day, another one 8 minutes, and so on. I do not see why there could not be such internal cycles in trees, although they might be modified by even slight environmental changes.

ALVIM: I think that something must have started this difference, and this something must come from the outside. I would not regard these cycles as autonomous before we know more about differences in microclimate around the plants.

BROWN: If those trees which do not produce any growth rings at all were transferred to a temperate zone, or to some alternating climatic conditions, would they be able to produce rings?

ALVIM: In Costa Rica cacao is grown in the wet lowlands on the Atlantic coast and on the dry lowlands of the Pacific coast. On the Atlantic coast the rings are very poorly defined, but there are clearly marked rings on the Pacific coast.

BROWN: It is difficult to explain this on the basis of an auxin mechanism.

WAREING: I do not see why it should be.

CLEMENT: Starting some 60 years ago the Harvard Station in Cuba has collected phenological data on trees brought in from the tropics all over the world. This is something a botanical garden is supposed to do, but all too often does not do. We did manage to get some records out of Cuba. If some good physiologist were to put his mind on these records, he could probably classify a whole series of different kinds of behavior. Your paper brought several things to mind. For instance, what happens to trees which are brought from no-annual-ring country to a more extreme climate? Our station was located at 20° north latitude. Here many conditions which normally did not produce rings did produce them, even if they were not annual rings. Another thing is the disturbance of flowering patterns. Plants which normally grow near the equator often have rather fixed flowering periods, perhaps in response to very slight changes in temperature, daylength, or moisture. At 20° north latitude these plants become utterly confused; they flowered whenever they felt like it. This was not the same from one year to the next. They might flower several times in one year and not at all the next. Other plants moved over 15 or 20° of latitude retained a very regular periodicity of flowering; they flowered almost on the same day every year. I think that an analysis of phenological records of this kind could give us some clues as to the classes of phenomena involved in this behavior.

THIMANN: You mentioned the Indian study by Chowdhury (1961) in which only 25% of the trees showed growth rings. Did this study cover the whole country?

ALVIM: I think it covered all of tropical India. It was a paper on the relation of growth rings to taxonomy.

THIMANN: Chowdhury's figure is lower than what you mentioned for Brazil.

ALVIM: He does not give many detailed figures, just that percentage. I obtained my data from a large number of studies done in São Paulo by Maniere (1958).

WAREING: Is it known how many of these are evergreen and how many are deciduous species? How far do these trees without growth rings show periodicity in extension growth and how many grow spasmodically?

ALVIM: As mentioned in my paper, Coster (1927-1928) suggested that rings are formed chiefly in deciduous trees, but Chowdhury (1961) found well-defined rings in some tropical evergreens.

WAREING: Do you find deciduous species among those that do not form rings?

ALVIM: Apparently, whenever they are deciduous they form rings.

WAREING: I mention this because a cambial stimulus almost certainly comes from fully developed leaves. I think that mature leaves produce significant amounts of auxin which can stimulate cambial activity. The trees that do not show rings should be examined to ascertain whether they are evergreen and whether they flush in a particular season or grow continuously.

ALVIM: Unfortunately the study by Maniere (1958) was purely anatomical; it gives no information on growth behavior of plants.

WAREING: Do you know if there are growth rings in individual shoots in cases where there are not in the main trunk? I can well imagine that if there are periodic flushes within the shoots there might be local growth rings, but these could disappear further down the trunk, where samples are usually taken. This disappearance would be expected, especially if the shoots do not flush simultaneously.

ALVIM: Each flush generally produces a mark in the wood below. In cacao there may be many marks per year. From general observation I believe each flush produces a ring in the branch, but I am not in a position to say how far down this ring goes.

FREY-WYSSLING: In its first year rubber (*Hevea brasiliensis*) has two periods of growth. In the second year, under appropriate conditions, there may be as many as four flushes. The 2-year-old base will then show six indistinct rings.

WAREING: On the other hand, when there are two flushes in European oak, the second one a lammas shoot, there are not necessarily two growth rings at the base of the first shoot. I came to the conclusion that something keeps the cambium active during the quiescent period of the bud. Even cutting out the developing bud had no effect. I was therefore led to the conclusion that a cambial stimulus can come from the mature leaves.

LARSON: This is also true in some of our temperate zone conifers. *Pinus banksiana,* for example, normally produces several flushes of growth in a season, but the flushes succeed each other so rapidly that no separating latewood layer is laid down in the wood.

ALVIM: In some trees there is more cambial activity when the buds are not growing; I mentioned this in the paper. Extension growth in intermittently growing species seems to represent such a drain on the resources of the tree that it decreases the rate of cambial activity.

FREY-WYSSLING: Suckers from stumps of old, cut rubber trees (*Hevea brasiliensis*) grow continuously. They form 100 to 300 leaves and a 2-centimeter-thick shoot. The old root system seems to supply enough material to enable these shoots to grow continuously.

ALVIM: Juvenile shoots have no periodicity; they flush and grow continuously. Rubber trees, or mango, can be propagated vegetatively when they are juvenile. When they get old and show periodicity propagation with cuttings becomes rather difficult. Juvenile shoots also do not shed their leaves. These facts clearly indicate that there are physiological differences associated with age that modify growth periodicity.

REFERENCES

Alvim, P. de T. (1956). *In* "VI Reunião Comite Tecnico Interam. Cacau," pp. 83-87. Bahia, Brazil.

Alvim, P. de T. (1956b). *In* "VI Reunião Comite Tecnico Interam. Cacau," pp. 117-125. Bahia, Brazil.

Alvim, P. de T. (1958). *Coffee Tea Ind.* 81, 17-25.

Alvim, P. de T. (1960). *Science* 132, 354.

Beard, J.S. (1946). *Oxford Forestry Mem.* 20.

Bünning, E. (1948). *In* "Vernalization and Photoperiodism" (A.E. Murneek and R.O. Whyte, eds.). Chronica Botanica, Waltham, Massachusetts.

Byram, G.M., and Doolittle, W.T. (1950). *Ecology* 31, 27-35.

Chowdhury, K.A. (1961). *Proc. 10th Pacific Sci. Congr. Pacific Sci. Assoc., Honolulu, Hawaii, 1961* (in press).

Corner, E.J.H. (1940). "Wayside Trees of Malaya." Singapore.

Coster, C. (1926). *Ann. Jard. Botan. Buitenz.* 35, 125-162.

Coster C. (1927-1928). *Ann. Jard. Botan. Buitenz.* 37, 49-160; 38, 1-114.

Downs, R.J. (1962). *In* "Tree Growth" (T.T. Kozlowski, ed.), pp. 133-148. Ronald Press, New York.

Franco, C.M. (1962). *In* "Curso Internacional de Fisiologia Vegetal." Piracicaba, Brazil.

Greenwood, M., and Posnette, A.F. (1950). *Hort. Sci.* 25, 164-174.

Huerta, A. (1962). Personal communication.

Humphries, E.C. (1944). *Ann. Botan. (London)* [N.S.] **8**, 259-267.
Koriba, K. (1958). *Garden's Bull. Singapore* **17**, 11-81.
Kozlowski, T.T., ed. (1962). *In* "Tree Growth," pp. 149-164. Ronald Press, New York.
Larson, P.R. (1962). *In* "Tree Growth" (T.T. Kozlowski, ed.), pp. 97-117. Ronald Press, New York.
Maniere, C. (1958). *Bol. Inst. Pesquisas Tecnicol. São Paulo* **46**.
McDonald, J.A. (1932-1933). *Ann. Rept. Cacao Res., Imp. Coll. Trop. Agr., Trinidad, 1931* **1**, 29-38; **2**, 88-iv.
Njoku, E. (1958). *J. West African Sci. Assoc.* **4**, 99-111.
Piringer, A.A., and Downs, R.J. (1955). *Turrialba* **5**, 72-77.
Piringer, A.A., and Downs, R.J. (1960). *Proc. 8th Inter-Am. Cacao Conf., Trinidad*, pp. 82-90.
Piringer, A.A., Downs, R.J., and H.A. Borthwick (1958). *Am. J. Botan.* **45**, 323-326.
Richards, P.W. (1957). "The Tropical Rain Forest." Cambridge Univ. Press, London and New York.
Rodrigues, W.A. (1962). *Inst. Nacl. Pesquisas Amazonia, Publ.* **14**, Manaus, Brazil.
Schimper, A.F.W. (1935). "Pflanzengeographie auf physiologischer Grundlage," 3rd ed. (Revised by F.C. van Faber) Jena.
Simão, S. (1960). "Estudos da planta e do fruto da mangueira (*Mangifera indica* L.)." Thesis. Escola Superior de Agricultura "Luiz de Queiroz," Piracicaba, Brazil.
Simon, S.V. (1914). *Jahrb. Wiss. Botan.* **54**, 71-187.
Volkens, G. (1912). "Laubfall und Lauberneuerung in den Tropen." Berlin.
Walter, H. (1962). "Die Vegetation der Erde in ökologischer Betrachtung." Fischer, Jena.
Went, F.W. (1957). "Experimental Control of Plant Growth." Chronica Botanica, Waltham, Massachusetts.
Wright, H. (1905). *Ann. Roy. Botan. Gardens Peradeniya* **2**, 415-517.

Recording Photosynthesis, Respiration, and Transpiration

Bruno Huber

Forstbotanisches Institut, Universität München, Germany

The present paper reviews some of the recent work on the ecology of gas exchange in trees by means of recording instruments, particularly the infrared recorder [the Ultrarot-Absorptionsschreiber (URAS) of the German literature]. Emphasis is placed on laboratory investigations in this paper; a review of research under field conditions is given by Tranquillini in his contribution to this volume.

Advances of recent years are primarily due to improved instrumentation. Not only do our modern gas analyzers have a greatly increased sensitivity, but they also produce a much denser series of figures. The increased quality of recent results does not by any means, however, curtail our appreciation of the efforts of the pioneers in the field of ecology of photosynthesis like Henrici or Lundegårdh.

To start with well-known facts, let us recall Blackman's discovery of the logarithmic relation between light intensity and rate of photosynthesis. The next important step was the discovery of Boysen Jensen (1932), who died in 1961, that shadow leaves of trees (ash) have a lower respiration and a lower light compensation point than sun leaves. On the other hand, photosynthesis of sun leaves increases with increasing light intensities to a much higher value than that of shadow leaves (Fig. 1); the curve of photosynthesis of sun leaves therefore crosses the curve of shadow leaves at a certain light intensity.

Recent investigations show that these two kinds of behavior are widely distributed. They not only hold true for light and shadow leaves and light and shadow plants, but also for single leaves and whole plants, and for needles and branches of pine (Kramer and Clark, 1947; further literature cited by Kramer and Kozlowski, 1960, p. 77). It is easy to understand that a forest reaches light saturation at a much higher light intensity than a single leaf illuminated at a right angle, because the actual illumination of leaves in a tree or forest is much lower than the light intensity indicated by a photometer.

Walter (1963) found a similar relation between precipitation and mass of vegetation; the open vegetation of deserts and semideserts is, according to Walter, saturated with plants, because the small amount of available

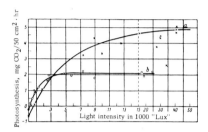

FIG. 1.   The effect of light intensity on net photosynthesis in sun leaves (a) and shadow leaves (b) of ash. The respiration of shadow leaves is lower in the dark (light intensity zero) than that of sun leaves. Photosynthesis is equal to respiration (light compensation point) at lower light intensities in shadow leaves than in sun leaves. Optimal photosynthesis is reached at lower light intensities in shadow leaves than in sun leaves. The curve of photosynthesis in sun leaves starts with a higher respiration and a higher light compensation point, but increases to much higher light intensities. It crosses the curve of shadow leaves at about 3000 lux. From Boysen Jensen (1932).

water does not allow a denser vegetation. The differences between desert and nondesert plants in transpiration per unit of leaf surface or leaf weight are surprisingly small.

The effect of temperature on photosynthesis was investigated by Pisek and Winkler (1959) (Fig. 2). The optimal temperature for photo-

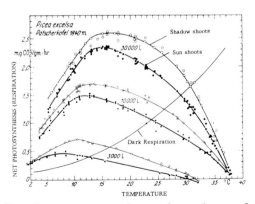

FIG. 2.   The effect of temperature on photosynthesis of sun and shadow leaves of spruce at different light intensities (3000, 10,000, and 30,000 lux). Optimal temperature rises from about 10° at 3000 lux to about 16° at 30,000 lux. The exponential curve indicates respiration. From Pisek and Winkler (1959).

synthesis increases with light intensity. Plants of the mountains such as Norway spruce in the Alps reach their optimum at temperatures below 20°C, some arctic and alpine lichens not much above the freezing point (Lange, 1963). In plants adapted to cold, apparent photosynthesis ceases at many degrees below the freezing point. This suggests that in tropical

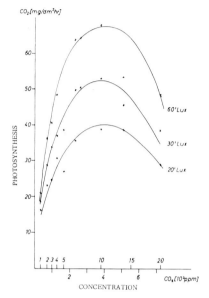

FIG. 3. The effect of carbon dioxide concentration on photosynthesis in poplar leaves at different light intensities. The optimal CO_2 concentration appears to be independent of the light intensity. This situation needs further investigation. From Koch (1963).

plants the optimal points of photosynthesis are much higher on the temperature scale. Modern recording methods have not yet been used in tropical regions.

The third essential factor of photosynthesis is carbon dioxide. In our modern laboratories we are faced with the two problems of stabilizing and of varying the amount of CO_2. The increasing motorization in the neighborhood of our laboratories causes serious fluctuations of the CO_2 content of the air. Every morning when the staff arrive at the building, the exhaust gases of their cars cause a remarkable increase of the CO_2 content of the air. This fluctuation can be eliminated by passing the air through a filter of diethanolamine (Koch, 1963). The effect of carbon dioxide concentration on the rate of photosynthesis can be studied by mixing CO_2-free air with given amounts of CO_2 from a gas container.

Infrared absorption values do not increase linearly with the concentration of carbon dioxide. For experiments over a wide range of concentrations, for example 300 to 10,000 ppm or 0.03 to 1% volume, Koch recommends the compensation method which was first used in the Patscherkofel climate house. Within a fixed scale, for example, between 240 and 360 ppm, he measured the quantity of CO_2–free air necessary

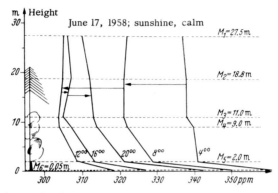

FIG. 4. Daily march of the carbon dioxide content of the air at different heights in a mixed forest stand. Between 4 A.M. and noon there is a rapid decrease of CO_2, due to vertical turbulence. There is a slow recovery during the afternoon, a more rapid one during the night. From Miller and Rüsch (1960).

to dilute a given air sample of the experimental setup to bring the analytical sample to within the scale. Figure 3 shows results obtained with poplar.

Photosynthesis increased considerably if the carbon dioxide content was raised above the natural concentration in air. An increase in light intensity did not increase the optimal CO_2 concentration of photosynthesis. The exact position of the CO_2 optimum needs further investigation; it may well depend on temperature as well as light.

Here it should be mentioned that investigation of photosynthesis of trees at higher CO_2 concenrations is more of a fundamental than a practical interest. The old opinion that in dense forests CO_2 accumulates to high values is erroneous according to recent records (Fig. 4). Within an hour after sunrise the CO_2 that accumulated during the night is removed, not by the intense photosynthesis of the vegetation, as formerly thought, but by vertical turbulence caused by temperature inversion. This is even true for the Swiss *Plenterwälder*, mixed stands of fir (*Abies alba*) of very different age classes, as Mitscherlich (1963) found in the Black Forest.

Every forester knows that wood productivity of forests depends on soil nutrition; he usually distinguishes among five *Bonitäten* (site indices) of different productivities. Keller and Koch (1963) showed that this difference is due to differences in photosynthesis (Fig. 5). Strangely enough, this relationship was formerly studied in algae and other lower plants but never in trees.

Finally a few remarks on evaluation of records. The rate of photosynthesis usually is expressed per surface or weight of leaves. However, it is better if photosynthesis (A) and respiration (R), or photosynthesis

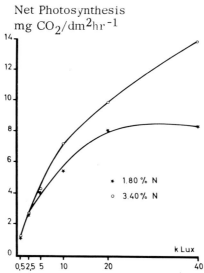

FIG. 5. Photosynthesis of poplar leaves at different light intensities and two different nitrogen contents of leaves. The nitrogen content becomes the limiting factor at high light intensities. The same holds true for iron. From Keller and Koch (1963).

and transpiration (T) of the same leaf or branch are compared directly. Thus we obtain values which are independent of leaf weight and surface.

$$\frac{A}{\text{weight}} : \frac{T}{\text{weight}} = A : T$$

$$\frac{A}{\text{weight}} : \frac{R}{\text{weight}} = A : R$$

$A : T$ is often called "productivity of transpiration"; $A : R$ (in the case of net photosynthesis), or $(A + R)/R$ (in the case of total photosynthesis), is called "economic coefficient." Under optimal conditions Huber and Rüsch (1961) found $(A + R)/R$ values above 20 for poplar leaves; this means that less than 5% (sometimes only 2%) of the total photosynthesis is lost by leaf respiration, while according to Eidmann (1962) 20–50% is lost by root respiration. Koch (1956) has investigated the daily march of $A : T$ ratio (Fig. 6) (see also Huber, 1958). He found a maximum in the morning soon after sunrise because photosynthesis follows radiation while transpiration rises more slowly with air temperature and the water-saturation deficit of the air.

The $A : T$ ratio has been investigated under increasing dryness. Let us recall what Stocker (1956) wrote in the "Encyclopedia of Plant Physiology": under dry conditions the plant has to balance between hunger and thirst. That is, it has to avoid a lethal water deficit without preventing photosynthesis. Vieweg (1960) claims that there is a sudden drop of photosynthesis at a certain point of water-saturation deficit. But

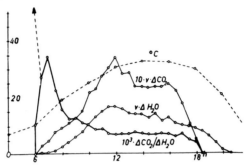

FIG. 6. Daily march of the ratio (heavy line) between vertical CO_2 flux (v. Δ CO_2) and water vapor flux (v. Δ H_2O). Abscissa, time of day; ordinate, arbitrary units. From Koch (1956).

Larcher (1960, 1961a, b, 1962) has published comparative investigations of A and T on detached branches of the evergreen oak *Quercus ilex* and the deciduous oak *Quercus pubescens* (Fig. 7). *Quercus ilex* shows a rise of the $A : T$ ratio to higher water-saturation deficits and then a sudden drop due to a very effective closure of the stomata. Polster *et al.* (1960) published similar observations from the Hungarian *Quercus cerris–Quercus robur* stand at the timber line bordering the steppe. They found

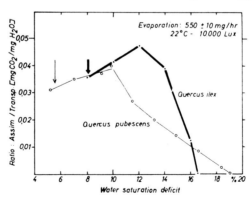

FIG. 7. The effect of water-saturation deficits on the ratio photosynthesis: trans-piration in *Quercus pubescens* and *Quercus ilex*. The evergreen oak continues photo-synthesis to higher saturation deficits than the deciduous oak. From Larcher (1962). (See also Tranquillini, 1963.)

a negative balance of the outer, especially sunny branches, on sunny days, but the shadow of these branches allows active photosynthesis in the inner parts of the crown.

Brix (1962) measured the effect of diffusion-pressure deficits (DPD) on photosynthesis and respiration in Kramer's laboratory. Photosynthesis

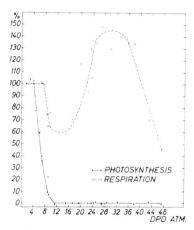

Fig. 8. The effect of diffusion-pressure deficits on photosynthesis and respiration of loblolly pine seedlings. From Brix (1962).

dropped sharply with increasing DPD, while respiration decreased more slowly and showed a sublethal rise (Fig. 8) (see also Huber and Ziegler, 1960).

An early observation of Bosian (1933) that respiration (R) also drops during midday because of stomatal closure has not been confirmed by later investigations. Pisek and Winkler (1953, 1959) found in their observation of gas exchange with detached branches without water supply a slow and much lower decrease of R than of A and T. Ziegler might be right in his remark at the Innsbruck Symposium that closing the stomata has little influence on respiration because oxygen supply from air containing more than 20% CO_2 is not as limiting for respiration as 0.03% CO_2 is for photosynthesis.

References

Bosian, G. (1933). *Z. Botan.* **26**, 209-290.
Boysen Jensen, P. (1932). "Die Stoffproduktion der Pflanzen." Fischer, Jena.
Brix, H. (1962). *Physiol. Plantarum* **15**, 10-20.
Eidmann, F. (1962). *Intern. Symp. Baumphysiol., Innsbruck, 1961* pp. 43-45 (mimeo).
Huber, B. (1958). *In* "The Physiology of Forest Trees" (K.V. Thimann, ed.), pp. 367-379. Ronald Press, New York.

Huber, B., and Ziegler, H. (1960). *In* "Encyclopedia of Plant Physiology" (W. Ruhland, ed.), Vol. XII/2, pp. 150-169. Springer, Berlin.

Intern. Symp. Baumphysiol. (1962). *Innsbruck, 1961.* Zusammenfassung der Vorträge und Diskussionen (mimeo).

Keller, Th., and Koch, W. (1963). *Mitt. Eidgen. Anst. Forstl. Versuchswesen* **38**, 253-318.

Koch, W. (1956). "Der Tagesgang der 'Produktivität der Transpiration,'" Diss. München.

Koch, W. (1963). *Allgem. Forst- Jagdztg.* **134**, 54-57.

Kramer, P.J., and Clark, W.S. (1947). *Plant Physiol.* **22**, 51-57.

Kramer, P.J., and Kozlowski, T.T. (1960). "Physiology of Trees." McGraw-Hill, New York.

Lange, O.L. (1963). *Ber. Deut. Botan. Ges.* **75**, 351-352.

Larcher, W. (1960). *Bull. Res. Council Israel Sect. D.* **8**, 213-214.

Larcher, W. (1961a). *Planta* **56**, 575-606.

Larcher, W. (1961b). *Planta* **56**, 606-617.

Larcher, W. (1962). *Intern. Symp. Baumphysiol., Innsbruck, 1961* pp. 6-8 (mimeo).

Miller, R., and Rüsch, J. (1960). *Forstw. Zentr.* **79**, 42-62.

Mitscherlich, G. (1963). *Allgem. Forst- Jagdztg.* **134**, 1-12.

Pisek, A., and Winkler, E. (1953). *Planta* **42**, 253-278.

Pisek, A., and Winkler, E. (1959). *Planta* **53**, 532-550.

Polster, H., Weise, G., and Neuwirth, G. (1960). *Arch. Forstw.* **9**, 947-1014.

Stocker, O. (1956). *In* "Encyclopedia of Plant Physiology" (W. Ruhland, ed.), Vol. III, pp. 646-741. Springer, Berlin.

Tranquillini, W. (1963). *Ber. Deut. Botan. Ges.* **75**, 353-364.

Vieweg, G. H. (1960). "Wasserhaushalt und Phytosynthese des Kormophytenblattes, mit besonderer Berücksichtigung der refraktometrischen Saugkraftbestimmung." Auszug. Diss., Darmstadt.

Walter, H. (1963). *Ber. Deut. Botan. Ges.* **75**, 349-350.

Photosynthesis and Dry Matter Production of Trees at High Altitudes

WALTER TRANQUILLINI

Forstliche Bundesversuchsanstalt Mariabrunn, Forschungsstelle für Lawinenvorbeugung, Innsbruck, Austria

Advances in Methods

Measurements of CO_2 exchange in plants under field conditions are still a matter of argument because of the so-called "cuvette climate." If the CO_2 uptake or output of leaves has to be measured, the leaves must be enclosed in containers where they heat up much more than in the open air. In addition, the air in the cuvette is always more humid because the transpired water vapor accumulates and, as a rule, the air in the cuvette moves less than in the field.

These climatic changes in the cuvette, especially overheating and its effects on photosynthesis and respiration, were already known in principle to the pioneers of ecological research of gas exchange (Henrici, 1921; Bosian, 1933).

Recently I showed by experimenting in a climatized wind tunnel that photosynthesis of several tree seedlings was also strongly influenced by the relative air humidity (Tranquillini, 1963). The rate of photosynthesis was measured at values of 85, 50, and 25% relative air humidity, while other factors such as light, temperature, wind, CO_2 concentration, and soil moisture were maintained constant. Figure 1 shows that photosynthesis of all tree species decreases considerably in dry air; in the case of spruce the value is less than 10% of the value measured in humid air. This decrease was especially marked with plants which were grown in the shade and constantly wet soil. It had to be attributed to severe dehydration of photosynthetic tissue. When transpiration in dry air was high, the plant seemed to be unable to absorb sufficient water although the soil was saturated with water. This occurs often under field conditions and Kramer (1958, 1962) has emphasized the fact several times.

Great efforts have been made to make the climate within the cuvette similar to the climate outside. The most important methods are cooling the walls of the cuvette with water (Bosian, 1933), cooling and drying the air entering the cuvette (Bosian, 1960), reducing the time of the experiment (Holdheide *et al.*, 1936), the use of a *Klappcuvette* (Lange, 1962a), reduction of insolation (Pisek and Tranquillini, 1954), and absorption of the infrared radiation (Tranquillini, 1954).

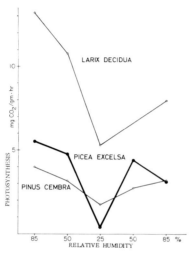

Fig. 1.   Photosynthesis of larch, spruce, and pine seedlings at various degrees of air humidity in a wind tunnel. The other climatic factors remained constant (40,000 lux, 17°C, 4 meters/sec, 300 ppm CO_2). The soil moisture content amounted to 50% of field capacity. From Tranquillini (1963).

I have tried to solve the problem by increasing the rate of air flow through the cuvette, a method which has already been used by Bourdeau (1962). The experiments were performed at 1900 meters above sea level at the Patscherkofel near Innsbruck during August and September 1961. A branch of larch was enclosed in a cuvette and photosynthesis and microclimate were determined at various rates of air flow through the cuvette.

From all the values measured I selected only those which were obtained at noon time on clear sunny days where the cuvette climate is extreme.

The difference in temperature between the needles of larch enclosed in the cuvette and those in the open air was found to be 11°C at a rate of air flow of 30 liters per hour (Fig. 2). With increasing rate of air flow the difference decreased rapidly at first and more slowly later on. At a rate of 2000 liters per hour the difference was only 0.5°C. This difference is negligible, especially with ecological measurements of gas exchange.

We measured not only the temperature, but also evaporation from disks of green filter paper, so-called "Piche disks" inside and outside the cuvette, in order to determine the transpiration stress of the leaves. Figure 2 shows the rates of evaporation at different air flow rates in percent of the rates of evaporation measured at the same time outside

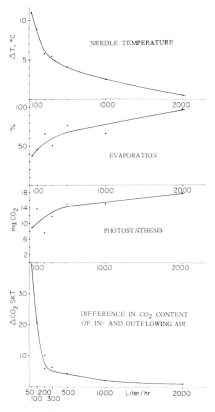

Fɪɢ. 2. The effects of air flow on the climatic conditions in the cuvette in full sunlight at noon. Temperature differences are given in degrees C, evaporation from filter paper disks in percent of evaporation from disks outside the chamber, photosynthesis in mg CO_2 absorbed, and the difference of CO_2 concentration between in- and out-flowing air in scale units of the instruments.

the cuvette. At an air flow of 30 liters per hour evaporation in the cuvette in sunny weather about noon time is only 40% of the evaporation outside the cuvette. With increased rate of air flow the relative evaporation increases; at 2000 liters per hour the same values were obtained for measurements inside and outside of the cuvette.

Figure 2 shows how much net photosynthesis is influenced by the rate of air flow and by the previously discussed changes of temperature and evaporation in the cuvette. The decrease in photosynthesis at low rates of air flow is the result of high temperature and poor CO_2 supply to the leaves in the cuvette. (See also the paper by Huber in this volume.)

It may be inferred from these experiments that the climate in a cuvette can become the same as the climate in the field and appropriate values of photosynthesis can be obtained if the rate of air flow in the cuvette is great enough. In our case this was at least 2000 liters per hour corresponding to an air movement of 50 cm per second. At this rate of air flow the larch needles started to tremble slightly. Diaphragm pumps cannot handle such large quantities of air; therefore we used a blower (Boepple & Co. K.G., Giessen, Germany) with which air could be blown through the cuvette at a rate of 10 cubic meters per hour. This blower could be operated continuously for very long periods of time.

At these high rates of air flow the CO_2 difference between the in-going and out-going air was very small. With the infrared gas analyzer set at its highest sensitivity (3 ppm CO_2 per unit of scale division) and maximum photosynthesis of a twig of larch (10–18 mg CO_2 per gram of needle dry weight and hour), the CO_2 difference was only one scale unit at a rate of air flow of 2000 liters per hour (Fig. 2). This was within the limit of error of the analyzer. Experiments with high rates of air flow require therefore a recording instrument with a sensitivity 50 times as great as the standard ones. The firm of Hartmann and Braun in Frankfurt has designed such an instrument and called it "Super-URAS." The first apparatus is being tested now.

The Annual Course of the Net Photosynthesis of *Pinus cembra L.* and *Larix decidua Mill.* at the Timber Line (2000 Meters above Sea Level)

The experiments were carried out near Obergurgl in the Ötz Valley in the Tyrol at 2000 meters above sea level just above the timber line (Tranquillini, 1957, 1959a, b). A hut was put up in which the recording instruments for CO_2 exchange and microclimate could be installed. Several pine and larch trees within a radius of 100 meters from the observation hut were selected. Both tree species grow at the timber line in the Central Alps and are well adapted to the rough climate of high elevations. The pine mainly regenerates in raw humus, the larch in

FIG. 3. Needle temperature in the cuvette (daily mean, maxima, minima) and needle temperature in the open air (horizontal marks), global radiation, precipitation, height of snow cover and daily sum of net photosynthesis and night respiration of several pine trees at the field station near Obergurgl (2000 meters) during the growing season 1955. From Tranquillini (1959a).

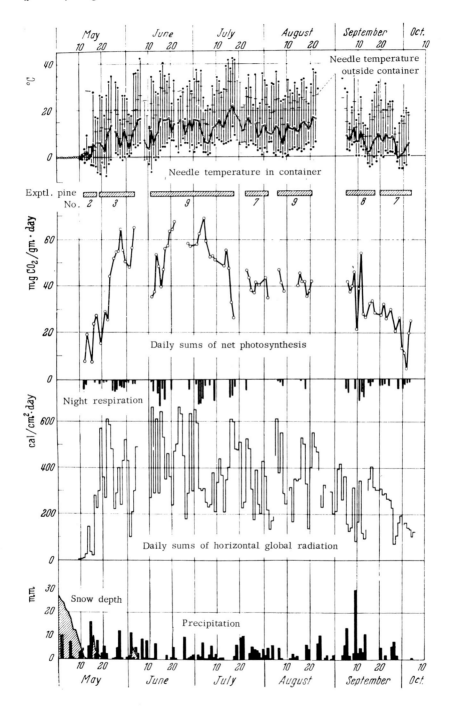

Needle temperature outside container

Needle temperature in container

Exptl. pine No.

Daily sums of net photosynthesis

Night respiration

Daily sums of horizontal global radiation

Snow depth

Precipitation

mineral soil. The rate of growth of the trees at the timber line is extremely slow. Even in the most favorable habitats, both species attain a height of only 80 centimeters in 25 years.

The cuvettes and the measuring instruments were placed near the plants and connected with wires and tubes to the recording instruments

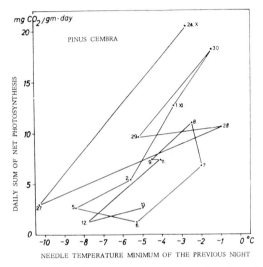

Fig. 4. Daily CO_2 uptake of young pine trees as a function of the needle temperature minimum of the preceding night. From Tranquillini (1957).

in the hut. Measurements were carried out throughout the year. We shall first discuss results obtained with pine.

In May, when the area became free from snow, the CO_2 exchange was at once positive (Fig. 3). The daily uptake of CO_2 was, however, still very small and fluctuated about 20 mg per gram of dry weight of needles. Photosynthesis suddenly increased toward the end of May; the daily uptake was then about 50–60 mg. This was the effect of several very warm days (leaf temperature above 30°C for short periods, daily average above 10°C; Fig. 3). High temperature promoted photosynthesis. In the following period photosynthesis decreased again: the daily rate was about 40 mg. As pine sprouts in July, we first assumed that photosynthesis was inhibited by sprouting because Clark (1956) has already shown that the current year's needles are not as efficient as the older needles. Now we know from similar behavior of the larch that the decrease was caused by a change of the internal condition of the plant also. This assumption was substantiated by the fact that during this period other processes were carried on more slowly or came to a complete stop; for instance, water movement (Huber and Plankl, 1956), diameter growth

(Kern, 1960), and rooting capacity of cuttings (Raschendorfer, 1953; Schiechtl, 1958).

In September photosynthesis gradually fell to a low rate because of a decrease in temperature, light intensity, and photoperiod.

With the first frosts, especially when the temperature dropped below

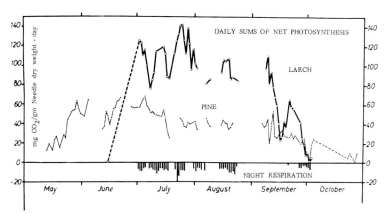

Fig. 5. Annual course of daily CO_2 uptake of young larch and pine trees, and night respiration of larch trees at the timberline near Obergurgl (2000 meters). From Tranquillini (1962).

—4°C, photosynthesis was severely inhibited. I plotted the daily rates of photosynthesis during that period as a function of the minimum needle temperature of the preceding night (Fig. 4). It is quite obvious that photosynthesis is very low after a severe night frost. If warm weather follows, photosynthesis increases but does not reach the same values again. With more frequent and more severe frosts photosynthesis is further inhibited. Thus a gradual decline of photosynthesis was observed in October.

Water freezes in the needles below —4°C (Tranquillini and Holzer, 1958). When ice is formed, water is rigorously removed from protoplasm. The structures of the protoplasm and the plastids are changed. This change cannot be reversed at this time of the year because the necessary heat is missing.

The CO_2 intake is completely stopped in winter. This is the effect of two causes:

(1) The stomata are closed because the plants suffer from water deficiency. The ground is frozen and absorption of water has stopped.

(2) Photosynthesis is so severely inhibited that even the CO_2 produced by respiration in the leaves cannot be reassimilated. Respiration as an enzymic process is less severely inhibited by frost and starts rapidly at

temperatures above the freezing point. The CO_2 balance of plants is therefore negative in midwinter during warm periods, i.e., the leaves release CO_2 in light and suffer substantial losses of dry matter.

This dormancy or negative CO_2 balance in winter lasts until it gets warm enough so that (1) frost leaves the ground and the stomata can be reopened, and (2) photosynthesis is no longer inhibited, that is, the protoplasm is changed back into its original state.

These conditions were not met in our habitat until the end of April. Photosynthesis started slowly from that time on.

Comparing the annual course of the CO_2 exchange of the pine with that of the larch (Tranquillini, 1962), we saw that the leaf buds of this species open at the timber line in mid-June. At the end of June the needles were fully grown. This late budding was a result of the climate. These young larch needles, rich in water content, are extremely sensitive to frost. If they budded earlier, they would be damaged by late frosts.

Therefore photosynthesis of larch started at a time when the evergreen pine had already been photosynthesizing at maximum rate for about a month (Fig. 5). In July photosynthesis was very high. But a month later there was a marked drop for reasons already discussed. From the fact that the depression of photosynthesis starts later with the larch, it is to be inferred that this depression does not depend on the climate but on the duration of great photosynthetic activity.

During September photosynthesis of the larch was rapidly reduced. The same effects are probably responsible for the drop as in the pine, that is decreasing light intensity and temperature. Photosynthesis in the pine was only decreased by the first frosts, but remained positive until November. In larch, however, the same frosts rapidly caused decomposition of the chlorophyll, needles became discolored, and photosynthesis came to a stop 1 month earlier than in pine.

The growing season of the larch (107 days) is remarkably shorter than that of the pine (181 days), but the shorter period of photosynthesis of larch is more than compensated by its high photosynthetic rate during the summer. The annual total of CO_2 uptake per gram dry weight of needles (9,243 mg) is 47% higher in larch than in pine (6,278 mg).

A comparison of the annual course of CO_2 exchange with the annual course of the various factors of climate shows clearly what an important factor temperature is. It not only influences photosynthesis and respiration directly (see the paper by Huber in this volume), but causes changes in the structure of the protoplasm, especially of the plastids, the apparatus for photosynthesis. In autumn the frosts force the plant into dormancy, hinder photosynthesis, or even stop it. The earlier they occur, the more frequent and more severe they are, the earlier plants become dormant, the more thorough dormancy is and the more difficult it is to bring about a reversal of this state. Besides the inhibition of photosynthesis, other far-reaching changes take place in the plant: frost resistance is increased, the chloroplasts are moved to the center of the cells, the chlorophyll becomes more sensitive to light and is partly photochemically destroyed, the needles get a yellowish hue.

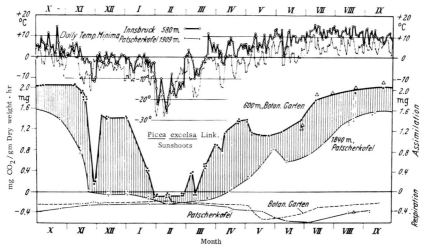

FIG. 6. Annual variations in photosynthetic capacity of sun leaves of *Picea excelsa* in Innsbruck (600 meters) and Patscherkofel (1900 meters). Above: daily temperature minima at Innsbruck and Patscherkofel. The hatched area shows how much more is produced by spruce in the warmer valley climate than at the timber line.

In spring all these changes are reversed for the most part: dormancy is broken, photosynthesis is resumed, frost hardiness decreases, the chloroplasts move back to their original position, new chlorophyll is produced, and the needles become green again.

It is obvious that these changes depend on a certain amount of heat. It is, however, not yet known whether a certain threshold of temperature has to be exceeded, or whether the breaking of dormancy is due to the influence of a certain heat sum. The only fact known is that the period of dormancy gets longer, and the production of the trees less, the colder the climate is.

It is well known that climate gets colder with increasing geographical latitude and altitude. Pisek and Winkler (1958) have made a comparative investigation of the photosynthetic capacity of spruce in various regions. At certain times of the year twigs were brought into the laboratory and photosynthesis and respiration determined under standard conditions. The results are shown in Fig. 6. Temperature minima are much lower at the Patscherkofel (1900 meters) than at Innsbruck (600 meters). Frosts occur much earlier in autumn and much later in spring. Therefore photosynthesis is stopped 2 months earlier at the timber line than in the valley and is resumed in the spring 1 month later. The degree of dormancy is also different. At the timberline the CO_2 balance is continuously negative for 5 months, branches down in the valley make use of each warm period for dry matter production during winter. Their gas exchange comes to a complete rest only during the cold days in February. The hatched area in Fig. 6 shows very impressively how much more dry matter is produced by spruce in the warmer valley climate than at the timber line.

From these investigations we may draw the conclusion that decreasing temperature with increasing altitude plays an important part in dry matter production and therefore temperature is also important for the upper forest limit and the timber line, both in the mountains and extreme northern latitudes. The limits, as far as they are caused by nature, are where the summer heat is not sufficient for dry matter production to make up for the substantial losses during the winter and achieve at least a small surplus production for growth.

Analysis of Dry Matter Production of Trees at the Timber Line

Since Boysen Jensen (1932) and his collaborators in Denmark and Polster (1950) in Germany have made the analysis of dry matter production in forest trees, we know that a surprisingly small part of carbon, assimilated by the leaves in gross photosynthesis, is converted into stem wood. The greater part is lost again by (1) respiration of the leaves, twigs, stems and roots, (2) loss of leaves, twigs, bark, roots and seed, and (3) excretion of organic substances (excretion of the roots, transfer to the mycorrhizal mycelia).

This problem was the subject of two recent international symposia, the ecological symposium about dry matter production of vegetation at Stuttgart-Hohenheim in 1960 (Lieth, 1962) and the symposium of tree physiologists at Innsbruck in 1961 (published in 1962).

According to Polster (1950) only 24–45% of the total photosynthesis of several European tree species goes into increment and 17–33% into usable wood. Similar results were obtained by the Danish scientists when they analyzed the dry matter production of beeches (Möller et al., 1954).

I have analyzed the dry matter production of young pine plants at the timber line by measuring growth increments and comparing this with values calculated from gas exchange measurements (Tranquillini, 1959b). Experiments with larch are under way now.

The sum of the annual gross photosynthesis of young pines amounted to 7,830 mg CO_2 per gram of needle dry weight (Fig. 7). During the vegetation period 1,551 mg CO_2 (20%) is consumed in respiration by the leaves during the daytime. This is little compared with tree species in lower regions. According to Polster (1950), loss through respiration amounts to 21% in beech and 46% in pine. These are extreme values.

At night a further amount of 556 mg CO_2 (7% of the total photosynthesis) is consumed in respiration. This loss is also less than that of trees in lower regions because the nights are warmer there and respiration is higher. Just to give an example, spruce and beech near Munich consume on the average about 17% of the gross photosynthesis at night during the vegetation period (Pisek and Tranquillini, 1954).

Another loss of 447 mg of CO_2, that is, 6%, occurred through the respiration of the roots of pine. This loss is debated because respiration

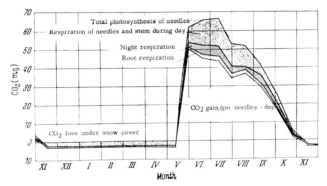

FIG. 7. Annual course of the CO_2 balance of young pine plants at the timber line. From the amount of CO_2 assimilated by the leaves by gross photosynthesis a part is lost by respiration of the shoots and roots immediately and by respiration during the nights. The CO_2 gain of the plant during the growing season is diminished by respiration of the whole plant in winter under snow cover.

was determined with isolated roots. Eidmann (1962) stated that roots have considerably less respiration in the air than in the ground. According to his measurements the roots of various tree species respire 20–40% of the gross photosynthesis. But it has to be taken into account that my pine seedlings had a surprisingly small mass of roots compared to the mass of leaves; besides, the soil temperature at the root horizon is very low at 2,000 meters above sea level. Both factors greatly reduce root respiration.

During the period of snow cover the parts of the plants above ground consume 439 mg of CO_2 in respiration, that is, 6% of gross photosynthesis.

As stem respiration of seedlings has already been taken into account in considering respiration of needles, and the loss in leaf, bark, and root of seedlings is not worth considering, we get a total loss of 2,993 mg of CO_2. This is 38% of the gross photosynthesis.

Each gram of needles converts 4,837 mg of CO_2 or 1.3 gm carbon into organic matter. As the dry matter substance of pine seedlings consists of 60% carbon, this equals about 2.2 gm of dry matter.

The actual increment of dry matter for the seedlings was only 0.65 gm. This is only one-third of the value calculated from the measurements of gas exchange.

Such a discrepancy was rather surprising because both methods for the determination of dry matter had been worked out very carefully. I had thought earlier that the plants gave off considerable quantities of carbon compounds to the mycorrhizal fungi (Melin and Nilsson, 1957). How much the quantity actually is, has not yet been investigated.

Now I am inclined to assume that the pine needles in the cuvettes assimilated much more vigorously than the plants in the field. At the time these measurements were taken we could not eliminate the overheating of the leaves in the cuvettes. Overheating was quite noticeable on sunny days (Fig. 3). Therefore photosynthesis in cuvettes may have attained rates similar to those of a warmer climate, rates which are never reached under natural conditions. This interpretation has been confirmed by experiments in the climate house at the Patscherkofel. Larch seedlings which were kept at 10°C in a cool greenhouse assimilated much less under optimum conditions in the wind tunnel than those which had been transferred to a warmer greenhouse (20°C) a few weeks before the experiments were started.

DISCUSSION

HELLMERS: From your last graph (Fig. 6), I gather that it takes an extended cold period to knock out the photosynthetic mechanism of your trees. Those in the valley were able to recover after one short cold spell and then photosynthesized most of the winter, but those on the mountain were inactivated completely because of the extended cold period. This suggests that one cold spell will not completely eliminate photosynthesis, but reduces it. Is there a relationship between the length or degree of cold and the recovery rate?

TRANQUILLINI: The differences in photosynthetic capacity on the mountain and down in the valley are primarily based upon the different frequencies of severe frosts. On the Patscherkofel we also have warm weather during the daytime, but the minima do not exceed the freezing point for a period of 5 months. Therefore the photosynthesis remains negative.

FREY-WYSSLING: As a matter of fact, it is not real dormancy, because as soon as the temperature rises above zero photosynthesis starts up again. You can see that peak in early March. Is this real dormancy or just induced dormancy?

TRANQUILLINI: Spruces appear to have some sort of endogenous rhythm: photosynthetic capacity decreases during the winter even if the trees are grown in the greenhouse under summer conditions. However, a complete cessation of photosynthesis is brought about only upon repeated exposure to temperatures below the point where water freezes in the needles.

THIMANN: Does photosynthesis stop at exactly 0°C?

TRANQUILLINI: The temperatures in the figure are air temperatures. The needle temperatures are quite different. Needle temperatures are as a rule lower at night and higher in the day.

THIMANN: What temperature is it in the needles when photosynthesis stops?

TRANQUILLINI: About minus 4°C, the temperature at which water freezes in the needles of *Pinus cembra.*

ZIEGLER: It is not necessary that photosynthesis stop when the water freezes. Dr. Lange, in my department, has lichens (*Stereocaulon alpinum* and *Cladonia alcicornis*) which show some net photosynthesis at —24°C (temperature of the lichen, not of the air). They are completely frozen (Lange, 1962b). He confirmed this with $C^{14}O_2$. But I think there is no question that photosynthesis stops in pine at temperatures a little below zero.

TRANQUILLINI: Yes, the plastids of pine are different from those of an algal cell.

WAREING: How can these enzyme-controlled reactions go on in frozen preparations?

ZIEGLER: We do not know. He has at present only the effect.

THIMANN: Is it really frozen? Is it possible that it is still fluid?

ZIEGLER: The thallus is frozen (there is a distinct, determinable, species-characteristic freezing point), but I cannot say whether the functioning plastids are really frozen.

COLVIN: Even if it is supercooled to that degree it is still extraordinary.

THIMANN: We know that the first reaction, the photoreaction involving the chlorophyll and the cytochrome, goes on at liquid-air temperature (Chance and Nishimura, 1960).

ZIEGLER: But Dr. Lange determined the light-dependent CO_2 consumption.

HELLMERS: Probably one of the problems is that when light enters the cell, the temperature inside the plastid may be quite different from what it is in the vacuole.

ZIEGLER: Possibly the plastids are at —15°C, not —24°C like the rest of the thallus. It is also true that —24°C is only the lower limit of our present device, not that of the capacity of the lichens.

PRESTON: Did not Blackman show photosynthesis at —20°C in his work 20 years ago?

TRANQUILLINI: Even Henrici (1921) found photosynthesis below —20°C, if I remember correctly, but these older measurements were not very reliable.

ZIEGLER: When you take needles of the Patscherkofel trees, how long must you hold them above zero to break their dormancy?

TRANQUILLINI: This depends on their dormancy. If shoots are brought to +10°C in the middle of the winter, it takes about 3 days until they show a net photosynthesis, but they do not reach a photosynthetic capacity as high as that of the summer. If, on the other hand, the twigs are warmed up toward the end of the winter, they show net photosynthesis immediately.

WILCOX: Are these 1-year-old needles when you start the experiment? Do you measure the same needles continuously?

TRANQUILLINI: There are several branches with 5 years' growth of needles on them.

HELLMERS: This raises a question about the relationship of the larch to the pine. Freeland (1952) has shown that the photosynthetic rate decreases with the age of the needles. But you are comparing pine needles, with a 3- or 5-year life span, with larch, which has only 1 year's needles.

TRANQUILLINI: We have not compared the various years' needles; we have only measured the whole branch.

THIMANN: What about differences between the top and the bottom of the tree?

TRANQUILLINI: We have not investigated this in pine, but in spruce and beech. There are marked differences in tall trees. The pines were short.

THIMANN: Are the upper leaves more effective or less so?

TRANQUILLINI: This depends on their water stress. In water-stressed plants the top of the crown is more effective, but when there is much water in the soil the basal leaves are more effective.

REFERENCES

Bosian, G. (1933). Z. Botanik **26**, 209-284.

Bosian, G. (1960). Flora (Jena) **149**, 167-188.

Bourdeau, P. F. (1962). Intern. Symp. Baumphysiol., Innsbruck, 1961, p. 63 (mimeo).

Boysen Jensen, P. (1932). "Die Stoffproduktion der Pflanzen." Fischer, Jena.

Chance, B., and Nishimura, M. (1960). Proc. Natl. Acad. Sci. U.S. **46**, 19-24.

Clark, J. (1956). Bimonthly Progr. Rept. Div. Forest Biol. Dept. Agr. Can. **12**, 1-2.

Eidmann, F. (1962). Intern. Symp. Baumphysiol., Innsbruck, 1961. pp. 43-45 (mimeo).

Freeland, R. O. (1952). Plant Physiol. **27**, 585-690.

Henrici, M. (1921). Verhandl. Naturforsch. Ges. Basel **32**, 107-168.

Holdheide, W. V., Huber, B., and Stocker, O. (1936). Ber. Deut. Botan. Ges. **54**, 168-188.

Huber, B., and Plankl, L. (1956). Forstwiss. Zentr. **75**, 350-357.

Kern, K. G. (1960). Allgem. Forst- Jagdztg. **131**, 97-116.

Kramer, P. J. (1958). In "The Physiology of Forest Trees" (K. V. Thimann, ed.), pp. 157-186. Ronald Press, New York.

Kramer, P. J. (1962). In "Tree Growth" (T. T. Kozlowski, ed.) pp. 171-182. Ronald Press, New York.

Lange, O. L. (1962a). Ber. Deut. Botan. Ges. **75**, 41-50.

Lange, O. L. (1962b). Ber. Deut. Botan. Ges. **75**, 351-352.

Lieth, H. (1962). "Die Stoffproduktion der Pflanzendecke." Fischer, Stuttgart.

Melin, E., and Nilsson, H. (1957). Svensk Botan. Tidskr. **51**, 166-186.

Möller, C. M., Müller, D., and Nielsen, J. (1954). Ber. Schweiz. Botan. Ges. **64**, 487-494.

Pisek, A., and Tranquillini, W. (1954). Flora (Jena) **141**, 237-270.

Pisek, A., and Winkler, E. (1958). Planta **51**, 518-543.

Polster, H. (1950). "Die physiologischen Grundlagen der Stofferzeugung im Walde." Bayr. Landwirtsch.-Verlag, München.

Raschendorfer, I. (1953). Forstwiss. Zentr. **72**, 159-171.

Schiechtl, H. M. (1958). Mitt. Forstl. B.-Versuchsantalt Mariabrunn **55**, 1-273.

Tranquillini, W. (1954). Ber. Deut. Botan. Ges. **67**, 191-204.

Tranquillini, W. (1957). Planta **49**, 612-661.

Tranquillini, W. (1959a). Planta **54**, 107-129.

Tranquillini, W. (1959b). Planta **54**, 130-151.

Tranquillini, W. (1962). Ber. Deut. Botan. Ges. **75**, 353-364.

Tranquillini, W. (1963). Planta **60**, 70-94.

Tranquillini, W., and Holzer, K. (1958). Ber. Deut. Botan. Ges. **71**, 143-156.

The Role of Water in Wood Formation

PAUL J. KRAMER

Duke University, Durham, North Carolina

Introduction

It is well known that there is a relationship between water supply and wood formation. Trees usually form wider annual rings and make more diameter growth in wet than in dry summers and even temporary water deficits decrease or sometimes stop diameter growth. The classic work on water in relation to diameter growth was done by MacDougal (1921, 1924) and the extensive literature is cited by Glock (1955), Schulman (1956), and Zahner (1963). The science of dendrochronology is based on existence of a relationship between rainfall, soil moisture, and diameter growth of trees.

In spite of several decades of research, the relationship between water supply and wood formation is not completely understood. There are many discrepancies between rainfall and tree growth and the relationship differs in regions with different patterns of rainfall, as for example, California and northern Arizona (Glock and Agerter, 1962). Because of the effect of temperature on transpiration which in turn affects tree water stress, more growth might even occur in a summer of below-average rainfall if the temperature were below average than in a summer with high rainfall, but with high temperatures which cause excessive water loss (Coile, 1936). Furthermore, trees on a wet site may grow more in a dry year than in a wet year when saturated soil and poor aeration reduces absorption (Fraser, 1962). It also has been shown that the rainfall of one season sometimes has significant effects on diameter growth the following season (Fritts, 1962; Schulman, 1956; Schumacher and Meyer, 1937).

The existence of these inconsistent relationships between water supply and tree growth is more comprehensible when we recall that rainfall and soil moisture affect growth only indirectly. Growth is controlled by a complex of biochemical and physiological processes which are affected by the degree of water stress existing in the tree. The water stress of a

519

tree is determined by the relative rates of water loss and water absorption, processes which depend on atmospheric and soil moisture conditions. Thus the direct correlation is between growth and tree water stress and the correlation between growth and environmental moisture conditions is indirect and variable.

The exact manner in which water deficit reduces tree growth is not fully understood because it affects growth in many ways, some direct and some indirect, and it is very difficult to evaluate their relative importance (Zahner, 1963).

Requirements for Cambial Activity

In order to discuss the role of water in wood formation we will list the principal requirements for cambial activity and wood formation and then consider their role at various stages in cambial activity.

The important requirements for cambial activity are as follows: (1) a temperature suitable for a high level of metabolic activity; (2) a supply of growth regulators, especially auxin; (3) a supply of carbohydrates and nitrogen-containing substances; (4) a supply of mineral nutrients; and (5) sufficient water to maintain cells in a turgid condition.

Water supply and temperature affect nearly all of the processes involved in the synthesis of food, its translocation to the cambium, and its conversion into new tissue. Temperature also influences the availability of soil water and the rate of transpiration and thus affects the degree of water stress occurring in trees; hence these factors are highly interrelated.

The Role of Water

There are many ways of dealing with the role of water in wood formation, but perhaps the most effective approach is to consider its role in connection with the various phases or stages in growth during a season. These major phases will be listed and the effects of water stress will be discussed for each one separately, so far as that is possible.

The principal stages in wood formation during a season are: (1) enlargement of existing cells; (2) initiation of cell division; (3) earlywood formation; (4) latewood formation; (5) occasional formation of false rings; and (6) permanent cessation of growth.

Enlargement of Existing Cells

According to Ladefoged (1952), Wilcox (1962), and others, the first evidence of cambial activity is radial enlargement of existing cells. In upper New York State cambial cells of several species begin to enlarge radially as soon as the mean temperature rises above 40°F for a week (Wilcox, 1962). This is about 3 weeks before the buds open and 4 weeks before cambial cells begin to divide.

The time at which this stage starts presumably depends on the temperature rising high enough to permit the required level of metabolic activity. Any auxin required must already be present because it could not have been supplied from the buds which are not yet swelling. Water does not appear to be a limiting factor for this stage in cambial activity.

Initiation of Cell Division

There is general agreement that cambial cells begin to divide in the spring about the time the buds begin to swell, presumably in response to downward movement of auxin produced in the opening buds (see Larson, 1962; Wilcox, 1962; Wort, 1962; for the extensive literature on this topic). In cool climates the opening of buds occurs about the same time that a marked increase in water content occurs (Craib, 1918; Gibbs, 1958) and this led Priestley and Scott (1936), Scarth (1936) and others to suggest that increase in water content is responsible for the opening of buds. Bannan (1962) states, "When frost leaves the ground and water becomes available, cambial reactivation takes place." Presumably this occurs because the buds begin to grow and supply auxin when water becomes available.

This dependence on uptake of water may exist in cold climates, although the writer doubts if even in Canada the water content of trees falls low enough to be limiting. It is true that the water content of tree trunks decreases in late winter and then increases after the soil thaws, but the winter low often is higher than the water content in early summer when growth is occurring (Clark and Gibbs, 1957; Gibbs, 1958). Lack of water certainly is not the factor limiting the opening of buds and resumption of cambial activity in warmer climates such as California or the southern states. This view also is supported by Huber's (1948) observation that cambial activity sometimes is resumed in the spring in felled trees, which obviously cannot absorb more water. It is much more probable that in general the opening of buds depends on occurrence of temperatures high enough for the necessary level of metabolic activity than that it depends on an increase in water content. However, the role of temperature sometimes is questioned. For example, Daubenmire (1949) stated that the beginning of diameter growth in 17 species of trees in northern Idaho was not clearly related to air or soil temperature. Growth began about the same time each spring, suggesting that resumption might be controlled by photoperiod rather than temperature.

Earlywood Formation

Formation of the thin-walled cells of large diameter characteristic of earlywood seems to be associated with an abundant supply of auxin and carbohydrate, sufficient water to maintain a high level of turgidity, and temperatures high enough for rapid metabolism. The importance of temperatures in early season growth is shown by the existence of a high correlation between temperature and growth early in the season which disappears later when soil moisture is likely to be more limiting (Fritts, 1958; Kozlowski, *et al.*, 1962). Water is seldom a limiting factor early in the season, except where the soil is frozen to a considerable depth.

Early growth probably is dependent largely on carbohydrates formed the preceding season, but rapid growth will soon deplete the supply unless conditions are favorable for current photosynthesis. The new shoots provide adequate auxin, and nitrogen and minerals are not likely to be limiting. However, competition between cambium and new cells for carbohydrates must be keen, and Zahner (1963) suggests that this may be responsible for the short life and thin walls of the first-formed xylem elements.

Rudinsky and Vité (1959) proposed that rapid flow of water through the xylem is a factor in the vertical alignment of xylem elements. Zahner (1963) suggested that this rapid flow through the earlywood may speed up the maturation of the newly formed cells and result in loss of protoplasm before much wall thickening has occurred. Perhaps the orienting effect of the transpiration stream also is involved in the alignment of new xylem elements to form effective pathways for conduction around wounds in trees.

Latewood Formation

As the season progresses there is a transition from the large-diameter, thin-walled cells of earlywood to the smaller, thicker-walled cells of latewood. According to Zahner (1962, 1963) this transition usually begins after the first severe water deficit occurs. It can be delayed until late summer by irrigation or by an even distribution of summer rainfall, or it may occur very early in the summer if there is an early drought. It may occur gradually if water stress develops gradually or it may occur abruptly if water stress develops rapidly.

Although there is much evidence that the transition from earlywood to latewood is closely related to the occurrence of water stress, there is considerable uncertainty concerning the mechanism by which the transition is brought about. Water stress might act directly by reducing cell division and cell enlargement, but it might also act indirectly by reducing photosynthesis, auxin synthesis, and the translocation of carbohydrates and auxin to the cambium.

Some investigators, such as Larson (1962, 1963), claim that the transition from earlywood to latewood is caused primarily by a decreasing supply of auxin. They argue that water stress operates indirectly by reducing shoot and leaf growth which results in decreased synthesis of auxin, and the decreased supply of auxin causes the change in cell type from earlywood to latewood and eventually brings about the cessation of wood formation. The importance of auxin is supported by the results of experiments in which photoperiod, disbudding, and the application of exogenous supplies of auxin all affected the amount and type of wood formed. According to Wareing and Roberts (1956) a stimulus originating in the mature leaves under long photoperiod, but not under short photoperiod, keeps the cambium active in *Robinia pseudacacia*. However, growing stem tips were not required, either in *Robinia* or in *Pinus silvestris*, where cambial activity continues 4 to 6 weeks after leaf growth ceases (Wareing, 1951). Cambial activity often continues in other species for some weeks after shoot and leaf growth has ceased, indicating that growing shoots and leaves are not always essential as a source of auxin.

Perhaps after it is once stimulated the cambium can produce enough auxin to support growth for a time. Hatcher (1959) found that the auxin content of the trunks of apples trees fell very low during a drought, but rose rapidly after a rain. Apparently, in this instance auxin was produced in the cambium rather than in the leaves or buds, suggesting that the increase was the result of increased cambial activity rather than the cause. Wareing (1951) reported that debudded ring-porous species continued to form wide vessels, but debudding restricted cambial activity of diffuse-porous species. He suggested that ring-porous species may have a large reserve of auxin precursor in the cambium so that only a small amount is required to cause initiation of growth. Apparently the relationships of auxin to cambial activity may vary considerably among different species.

If sufficient water stress develops in a tree to slow down or stop shoot growth one would expect cambial activity to be affected also, unless the cambium of a tree is subjected to less water stress than the stem tips. This is unlikely in view of the shrinkage observed in trunks of trees during periods of water stress. The direct effects of water stress on cell division and cell enlargement would be exerted as soon as stress developed, but the effects of water stress on auxin and carbohydrate supply would develop considerably more slowly. It seems probable that cell enlargement in the cambial region will have been modified by the direct effects of water stress some days before a sufficient shortage of auxin or carbohydrate develops to seriously modify growth.

The amount of latewood formed depends largely on the water supply late in the growing season. If an abundance of rainfall is uniformly distributed throughout the summer, earlywood formation may continue until the end of the growing season. On the other hand, severe drought often stops latewood formation early in the season (Zahner, 1962), but if moisture stress does not become too severe growth may continue into the early autumn, resulting in a wide band of latewood.

Water supply also affects the amount of secondary thickening occurring in the walls of latewood cells. The amount of secondary thickening is supposed to be controlled chiefly by the supply of carbohydrates and Zahner (1963) states that mild water deficits which restrict cambial cell division without seriously reducing photosynthesis probably are most favorable for secondary thickening.

False Rings

False or double rings develop occasionally, if after the formation of some latewood a return to more favorable conditions results in formation of a second layer of earlywood. According to a review by Zahner (1963), false rings are caused by severe water stress produced by midsummer drought, followed by sufficient rainfall to cause resumption of growth. Defoliation by insects or storms also is said to cause double rings. Larson (1962, 1963) points out that double rings occur only if shoot growth is interrupted and then resumed and claims the resumption of earlywood production occurs because of the increased auxin supply from the renewed growth of shoots. It is likely that auxin is effective only if the water stress is eliminated; hence it might be argued that an increased supply of water is as important as an increased supply of auxin. Furthermore, an increase in carbohydrate caused by increased photosynthesis may be involved.

Cessation of Growth

In dry seasons wood formation usually stops quite early in the summer because of water stress, but in wet seasons it may continue until September or October and finally is slowed down and stopped by processes associated with low temperature and decreasing photoperiod. Larson (1962, 1963) claims that cambial activity ceases because cessation of shoot and leaf growth reduces the supply of auxin. Among the arguments advanced to support this view is the fact that growth ceases at the bases of trees before it ceases toward the crowns, presumably because the base of the trunk is farthest from the crown, where auxin is produced. It should be remembered, however, that the base of a tree trunk also is farthest from the leaves, where carbohydrates are produced. The production of carbohydrate presumably is reduced as promptly by water stress as the production of auxin, and the translocation of both is reduced by water stress. Furthermore, cambial activity often continues for several weeks after shoot and leaf growth ceases (Wareing, 1951).

We do not have enough information to evaluate accurately the relative importance of decreasing auxin and carbohydrate on wood formation. However, we do have evidence from laboratory research that moderate water stress will reduce or stop cell enlargement even in the presence of adequate auxin and carbohydrate. This is discussed later.

Physiological Effects of Water Stress

As stated earlier, water stress affects wood formation by modifying various physiological processes and conditions which control cell division, enlargement, and differentiation. A few of these effects will be discussed individually in order to show more clearly some examples of the direct and indirect consequences of water stress.

Cell Turgor

It appears that low cell turgor is one of the most common limitations on cell expansion because it has been shown repeatedly that reduction in turgor reduces cell enlargement, even in the presence of auxin (Ordin, 1958, 1960; Thimann, 1954, Thimann *et al.*, 1950). Apparently sufficient turgor pressure must exist to keep the protoplasts pressed firmly against the cell walls if deposition of new wall material and cell enlargement is to continue. Furthermore, turgor of the guard cells determines the degree of stomatal opening and thus controls the pathway available for entrance of the carbon dioxide used in photosynthesis.

Besides the direct effects on cell enlargement, the turgidity or the DPD has important effects on cell metabolism. Even a low DPD is said to reduce incorporation of C^{14} into cell walls (Ordin, 1958, 1960; Ordin *et al.*, 1957). Gates and Bonner (1959) reported that water stress increased the destruction of RNA in tomato leaves and it probably has important effects on other aspects of nitrogen and carbohydrate metabolism. Water stress must have considerable effect on enzyme systems and this topic ought to be investigated further.

Auxin

In addition to some minimum degree of turgor, a supply of auxin seems to be necessary for normal cell enlargement. Apparently it affects the plasticity of cell walls and the metabolic processes responsible for production and deposition of new material in growing walls (Cleland, 1958; Ordin *et al.*, 1956; Thimann, 1954).

The experimental data cited by Larson (1962) and others indicates the importance of auxin in controlling the amount and kind of wood formed by trees supplied with adequate water. However, it is equally clear that a deficiency of water also can modify or stop cambial activity very quickly, just as it can stop shoot growth. There is uncertainty, therefore, as to whether water stress usually reduces or stops growth by direct effects on cell turgidity or by reducing the auxin supply. Perhaps it operates both ways. One or two days of high transpiration might produce sufficient water stress to reduce or stop growth immediately and directly because of reduced turgor, before a deficiency of auxin or carbohydrate could develop. On the other hand, a water deficit developed slowly over many days probably will be accompanied by a reduction in the supply of both auxin and carbohydrates to the cambium.

It seems possible that too much emphasis is placed on auxin in connection with cambial activity. According to Kefford and Goldacre (1961), auxin is not a determining agent, but a predisposing agent which probably operates with kinins in activating cell division and with gibberellins in activation of cell enlargement. Perhaps more attention should be given to the possible roles of substances other than auxin in the regulation of cambial activity. Overbeek (1962) suggested that the pre-eminence given auxin results largely from the historical fact that it was the first growth regulating substance to be discovered. He describes the roles of auxin, kinins, and gibberellins in fruit enlargement and also emphasizes the importance of water and carbohydrates. All of these substances probably are likewise important in cambial activity and wood formation.

Carbohydrate Supply

Formation of wood requires large amounts of carbohydrates. Kremers (1957) estimated that for each gram of cell wall material present in the primary stage 20 grams are added by maturity. Perhaps another 10 grams of carbohydrate are used in respiration. The carbohydrate used in the early part of the season comes chiefly from photosynthate produced the previous year, hence growth early in one year often shows a correlation with rainfall of the preceding summer and autumn (Fritts, 1962; Schulmann, 1956; Schumacher and Meyer, 1957). However, growth later in the season uses the products of current photosynthesis and the large carbohydrate requirements of secondary thickening make it particularly sensitive to factors which decrease photosynthesis.

Photosynthesis is relatively sensitive to water stress (Kramer, 1958; Kramer and Kozlowski, 1960; Stalfelt, 1956). Brix (1962) recently made measurements of photosynthesis of loblolly pine subjected to increasing DPD and found that photosynthesis began to decrease rapidly at a relatively low water stress. This reduction probably is caused by closure of stomates cutting off the supply of carbon dioxide, because the decrease in rate of photosynthesis parallels the decrease in transpiration. Roberts (1963) found the same relationship between photosynthesis and transpiration with increasing water stress in yellow poplar.

Summer droughts can be expected to drastically reduce photosynthesis and decrease the supply of carbohydrates available for latewood formation and secondary thickening of cell walls. Presumably water deficits also reduce the synthesis of auxin by limiting the growth of stems and leaves.

Translocation

Reduction in rate of translocation can limit the supply of auxin and carbohydrates to the cambium. Other papers in this volume discuss possible mechanisms of translocation, but we will venture the statement that the effectiveness of any translocation mechanism will be reduced by water stress. Roberts (1963) has shown that even a moderate water stress severely reduces the translocation of C^{14}-labeled carbohydrate out of the leaves of yellow poplar. Wiebe and Wihrheim (1962) also found that a moderate water stress significantly reduced translocation of C^{14}-labeled compounds out of sunflower leaves.

As auxin appears to be translocated out of leaves in association with carbohydrates, reduction of movement of the latter would be expected to reduce translocation of the former. Various experiments on translocation of herbicides from leaves indicate that movement is greatly reduced by water stress (Basler *et al.*, 1961; Pallas and Williams, 1962).

It seems clear that water stress reduces translocation of both auxin and carbohydrates out of the crowns of trees. Such reduction may be involved in the earlier change to latewood and earlier cessation of growth in the lower than in the upper part of tree trunks and in suppressed as compared with dominant trees (Kozlowski and Peterson, 1962).

Measurement of Water Stress

Regardless of whether its effects are exerted directly by reduction in turgor or indirectly by reduction in the supply of auxin and carbohydrates, it is clear that water stress has very important effects on wood formation and diameter growth. In order to understand these effects we need to measure tree water stress in connection with research on cambial activity and wood production. As pointed out in the introduction, the level of tree water stress cannot be reliably estimated from measurements of soil moisture conditions, but must be measured directly.

The best measure of water stress in plants probably is the diffusion pressure deficit (DPD) or water potential. This can be measured by the electric hygrometer techniques of Monteith and Owen (1958) or Richards and Ogata (1958), which probably can be used equally well for leaves and pieces of wood or twigs. Another promising method is the Schardakow dye method described by Mouravieff (1959) and others. Thus far no one seems to have made measurements of the DPD of pieces of wood cut out from the cambial region. Although there would be operational difficulties in sampling wood such measurements might be preferable to those made on leaves.

A second method of measuring water stress is to determine the relative turgidity (Weatherly, 1950; Harms and McGregor, 1962) or water deficit of leaves by the method of the Stocker (1929). Hewlett and Kramer (1963) prefer to determine the water deficit on more or less intact leaves rather than on leaf disks because there is error from infiltration and temperature changes. Measurements of water deficit are easily made and show trends in water stress, but the percentages obtained are not comparable among different species as DPD values would be. Measurements of DPD or water potential would be preferable when they can be made. The important point is that the water stress of the tree must be measured directly if we are to understand the relationship between water supply and the physiological processes which control wood formation.

Conclusions

It generally is agreed that the development of water stress in trees influences almost every aspect of wood formation, including the duration of cambial activity, the transition from earlywood to latewood, the amount of secondary thickening, and the total width of annual rings. However, it is not certain how many of these effects are caused directly and how many indirectly. Water stress can reduce growth directly by reducing cell turgor and interfering with metabolism and cell enlargement. It might reduce growth indirectly by decreasing the synthesis of auxin and carbohydrates and slowing down their translocation to the cambium.

Some investigators claim that water stress usually operates indirectly by reducing shoot and leaf growth and thereby reducing the supply of auxin. However, water stress severe enough to reduce or stop shoot growth probably will also reduce or stop cambial activity at the same time, long before an auxin deficiency could develop. Water deficits also decrease photosynthesis, thereby reducing the supply of carbohydrates available for secondary thickening and other processes in the cambial region. However, the effects of water stress operating through reduced auxin and carbohydrate probably occur much more slowly than the direct effects operating through cell turgor. A severe water stress developed rapidly would operate directly, at least at first, while a stress developed slowly over a longer period might operate principally through indirect effects.

Separation and evaluation of the relative importance of direct effects of reduced cell turgor and the indirect effects of reduced auxin and carbohydrate supply is difficult. It will require simultaneous measurements of cambial activity auxin content, carbohydrate supply, and water stress in the cambial region. Direct measurement of tree water stress is particularly important because plant water stress cannot always be estimated reliably from soil moisture measurements. The processes controlling growth are affected directly by the tree water stress and growth is correlated only indirectly with soil and atmospheric moisture conditions.

DISCUSSION

WAREING: I think that none of us would disagree with the idea that in a complex process like cambial activity, which requires a variety of different environmental conditions, nutrients, hormones, etc., any one of the factors can be limiting. Thus, under certain conditions lack of water may be limiting, or low temperatures, or light intensity. If none of these external conditions are limiting, then cambial activity may be limited by internal conditions; this is where one tends to stress the role of auxin. There is really no fundamental difference of opinion about this. It is a difference of approach. If one is interested in ecological problems and trees growing in the forest, one stresses the effect of external factors. If one is more interested in developmental problems, the plants are supplied with adequate water so that this is not limiting.

KRAMER: To a degree, that is correct. However, I could not agree with Dr. Larson when he said that water stress interferes with cambial activity by first reducing shoot growth. I would argue that the cambial cells were already inhibited by water stress.

LARSON: I agree that water stress is involved in the effect of auxin on any cell system. Turgor pressure is certainly involved in cell enlargement, once the cell has been "conditioned" for expansion in some way by auxin. With regard to the effect of drought on wood formation, it is perhaps true that we cannot adequately segregate the two factors at the present time. However, the fact that the drought-induced false ring exhibits a gradient from a very abrupt latewood zone at the stem base to a very transitional type within the crown suggests a hormonal stimulus.

THIMANN: In tuber tissue when conditions are set up to make the cell lose water, then after a time, even though the external conditions remain constant, the cell gains water again. In other words, it has at its disposal a supply of osmotically inactive material which it turns into osmotically active material. These somehow seem to be influenced by reducing turgor.

KRAMER: In whole plants if the osmotic pressure of the substrate of the plant is increased, the osmotic pressure of the whole plant goes up relatively soon. Then there will be about the same osmotic gradient of, say, 4 atm from the substrate to the roots that there was before the osmotic pressure was increased. This does not mean that the plant grows as well, because each cell is subjected to a DPD which is 4 atm greater than before. In this case the plant seems to accumulate some salt.

ALVIM: In some cases the water acts through hormones. Flowering of coffee can be induced by moisture stress. Without moisture stress the plants eventually become dormant. If kept watered constantly, they do not grow. Moisture stress breaks their dormancy. The chilling requirement of fruit trees like apple and pear is very similar. When these trees are grown in tropical areas where the temperature does not become low enough to break dormancy, they can be grown successfully if irrigation is suppressed for a period. If this is not done, they flower very poorly.

KRAMER: It seems, therefore, that some trees can have their cold requirement replaced by water stress. Obviously this must affect internal metabolism and the supply of whatever substances are controlling growth. I was not aware of that situation.

HELLMERS: We transferred growing redwood trees from cool to warm temperature conditions at night. This caused the trees to wilt during the night and reduce growth. After a period of wilting every night for several weeks they ceased to wilt and assumed their previous growth rate.

KRAMER: Could there have been a considerable increase in leaf area which was more heavily cutinized? If tree seedlings are moved from shade to bright sun, the leaves are almost always damaged because they are not heavily cutinized and the interveinal areas are quite large. Leaves produced under the new conditions will be adapted and do not suffer in direct sunlight. Another possibility is that your plants adjusted the root shoot ratio to provide more water. Sugar cane plants in Hawaii are said to have a very high capacity to compensate for a period of time under unfavorable conditions by increased rate of growth when returned to favorable conditions.

HELLMERS: If watering of 2-year-old pines in pots is gradually reduced from watering once a day to once a week, and finally to once every 6 weeks, the plants survive. On the other hand, if all watering is stopped suddenly, the plants die. Therefore, there must be some adaptation mechanism.

KRAMER: Most of this is probably associated with increased cutinization and increased root/shoot ratio.

RICHARDSON: I think that this is related to the development of new roots in many cases. In Holland we did some experiments in flooding seedlings with salt water. The immediate reaction was wilting. Species differed in their ability to regenerate new root systems in this relatively high concentration; oak regenerated a new root system and was quite healthy, but sycamore, and all the conifers, were very sensitive. The old system did not function in the new environment and they did not regenerate a new one.

I would like to make a comment on the methodology of correlating ring width with soil moisture. A lot of tree-ring analysis has distinct limitations in the methodology used. Duff and Nolan in Canada have analyzed tree growth intensively; they took transverse sections through each internode of the tree and measured the width of the rings from the pith outwards in every internode. They then plotted these measurements in different ways. First of all they plotted the width of ring from the apex downwards within one growth sheath. They got a certain pattern of variation. The second method was to plot ring width from the pith outwards, the usual way to measure ring width for correlating with environmental factors. Again there was a distinct pattern. If this is done for every internode, there is some variation, but there is a systematic pattern, because the rings tend to get narrower further from the pith. If the ring width is plotted at a fixed distance from the pith, that is, ring widths formed by cambia of the same age, there is no systematic pattern at all; it resembles more a series of straight lines. If these ring widths are plotted according to the year of formation, they coincide much more closely than if they are plotted within one stem section from the pith outwards. A student of mine at Aberdeen carried out this type of analysis and attempted to relate ring width to moisture and temperature, using trees from the top and bottom of a sand dune. He got no correlations using the first two types of analyses. But when he used the third type, where there is no systematic variation, he got correlation coefficients of around 0.9, from the trees at the top of the dune with rainfall and from trees at the bottom of the dune with summer temperature. Another student found the same thing for wood density and tracheid length. By using the third type of sequence the systematic pattern of variation within the tree can be eliminated. This is obvious in ring width, but not so obvious in tracheid length, although it is there. Therefore, if anyone is looking for correlations with ring widths, he should compare rings formed by cambia of the same age.

REFERENCES

Bannan, M. W. (1962). *In* "Tree Growth" (T. T. Kozlowski, ed.), pp. 3-21. Ronald Press, New York.

Basler, E., Todd, G. W., and Meyer, R. E. (1961). *Plant Physiol.* 36, 573-576.

Brix, H. (1962). *Physiol. Plantarum* 15, 10-20.

Clark, J., and Gibbs, R. D. (1957). *Can. J. Botany* 35, 219-253.

Cleland, R. (1958). *Physiol. Plantarum* 11, 599-609.

Coile, T. S. (1936). *Ecol. Monographs* 6, 533-562.

Craib, W. G. (1918). *Roy. Botan. Gardens Edinburgh Notes* 11, 1-18; 12, 187-190; 14, 1-8 (1923).

Daubenmire, R. F. (1949). *Botan. Gaz.* 110, 464-475.

Fraser, D. A. (1962). *In* "Tree Growth" (T. T. Kozlowski, ed.), pp. 183-204. Ronald Press, New York.

Fritts, H. C. (1958). *Ecology* 39, 705-720.

Fritts, H. C. (1962). *Tree-Ring Bull.* 25, 2-10.

Gates, C. T., and Bonner, J. (1959). *Plant Physiol.* 34, 49-55.

Gibbs, R. D. (1958). *In* "The Physiology of Forest Trees" (K. V. Thimann, ed.), pp. 43-69. Ronald Press, New York.

Glock, W. S. (1955). *Botan. Rev.* 21, 73-188.

Glock, W. S., and Agerter, S. R. (1962). *In* "Tree Growth" (T. T. Kozlowski, ed.), pp. 23-56. Ronald Press, New York.

Harms, W. R., and McGregor, W. H. D. (1962). *Ecology* 43, 531-532.

Hatcher, E. S. J. (1959). *Ann. Botan.* 23, 409-423.

Hewlett, J. D., and Kramer, P. J. (1963). *Protoplasma* 57, 381-391.

Huber, B. (1948). *Forstwiss. Zentr.* 67, 129-164.

Kefford, N. P., and Goldacre, P. L. (1961). *Am. J. Botany* 48, 643-650.

Kozlowski, T. T., and Peterson, T. A. (1962). *Botan. Gaz.* 124, 146-154.

Kozlowski, T. T., Winget, C. H., and Torrie, J. H. (1962). *Botan. Gaz.* 124, 9-17.

Kramer, P. J. (1958). *In* "The Physiology of Forest Trees" (K. V. Thimann, ed.), pp. 157-186. Ronald Press, New York.

Kramer, P. J., and Kozlowski, T. T. (1960). "Physiology of Trees." McGraw-Hill, New York.

Kremers, R. E. (1957). *Tappi* 40, 262-268.

Ladefoged, K. (1952). *Kgl. Danske Vid. Selsk., Biol. Medd.* 7, 1-98.

Larson, P. R. (1962). *In* "Tree Growth" (T. T. Kozlowski, ed.), pp. 97-117. Ronald Press, New York.

Larson, P. R. (1963). *Forest Sci.* **9**, 52-62.

MacDougal, D. T. (1921). *Carnegie Inst. Wash. Publ.* **307**.

MacDougal, D. T. (1924). *Carnegie Inst. Wash. Publ.* **373**.

Monteith, J. L., and Owen, P. C. (1958). *J. Sci. Instr.* **35**, 443-446.

Mouravieff, I. (1959). *Bull. Soc. Botan. France* **106**, 306-309.

Ordin, L. (1958). *Sci. Res.* **4**, 553-564.

Ordin, L. (1960). *Plant Physiol.* **35**, 443-450.

Ordin, L., Applewhite, T. H., and Bonner, J. (1956). *Plant Physiol.* **31**, 44-53.

Ordin, L., Cleland, R., and Bonner, J. (1957). *Plant Physiol.* **32**, 216-220.

Overbeek, J. van. (1962). *Proc. Campbell Soup Co. Plant Sci. Symp., Camden, New Jersey*, pp. 37-58.

Pallas, J. E., and Williams, G. G. (1962). *Botan. Gaz.* **123**, 175-180.

Priestley, J. H., and Scott, L. I. (1936). *Proc. Leeds Phil. Lit. Soc.* **3**, 235-248.

Richards, L. A., and Ogata, G. (1958). *Science* **128**, 1089-1090.

Roberts, B. R. (1963). Ph.D. Dissertation, Duke University, Durham, North Carolina; see also Roberts' paper, this volume, p. 273.

Rudinsky, J. A., and Vité, J. P. (1959). *Forest Sci.* **5**, 259-266.

Scarth, G. W. (1936). *Trans. Roy. Soc. Can.* [3] **30**, 1-10.

Schulman, E. (1956). "Dendroclimatic Changes in Semi-arid America." Univ. of Arizona Press, Tucson, Arizona.

Schumacher, F. X., and Meyer, H. A. (1937). *J. Agr. Res.* **54**, 79-107.

Stalfelt, M. G. (1956). *In* "Encyclopedia of Plant Physiology" (W. Ruhland, ed.), Vol. III, p. 654. Springer, Berlin.

Stocker, O. (1929). *Planta* **7**, 382-387.

Thimann, K. V. (1954). *Am. Scientist* **42**, 589-606.

Thimann, K. V., Slater, R. R., and Christiansen, G. S. (1950). *Arch. Biochem.* **28**, 130-137.

Wareing, P. F. (1951). *Physiol. Plantarum* **4**, 41-56.

Wareing, P. F., and Roberts, D. L. (1956). *New Phytol.* **55**, 356-366.

Weatherley, P. E. (1950). *New Phytol.* **49**, 81-97.

Wiebe, H. H., and Wihrheim, S. E. (1962). "Radioisotopes in Soil-Plant Nutrition Studies," pp. 279-288. Intern. Atomic Energy Agency, Vienna.

Wilcox, H. (1962). *In* "Tree Growth" (T. T. Kozlowski, ed.), pp. 57-95. Ronald Press, New York.

Wort, D. J. (1962). *In* "Tree Growth" (T. T. Kozlowski, ed.), pp. 89-95. Ronald Press, New York.

Zahner, R. (1962). *Forest Sci.* **8**, 345-352.

Zahner, R. (1963). *Forest Prods. J.* **13**, 240-247.

Distribution of Growth in Tree Seedling Stems as Affected by Temperature and Light

Henry Hellmers

Pacific Southwest Forest and Range Experiment Station, Forest Service, U. S. Department of Agriculture, and the California Institute of Technology, Pasadena, California

Introduction

Environment, within genetic limitations, governs the general form of tree seedlings. Two environmental factors that affect the distribution of growth in the stem, and therefore the form, are temperature and light.

Quantitative information on the distribution of growth in stems is available from relatively few controlled temperature and controlled light investigations. However, the information available illustrates the types of response obtained and also indicates the complexity of the problem in studying these factors, even under controlled environmental conditions.

The complexity of environmental factor interaction upon plant growth has been reviewed and discussed by many, including Shirley (1945), Billings (1952), Glock (1955), Kramer and Kozlowski (1960), and Mirov and Stanley (1959). Downs and Borthwick (1956) and Larson (1962) clearly demonstrated in laboratory studies the effect of factor interaction.

Downs and Borthwick found that photoperiodic effects can vary not only with changes in the light period, but also with temperature. On the basis of their results they suggest that some of the discrepancies found in studies of photoperiodism may be in fact due to temperature. Larson studied the effect of temperature on the development of young ponderosa pine (*Pinus ponderosa* Laws.) seedlings. He obtained the maximum effect of air temperature upon growth when root temperature was optimal and maximum root temperature effect upon growth when air temperature was optimal. In other words, the maximum variation caused by a change in one environmental factor was obtained when the other factors were optimal. These results emphasize the importance of holding

533

all conditions, except the one being varied, as close to the optimum as possible.

Temperature, light intensity, temperature-light intensity interaction, and light intensity–photoperiod interaction vary in their effects upon the distribution of growth in tree seedling stems. Direction and extent of the variation are considered in this paper.

Measurements usually made in determining stem growth are height and diameter. A more precise value for total growth made by seedlings is obtained by considering the volume of the stem. Because volume is directly related to height and basal area, the data presented in this paper are in these terms.

Temperature Effect

Most temperature studies with seedlings have not been concerned with the distribution of growth in the stem. Consequently, diameter measurements were omitted. On the other hand, minimum or optimum temperatures needed for either top or root elongation or increased dry weight have been the objectives of many investigations (Barney, 1951; Hellmers, 1962, 1963b; Larson, 1962; Richardson, 1957; Stone and Schubert, 1959; Stone et al., 1962). Also, temperature studies have been made to determine the effect of soil temperature on top growth and of air temperature on root growth (Franco, 1958; Hellmers, 1963a; Larson, 1962; and Nightingale, 1935).

Diameter growth of older trees, however, has been investigated extensively. Glock (1955) reported that Eidem (1943) found temperature to be the leading factor in determining annual ring thickness in fir in Norway. Huber (1948) reported a correlation between mean summer temperature and ring width on high-altitude trees. Through a series of multiple regression analyses of radial growth of trees in Ohio and Illinois, Fritts (1958, 1960, 1962) concluded that the growth of beech (*Fagus grandifolia* Ehrh.) was closely correlated with maximum temperature but not minimum temperature. In addition, he determined optimum temperatures for radial growth of white oak (*Quercus alba* L.), red oak (*Q. rubra* L.), and sugar maple (*Acer saccharum* Marsh.). Earlywood production in white oak was inversely related to April temperatures. Lodewick (1930) could find no effect of monthly mean temperatures on diameter growth of longleaf pine in Florida.

Pinus ponderosa and *P. jeffreyi* in 20-year-old plantations showed that elevation of both seed source and plantations affected stem taper (Callaham and Liddicoet, 1961). Increased elevation increased the stockiness of the trees. Temperature, along with moisture and wind conditions, were suggested as possible causes for the growth pattern.

The role of temperature in the growth of first-year red fir (*Abies magnifica* A. Murr.) seedlings was investigated recently. The experiment was conducted in the temperature-controlled rooms of the Earhart Plant Research Laboratory (Went, 1957). The light, a combination of fluorescent and incandescent bulbs, provided approximately 500 ft-c at the top of the pots. The seedlings grew under the test conditions for 6 months from the cotyledon stage. The design of the experiment included the growing of 13 plants in each of 15 day-night temperature combinations. Day temperatures of 10 and 23°C were used in conjunction with night temperatures of 4, 10, 17, and 23°C. With the warmer day, an additional night temperature of 26°C was used. Additional day-night combinations were used to provide a range of 4, 10, 17, 23, and 26°C day temperatures with 4 and 17°C night temperatures. The photoperiod and day temperatures were given simultaneously for 16 hours. Further details on the design and conduction of the experiment have been published (Hellmers, 1963b). Measurements were made of the height from the cotyledons to the bud and of the stem diameter below the cotyledons.

The results showed that the tallest plants did not have the largest basal areas (Fig. 1). The tallest trees occurred under the two day temperature conditions associated with 13°C cooler nights, 23°C day with a 10°C night and a 17°C day with a 4°C night (Fig. 1,B, C). A similar thermoperiodic effect upon height growth was observed on loblolly pine by Kramer (1957) and Hellmers (1962). Fir seedlings developing the largest basal areas grew under different sets of temperature conditions, a 10°C day with a 23°C night (Fig. 1,A) and a 23°C day with a 17°C night (Fig. 1,B, D). Terminal bud formation appeared to affect height growth more than basal area development. Of the 26 trees in the two conditions with the tallest trees, only two formed terminal buds, and these were the shortest trees. Of the trees in the two conditions with the largest basal area trees, a total of six trees produced terminal buds but these six trees ranged from the largest to the smallest in basal area. Terminal bud formation increased with increased temperature. No terminal buds were formed under the constant 4 or 10°C day with 4°C night temperatures. All plants under a 23°C day, with a 26°C night temperature, formed terminal buds.

The differences in response of height and basal area resulted in changes in the height : basal area ratio with temperature (Fig. I,A, B, C, D). The ratio of average height to average basal area under the different temperature conditions ranged from 6.1 to 14.7. On the graphs (Fig. 1) where the basal area point falls below the height point, the height : basal area ratio is greater than 10. The lowest ratio occurred under a 4°C day with a 17°C night condition (Fig. 1, D), while the highest ratio developed under a 23°C day with a 10°C night (Fig. 1,B). A decrease of 6°C in both day and night temperature only slightly affected the high ratio as shown by the 17°C day with 4°C night condition in which the ratio was 14.6.

Height growth responded more to the temperature conditions than did basal area growth. Under conditions of cool days, 10°C and cooler, the

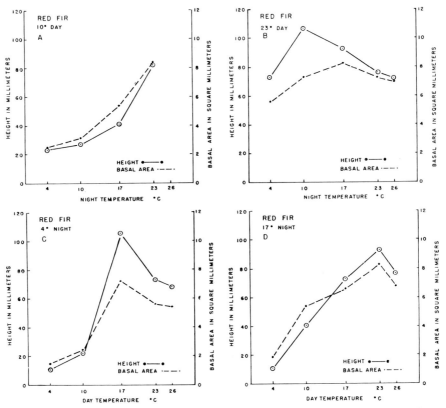

FIG. 1.   The height and basal area of red fir seedlings grown from the cotyledon stage for 6 months under various day-night temperature combinations and a 16-hour photoperiod of 500 ft-c of light. Relation of scales is such that a common point on the graph indicates a height : basal area ratio of 10.

trees' height growth appeared to be restricted more than basal area (Fig. 1,A, C, D). This would be evident to a greater extent if the graphs were plotted on a 1:1 ratio as used in calculating the volume of growth. When conditions became favorable for stem elongation, it again responded more than did basal area. This indicated that height growth for this species was more sensitive to temperature than basal area growth. Consequently, the tallest trees are associated with the largest height: basal area ratios and the shortest trees with the lowest ratios.

Light Intensity Effect

Light intensity as a factor in tree growth has been reviewed by Shirley (1935, 1945). As with temperature, most studies have been concerned with height growth rather than basal area growth. In general, the greatest amount of height growth occurs under less than full sunlight. No general statement about light intensity effects upon basal area growth appear in the reviews. Since the reviews, height and basal area development of several species of tree seedlings have been studied using different light intensities. The results which follow indicate great variability between species for both growth responses. Artificial light was provided by a combination of fluorescent and incandescent lights. This combination has been found to produce good plant growth but the quality is not identical with that of sunlight (Went, 1957).

Two of the constant temperature conditions, 17 and 23°C, used in the red fir temperature study were replicated with the substitution of natural light for 8 hours of artificial light. Thus, the photoperiod was maintained at 16 hours. The natural light varied in intensity up to 10,000 ft-c during the day in the temperature-controlled greenhouses.

The basal areas of the trees in the 17°C natural light condition were significantly larger than in the 23°C natural light condition. In turn the trees in the 23°C natural light conditions were significantly larger in basal area than either set of trees under artificial light. The trees under artificial light were not significantly different from each other. Under these artificial light-constant temperature conditions, red fir did not produce the tallest plants nor the largest basal area (Fig. 1).

Half or more of the plants under both light regimes and both temperatures set terminal buds. In contrast, among trees that attained maximum height or basal area under artificial light, relatively few had set terminal buds by the termination of the experiment.

The large basal area produced under natural light reduced the height: basal area ratio of these trees by 39 and 53% of that of the trees grown under artificial light.

Height growth showed no significant differences among the four conditions (Table I and Fig. 2). Marked differences occurred in branch development (Fig. 2). The high intensity light caused an increase in branch growth under both temperatures but especially under 17°C.

Redwood, *Sequoia sempervirens* (D. Don) Endl., seedlings were grown under the same two light conditions as were the fir, but at 19 and 23°C constant temperatures. Each treatment included eight plants.

High light intensity increased both height and basal area of the redwood seedlings (Table I). The largest difference caused by light intensity

TABLE I

TEMPERATURE AND LIGHT INTENSITY EFFECT UPON REDWOOD SEEDLINGS[a]

Species	Constant temperature (°C)	500 ft-c for 16 hr			Natural light for 8 hr plus 500 ft-c for 8 hr		
		Ht. (mm)	Basal area (mm²)	Ht./BA	Ht. (mm)	Basal area (mm²)	Ht./BA
Red fir	17	74	6.6	11.2	73	13.7	5.3
	23	77	7.3	10.5	64	10.0	6.4
Redwood	19	358	22.1	16.2	773	49.0	15.8
	23	414	22.9	18.1	542	40.7	13.8

[a] Grown under test conditions for 6 months; each treatment included 13 trees.

occurred in the development of height and basal area under the 19°C temperature condition. Under the 23°C condition, high light intensity caused a proportionally greater increase in basal area than in height, resulting in a significantly lower height:basal area ratio.

The fir and redwood have different growth characteristics. The redwood does not set buds (Sterling, 1945), and hence its height growth is fairly continuous under favorable environmental conditions. For this reason the distribution of growth is different in the redwood seedlings from that in the fir. The ratios of height to basal area in redwood are greater than those in the fir (Table I). These large ratios are comparable to those of 14.7 for fir when grown under optimum temperature conditions for height growth.

Skok (1961) grew giant sequoia, *Sequoia gigantea* (Lind.) Decne., under both low- and high-intensity light conditions. A photoperiod of 16 hours with 1500 ft-c of artificial light and a temperature of 24°C was maintained in a growth chamber for the low-intensity condition. For high intensity, natural light in a greenhouse was used. The photoperiod was extended to 16 hours with very low-intensity light of 28 to 40 ft-c. The seedlings were 12.7 months old at the termination of the test.

The height:basal area ratio for Skok's seedlings grown under artificial light was less than half of that for those receiving the 8 hours of natural light (Table II). Under low light intensity, the basal area doubled in size while height was not affected. In two other studies (Skok, 1961) in which he varied the photoperiod, a 16-hour photoperiod consistently produced the lowest height:basal area ratio. In each case the low ratio resulted from growing these plants under artificial light only, while all other photoperiods included at least 8 hours of natural light (Table II).

Results with red fir, redwood, and giant sequoia clearly demonstrate the variability that occurs between species. High light intensity only slightly affected the distribution of growth in the redwood seedlings compared to the strong effect upon the distribution of growth in seedlings of the other two species. For fir and giant sequoia the effects were primarily upon basal area growth rather than height growth. Height increased only slightly, if at all. However, the action of the light on basal area was opposite for the two species. Fir developed a much larger

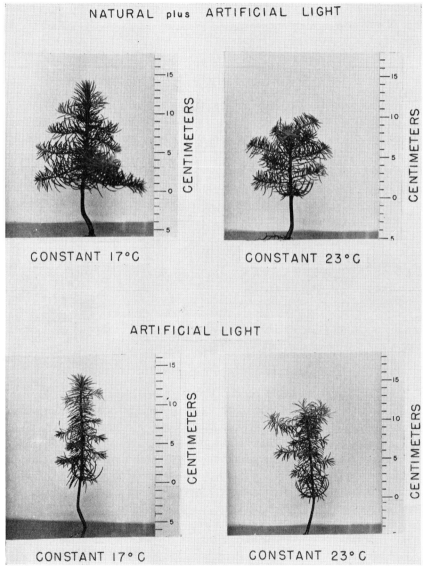

FIG. 2. Largest red fir seedlings grown in 6 months under two constant temperatures and two light intensities.

TABLE II

DISTRIBUTION OF GROWTH IN STEMS OF GIANT SEQUOIA
SEEDLINGS UNDER VARIOUS PHOTOPERIODS[a]

Photoperiod[b] (hours)	Height (mm)	Basal area (mm²)	Ht./basal area
Grown for 12.7 months			
8	60	6.6	9.09
12	104	13.2	7.88
14	133	18.9	7.04
16	137	23.8	5.76
16[c]	124	46.6	2.66
18[d]	173	31.2	5.54
Grown for 17.6 months			
8	91	13.9	6.55
12	145	30.2	4.80
16[c]	393	235.1	1.67
18[d]	536	216.4	2.47
Grown for 18.7 months			
8	88	18.9	4.66
12	131	36.2	3.62
16[c]	359	283.5	1.27
18[d]	524	232.4	2.25

[a] Data from Skok (1961).
[b] 8 Hours natural light plus low-intensity light, 23–40 ft-c.
[c] 16 Hours artificial light, 1500 ft-c.
[d] Natural daylength plus low-intensity light, 23–40 ft-c.

basal area under high light intensity; giant sequoia developed a much larger basal area under low light intensity.

Temperature-Light Intensity Interaction

The light intensity effect on the fir was much greater than the temperature effect. This was true under both temperatures and under either light condition (Table I). Neither of the constant temperatures, 17 or 23°C, was optimum for either height or basal area growth. I do not know whether the light intensity effect on height and basal area would increase or decrease under optimum temperature conditions. This relationship is complicated because the temperature optimum under the two light intensities may well be different. Differences in optimum temperature for photosynthesis in conifers under different light intensities have been demonstrated by Pisek and Winkler (1959).

Redwood seedlings responded in both height growth and basal area growth to temperature and light intensity. An interaction of the two environmental factors is evident (Table I). The light intensity effect was greatest under a 19°C temperature; the temperature effect was greatest under high light intensity. Furthermore, under high light intensity only height growth was affected significantly by temperature. It should be noted, even though the differences were not significant, that increased temperature resulted in increased height growth and basal area growth with low light intensity but *vice versa* with high light intensity. Therefore, for both redwood and red fir, there appear to be different optimum temperatures under different light intensities.

Photoperiod Effect

Photoperiodicity controls the growth and development of many species of woody plants. The roles of photoperiod in stem elongation, cambial activity, and dormancy are reviewed by Wareing (1956), Nitsch (1959), and Kramer and Kozlowski (1960). Trees with determinate growth increase in height by flushes. Although the growth of the flushes in some species is photoperiodically controlled, the growth period is of relatively short duration. Radial growth also appears to be photoperiodically controlled, but the period of radial growth is longer than the period of height growth. Thus, the height:basal area ratio of seedlings must undergo rather marked changes during the first and subsequent growing seasons.

The distribution of growth in tree seedling stems has been shown to be affected by photoperiod during seedling growth. Skok (1961), in addition to the 16-hour photoperiod conditions previously described, used a range of photoperiods from 8 to 18 hours. Each condition, except the 16-hour photoperiod, received 8 hours of natural light, extended where necessary with light of low intensity (Table II). The longest photoperiod was different in that it consisted of natural light for the duration of the day, and then the photoperiod was extended to 18 hours with low-intensity light. Seedlings of giant sequoia were grown from seed and kept in the study for 12.7, 17.6, or 18.7 months, apparently without cessation of growth. At all three ages the distribution of growth within the stems showed a definite trend with a change in photoperiod (Table II). The basal area increased proportionately more than did height growth with increased photoperiod. This resulted in a lowering of the height:basal area ratio.

Virginia pine (*Pinus virginiana* Mill.) and ponderosa pine (*P. ponderosa* Laws.) seedlings also showed differences in the distribution of growth in the stem under different photoperiods (Downs and Piringer, 1958). All plants were in the greenhouse for 8 hours, and when necessary the photoperiod was extended with 30 ft-c of artificial light. The height:basal area ratio for Virginia pine decreased with increased photoperiod (Table III). Basal area increased consistently with increased photo-

TABLE III

DISTRIBUTION OF GROWTH IN STEMS OF VIRGINIA PINE AND PONDEROSA PINE
SEEDLINGS GROWN UNDER DIFFERENT PHOTOPERIODS[a]

Photo-period[b]	Virginia pine			Ponderosa pine		
	Height (mm)	Basal area (mm²)	Ht./basal area	Height (mm)	Basal area (mm²)	Ht./basal area
8	71	2.84	25.00	27	3.46	7.80
12	116	4.91	23.63	91	6.16	14.77
14	106	10.18	10.41	77	6.16	12.50
16	109	13.20	8.26	53	6.61	8.02

[a] Data from Downs and Piringer (1958).
[b] 8 Hours natural light plus low-intensity light, approximately 30 ft-c.

period; height growth increased only when the photoperiod increased
from 8 to 12 hours. Ponderosa pine was erratic in its growth pattern, but
with one exception it also exhibited a decrease in height:basal area ratio
with increased photoperiod (Table III). The maximum ratio was obtained under a 12-hour photoperiod. Height growth decreased with
longer and shorter photoperiods, and basal area increased as photoperiod
increased from 8 to 16 hours.

Thus, photoperiod appears to be an important factor in controlling
the distribution of growth. Long photoperiods result in stocky seedlings.
The optimum photoperiod for height growth may not be the optimum
photoperiod for basal area growth.

Photoperiod–Light Intensity Interaction

Chailakhian (1954) suggested that many factors other than the duration of light influence the photoperiodic effect. Downs and Borthwick
(1956) demonstrated that temperature is one of these factors. With data
from Skok (1961, 1962) it can be shown that light intensity interacts with
photoperiod in influencing the distribution of stem growth within giant
sequoia seedlings.

A previous section shows that when Skok (1961) grew seedlings under
a 16-hour photoperiod, different height:basal area ratios developed under
high and low light intensities. With only low-intensity light (1500 ft-c)
basal area increased. Also, with longer photoperiods basal area growth
increased. However, plants under the longer photoperiods received
longer periods of low intensity light. Thus, all or part of the photoperiodic
effect upon growth distribution in the stem may have been due to an
increase in the duration of low-intensity light.

Results from a second study by Skok (1962) suggest that the growth-
distribution effect is entirely due to the duration of low intensity light

received by the plants. He observed significant increases in both height growth and basal area in giant sequoia seedlings when the 16-hour dark period was interrupted with 1 hour of low-intensity light (23–40 ft-c). However, the ratio of height to basal area was not altered by this treatment.

Effect of Age and Other Factors

Age has been shown to affect rate of height growth in tree seedlings (Wareing, 1956; Hellmers, 1963a). Age or length of time the giant sequoia seedlings were in the study also affected the distribution of growth in Skok's photoperiodic study (Table II). The height:basal area ratio decreased with age again because of a proportionately greater increase of growth in basal area than height.

The difference in distribution of growth between the 17.6- and the 18.7-month-old seedlings apparently involves some other factor than age. One possibility is the season of the year and the attendant variation of light intensity. The older seedlings were shorter and larger in basal area than plants which were a month younger in the corresponding photoperiod.

Summary and Conclusions

Light and temperature control the distribution of growth in a tree seedling stem. The control varies with the species and the conditions under which the heat and light are applied.

Both height growth and basal area of red fir are influenced by temperature. Height growth is more plastic than basal area growth and exhibits optimal temperatures different from those for radial growth. As a result, height:basal area ratios under the various temperature conditions ranged from 6.1 to 14.7.

Light intensity effects vary with the species. High-intensity light in a greenhouse causes an increase in both height and basal area growth in redwood. However, a high-intensity light had little effect upon height growth of red fir or giant sequoia seedlings but did affect basal area growth. Basal area of the fir increased under high-intensity light while that of giant sequoia decreased.

A temperature–light intensity interaction is evident in the growth of red fir and redwood. The interaction indicated that the optimum temperatures for seedling growth vary with the light intensity.

Photoperiod affects the distribution of growth in giant sequoia, Virginia pine, and ponderosa pine seedlings. An increase in photoperiod decreased the height:basal area ratios. However, a photoperiod–light intensity interaction occurred with the giant sequoia seedlings that was sufficient to make the effect of photoperiod per se questionable for this species.

Age of seedlings also affects the distribution of growth in the stem of giant sequoia seedlings.

As information on the effects of individual factors accumulates, the next logical use for controlled-environment equipment is to extend the study of factor interactions. The complications in studying the interaction of even two environmental factors, such as light and temperature, are demonstrated in this paper. These complications emphasize the desirability of obtaining rather complete information on the effect of the individual factors over a wide range of their natural variation.

DISCUSSION

RICHARDSON: I am bothered by your use of basal area. A better measure would have been the area or diameter at the midpoint of the stem. One could get some idea of this by comparing the dry weight data with your theoretical volume to get some sort of stem density. Have you ever done this? Is it a valid measure of growth?

HELLMERS: No; I measured the basal area below the cotyledons, and assumed that the tree stem in the crown is a cone.

RICHARDSON: Is it in fact a cone? Have you derived this from your dry weight figures?

HELLMERS: All I know is that they are pointed at the top, and therefore there is a taper in the crown.

RICHARDSON: What effect does thinning these plants have? You started with 50 and ended up with 4.

HELLMERS: I did not have to thin the firs as there was only one plant per pot. The redwoods I thinned in later stages by removing pots from the growing area.

WILCOX: I was concerned about the effect of light quality. In growing pines the extent of elongation is extremely sensitive to the balance between incandescent and fluorescent light. What was the quality of the lights you used? Did you turn the fluorescent lights off after or before the incandescent lights?

HELLMERS: We used a combination of fluorescent and Mazda lights. They were turned off simultaneously.

LARSON: According to your photographs, there seemed to be a tendency for the trees under the longer photoperriod to have larger basal branches. If this were the case it would account for your increase in basal area.

HELLMERS: The size of the basal branches could be a contributing factor in stem basal area growth. However, it would be difficult to isolate the contribution of this one part of the crown to basal area growth.

WAREING: Under conditions of limiting light intensity the apical meristems are at an advantage in competition with the cambium for available nutrients. This is shown, for example, by the fact that when trees are grown in dense plantations you get extension growth but reduced diameter increment. Given limiting photosynthates, you seem to get elongation growth at the expense of diameter growth. I would have thought that what you have reported is the same phenomenon.

HELLMERS: Yes, in red fir the height growth was almost the same under both light intensities (Table I).

WILCOX: *Abies magnifica* may not have been a happy choice, because at least in *Abies procera,* there is some mechanism built in that is a deterrent on height growth. Seedlings will remain static in the nursery before they start growing. When they finally do start they grow very rapidly.

RICHARDSON: The differences are not necessarily brought out by your ratios. It seems to me that we have reached the stage where we must us clonal material for the sort of experiment where processes are studied. In herbaceous material the populations are often far less variable than tree populations. This material is very heterozygous; even under closely controlled conditions it shows an enormous variability.

HELLMERS: I am convinced that, even under optimal conditions, one obtains great variability in the growth of tree seedlings. In the field many trees are lost which are not even considered in the population, while under optimal conditions these weaker trees survive and have to be counted. In Jeffrey pine I could attribute approximately 23% of the variability to genetic variability, even though the seeds were from a single mother tree (Hellmers, 1963b).

RICHARDSON: It is often argued that environmental control will replace statistical control, but this is not true, at least as far as trees are concerned.

RAUP: What control did you have over your seed source?

HELLMERS: The seeds used in these experiments were taken from lots representing a geographic area; they were probably taken from several trees. There is always the choice to be made of using the seed from one tree with known parents, or of using a seed collection as the foresters use it. If seed from known parents is used the question arises as to how representative this seed is of the seed produced by the species.

RAUP: I agree with Dr. Richardson that clonal material should be used. In dealing with such small variations as you have, you are in danger of having genetic variation which is equal to or greater than any variation you are measuring.

HELLMERS: This could well be true. However, my one experience with clonal material of woody plants showed the growth rates of the clones to be extremely variable, which was probably caused by differences in rooting.

WILCOX: I had one collection of incense cedar seed which I thought was relatively uniform. Three months after germination I could rank the seedlings along the whole side of the greenhouse on the basis of height and color. One color extreme corresponded to minimum height and the other extreme to maximum height. There were even some albinos.

HELLMERS: Although I grew one seedling per pot, I started with approximately six seedlings per pot. The plants were grown for a month to the cotyledon stage, under one set of conditions. Then the seedlings were moved to the test conditions. At that point I thinned to seedlings of uniform size and appearance. This eliminated some of the variation.

RAUP: I was impressed by the Swedish foresters and their attempts to achieve uniformity in their pulp. They finally ended up by grafting to form clones of known fiber length.

RICHARDSON: There is probably more fiber length variation within an individual tree than there is between trees.

COLVIN: I would like to draw your attention to the recent developments in multivariate analysis. Populations can be raised under natural conditions and almost any number of factors can be studied provided one has methods of expressing the factors in the environment quantitatively. One also needs a good mathematician and a computer. I know of cases where they are handling simultaneously thirty different factors. I do not believe that there is any theoretical limit on the number of variables. At the

546 HENRY HELLMERS

end usually most of the variables can be thrown away and five or six of them will account for most of the variability.

BROWN: We just finished a study of this sort over a 5-year period. We studied 38 different variables as factors influencing seed production in clonal seed orchards. We came out with a lot of information but to interpret it biologically was extremely difficult (Georgia Forestry Commission, unpublished).

HELLMERS: Unfortunately it is possible to get very nice correlations between factors which biologically have no relation whatsoever. However, with controlled environment conditions one can determine which environmental factors are important and then use this information to establish large-scale field studies. In a growth chamber one can find the trend of a response while in the natural populations one obtains the whole range of variability.

COLVIN: I agree; one has to be careful of spurious correlations. In addition, one of the multivariate programs may be as costly as an equivalent number of growth chambers.

REFERENCES

Barney, C. W. (1951). *Plant Physiol.* **26**, 146-163.
Billings, W. D. (1952). *Quart. Rev. Biol.* **27**, 251-265.
Chailakhian, M. Kh. (1954). *Zhur. Obshchei Biol.* **25**, 629. (From Mirov and Stanley, 1959.)
Callaham, R. Z., and Liddicoet, A. R. (1961). *J. Forestry* **59**, 814-820.
Downs, R. J., and Borthwick, H. A. (1956). *Botan. Gaz.* **117**, 310-326.
Downs, R. J., and Piringer, A. A. (1958). *Forest Sci.* **4**, 185-195.
Eidem, P. (1943). *Nytt. Mag. Naturv. B.* **83**, 145-189. (From Glock, 1955.)
Franco, C. M. (1958). IBEC Research Institute Bull. No. 16., 24 pp.
Fritts, H. C. (1958). *Ecology* **39**, 705-720.
Fritts, H. C. (1960). *Forest Sci.* **6**, 334-349.
Fritts, H. C. (1962). *Tree-Ring Bull.* **25**, 2-10.
Glock, W. S. (1955). *Botan. Rev.* **21**, 73-188.
Hellmers, H. (1962). *In* "Tree Growth" (T. Kozlowski, ed.), pp. 275-287. Ronald Press, New York.
Hellmers, H. (1963a). *Botan. Gaz.* **124**, 172-177.
Hellmers, H. (1963b). *Forest Sci.* **9**, 189-201.
Huber, B. (1948). *Naturwissenschaften* **35**, 151-154.
Kramer, P. J. (1957). *In* "The Physiology of Forest Trees" (K. V. Thimann, ed.), pp. 573-580. Ronald Press, New York.
Kramer, P. J., and Kozlowski, T. T. (1960). "Physiology of Trees." McGraw-Hill, New York.
Larson, M. M. (1962). Ph.D. Thesis. Univ. of Washington, Seattle. 146 pp.
Lodewick, J. E. (1930). *J. Agr. Res.* **41**, 349-363.
Mirov, N. T., and Stanley, R. G. (1959). *Ann. Rev. Plant Physiol.* **10**, 223-238.
Nightingale, G. I. (1935). *Botan. Gaz.* **96**, 581-639.
Nitsch, J. P. (1959). *Bull. Soc. Botan., France* **106**, 259-287.
Pisek, A., and Winkler, E. (1959). *Planta* **53**, 532-550.
Richardson, S. D. (1957). *In* "The Physiology of Forest Trees" (K. V. Thimann, ed.), pp. 409-425. Ronald Press, New York.
Shirley, H. L. (1935). *Botan. Rev.* **1**, 355-381.
Shirley, H. L. (1945). *Botan. Rev.* **11**, 497-532.
Skok, J. (1961). *Botan. Gaz.* **123**, 63-70.

Skok, J. (1962). *Botan. Gaz.* **124**, 17-19.

Sterling, C. (1945). *Am. J. Botany* **32**, 118-126.

Stone, E. C., and Schubert, G. H. (1959). *Forest Sci.* **5**, 322-332.

Stone, E. C., Jenkinson, J. F., and Krugman, S. L. (1962). *Forest Sci.* **8**, 288-297.

Wareing, P. F. (1956). *Ann. Rev. Plant Physiol.* **7**, 191-214.

Went, F. W. (1957). "Experimental Control of Plant Growth." Chronica Botanica, Waltham, Massachusetts.

Author Index

Numbers in parentheses are reference numbers and are included to assist in locating references in which authors' names are not mentioned in the text. Numbers in italics refer to pages on which the references are listed.

A

Abbe, L. B., 253, *257*
Acerbo, S. N., 204, *217*, 223, 226, *237*
Adams, E., 224, 229, *239*
Adamson, R. S., 76, *85*
Adler, E., 137, *151*, 215, *217*
Aeberli, H., 87, *132*
Agerter, S. R., 519, *531*
Agranoff, B. W., 233, *238*
Albersheim, P., 88, *131*, 415, *454*
Aldrich-Blake, R. N., 459, 460, 462, 473, 474, *478*
Altermatt, H., 222, *237*
Alvim, P. de T., 482, 489, 490, 491, *494*
Amos, G. L., 88, *134*, 411, *454*
André, H., 357, *364*
Andrews, H. N., 9, *17*
Applewhite, T. H., 526, *532*
Arber, A., 71, *85*
Arnon, N., *457*
Aronoff, S., 282, *288*
Aronson, J. M., 170, *187*
Aspinall, G. O., 146, *151*
Astbury, W. T., 170, *187*
Asunmaa, S., 88, 91, *131*, *132*, 147, *151*

B

Bailey, A. J., 89, *132*, 166, *166*
Bailey, I. W., 4, 21, 23, 32, 35, 88, 92, 94, 95, 100, 103, 104, 110, 111, 113, *132*, 133, 334, 342, *344*, 369 (1, 2, 3, 66), *386*, 388, 428, *452*, *456*, 467, *478*
Bailey, L. H., 69, *85*
Baker, D. B., 331, *344*
Balashov, V., 190, *200*
Ball, E., 70, *85*, 390, *404*
Bamber, R. K., 46, *50*
Bannan, M. W., 19, 20, 21, 22, 24, 32, 33, 35, 111, 113, 114, *132*, 318, *320*, 333, 343, 369 (4, 5, 6, 7, 8), 374, *386*, 521, *531*
Barghoorn, E. S., 3, 10, 12, *17*, 21, 35
Barker, E., 81, *85*

Barker, H. A., 230, *237*
Barlow, H. W. B., 428, *454*
Barney, C. W., 534, *546*
Basler, E., 274, 277, 281, *288*, 527, *531*
Bassett, K. H., 176, *187*
Bate-Smith, E. C., 227, 228, *237*
Battersby, A. R., 228, *237*
Bayley, S. T., 179, 185, *188*, 190, 191, 192, 196, 197, 198, *201*
Beard, J. S., 485, *494*
Beer, M., 124, *132*, 179, *187*, 192, 194, 196, *200*
Beevers, H., 311, *320*
Belford, D. S., 176, *187*
Benziman, M., 191, *200*
Berkeley, E. E., 94, *132*
Berlyn, G. P., 438, *454*
Biddulph, O., 274, 284, *288*, 299, *301*
Biddulph, S., 284, *288*
Bierhorst, D. W., 467, *478*
Billek, G., 204, *218*, 223, 226, *238*
Billings, W. D., 533, *546*
Bisalputra, T., 269, *272*
Bishop, C. T., 142, *151*
Bisset, I. J. W., 368 (9, 10), 369 (10), 384, *386*, 411, *454*
Bittner, F., 204, *217*
Björkman, E., 245, *257*
Bland, D. E., 431, 435, *454*
Boesenberg, H., 205, *217*, 343, *344*
Bogorad, L., 227, *237*
Bolker, H. I., 150, *151*
Bonner, J., 525, 526, *531*, *532*
Borthwick, H. A., 484, *495*, 533, 542, *546*
Bosian, G., 503, *503*, 505, 506, *518*
Bosshard, H. H., 103, 105, 113, *132*, *457*
Bourdeau, P. F., 358, *364*, 506, *518*
Bourne, E. J., 191, *200*
Bouveng, H. O., 142, 143, *151*
Bower, F. O., 474, *478*
Boysen Jensen, P., 497, 498, *503*, 514, *518*
Bradley, M. V., 324, *343*
Branner, J. C., 71, 72, 83, *85*
Braun, H., 303, *320*

Brauns, D. A., 219, *237*
Brauns, F. E., 219, *237*
Brebner, G., 76, *86*
Bretz, C., 330, *344*
Briggs, W. R., 356, *364*
Brix, H., 278, 285, 288, 503, *503*, 527, *531*
Brown, A. G., 367 (17, 25), *387*
Brown, A. M., 192, 196, *200*
Brown, C. L., 391, 394, *404*
Brown, H. P., 21, 22, *35*
Brown, R. M., 367 (58), *388*
Brown, S. A., 204, *217*, 219, 221, 224, 225, 226, 228, 229, 230, 231, *237*, *239*
Bucher, H., 94, 128, *132*, 149, *151*, 438, *454*
Buchtela, K., 223, *238*
Bünning, E., 19, *35*, 411, *455*
Büsgen, M., 307, 315, *320*, 407, 442, *455*, 477, *478*
Burch, W. D., 437, *455*
Burger-Rachamimov, H., 191, *200*
Burns, G. P., 412, 438, 439, 454, *455*
Burr, G. O., 287, *288*
Byram, G. M., 487, 489, *494*

C

Callahan, R. Z., 534, *546*
Camus, G., 331, 343, *343*
Canny, M. J., 259, 260, 265, 266, *272*, 282, 284, *288*
Carano, E., 74, *85*
Cardinale, G., 207, 208, *217*
Casperson, G., 428, 448, 452, *455*
Chailakhian, M. Kh., 542, *546*
Chalk, L., 369 (11), *386*
Champion, H. G., 367 (12), *386* (12)
Chance, B., 517, *518*
Chang, Y.-P., 40, *50*
Chattaway, M. M., 43, 46, *50*
Cheadle, V. I., 51, 53, 55, 56, *63*, 75, 76, *85*
Chen, C.-L., 207, 208, *217*
Chisholm, M. D., 204, *217*, 219, 222, 224, 229, 233, *237*, *239*
Chow, K. Y., 410, 411, *455*
Chowdhury, K. A., 487, 489, 493, *494*
Christiansen, G. S., 525, *532*
Church, A. H., 235, *237*
Claire, F. H., 204, *217*

Clark, D. G., 260, *272*
Clark, J., 358, *364*, *518*, 521, *531*
Clark, W. S., 497, *504*
Clarke, F., 3, *17*
Clarke, G. L., 100, *132*
Clarke, S. H., 409, *455*
Cleland, R., 525, 526, *531*, *532*
Clowes, F. A. L., 30, 32, *35*
Clutter, M. E., 331, *344*
Cocking, E. C., 248, *257*
Coile, T. S., 519, *531*
Cole, D., 367 (85), *388*
Colvin, J. R., 123, *132*, 179, *187*, 191, 192, 193, 194, 195, 196, 197, *200*, *200*
Conn, E. E., 219, 228, 230, 232, *238*
Cook, C. D., 176, *187*
Cordemoy, A. J. de, 76, *85*
Corner, J. J., 228, *238*
Correns, E., 418, 434, *455*
Cory, R., 284, 288, 299, *301*
Coster, C., 488, 489, 490, 493, *494*
Côté, W. A., 110, *132*, 424, *455*
Crafts, A. S., 253, *257*, 282, *288*, 403, *404*
Craib, W. G., 521, *531*
Crane, J. C., 324, *343*
Creighton, R. H. J., 216, *217*
Critchfield, W. B., 298, *301*
Cronshaw, J., 99, 104, 105, 107, 111, 124, *132*, 170, *187*
Crosby, D. G., 200, *200*
Croon, I., 141, *151*
Currier, H. B., 51, *63*
Curtis, O. F., 260, *272*, 295, *301*

D

Dadswell, H. E., 88, 95, 98, 99, 100, 106, 118, 119, 121, *132*, *134*, 367 (13, 14, 15, 16, 17), 368 (9, 10), 369 (10, 47, 52), 383 (52), 384 (52), *386*, *387*, *388*, 409, 411, 412, 415, 416, 417, 418, 422, 424, 431, *454*, *455*, *456*
Dahl, E., 361, *364*
Danon, D., 193, 194, 195, *200*
Das, N. K., 390, *404*
Daubenmire, R. F., 521, *531*
Davies, G. W., 91, 103, 108, 110, *134*, 434, *456*

Davis, B. D., 219, 224, 229, *238*
Day, A. C., 110, *132*, 424, *455*
Day, B. E., 281, *288*
Dearing, G. G., 191, *200*
Dennis, D. T., 170, 176, *187*, 193, *200*
Dinwoodie, J. M., 356, 361, *364*, 367 (19, 62), 368 (18), 369 (18, 62), 370 (20), 377 (20), 381 (62), 382 (20), 383 (18)
D'Iorio, A., 231, *239*
Dixon, G. H., 311, *320*
Doak, K. D., 459, 476, *478*
Dobbs, C. G., 379 (21), *387*
Dominik, T., 462, *478*
Doolittle, W. T., 487, 489, *494*
Downs, R. J., 484, 491, *494, 495*, 533, 541, 542, *546*
Drabble, E., 72, *86*
Drodie, H. W., 287, *288*
Dürr, W., 154, 155, 166, *166*
Duloy, M., 51, *63*
Dyer, D., 440, *455*

E

Eagles, C. F., 332, *344*
Eberhardt, G., 204, *217*
Echols, R. M., 367 (22, 23), 369 (22, 23), *387*
Eckardt, T., 70, *86*
Eggerer, H., 233, *238*
Eggert, D. E., 7, *17*
Eidem, P., 534, *546*
Eidmann, F., 501, 515, *518*
Elliott, G. K., 369 (24), *387*
Elliott, J. H., 333, *344*
Ellis, D. J., 95, *132*
El-Shishiny, E. D. H., 274, *288*, 299, *301*
Emerton, A. W., 95, *132*
Engelman, E. M., 269, 272
Esau, K., 51, 53, 55, 56, 58, 60, *63*, 81, 82, *86*, 87, *132*, 269, *272*, 295, *301*, 328, *344*
Eschrich, W., 48, *50*, 63, *63*, 295, *301*
Evert, R. F., 41, *50*, 333, *344*
Ewart, A. C. J., 438, *455*

F

Fahn, A., *457*
Faigle, H., 223, *238*
Faull, A. F., 369 (3), *386*

Feingold, D. S., 191, 198, *200*
Ferguson, J. J., 233, *238*
Fielding, J. M., 367 (17, 25), *387*
Finck, F., 159, *167*
Foil, R. R., 374 (26), *387*
Forsaith, C. C., 22, *35*
Forward, D. F., 21, *35*
Foster, R. D., 170, *187*
Fraenkel, G. S., 234, *238*
Franco, C. M., 490, 491, *494, 534, 546*
Fraser, D. A., 519, *531*
Freeland, R. O., 358, *364*, 517, *518*
Frei, E., 95, 127, *132*, 170, 171, 175, 177, 178, 179, 180, *187*
Frenzel, P., 104, *132*
Freudenberg, K., 144, *151*, 154, 155, 166, *166*, 203, 204, 205, 207, 208, 212, 213, 214, 215, 217, *218*, 219, 221, 232, 236, *238*, 343, *344*
Frey, A., 153, 155, *166*, 424, *455*
Frey, H. P., 157, 158, 159, *167*
Frey-Wyssling, A., 87, 88, 89, 90, 100, 103, 105, 108, 116, 128, *132, 167*, 170, 185, *187, 238*, 415, 418, 448, *454, 455, 457*
Friedmann, M., 214, *217*
Fritts, H. C., 519, 522, 526, *531*, 534, *546*
Fuchs, W., 203, 204, 205, *217*
Fukuzumi, T., 204, *217*

G

Gamborg, O. L., 219, 222, 224, 227, 229, 233, *238*
Ganguli, N. C., 229, *238*
Garegg, P. J., 142, 143, *151*
Gascoigne, J. A., 189, 192, *200*
Gates, C. T., 273, *288*, 525, *531*
Gautheret, R. J., 330, 331, *344*, 390, 403, *404*
Geiger, H., 213, *217*
Geissbühler, H., 390, *404*
Geissmann, T. A., 222, 227, *238*
Gerry, E., 367, 369 (28), *387*
Gibbs, R. D., 216, *217*, 521, *531*
Gierer, J., 137, *151*
Gillespie, B., 341, 343, *344*
Gillett, E. C., 67, *86*
Gilvarg, C., 229, *239*
Giovanni, M. V. di, 411, 412, *455*

Glaser, L., 191, *200*
Glaudemans, C. P. J., 143, *151*
Glock, W. S., 519, *531*, 533, 534, *546*
Goggans, J. F., 374 (29), *387*
Goldacre, P. L., 526, *531*
Goldsmith, M. H. M., 356, *364*
Goldsmith, V., 95, *132*
Gorham, P. R., 245, 257, 271, 272, 281, 282, 283, *288*
Goring, D. A. I., 137, *151*
Gracza, L., 332, *344*
Graf, A., 204, *218*
Grafflin, M. W., 189, 194, *201*
Green, P. B., 178, *187*, 198, 200
Greene, J. T., 367 (37), *387*
Greenwood, M., 482, *494*
Grillos, S. J., 33, *35*
Grion, G., 214, *217*
Grisebach, H., 219, 227, *238*
Gross, S. T., 100, *132*
Grossenbacher, J. G., 407, *455*

H

Haberlandt, G., 437, *455*
Hacskaylo, E., 478, *478*
Hägglund, E., 367 (53), 369 (53), *388*
Hale, C. R., 299, *301*
Hamilton, J. K., 141, *151*
Hancock, C. R., 428, *454*
Handley, W. R. C., 286, *288*
Hanney, C. E. A., 328, 334, *344*
Harada, H., 89, 92, 93, 95, 96, 97, 99, 100, 103, 104, 105, 113, 114, 117, 118, 119, 125, 127, *132*, *133*, *134*
Harborne, J. B., 227, 228, *238*
Harkin, J. M., 203, 204, 214, 215, *217*, *218*
Harlow, W. M., 369 (30), *387*
Harms, W. R., 528, *531*
Harper, A. G., 376 (31), *387*
Harper, B. J. T., 228, *237*
Hartig, R., 315, *320*, 342, *344*
Hartig, Th., 289, *301*, 403, *404*
Hartley, W. R., 369 (32), 384, *387*
Hartmann, F., 407, 438, 440, 441, *455*
Hartmann-Fahnenbrock, M., 103, 107, *133*
Hartt, C. E., 287, *288*
Harvey, L. J., 88, *134*
Hassid, W. Z., 191, 198, *200*
Hata, K., 369 (33), *387*

Hatch, A. B., 459, 473, 476, *478*
Hatcher, E. S. J., 523, *531*
Hejnowitz, Z., 21, 35, *133*
Helander, A. B., 369 (34), *387*
Hellmers, H., 534, 535, 543, 545, *546*
Helm, J., 70, *86*
Hengartner, H., 160, 162, 163, 164, *167*
Hengstenberg, J., 89, *133*
Henning, U., 233, *238*
Henrici, M., 505, 517, *518*
Henson, F., 349, *365*
Hepting, G. H., 256, *257*
Hepton, C. E. L., 58, 60, *63*, 259, *272*
Herrmann, K., 228, *238*
Hess, K., 189, *200*
Hestrin, S., 190, 191, 193, 194, 195, *200*
Hewlett, J. D., 275, *288*, 528, *531*
Hibbert, H., 216, *217*
Higuchi, T., 434, *455*
Hildebrandt, G., 374 (35), *387*
Hill, G. P., 259, 264, *272*, 285, *288*, 293, 296, 297, 300, *301*
Hodge, A. J., 89, 92, 95, 107, *133*
Høeg, O. A., 5, *17*
Hofbauer, G., 204, *218*
Hohl, H. R., 111, *133*
Holdheide, W., 37, 40, 41, 43, 46, 47, 48, *50*, 292, *301*, 307, *320*, 506, *518*
Holm, T., 76, *86*
Holmberg, B., 216, *218*
Holttum, R. E., 66, 67, 69, 76, 78, *86*
Holzer, K., 511, *518*
Horowitz, N. H., 235, *238*
Houwink, A. L., 114, *133*, 171, 178, *187*
Howsmon, J. A., 89, *133*
Hsving, W.-Y., 374 (67), *388*
Huber, B., 49, *50*, 287, *288*, 292, 298, *301*, 306, *320*, 501, 503, *504*, 506, 510, *518*, 521, *531*, 534, *546*
Huber, F., 318, *320*
Hübner, H. H., 212, *217*
Huerta, A., 481, *494*
Humphries, E. C., 482, *495*
Hunger, G., 104, *133*
Husemann, E., 195, *200*
Hutchinson, J., 65, *86*
Hyvärinen, M. J., *388*

I

Ibrahim, R. K., 226, *238*
Imaseki, I., 228, *238*

Ingle, H. D., 110, *134*
Iterson, G. van, 92, *133*
Ito, T., 227, *239*

J

Jaccard, P., 408, 409, 424, 436, 438, 439, 440, 442, 446, 452, 454, *455*
Jackson, C. P., 195, *200*
Jackson, L. W. R., 367 (37), 369 (36), *387*
Jacobs, M. R., 407, 438, 445, 446, *455*
Jacobs, W. P., 331, 343, *344*, 426, *455*
Jacquiot, C., 390, *404*
Jayme, G., 104, *133*, 159, *167*, 415, 431, *455*
Jenkinson, J. F., 534, *547*
Jensen, W. A., 32, *35*
Jodl, R., 154, *167*
Johnson, H. A., 20, 30, *35*
Jones, H., 287, *288*
Jost, L., 346, *364*, 405, 441, *455*
Jovanović, V., 213, *217*
Jutte, S. M., 413, *455*

K

Kamiya, N., 263, *272*
Kaul, K. N., *86*
Kavaljian, L. G., 32, *35*
Kefford, N. P., 526, *531*
Keller, Th., 500, 501, *504*
Kennedy, R. W., 367 (38, 39), *387*
Kephart, J. E., 124, *134*
Kern, K. G., 511, *518*
Kerr, T., 88, 92, 94, 95, *132, 133*
Kersten, H., 477, *478*
Kessler, G., 58, *63,* 295, *301*
Khan, A. W., 192, *200*
Kienholz, R., 361, *364,* 369 (40), *387*
Kisser, K. W., 204, *218*
Kjaer, A., 88, 91, *133*
Klein, E., 223, *238*
Klungsöyr, S., 191, *200*
Knappe, J., 233, *238*
Knight, T. A., 438, *455*
Kny, L., 408, *455*
Kobayashi, K., 107, *133*
Koch, W., 499, 500, 501, 502, *504*
Kochneva, M. N., 14, *17*

Kollmann, R., 51, 60, 61, *63,* 259, *272,* 295, *301*
Koontz, H., 274, *288*
Koriba, K., 481, 484, 486, 489, 490, 492, *494*
Kornberg, H. L., 311, *320*
Kosuge, T., 228, 232, *238*
Koukol, J., 219, 230, *238*
Kozlowski, T. T., 31, *35,* 253, *257,* 307, 308, *320,* 487, 489, *495,* 497, *504,* 522, 527, *531,* 533, 541, *546*
Kramer, P. J., 253, *257,* 275, *288,* 307, 308, *320,* 360, *364,* 497, *504,* 505, *518,* 527, 528, *531,* 533, 535, 541, *546*
Kramer, P. R., 369 (41), *387*
Kratzl, K., 204, *218,* 221, 223, 226, *238*
Kreger, D., 314, *320*
Kreger, D. R., 171, *187*
Kremers, R. E., 227, 228, *238,* 526, *531*
Kretovich, W. L., 229, *238*
Krotkov, G., 243, 244, *257*
Krugman, S. L., 534, *547*
Küster, E., 404, *404*
Kuroda, K., 260, 263, *272*
Kursanov, A. L., 246, 253, 254, *257,* 260, *272,* 358, *364*
Kuyper, B., 179, *188*

L

Lacy, H. J., 428, *454*
Ladefoged, K., 520, *531*
Lam, S. L., 356, *364*
Lamport, D. T. A., 124, *133*
Lang, A., 330, *344*
Lange, O. L., 499, *504,* 506, 517, *518*
Lange, P. W., 88, 91, *132, 133,* 147, *151,* 154, 162, *167,* 413, *455*
Larcher, W., 502, *504*
Larson, M. M., 533, 534, *546*
Larson, P. R., 32, *36,* 323, *344,* 346, 347, 351, 352, 353, 355, 356, 359, *364,* 367 (44), 374 (44), 375, 379 (42), *387,* 487, 488, *495,* 521, 523, 524, 526, *531, 532*
Laurencot, H., 224, *239*
Ledbetter, M. C., 108, *133*
Leete, E., 228, *238*
Lehmann, B., 204, *217*
Leopold, A. C., 356, *364*

Levy, C. C., 231, 233, *238*
Liang, C. Y., 176, *187*
Liang, S.-C., 367 (46), 369 (46), *387*
Liddicoet, A. R., 534, *546*
Liese, J., 465, 466, *478*
Liese, W., 103, 104, 105, 107, 108, *133,* *134*, 369 (47), 386, *387*
Lieth, H., 514, *518*
Lindberg, B., 140, 141, 142, 143, *151,* 216, *218*
Lindinger, L., 76, *86*
Lister, G. R., 243, *257*
Lizandr, A. A., 273, 281, *288*
Lodewick, J. E., 534, *546*
Luckwill, L. L., 427, *455*
Lynen, F., 233, *238*
Lyon, C. T., 453, *455*

M

McCalla, D. R., 219, 222, 224, 226, 228, 231, *238*
McDonald, J. A., 482, *495*
MacDougal, D. T., 519, *532*
McGinnes, E. A., 176, *187*
McGregor, W. H. D., 528, *531*
McKell, C. M., 273, 276, 281, 282, 288
MacMillan, W. B., 369 (48), *387*
Malins, M., 426, *456*
Malysheva, K. M., 273, 281, *288*
Maniere, C., 487, 493, *495*
Manskaya, S. M., 14, *17*, 233, *238*
Mapes, M. O., 390, *404*
Marchessault, R. H., 161, *167*, 176, *187*
Margarie, C., 193, *200*
Marion, L., 228, *238*
Mark, H., 89, *133*
Martin, R. V., 287, *288*
Martin, S. M., 191, *200*
Marts, R. O., 374 (56), *388*
Maskell, E. J., 316, *320*
Mason-Jones, A. G., 438, *455*
Mason, T. G., 316, *320*
Mathur, S. N., 329, *344*
Mayer, R., 213, *218*
Mears, K., 390, *404*
Mehler, A. H., 230, *239*
Meier, H., 88, 95, 107, 108, 128, *133,* 140, 141, 143, 147, *151*
Meister, A., 229, *238*

Melin, E., 459, 462, *478*, 516, *518*
Mercer, F. V., 51, *63*
Meredith, R., 98, *133*
Merritt, C., 473, *478*
Messeri, A., 418, *455*
Metzger, K., 412, 424, 436, *456*
Meyazaki, Y., 95, 96, 103, 104, 105, *133*
Meyer, F. J., 74, *86*
Meyer, H. A., 519, *532*
Meyer, R. E., 274, 277, 281, 288, 527, *531*
Mian, A. J., 146, *151*
Middlebrook, Mavis, 178, *187*
Milanez, F. R., 40, *50*
Miller, C. O., 390, *404*
Miller, R., 500, *504*
Millman, B., 194, 196, 197, *200*
Mirov, N. T., 533, *546*
Misra, P., 369 (49), *387*
Mitchell, G. L., 100, *133*
Mitscherlich, G., 500, *504*
Mitrakos, K., 90, *132*
Mitsuhashi, S., 229, *238*
Mittler, T. E., 259, 272, 292, 293, 296, *301*
Mizutani, A., 227, *239*
Möller, C. M., 514, *518*
Moeller, J., 43, *50*
Mollenhauer, H. H., 124, *134*
Molski, B., 348, 363, *364*, 375 (50), *387*
Monoyer, A., 71, 72, 73, *86*
Monteith, J. L., 528, *532*
Moor, H., 185, *187*
Mork, E., 361, 369 (51), *364*, 387
Morris, D., 79, *86*
Mouravieff, I., 528, *532*
Mühlethaler, K., 88, 89, 103, *131, 132, 133*, 154, *167*, 185, *187*, 194, 195, *200*, 415, *454*
Müller, D., 514, *518*
Müller, E., 213, *218*
Münch, E., 284, *288*, 295, 300, *301*, 307, 315, *320*, 407, 442, 446, 453, *455, 456*
Mukherjee, S. M., 90, *133*
Myers, A., 170, 176, *187*

N

Nagatomo, S., 95, *133*
Nandy, M., 229, *238*

Nasr, T. A. A., 444, *456*

Nečesaný, V., 334, 340, 342, *344*, 408, 409, 411, 427, 428, *456*

Neish, A. C., 189, 191, 198, *200*, 204, *217*, 219, 221, 222, 223, 224, 225, 226, 227, 228, 229, 230, 231, 233, *237*, *238*, *239*

Nelson, C. D., 243, 244, 245, *257*, 271, *272*, 281, 282, 283, 288

Neufeld, E. F., 191, 198, *200*

Neuwirth, G., 358, *364*, 502, *504*

Nevard, E. H., 176, *187*

Newman, I. V., 9, *17*, 20, 33, 34, *36*, 111, *133*

Nicholls, J. W. P., 367 (16, 17), 369 (52), 383 (52), 384 (52), 387, *388*

Nicolai, E., 170, *188*

Niedercorn, F., 204, *217*

Nielsen, J., 514, *518*

Nightingale, G. I., 534, *546*

Nilsson, H., 516, *518*

Nimz, H., 213, *217*

Nishimura, M., 517, *518*

Nitsch, J. P., 541, *546*

Njoku, E., 484, *495*

Noelle, W., 459, 460, 462, 465, 466, 473, 474, 476, *478*

Nolan, N. J., 21, *35*

Nord, F. F., 204, *217*, 223, 226, *237*

Northcote, D. H., 124, *133*

Nylinder, P., 367 (53), 369 (53), *388*

O

Ogata, G., 528, *532*

Ohad, I., 193, 194, 195, *200*

Ollinmaa, P. J., 410, 411, 428, *456*

Ollis, W. D., 219, 227, *238*

Onaka, F., 408, 409, 410, 411, 412, 424, 426, 428, 431, 438, 444, 454, *456*

Oppenheimer, H. R., 376 (54), *388*

Ordin, L., 525, 526, *532*

Orman, H. R., 368 (55), 383 (55), 384 (55), *388*

Ott, E., 189, 194, *201*

Ourr, I. F., 233, *238*

Overbeek, J. van, 526, *532*

Ovington, J. D., 21, *36*

Owen, P. C., 528, *532*

P

Pallas, J. E., 273, 276, 277, 281, *288*, 527, *532*

Pansain, A. J., 22, *35*

Patau, K., 390, *404*

Paul, B. H., 374 (56), *388*

Péaud-Lenoël, C., 193, *200*

Peel, A. J., 259, 264, *272*, 285, *288*, 293, *301*

Pellerin, J., 231, *239*

Perilä, O., 146, *151*

Perkins, H. J., 271, *272*, 281, 282, *288*

Peterson, T. A., 31, *35*, 527, *531*

Petinov, N. S., 273, 281, *288*

Piringer, A. A., 484, 491, *495*, 541, 542, *546*

Pisek, A., 498, 503, *504*, 506, 513, 514, *518*, 540, *546*

Plankl, L., 510, *518*

Plumstead, E. P., 10, *17*

Pollard, J. K., 184, *188*

Polster, H., 502, *504*, 514, 515, *518*

Porter, C. A., 224, *239*

Porter, H. K., 287, *288*

Posnette, A. F., 482, *494*

Prescott, D. M., 30, *36*

Preston, R. D., 16, *17*, 58, *60*, *63*, 92, 94, 95, 98, 100, 115, 127, *132*, *133*, *134*, 170, 171, 174, 175, 176, 177, 178, 179, 180, 184, 185, *187*, 190, 193, 196, 197, *201*, 259, 260, *272*, 418, 451, 452, *456*

Priestley, J. H., 67, *86*, 346, *364*, 369 (57), 376 (57), *388*, 407, 408, 409, 426, 435, *456*, 521, *532*

Priestley, J. M., 338, *344*

Probine, M. C., 115, *133*, 173, 174, 178, *188*

Prusakova, L. D., 273, 281, *288*

Q

Quastel, J. H., 230, *239*

Queva, C., 70, *86*

R

Ramamurti, K., 195, *200*

Rånby, B. C., 89, *133*, 451, *456*

Ranganathan, S., 418, *456*

Raschendorfer, I., 511, *518*

Rasdorsky, W., 437, *456*

Rasenack, D., 205, *217*, 343, *344*

Rathgeber, N., 51, *63*
Raven, H. M., 314, *320*
Rawitscher, F., 407, 408, *456*
Ray, P. M., 331, *344*, 453, *456*
Reed, J. F., 256, *257*
Rees, L. W., 367 (58), *388*
Reichert, M., 203, 204, 205, *217*
Reinders-Gouwentak, C. A., 323, 330, *344*
Reinhart, O., 374 (73), *388*
Rendle, B. J., 349, *364*
Reznick, H., 203, 204, 205, *217*, 219, 220,
    222, 227, 228, 234, *239*, 343, *344*
Rhodes, R. R., 367 (84, 85), *388*
Richards, L. A., 528, *532*
Richards, P. W., 485, 488, 490, 491, *495*
Richardson, S. D., 356, 361, *364*, 367
    (61, 62), 369 (62), 370 (20), 377
    (20), 379 (59), 381 (62), 382
    (20), 384 (60), *387*, *388*, 534, *546*
Ridley, H. N., 79, *86*
Ripley, G. W., 95, *132*, 259, *272*
Risley, E. B., 53, 55, 56, *63*
Ritter, G. J., 100, *132*, *133*
Roberts, B. R., 527, *532*
Roberts, D. C., 10, *17*
Roberts, D. L., 332, *344*, 523, *532*
Roberts, R. H., 356, *364*
Robinson, R., 227, *239*
Rodrigues, W. A., 491, *495*
Roelofson, P. A., 114, *133*, 178, 185, *188*,
    189, 194, 196, 197, *201*
Röseler, P., 76, *86*
Rouschal, E., 292, *301*
Roussel, L., 361, *364*
Ruch, F., 157, 162, 163, 164, *167*
Rudinsky, J. A., 522, *532*
Rudney, H., 233, *238*
Rüsch, J., 500, 501, *504*
Ruscher, C., 418, *455*
Russell, E. S., 444, *456*
Rutten, M. G. T., 3, *17*
Rutter, A. J., 359, *364*

S

Sachs, I. B., 95, 103, *133*
Sachs, J., 411, *456*
Sachs, R. M., 330, *344*
Sachsse, H., 410, 411, 424, *456*
Sakakibara, A., 213, *217*
Sanio, K., 367, *388*
Santos, C. R. de Oliveira, 37, 40, *50*

Sax, K., 391, 394, *404*
Scaife, E., 432, *456*
Scarth, G. W., 262, 272, 521, *532*
Scheffler, K., 213, *218*
Schick, A., 213, *218*
Schiechtl, H. M., 511, *518*
Schimper, A. F. W., 491, *495*
Schneider, H., 43, *50*, 298, *301*
Schoch-Bodmer, H., 130, *133*
Schoute, J. C., 66, 71, 72, 73, 74, 75, 76,
    77, 78, 79, *86*
Schreiner, E. J., 367 (64), *388*
Schubert, G. H., 534, *547*
Schubert, W. J., 204, *217*, 223, 226, 237
Schulman, E., 519, 526, *532*
Schultze-Dewitz, G., 369 (65), 374 (65),
    388
Schumacher, F. X., 519, *532*
Schumacher, W., 60, 61, *63*, 74, *86*, 259,
    272, 295, *301*
Schwinck, I., 224, 229, *239*
Scott, D. H., 76, *86*
Scott, F. M., 262, *272*
Scott, L. I., 67, *86*, 426, *456*, 521, *532*
Scott, T. K., 356, *364*
Scurfield, G., 411, 420, 422, 424, 425,
    426, 429, 430, 432, 433, 447, *456*
Setterfield, G., 185, *188*, 190, 191, 192,
    196, 197, 198, *201*, 438, *456*
Shepard, H. B., 369 (66), *388*
Shibata, S., 222, 228, *238*, *239*
Shirley, H. L., 533, 537, *546*
Shiroya, T., 244, *257*
Sidhu, G. S., 215, *217*
Siegel, S. M., 331, *344*, 434, *456*
Simão, S., 484, 492, *495*
Simon, S. V., 488, *495*
Sinnott, E. W., 312, *320*, 341, *344*
Skok, J., 538, 540, 541, 542, *546*
Skoog, F., 390, *404*
Slankis, V., 244, *257*
Slater, R. R., 525, *532*
Smith, F. H., 33, *35*
Smith, G. F., 477, *478*
Smith, H., 341, *344*
Smith, J. H. G., 367 (38), *387*
Smyth, R. D., 230, *237*
Snow, R., 346, *364*
Söding, H., 330, *344*, 346, *364*
Solereder, H., 74, *86*
Sorokin, H. P., 329, *344*

Sorokin, S., 331, 343, *344*, 390, *404*
Spanner, D. C., 259, 260, 272
Spurlin, H. M., 189, 194, *201*
Spurr, S. H., 374 (68), *388*
Stafford, H., 216, *218*, 232, *239*
Stalfelt, M. G., 527, *532*
Stanley, R. C., 533, *546*
Steenberg, B., 91, *132*
Stein, W. D., 199, *201*
Stemsrud, F., 104, *134*
Sterling, C., 21, *36*, 538, *547*
Steward, F. C., 184, *188*, 390, *404*
Stewart, C. M., 88, *134*
St. John, H., 77, *86*
Stocker, O., 275, *288*, 502, *504*, 506, *518*, 528, *532*
Stone, B. A., 189, *201*
Stone, E. C., 534, *547*
Stone, J. E., 204, *217*
Stonecypher, R., 367 (85), *388*
Strasburger, E., 74, 84, *86*, 305, *320*
Struckmeyer, B. S., 356, *364*
Susmel, L., 369 (69), *388*
Swain, T., 222, *238*
Swanson, C. A., 274, *288*, 299, *301*
Synge, R. L. M., 3, *17*
Szalai, I., 332, *344*

T

Tabor, H., 230, *239*
Takahashi, D., 287, *288*
Takahashi, M., 227, *239*
Tanimoto, T., 287, *288*
Tanner, G. K., 204, *217*
Thaine, R., 260, 261, *272*
Theander, O., 216, *218*
Thimann, K. V., 329, 341, 343, *344*, 356, *364*, 453, *456*, 525, 526, *532*
Thompson, N. S., 141, *151*
Timell, T. E., 137, 143, 146, *151*
Todd, G. W., 274, 277, 281, *288*, 527, *531*
Tomlinson, P. B., 65, 66, 67, 68, 69, 70, 71, 72, 73, 75, 79, 81, *86*
Tong, D., 407, 408, 409, 426, 435, *456*
Topfmeier, F., 213, *217*
Torres-Serres, J., 203, *217*
Torrey, J. G., 21, *36*, 474, *478*
Torrie, J. H., 522, *531*
Toryama, H., 262, *272*
Towers, G. H. N., 226, *237*, *238*

Tranquillini, W., 502, *504*, 505, 506, 508, 510, 511, 512, 514, *518*
Trendelenburg, R., 349, *364*, 369 (70), *388*
Tronchet, A., 361, *364*
Turner, L. M., 256, *257*
Tuszon, J., 100, *134*
Tyler, S., 3, *17*

U

Underhill, E. W., 222, 226, *239*
Utsumi, N., 107, *132*

V

Van Buijtenen, J. P., 376, 379, *388*
Vasiljevic, S., 368 (72), 369 (72), *388*
Vernon, L. P., 282, *288*
Vestal, M. R., 94, 100, 103, *132*
Vieweg, G. H., 502, *504*
Vité, J. P., 522, *532*
Vlitos, A. J., 200, *200*
Vöchting, H., 436, 438, *456*
Voegeli, H., 374 (73), *388*
Volkens, G., 485, *495*
von Alten, H., 459, *478*
von Mohl, H., 71, 72, 84, *86*

W

Wälchli, O., 429, *456*
Wahlgren, H. E., 413, *456*
Wakashima, T., 95, 96, 103, 104, 105, *133*
Wakil, S. J., 310, *320*
Walter, H., 485, 486, 490, 491, *495*, 498, *504*
Wandt, R., 349, *364*
Wang, C. H., 191, *201*
Warburg, O., 74, *86*
Wardlaw, C. W., 474, *478*
Wardrop, A. B., 87, 89, 90, 91, 92, 93, 94, 95, 97, 98, 99, 100, 103, 105, 106, 107, 108, 110, 111, 113, 114, 117, 118, 119, 121, 124, 125, 127, 128, *132*, *133*, *134*, 341, *344*, 367 (15), 368 (10), 369 (10), 384, *386*, *387*, *388*, 408, 409, 410, 411, 412, 415, 416, 417, 418, 420, 422, 423, 424, 425, 426, 428, 429, 430, 431, 432, 433, 434, 435, 440, 445, 447, *455*, *456*
Wareing, P. F., 32, *36*, 332, *344*, 346, 347, *364*, 375, *388*, 444, *456*, 523, 525, *532*, 541, 543, *547*

Watkin, J. E., 219, 222, 223, 226, *239*
Weatherley, P. E., 259, 264, 272, 285, 288, 293, *301*, 528, *532*
Weaver, R. J., 299, *301*
Webb, C., 349, *365*
Webb, T. E., 200, *201*
Weber, R., 315, *320*
Weigel, H., 191, *200*
Weigl, J., 191, 193, 195, *201*
Weinstein, L. H., 224, *239*
Weise, G., 502, *504*
Weissbach, H., 230, 237
Went, F. W., 490, *495*, 535, 537, *547*
Wergin, W., 408, 418, 434, 435, *455*, *456*
Werkman, C. H., 278, *288*
Werner, H.-K., 215, *218*
Werner, R., 195, *200*
Wershing, H. F., 334, 342, *344*, 428, 452, *456*
Westing, A. H., 340, *344*
Wetmore, R. H., 331, 343, *344*, 390, *404*
Wetter, L. R., 229, *238*
Whaley, W. G., 124, *134*
Whalley, B. E., 111, *132*
White, D. J. B., 408, 410, *456*
White, G. A., 191, *201*
White, J., 440, *456*
Whitemore, T. G., 41, 43, 47, *50*
Wiebe, H. H., 273, 281, 282, 287, *288*, 527, *532*
Wiederskehr-Scherb, L. P., 94, 128, *132*
Wieler, A., 289, *301*
Wiener, O., 155, 157, 158, *167*
Wight, W., 20, 21, 22, *36*, 256, *257*
Wightman, F., 219, 222, 224, 229, *239*
Wihrheim, S. E., 273, 281, 282, 287, *288*, 527, *532*
Wilcox, H., 323, *344*, 346, *365*, 465, 474, *478*, 520, 521, 522, *532*
Wilhelmi, T., 361, *365*
Wilkie, K. C. B., 147, *151*
Williams, G. G., 273, 276, *288*, 527, *532*
Williams, R. C., 89, *134*
Wilson, A. M., 273, 276, 278, 281, 282, *288*
Wilson, B. F., 20, 24, 32, 33, *36*

Wilson, J., 393, *404*
Wilson, J. W., 367 (39), *387*
Wilson, P. M., 393, *404*
Wilson, R. M., 230, *237*
Wimber, D. E., 32, *36*
Winget, C. H., 522, *531*
Winkler, E., 498, 503, *504*, 513, *518*, 540, *546*
Witkowska, L., 375 (79), 379 (79), *388*
Wodzicki, T., 348, 356, 358, 363, *365*, 375 (76, 77, 78, 79), 379 (77, 79), 384 (77, 78), *388*
Wolfe, J. A., 12, *17*
Wood, H. G., 278, *288*
Woods, H. S., 90, *133*
Woolf, B., 230, *239*
Wort, D. J., 323, *344*, 521, *532*
Wright, D., 221, 224, 225, 228, 229, 230, 231, *237*, *239*
Wright, H., 485, 486, 490, *495*
Wyckoff, R. W. G., 89, *134*

Y

Yamazaki, M., 222, 228, *238*, 329
Yaniv, H., 229, *239*
Yemm, E. W., 248, *257*
Yllner, S., 108, 128, *133*

Z

Zahner, R., 374 (80), *388*, 519, 520, 522, 524, *532*
Zahur, M. S., 37, *50*
Zeeuw, C. De., 47, *50*
Zelawski, W., 348, 363, *364*, *365*, 375 (50), *387*, *388*
Zholkevich, V. N., 273, 281, *288*
Ziegler, H., 293, *301*, 308, 310, 318, 319, *320*, 503, *504*
Ziegler, I., 308, 310, *320*
Zimmermann, M. H., 41, *50*, 284, *288*, 292, 293, 294, 298, *301*
Zimmermann, W. A., 346, *365*
Zobel, B. J., 349, *365*, 367 (82, 84), 374 (82), *388*
Zocher, H., 154, 155, 166, *166*
Zucker, M., 231, 233, *238*

Subject Index

A

Alkaloids, 228
Amino acids,
    aromatic, biosynthesis, 224
    in phloem, 293, 296
    origin of pool, 229
Apical dominance, 15
Apical meristem, 70, 74, 84
Auxin, *see* also Growth hormones,
    effects on reaction wood formation,
        333-343, 354, 452-454
    in tissue culture, 390
    in xylem differentiation, 323-333

B

Branching,
    of fossil plants, 15
    of monocotyledons, 66, 73-80, 84
    of roots, 460-465

C

Callose,
    dormancy-, 49, 58-60, 81, 290, 293-300
    during cell development, 53-58, 61
    wound-, 48, 63
Cambial activity,
    distribution along axis, 332-342, 353-
        356, 362, 530, 531
    effect of daylength on, 347-352, 541-
        543
        of gravity on, 333-343
        of hormones on, 323-333, 345-365,
            525, 526
        of light intensity on, 537-543
        of pressure on, 391-402
        of temperature on, 534-536, 540, 541
    first sign of, 49
    in conifers, 19-36
    in monocotyledons, 66, 75
    in tropical trees, 487-489
    periodicity of, 332, 333
    role of water in, 352, 353, 520-525,
        529
Cambium,
    cell divisions in, 19-36, 111
    definition of term, 20, 24, 34-35
    evolution of, 3-17
    in Agavaceae, 75, 76

    regeneration of, 393, 394, 404
    tissue culture of, 389-391
Cell walls,
    chemistry of, 88, 89, 137-151, 170
    dehydration of, 451-452
    growth of, 49, 111-118, 129, 173-187
    in reaction wood, 412-424
    of algae, 169-187
    optical properties of, 87-128, 153-167,
        176
    organization of, 89-131, 169, 176-187
    sculpturing of, 103-110, 467
    structure and formation of, 87-134
Cellulose,
    antiparallel structure of, 185, 186, 199
    biosynthesis of, 179-184, 189-201
    crystallinity of, 89, 90, 124, 150, 170,
        171, 175, 176, 185, 193, 194,
        418-424, 451
    degree of polymerization of, 137
    in fossil plants, 13
    isolation, purification, determination of,
        139, 140
    microfibril formation, 179-184, 193-
        197, 200
    optical properties of, 161 (*see* also
        Cell walls)
    orientation in cell walls, 87-134, 137-
        151, 169-186, 197, 198
Cinnamic acid derivatives,
    conversion to lignin, 232
    formation of, 228, 230, 231, 235, 236
Cyclosis, *see* Streaming

D

Dormancy,
    at low temperatures, 511-514, 516, 517
    in monocotyledons, 85
    in tropical trees, 484, 490
    of phloem, *see* Callose
    of roots, 462, 469, 473, 475
Dry matter production, 514-516

E

Evolution of land plants, 3-17

F

Fibers, *see* also Cell walls
    chemistry of, 137-151

growth of, 111-118, 178, 186
  in palms, 71, 72
  in phloem, 37-40, 46
  in reaction wood, 411
  in xylem, 40, 87, 92-99, 130, 170
  secondary wall formation in, 118-128
Flowering,
  in monocotyledons, 67, 73-75, 82, 85
  in tropical trees, 489-491, 493, 530

G

Gibberellin, 323-333
Growth, *see* also Cell walls, Tracheids,
    etc.
  at the timber line, 508-514
  eccentric, 407-409
  in tropical regions, 479-495
  intrusive, 49, 129
  secondary, *see* Cambial activity
  surface, 111-118
  and translocation, 289-301
Growth hormones,
  and cambial activity, 289, 318, 345-
    365
  effect on cell-wall growth, 186, 187,
    363, 364
  in fossil plants, 14, 15
  production of, 362
  role in reaction wood formation, 333-
    343, 452-454
    in xylem differentiation, 323-333
  transport of, 334-343, 353, 356

H

Heartwood,
  biotin content, 308, 309
  formation, 235, 320, 457
  pyridoxine content, 310, 311
Hemicelluloses,
  chemistry of, 140-150
  distribution in cell wall, 146-149
  in algae, 171, 174-187
  in cell walls, 88, 89, 137-150
  in monocotyledons, 146
  isolation, purification, determination of,
    139, 140
  orientation in cell wall, 174-187

I

Indole acetic acid, *see* Auxin

J

Juvenile phase,
  in *Hevea,* 494
  of monocotyledons, 67-69, 73-77

K

Kinetin,
  effect on cambial activity, 329, 330
  in tissue culture, 390

L

Lacticifers, 61, 62
Laminarin, 171
Leaf,
  formation and fall, 482-487
  primordia in palms, 70
Lignification,
  effect of auxin on, 331
  in fossil plants, 13, 14
  in reaction wood, 431-435
  in relation to rigidity, 4, 5, 15, 16
  of cell walls, 88, 89, 128, 129, 146,
    165, 203-206
Lignin,
  degradation products of, 207-216
  distribution in cell walls, 153-167
  extraction from wood, 207
  in fossil plants, 13-15
  linkages to polysaccharides, 151, 165,
    166
  linkages within, 137, 138, 209-216
  optical properties of, 153-167
  precursors, application to plants, 203,
    221-224
  synthetic pathways, 208, 212-216, 219-
    237
  taxonomic significance of, 4, 5, 14,
    150, 215, 216, 226, 233-235
  to cellulose ratio, 203
Longevity of phloem, 41-46, 49, 80-82

M

Mitosis in cambium, 19-36
Monocotyledonae,
  arborescent, stem structure, 65-86
  secondary growth in, 11, 66, 75
Movements; *see* Orientation
Mycorrhizae, 245, 246, 465, 474, 476,
    478, 515

O

Orientation movements, 405-409, 444-449, 452, 454

P

Palms,
branched axis in, 66, 84
height of, 66
stem structure of, 66-73, 76-85
Parenchyma,
chemistry of, 146
in palms, 72
in phloem, 40-46, 54, 56
in reaction wood, 410, 411
in xylem, 99, 100
texture of, 99, 100, 170
Periderm, 37, 44-47
Phloem,
conducting, 41-43, 290-293
formation in conifers, 19-37
in dicotyledons, 326-329
in vitro, 390, 398-403
growth rings in, 41, 291, 326, 328
non-conducting, 43-46
of dicotyledons, 37-50
of *Tilia*, 41, 42, 48
protoplasmic streaming in, 259-272
reactivation, 49, 58-60, 290, 295-300
regulation of formation, 326-329, 333
storage in, 305-307
ultrastructure of, 51-63
Phloem transport,
direction of, 245-253, 282-284, 290-299
effect of light intensity on, 249-251
of mineral nutrition on, 246-249
of mycorrhizae on, 245, 246
of water stress on, 273-288, 527
in monocotyledons, 80
in relation to root growth, 255
mechanism of, 60-63, 259-272
of reserve materials, 289, 290, 295-298
seasonal variations of, 251-253, 255, 256, 290-299
Photoperiodism, 484, 486, 533, *see* also Cambial activity
Photosynthesis,
annual course of, 508-514
at the timber line, 508-514
at very low temperatures, 517
and dry matter production, 514-516
of pine, 243-257
Photosynthetic rate,
effect of air flow on, 506-508
of air humidity on, 505
of CO_2 concentration on, 499, 500
of light intensity on, 497
of mineral nutrition on, 501
of temperature on, 498, 505, 510-514
of water stress on, 275-278, 285, 502, 503, 518, 527
of sun and shadow leaves, 249-251, 256, 257, 497
Pits, 103-105, 110, 130

R

Rays,
formation in conifers, 20, 21
in fossil plants, 6, 14
in phloem, 37-46
radial transport in, 315-319
storage in, 303-307
Reaction phloem, 424-426, 454
Reaction wood,
anatomy, 409-424
causes of formation of, 436-444
chemistry, 144, 145
differentiation, 426-431
formation, 333-343, 354
lignification, 431-435
and orientation movements, 444-449
texture, 98, 131, 334, 415-424
Reserve materials, *see* also Starch
deposition and mobilization of, 307-315
hemicelluloses as, 139
in monocotyledons, 72, 82
translocation of, 289, 290, 295-298, 314-320
Rhythms, internal, 479, 492, 516
Rhytidome, 37, 44-47
Roots,
branching of, 460-465
growth of, 255, 256, 462, 469, 473, 475, 530
in monocotyledons, 67-69, 73-75, 77
induction of secondary growth in, 386
morphology, 460-465
of *Pinus resinosa*, 459-478

translation to, 245-253, 282-284
xylem development in, 465-477

S

Sclerenchyma,
  in monocotyledons, 70-73, 80
  in phloem, 37-40
Sieve areas (and sieve plates), 53-63,
  130
Sieve elements (sieve tubes),
  in monocotyledons, 81, 82
  longevity of, 41-46, 49
  nucleoli in, 48
  plasmodesmata in, 53-58
  plasmolysis of, 61, 62
  pressure in, 61, 271
  reactivation of, 49, 58-60, 290, 295-
    300
  ultrastructure of, 51-63
Slime bodies (slime plugs), 55-63
Starch, *see* also Reserve materials
  accumulation in palm stems, 72
  conversion to fat, 307-314, 319
  in roots, 256
  texture of, 171
Storage, *see* Xylem, Phloem, Reserve
  materials
Streaming, protoplasmic, 259-272

T

Tracheids, *see* also Cell walls
  diameter of, 346-361, 379-386
  general structure of, 92-99, 130, 170
  growth of, 111-118, 178, 186
  in roots, 459-477
  length of, 367-374, 382-386
  secondary wall formation in, 118-128
  thickenings in, 105-107, 131
  wall thickness of, 356-361, 363, 364,
    374-379, 382-386
  wart structure in, 107-110, 130

Transport in rays, 315-319 (*see* also
  Phloem transport)
Tropical regions,
  arborescent monocotyledons in, 65-86
  tree growth in, 479-495
Twisting of growing cells, 178, 184-186

V

Vascular tissue,
  fusion of, 71-72, 74, 83, 84
  in arborescent monocotyledons, 65-86
  in fossil plants, 3-17
Vessels,
  differentiation of, 324, 325
  in reaction wood, 410
  structure of, 100-103, 130

W

Water conduction,
  at low temperatures, 286
  in monocotyledons, 80
  in rays, 316, 319
Water stress,
  effect on cambial activity, 352-353, 529
    on flower induction, 490, 491, 530
    on phloem transport, 273-288, 527
    on photosynthesis, 275-278, 285, 502,
      503, 518
  inducing leaf fall, 485
  measurement of, 527, 528

X

Xylem,
  development in roots, 465-477
  differentiation, 323-333, 389-394
  formation in conifers, 19-36, 328, 329
    in vitro, 398-403
  in fossil plants, 3-17
  primary, definition, 471, 477
  storage in, 303-305